W9-ARY-497

Heath GENERAL MATHEMATICS

David W. Lowry
Earl G. Ockenga
Walter E. Rucker

HEATH
D.C. Heath and Company
Lexington, Massachusetts Toronto

PHOTO CREDITS:
Bettmann Archive, Inc. 116CL, 127, 230L; Paul Buddle 141, 166R, 298; Walter Chandoha 300; Stuart Cohen 4, 6, 11, 12, 17, 19, 22, 24, 27, 34, 41, 49B, 55, 63, 66L, 67, 68, 71, 80, 83, 84, 86, 91, 92, 94, 97, 103, 110, 114, 126, 130, 135, 151, 156, 157, 181, 190, 212, 213L, 215, 216B, 217, 232, 233R, 257, 261, 270, 279, 282, 285, 305, 307, 312L, 315, 327, 331L, 342, 369, 372, 384, 389, 391, 395, 396, 397, 446, 449, 455; CONTACT Press Images/Deborah Edelstein 31; Courtesy of Football Hall of Fame 7T; DPI 32, DPI/Leeanne Schmidt 206B; Focus on Sports, Inc. 7B, 117, 188T, 229, 456; Focus on Sports, Inc./Herbert Schreibel 13,/Mickey Palmer 200, 456; Granger Collection 36; P. Grant 166T; Image Book, © 1983 DISCOVER Magazine, Time Inc./Jean Pragen 377; Paul Johnson 1, 44, 45, 46, 49T, 53, 60–61, 66R, 88, 95, 99T, 121, 125, 131, 136, 140, 142, 143, 146, 148, 149, 164, 165, 178, 182, 184, 185T,C, 193, 198, 199, 204, 210, 213R, 214, 221, 225, 226, 227, 228, 233L, 247, 248–249, 265, 269, 289, 293, 309, 312R, 323, 324, 325, 330, 335, 340, 341, 344, 345, 350, 351, 357, 359, 381, 394; Susan Lapides 75, 76, 166L, 197, 203, 251, 260, 302, 319, 339, 352, 353, 385, 451, 459; Museum of Modern Art 2; NASA 65; Photo Researchers/Hans Namuth 155,/Russ Kinne 177,/Thomas E. Evans 206T,/Catherine Ursillo 237,/Georg Gerster 312,/Richard Hutchings 361; Rick Rizzotto 216C, 320, 354; Michael Rusnock 160, 238; Sports Illustrated 20T; Stock, Boston 96; Stock, Boston/Peter Menzel 170,/Bill Gillette 185B,/Bohdan Hrynewych 444; Stock/Globe Photos 106MR, 116L,R, 139; Stock/Globe Photos/Andrew Allen 188,/N. Cutler 106L,/R. Dominguez 106ML, 116R,/Mike Keza 116CL,/Gregg Mancuso 58,/Patrick Morrow 363, 388,/Robert Nese 104,/G. Trindl 106R; Taurus Photos/© 1982 Alex Dunca, 129; Hilary Wallace 99B, 104, 108, 113, 115, 119, 163, 168, 187, 202, 216T, 236, 255, 274, 284, 331R, 349, 382, 383, 445, 449, 453, 457; Wide World Photos 20B, 230R.

ART CREDITS:
Leo Abbett 7, 9, 28; Ron Colvin 89; Walter Fournier, 39, 77, 85, 93, 111, 118, 169, 207, 210, 211, 218, 219, 240, 241, 259, 275, 287, 341B, 342, 355, 386, 387, 392, 393; George Ulrich 96, 158, 195, 252.

From the Guinness Book of World Records © 1983 by Sterling Publishing Co., Inc. 17, 77, 95, 212, 213, 261.

Published simultaneously in Canada.

Printed in the United States of America.

International Standard Book Number: 0-669-06406-8

CONTENTS

CHAPTER 1
Adding Whole Numbers and Decimals

Reading standard numerals *2*
Writing standard numerals in words *4*
Adding whole numbers *6*
Adding larger numbers *8*
Cumulative Skill Practice *10*
Problem solving *11*
Rounding whole numbers *12*
Estimating sums *14*
Reading decimals *16*
Cumulative Skill Practice *18*
Problem solving *19*
Rounding decimals *20*
Adding decimals *22*
More on adding decimals *24*
Cumulative Skill Practice *26*
Problem solving *27*
Chapter Review *28*
Chapter Test *29*
Cumulative Test *30*

CHAPTER 2
Subtracting Whole Numbers and Decimals

Comparing whole numbers *32*
Subtracting 2- and 3-digit numbers *34*
Subtracting 3- and 4-digit numbers *36*
Subtracting larger numbers *38*
Cumulative Skill Practice *40*
Problem solving *41*
Comparing decimals *42*
Subtracting decimals *44*
More on subtracting decimals *46*
Cumulative Skill Practice *48*
Problem solving *49*
Chapter Review *50*
Chapter Test *51*
Cumulative Test *52*

CHAPTER 3
Multiplying Whole Numbers and Decimals

Multiplying by multiples of 10, 100, or 1000 *54*
Multiplying by a 1-digit number *56*
Multiplying by a 2-digit number *58*
Multiplying larger numbers *60*
Cumulative Skill Practice *62*
Problem solving *63*
Multiplying decimals *64*
Simplifying expressions *66*
Multiplying decimals by 10, 100, or 1000 *68*
Cumulative Skill Practice *70*
Problem solving *71*
Chapter Review *72*
Chapter Test *73*
Cumulative Test *74*

CHAPTER 4
Dividing Whole Numbers and Decimals

Dividing by a 1-digit number *76*
More on dividing by a 1-digit number *78*
Dividing by a 2-digit number *80*
Cumulative Skill Practice *82*
Problem solving *83*
Dividing by a 3-digit number *84*
Order of operations *86*
Dividing a decimal by a whole number *88*
Cumulative Skill Practice *90*
Problem solving *91*
Dividing by 10, 100, or 1000 *92*
Dividing a decimal by a decimal *94*
More on dividing a decimal by a decimal *96*
Cumulative Skill Practice *98*
Problem solving *99*
Chapter Review *100*
Chapter Test *101*
Cumulative Test *102*

CHAPTER 5
Graphs and Statistics

Organizing data *104*
Using bar graphs *106*
Using line graphs *108*
Reading circle graphs and picture graphs *110*
Cumulative Skill Practice *112*
Problem solving *113*
Analyzing data—finding the mean *114*
Analyzing data—finding the median, mode, and range *116*
Presenting data—constructing graphs *118*
Cumulative Skill Practice *120*
Problem solving *121*
Chapter Review *122*
Chapter Test *123*
Cumulative Test *124*

CHAPTER 6
Fractions, Mixed Numbers, and Decimals

Equivalent fractions *126*
Writing fractions in lowest terms *128*
Least common denominator *130*
Comparing fractions *132*
Cumulative Skill Practice *134*
Problem solving *135*
Writing whole numbers and mixed numbers as fractions *136*
Writing fractions as whole numbers or as mixed numbers *138*
Writing fractions and mixed numbers in simplest form *140*
Writing quotients as mixed numbers *142*
Cumulative Skill Practice *144*
Problem solving *145*
Writing fractions and mixed numbers as decimals *146*
Writing decimals as fractions or mixed numbers *148*
Cumulative Skill Practice *150*
Problem solving *151*
Chapter Review *152*
Chapter Test *153*
Cumulative Test *154*

CHAPTER 7
Adding and Subtracting Fractions and Mixed Numbers

Adding fractions with common denominators *156*
Adding fractions with different denominators *158*
Adding mixed numbers *160*
Cumulative Skill Practice *162*
Problem solving *163*
Subtracting fractions with common denominators *164*
Subtracting fractions with different denominators *166*
Subtracting mixed numbers without regrouping *168*
Subtracting mixed numbers with regrouping *170*
Cumulative Skill Practice *172*
Problem solving *173*
Chapter Review *174*
Chapter Test *175*
Cumulative Test *176*

CHAPTER 8
Multiplying and Dividing Fractions and Mixed Numbers

Multiplying fractions *178*
A fraction of a whole number *180*
Multiplying mixed numbers *182*
More on a fraction of a whole number *184*
Cumulative Skill Practice *186*
Problem solving *187*
Dividing fractions *188*
Dividing mixed numbers *190*
Cumulative Skill Practice *192*
Problem solving *193*
Chapter Review *194*
Chapter Test *195*
Cumulative Test *196*

CHAPTER 9
Measurement

Using a metric ruler *198*
Metric units of length *200*
Changing units in the metric system *202*
Liquid volume—metric system *204*
Weight—metric system *206*
Cumulative Skill Practice *208*
Problem solving *209*
Length—customary units *210*
Changing units of length—customary *212*
Liquid volume—customary units *214*
Weight—customary units *216*
Computing with customary units *218*
Cumulative Skill Practice *220*
Problem solving *221*
Chapter Review *222*
Chapter Test *223*
Cumulative Test *224*

CHAPTER 10
Ratio and Proportion

Ratios *226*
Proportions *228*
Solving proportions *230*
Rates *232*
Cumulative Skill Practice *234*
Problem solving *235*
Scale drawings *236*
Similar figures *238*
Indirect measurement *240*
Cumulative Skill Practice *242*
Problem solving *243*
Chapter Review *244*
Chapter Test *245*
Cumulative Test *246*

CHAPTER 11
Percent

Changing a percent to a fraction *248*
Changing a fraction to a percent *250*
Percents and decimals *252*
Cumulative Skill Practice *254*
Problem solving *255*
Finding a percent of a number *256*
More on finding a percent of a number *258*
Finding the number when a percent is known *260*
More on percent *262*
Cumulative Skills Practice *264*
Problem solving *265*
Chapter Review *266*
Chapter Test *267*
Cumulative Test *268*

CHAPTER 12
Consumer Mathematics

Earning money *270*
Buying on sale *272*
Comparison buying *274*
Bargain buying *276*
Cumulative Skill Practice *278*
Problem solving *279*
Checking accounts *280*
Savings accounts *282*
Borrowing money *284*
Paying bills *286*
Cumulative Skill Practice *288*
Problem solving *289*
Chapter Review *290*
Chapter Test *291*
Cumulative Test *292*

CHAPTER 13
Geometry—Perimeter and Area

Measuring and classifying angles *294*
Perpendicular and parallel lines *296*
Polygons *298*
Perimeter *300*
Circumference *302*
Cumulative Skill Practice *304*
Problem solving *305*
Area—squares and rectangles *306*
Area—parallelograms *308*
Area—triangles *310*
Area—circles *312*
Cumulative Skill Practice *314*
Problem solving *315*
Chapter Review *316*
Chapter Test *317*
Cumulative Test *318*

CHAPTER 14
Surface Area and Volume

Space figures *320*
More on space figures *322*
Surface area—rectangular prisms and cubes *324*
Cumulative Skill Practice *326*
Problem solving *327*
Volume—rectangular prisms and cubes *328*
Volume—cylinders *330*
Volume—pyramids and cones *332*
Cumulative Skill Practice *334*
Problem solving *335*
Chapter Review *336*
Chapter Test *337*
Cumulative Test *338*

CHAPTER 15
Probability

A basic counting principle *340*
Permutations *342*
Probability *344*
Sample spaces *346*
Cumulative Skill Practice *348*
Problem solving *349*
Probability—more than 1 event *350*
Odds *352*
Expectation *354*
Cumulative Skill Practice *356*
Problem solving *357*
Chapter Review *358*
Chapter Test *359*
Cumulative Test *360*

CHAPTER 16
Integers

Ordering and comparing integers *362*
Adding integers *364*
Subtracting integers *366*
Cumulative Skill Practice *368*
Problem solving *369*
Multiplying integers *370*
Dividing integers *372*
Graphing ordered pairs *374*
Cumulative Skill Practice *376*
Problem solving *377*
Chapter Review *378*
Chapter Test *379*
Cumulative Test *380*

CHAPTER 17
Algebra

Writing expressions *382*
Evaluating expressions *384*
Solving addition equations *386*
Solving subtraction equations *388*
Cumulative Skill Practice *390*
Problem solving *391*
Solving multiplication equations *392*
Solving division equations *394*
Solving two-step equations *396*
Cumulative Skill Practice *398*
Problem solving *399*
Chapter Review *400*
Chapter Test *401*
Cumulative Test *402*

Skill Test *404*
Extra Practice *412*
Extra Problem Solving *444*
Glossary *461*
Symbols and Formulas *468*
Index *469*

Chapter 1

Adding Whole Numbers and Decimals

Reading standard numerals

BOX OFFICE CHAMPS	COST OF PRODUCTION *	EARNINGS FROM RENTALS *
E.T., 1982	$10,001,096	$195,063,412
Star Wars, 1977	13,100,056	193,138,000
The Empire Strikes Back, 1980	21,002,500	134,209,000
Superman, 1978	35,001,098	82,500,000
Close Encounters of the Third Kind, 1977	21,040,600	77,000,000
Star Trek, 1979	42,998,700	56,000,000
2001: A Space Odyssey, 1968	10,499,056	24,100,000
Planet of the Apes, 1968	5,800,021	15,000,000
Journey to the Center of the Earth, 1959	3,400,144	4,777,000

Figures are approximate and are for exercise use only. Actual figures may differ.

Here's how *to read large numbers.*

13,100,056 — million | thousand

193,138,000 — million | thousand

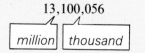

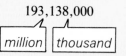

Star Wars cost 13 million, 100 thousand, 56 dollars to produce. The film earned 193 million, 138 thousand dollars.

1. Which film cost 10 million, 1 thousand, 96 dollars to produce?
2. Which film earned 24 million, 100 thousand dollars?
3. *Star Wars* was released in 1977. Which film was released in 1978?
4. Which films earned more than 100 million dollars?
5. Which films cost less than 10 million dollars to produce?
6. Which film earned about 134 million dollars?
7. Which film earned about 110 million dollars more than it cost?

EXERCISES

Study the clues. Use the chart on page 2 to name the movie.

8. Clues:
- This movie was released in 1977.
- It earned more than 100 million dollars.

9. Clues:
- This movie earned less than 90 million dollars.
- It was released in 1977.

10. Clues:
- This movie cost less than 10 million dollars to produce.
- It earned more than 10 million dollars.

11. Clues:
- This movie earned more than 100 million dollars.
- It cost more than 20 million dollars to produce.

12. Clues:
- This movie earned less than 70 million dollars.
- It was released before 1979.
- It cost more than 10 million dollars to produce.

13. Clues:
- This movie was released after 1977.
- It cost more than 30 million dollars to produce.
- It earned less than 60 million dollars.

14. Clues:
- This movie cost less than 15 million dollars to produce.
- It was released in 1968.
- It earned less than 20 million dollars.

15. Clues:
- This movie earned less than 80 million dollars.
- It cost more than 20 million dollars to produce.
- It was released after 1978.

Show time **Reading an ad**

Use the ad to answer the questions.

16. What movie is showing at Cinema 2?

17. What time is the first showing of *E.T.*?

18. Sonya went to see *E.T.* She arrived at the theater at 3:10. How long did she wait for the next movie to begin?

19. You live 15 minutes from Cinema 2. What time should you leave home to get to the theater 5 minutes before the start of the last showing?

Writing standard numerals in words

A famous fast-food chain served 2,400,000,000 slices of cheese last year. If you sliced one piece of cheese per second, 24 hours per day, it would take you more than 75 years to slice this much cheese.

Jack's fast food FACTS				
FOOD SERVED LAST YEAR				
	BILLIONS	MILLIONS	THOUSANDS	
Slices of cheese	2	400	000	000
Pounds of fish		46	205	500
Pounds of potatoes		542	840	000
Eggs		378	210	400

1. How many pounds of potatoes did the fast-food chain serve last year?

2. How many pounds of fish were served?

3. How many eggs were served?

Here's how *to write the standard numeral 46,205,500 in words.*

Short word-name: 46 million, 205 thousand, 500
Long word-name: forty-six million, two hundred five thousand, five hundred

4. Write the short word-name for the number of eggs the fast-food chain served.

5. Write the long word-name for the number of eggs served.

6. Write the short word-name for the number of slices of cheese served.

7. Write the long word-name for the number of slices of cheese served.

8. Write the long word-name for the number of pounds of potatoes served.

EXERCISES

Write the short word-name. *Hint: Study the* Here's how.

9. 47,258 **10.** 16,234 **11.** 776,039

12. 14,732 **13.** 520,066 **14.** 177,406

15. 6,835,270 **16.** 93,427,600 **17.** 74,000,050

18. 75,000,000 **19.** 60,600,600 **20.** 275,675,834

21. 14,360,220,000 **22.** 842,000,000,000 **23.** 5,000,600,000

Write the standard numeral.

24. 225 thousand, 16 **25.** 14 million **26.** 14 thousand, 616

27. 543 billion **28.** 8 million, 800 thousand **29.** 999 thousand, 50

30. six thousand two hundred four **31.** fifty-nine thousand, eight hundred

32. four million, three hundred eleven thousand, one hundred thirty-seven

33. twenty-one million, sixty-three thousand, three hundred

Write each short word-name as a standard numeral.

34. A fast-food chain serves **860 million** ounces of orange juice yearly. This is enough juice to fill **1 thousand 200** home-size swimming pools.

35. The same fast-food chain has served a total of **40 billion** hamburgers. This is enough hamburgers to make a stack **473 thousand, 500** miles high.

The check is in the mail! **Writing checks**

This check was mailed to the winner of Jack's Pot-of-Gold Sweepstakes. The amount of the check is written as a standard numeral and in words.

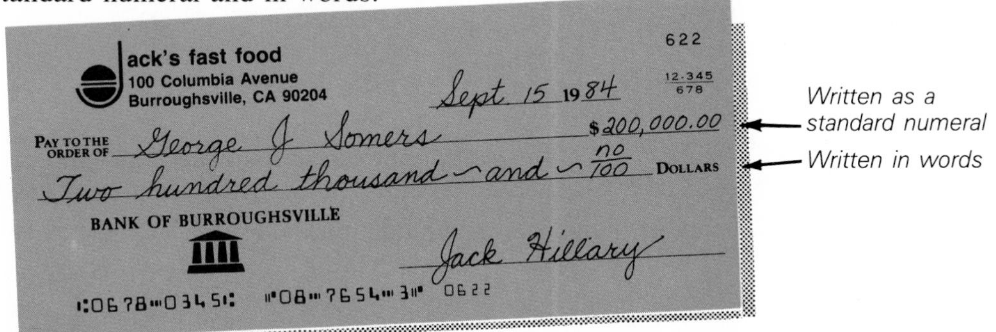

622
Jack's fast food
100 Columbia Avenue
Burroughsville, CA 90204
Sept 15 1984
12-345
678
PAY TO THE ORDER OF George J Somers
$200,000.00
Two hundred thousand and no/100 DOLLARS
BANK OF BURROUGHSVILLE
Jack Hillary
Written as a standard numeral
Written in words

Write the amount of each check in words.

36. \$350 **37.** \$1200 **38.** \$14,000 **39.** \$5710 **40.** \$26,010

41. \$12,900 **42.** \$9999 **43.** \$48,600 **44.** \$125,800 **45.** \$132,002

Adding whole numbers

Do you know these road signs? Two hundred people in each of three age groups were surveyed. This chart shows the number of people who identified each sign.

Age	Sign A	Sign B	Sign C
Under 10	**93**	**16**	**65**
10 to 15	**172**	**73**	**115**
16 and over	**197**	**157**	**183**

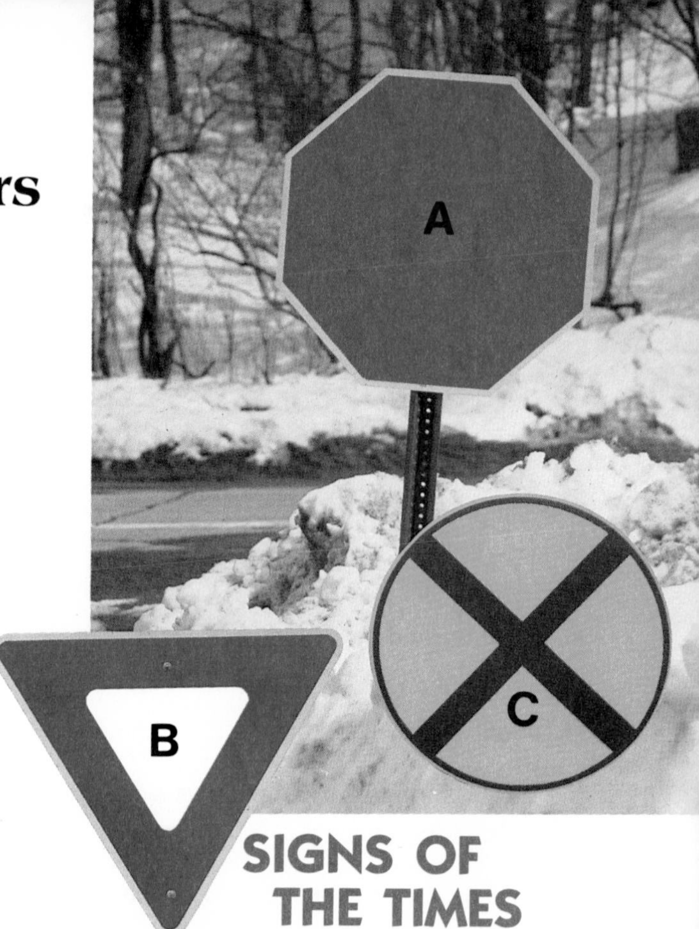

1. How many of the people 10 to 15 years old knew that Sign B was a yield sign?
2. How many of the people 16 and over knew that Sign C was a railroad-crossing sign?
3. Which three numbers would you add to find out how many of the people surveyed knew that Sign A was a stop sign?

Here's how *to add whole numbers.*

93 + 172 + 197 = ?

Line up the digits vertically.	Add ones. Regroup.	Add tens. Regroup.	Add hundreds.
93 172 +197	¹93 172 +197 2	²¹93 172 +197 62	¹93 ²172 +197 462

Look for the sums of 10.

The answer is called the **sum.**

4. Look at the *Here's how*. How many of the people could identify a stop sign?

EXERCISES

Add. *Here are scrambled answers for the next row of exercises: 94 131 101 71 87 77*

5. 72 + 15
6. 54 + 23
7. 69 + 25
8. 94 + 7
9. 55 + 76
10. 62 + 9

11. 247 + 462

12. 156 + 348

13. 436 + 86

14. 593 + 28

15. 297 + 886

16. 623 + 152

17. 57 + 38 + 13

18. 68 + 83 + 3

19. 883 + 96 + 741

20. 382 + 759 + 58

21. 426 + 18 + 4

22. 215 + 24 + 9

23. 526 + 28 + 104 + 71

24. 79 + 41 + 9 + 17

25. 142 + 85 + 98 + 444

26. 59 + 7 + 123 + 83

27. 164 + 646 + 88 + 3

28. 24 + 117 + 15 + 4

29. 68 + 13 + 428 + 7

30. 304 + 45 + 221 + 38

31. 723 + 372 + 86 + 197

32. 65 + 267 + 5 + 43

33. 597 + 64 + 563 + 314

34. 615 + 71 + 386 + 714

35. 231 + 316 **36.** 623 + 192 **37.** 154 + 480 **38.** 263 + 259

39. 176 + 87 **40.** 81 + 253 **41.** 253 + 57 **42.** 945 + 46

43. 236 + 61 + 9 **44.** 81 + 914 + 39 **45.** 7 + 38 + 214 **46.** 876 + 28 + 4

47. 47 + 567 + 8 **48.** 104 + 54 + 86 **49.** 92 + 7 + 163 **50.** 721 + 86 + 2

51. 68 + 219 + 6 **52.** 301 + 98 + 24 **53.** 68 + 9 + 252 **54.** 321 + 96 + 9

Solve. Use the survey information on page 6.

55. How many of the people surveyed identified the railroad-crossing sign?

56. How many people identified the yield sign?

57. How many people 10 or over identified the stop sign?

58. How many people under 16 identified the railroad-crossing sign?

On the road again **Reading road signs**

59. How many miles is it from Abilene to Odessa?

60. How far is it from Big Spring to Pecos?

61. When you are at Big Spring, how far are you from Odessa?

62. Which city is 218 miles from Pecos?

ABILENE 110 miles
BIG SPRING 25 miles
ODESSA 36 miles
PECOS 108 miles

Adding larger numbers

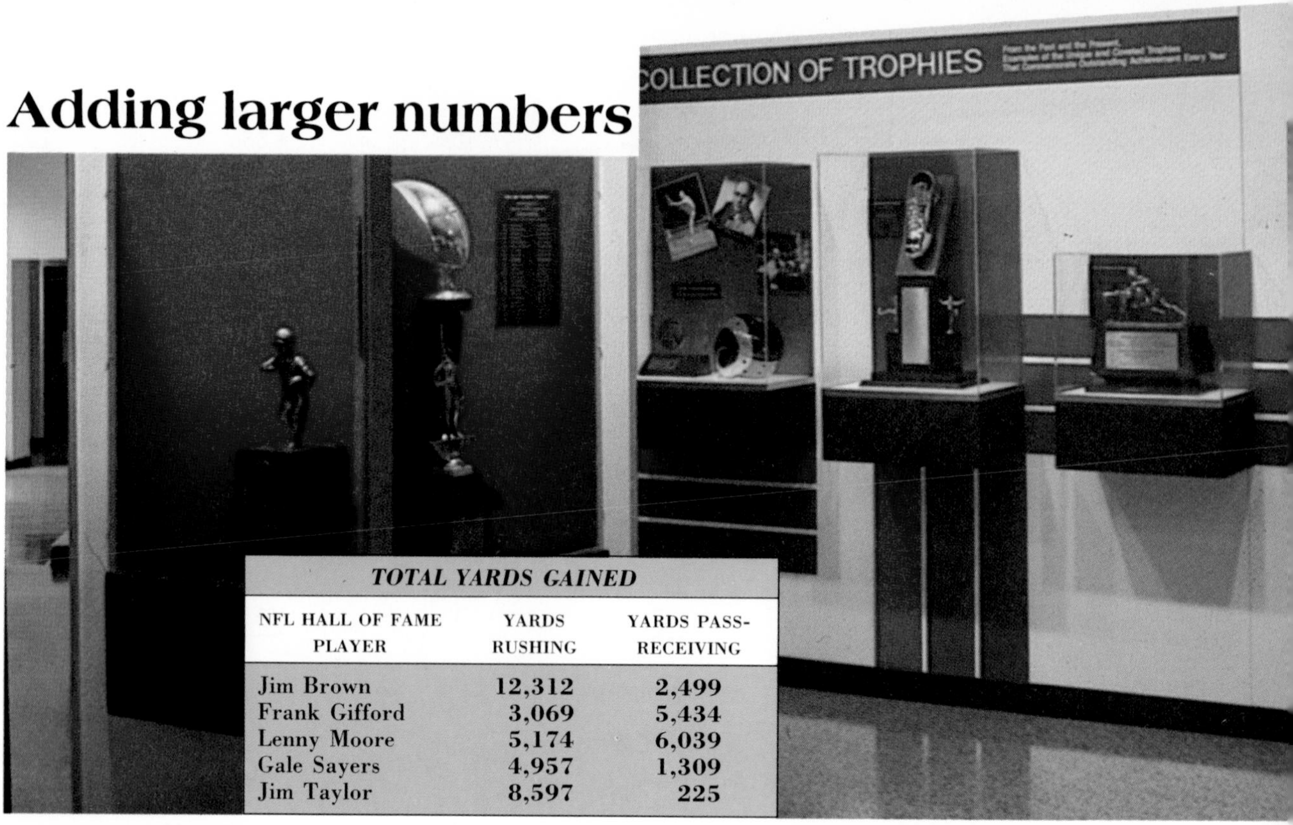

TOTAL YARDS GAINED		
NFL HALL OF FAME PLAYER	YARDS RUSHING	YARDS PASS-RECEIVING
Jim Brown	12,312	2,499
Frank Gifford	3,069	5,434
Lenny Moore	5,174	6,039
Gale Sayers	4,957	1,309
Jim Taylor	8,597	225

1. Which Hall of Fame player gained the most yards rushing?
2. Who had the most pass-receiving yards?
3. What two numbers would you add to compute Jim Brown's total rushing and pass-receiving yardage?

Here's how *to add large numbers.*

12,312 + 2499 = ?

Line up the digits that are in the same place and add.

4. Look at the *Here's how*. What was Jim Brown's total rushing and pass-receiving yardage?
5. Did Lenny Moore gain as many total yards as Jim Brown?

EXERCISES

Add. *Here are scrambled answers for the next row of exercises:*
12,316 8054 12,824 6673 5152

6. 6375 + 298	7. 4378 + 774	8. 9856 + 2968	9. 7409 + 4907	10. 6395 + 1659
11. 46,342 + 7,955	12. 62,237 + 8,073	13. 53,087 + 26,941	14. 34,668 + 62,951	15. 92,876 + 38,846
16. 7234 186 + 2145	17. 483 2964 + 192	18. 9263 4063 + 812	19. 12,610 8,715 + 24,025	20. 37,096 492 + 15,405
21. \$2.78 3.18 + 6.92	22. \$6.99 2.08 + 9.36	23. \$71.24 9.76 + 43.08	24. \$28.09 75.34 + 38.68	25. \$34.76 52.64 + 93.28

26. 24,198 + 9473
27. 543 + 1087
28. 19 + 9478
29. 7809 + 43,000
30. 38,624 + 1134
31. 356 + 2093
32. 1275 + 619 + 4235
33. 723 + 4263 + 82
34. 9261 + 2324 + 185
35. 256 + 1102 + 981
36. 6421 + 840 + 19
37. 618 + 5423 + 6
38. 14,726 + 8214 + 385
39. 24,426 + 902 + 6128
40. 83,280 + 4726 + 754
41. 25,002 + 312 + 1666
42. 72,016 + 354 + 14
43. 68,203 + 4204 + 8

Solve. Use the chart on page 8.

44. What was Gale Sayers' total rushing and pass-receiving yardage?
45. Which player had a total rushing and pass-receiving yardage of 11,213 yards?
46. What was the total rushing yardage of Jim Brown and Jim Taylor?
47. What was the total pass-receiving yardage of the five players?

Who wore this helmet? **Logical reasoning**

48. Study the clues. Use the chart on page 8 to name the player.

Clues:
- This player gained more than 5000 yards pass-receiving.
- This player gained less than 5000 yards rushing.

Cumulative Skill Practice

Write the short word-name. *(page 4)*
Hint: Think about where the commas go.

1. 35198	**2.** 4354	**3.** 12326	**4.** 36402
5. 443031	**6.** 92057	**7.** 180043	**8.** 200001
9. 45623926	**10.** 15481320	**11.** 82148099	**12.** 96000020
13. 1426005	**14.** 63128	**15.** 42000261	**16.** 86100000

Write the standard numeral. *(page 4)*

17. 347 thousand, 172
18. 18 million
19. 62 billion
20. 19 million, 418 thousand
21. 219 million, 76 thousand
22. 7 million, 3 thousand, 4
23. six hundred thirty-seven thousand, two hundred sixteen
24. fifty-one thousand, nine hundred sixty-seven
25. eighteen million, one hundred sixteen thousand
26. four hundred twenty-three thousand, fourteen
27. three billion, one hundred ten

Add. *(page 6)*

28. 83 +92	**29.** 69 +23	**30.** 78 +65	**31.** 82 +49	**32.** 53 +29	**33.** 24 +19
34. 964 +673	**35.** 857 + 95	**36.** 107 +682	**37.** 47 +90	**38.** 232 +563	**39.** 302 +191
40. 683 +457	**41.** 992 +193	**42.** 426 +150	**43.** 962 +193	**44.** 700 +538	**45.** 542 +619
46. 36 29 +18	**47.** 35 74 +81	**48.** 56 18 +66	**49.** 54 29 +93	**50.** 71 71 +39	**51.** 88 88 +88
52. 267 384 37 +115	**53.** 628 35 275 + 56	**54.** 57 629 38 +115	**55.** 342 708 56 + 86	**56.** 628 52 395 +544	**57.** 291 35 426 +184

Problem solving

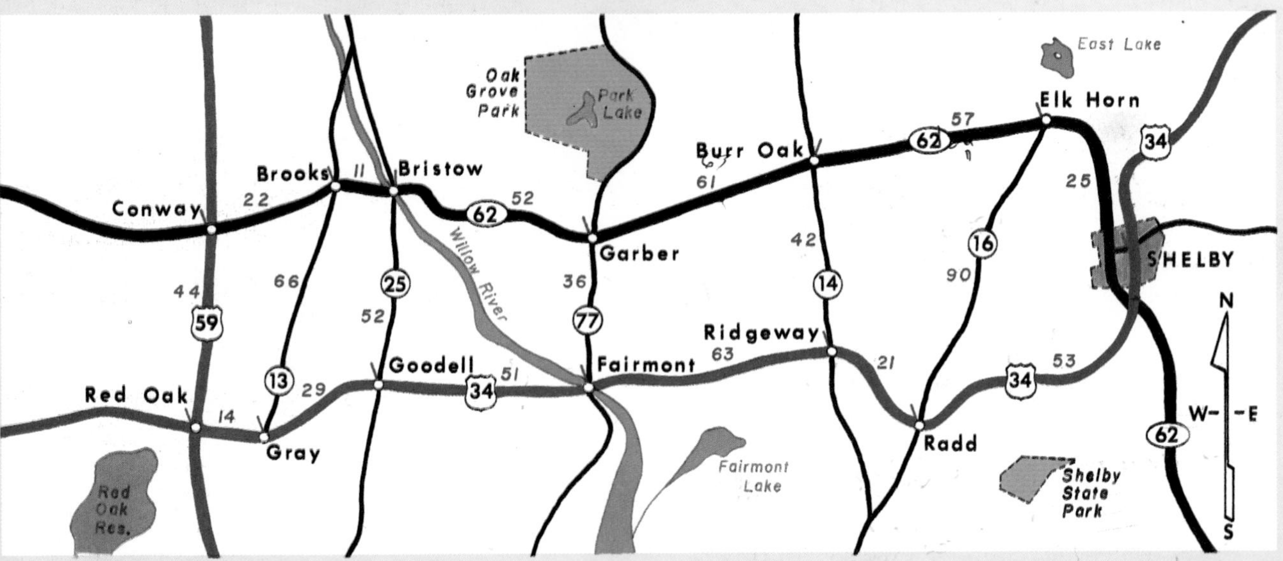

Use the map to answer the CB users' questions.

1. *I know it's 14 miles from Red Oak to Gray. How far is it from Gray to Fairmont?*

2. "How many miles is it from Conway to Garber?"

3. "Which city is about 180 miles east of Brooks?"

4. "I'm driving east on Highway 34. I'm 90 miles east of Red Oak. Which city will I drive through next?"

5. "I'm just crossing Willow River, traveling west on Highway 34. How far am I from Red Oak?"

6. "I'm at Red Oak on my way to Shelby. I plan to drive about 100 miles before lunch. At which city on Highway 34 should I stop and eat?"

7. "How far is it from Ridgeway to Bristow if I take Highways 14 and 62? Is that the shortest route?"

8. "I'm 150 miles west of Elk Horn on Highway 62. I'm headed for Conway. Is the next town Bristow or Brooks?"

9. "I want to take the shortest route from Elk Horn to Fairmont. What highways should I take?"

10. "I'm now traveling west on Highway 34. I just passed a sign that says Ridgeway is 15 miles ahead. How many miles am I from Goodell?"

11. "I'm 16 miles south of Bristow, going north on Highway 25. How far am I from Burr Oak?"

12. "I'm at Grant's Truckstop, 40 miles west of Burr Oak. How far am I from Shelby?"

Rounding whole numbers

EAST MEADOW MALL
GRAND OPENING
GUESS THE PRICE!
WIN THE CAR!
My guess is $________.
Name________
Address________
City________ State______ Zip______
Winner does not have to be present.

1. Carlos guessed $19,500. Joan guessed $19,600. The exact price of the sports car is $19,574. Whose guess was nearer the exact price?
2. Is $19,570 or $19,580 nearer the exact price?

Rounded numbers are often used in place of exact numbers.

Here's how *to round a whole number.*

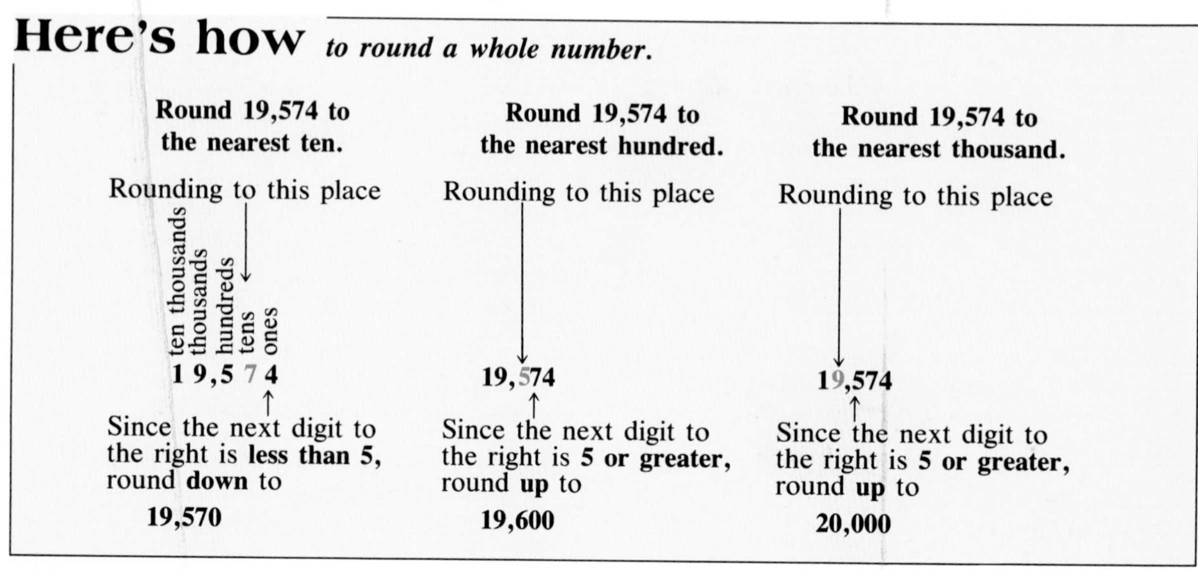

Round 19,574 to the nearest ten.
Rounding to this place
ten thousands
thousands
hundreds
tens
ones
1 9,5 7 4
Since the next digit to the right is **less than 5,** round **down** to
19,570
Round 19,574 to the nearest hundred.
Rounding to this place
19,574
Since the next digit to the right is **5 or greater,** round **up** to
19,600
Round 19,574 to the nearest thousand.
Rounding to this place
19,574
Since the next digit to the right is **5 or greater,** round **up** to
20,000

3. Look at the *Here's how*. In 19,574, which digit is in the ten thousands place? Is the next digit to the right 5 or greater?
4. Round 19,574 to the nearest ten thousand.

EXERCISES

Round to the nearest ten.

5. 73	**6.** 65	**7.** 6	**8.** 497	**9.** 521
10. 3	**11.** 2653	**12.** 4708	**13.** 6222	**14.** 6803

Round to the nearest hundred.

15. 378	**16.** 450	**17.** 99	**18.** 3692	**19.** 4987
20. 2509	**21.** 5621	**22.** 7770	**23.** 9050	**24.** 3021
25. 16,405	**26.** 25,980	**27.** 41,912	**28.** 53,950	**29.** 6092

Round to the nearest thousand.

30. 5732	**31.** 8026	**32.** 741	**33.** 8500	**34.** 203
35. 26,332	**36.** 41,582	**37.** 64,398	**38.** 50,225	**39.** 15,432
40. 236,479	**41.** 183,500	**42.** 379,199	**43.** 829,602	**44.** 699,999

Round to the nearest ten thousand.

45. 37,168	**46.** 42,600	**47.** 63,911	**48.** 9830	**49.** 17,302
50. 58,502	**51.** 47,300	**52.** 62,499	**53.** 92,888	**54.** 65,898
55. 239,100	**56.** 468,492	**57.** 623,619	**58.** 745,000	**59.** 99,999

Round.

60. During the first day of the grand opening at East Meadow, **13,721** shoppers entered the Guess the Sports-Car Price contest. Round the number to the nearest hundred.

61. A total of **173,517** shoppers entered the sports-car contest. Round the number to the nearest thousand.

Changing times

62. In 1921, you could buy this Model T for about $400. In an antique-car auction in 1982, this car sold for $[?].

To find [?], write a *6* in the tens place, a *9* in the hundreds place, a *4* in the ones place, and a *5* in the thousands place.

63. If the buyer at the auction used hundred-dollar bills to pay for the car, how many bills did he use? (*Hint: the buyer got back some bills in change.*)

Estimating sums

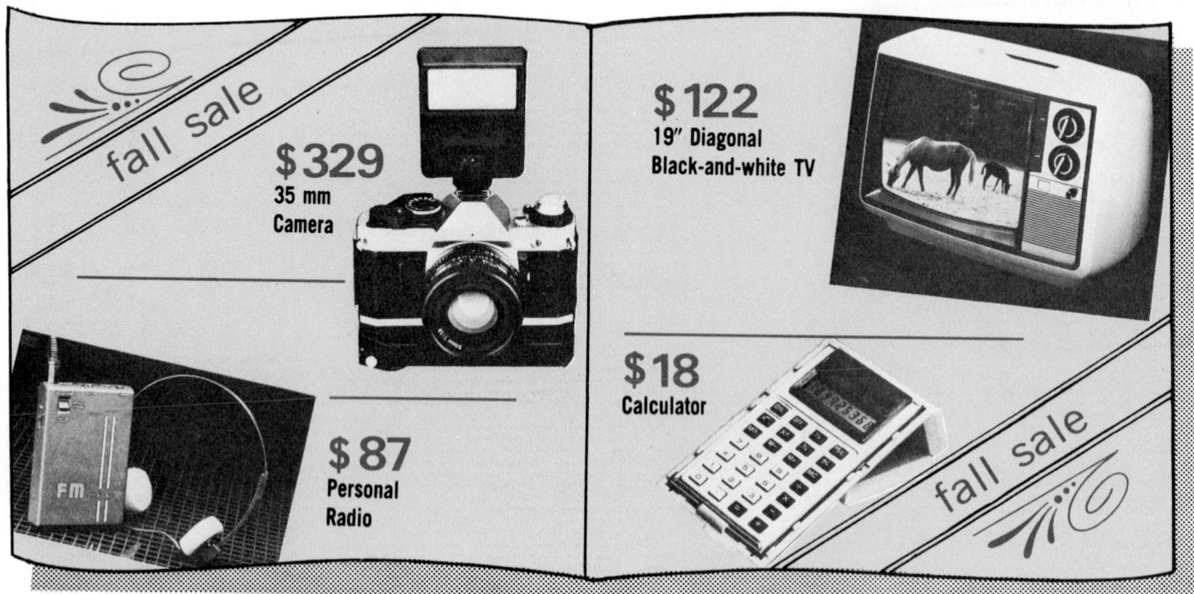

1. Which item costs about $300?
2. Which item costs about $90?
3. Which two prices would you round to estimate the total cost of the camera and the personal radio?

Here's how *to estimate sums.*

Round to the nearest ten dollars.

Ray
$329 → 330
$87 →+ 90
$420

Round to the nearest hundred dollars.

Cindy
$329 → 300
$87 →+100
$400

4. What is the actual total cost of the camera and the personal radio?
5. Look at the *Here's how*. Whose estimate was closer to the actual total cost, Ray's or Cindy's?
6. Use Ray's method. Which two items cost about $110?
7. Use Cindy's method. Which two items cost about $200?

EXERCISES

Which estimate would Cindy give? *Hint: Study the* Here's how.

	a.	b.	c.
8. \$325 + \$479	**a.** \$600	**b.** \$800	**c.** \$1000
9. \$281 + \$94 + \$319	**a.** \$700	**b.** \$1000	**c.** \$1300
10. \$631 + \$477 + \$819	**a.** \$1300	**b.** \$1600	**c.** \$1900

Which estimate would Ray give?

	a.	b.	c.
11. \$789 + \$42	**a.** \$810	**b.** \$830	**c.** \$850
12. \$37 + \$86 + \$129	**a.** \$230	**b.** \$260	**c.** \$290
13. \$29 + \$43 + \$68	**a.** \$140	**b.** \$170	**c.** \$200

Estimate each sum by rounding to the nearest hundred dollars.

14. \$428 + 583 (\$400 + 600)

15. \$685 + 519

16. \$867 + 109

17. \$929 + 409

18. \$789 + 239

19. \$581 + 302 + 18 (\$600 + 300 + 0)

20. \$106 + 18 + 289

21. \$ 22 + 599 + 372

22. \$928 + 82 + 614

23. \$871 + 28 + 79

Estimate each sum by rounding to the nearest ten.

24. 281 + 78 **25.** 329 + 19 **26.** 49 + 53 **27.** 39 + 43 + 19

28. 27 + 86 + 39 **29.** 78 + 23 + 49 **30.** 96 + 32 + 12 **31.** 448 + 89 + 72

32. 24 + 81 + 16 **33.** 305 + 17 + 29 **34.** 28 + 486 + 5 **35.** 16 + 24 + 111

36. 98 + 14 + 29 **37.** 15 + 82 + 199 **38.** 254 + 60 + 1 **39.** 14 + 86 + 999

40. 69 + 35 + 42 **41.** 38 + 246 + 10 **42.** 521 + 62 + 15 **43.** 87 + 6 + 981

Jewelry juggle Estimating costs

WALKER'S
GRAND OPENING SALE
14K Gold Chain \$209
Quartz Watch \$415
Emerald Ring \$88
Diamond Pendant \$679
Silver Charm \$19
East Meadow Mall

Use your estimation skills. Which two items cost about

44. \$500? **45.** \$1100? **46.** \$300?

47. \$110? **48.** \$700? **49.** \$900?

Which three items cost about

50. \$700? **51.** \$500? **52.** \$300?

53. \$1200? **54.** \$800? **55.** \$1300?

Reading decimals

The decimal shows the time (in seconds) that it took the skier to complete her first downhill run.

SPLIT SECONDS!

Tens	Ones		Tenths	Hundredths
5	7	.	6	8

1. In what place is the digit *6*?

2. In what place is the last digit?

Here's how *to read decimals.*

Her first run took **57 and 68 hundredths** seconds. Notice that the decimal point is read as "and" and the place of the last digit is read last.

Here are some more examples of how to read decimals:

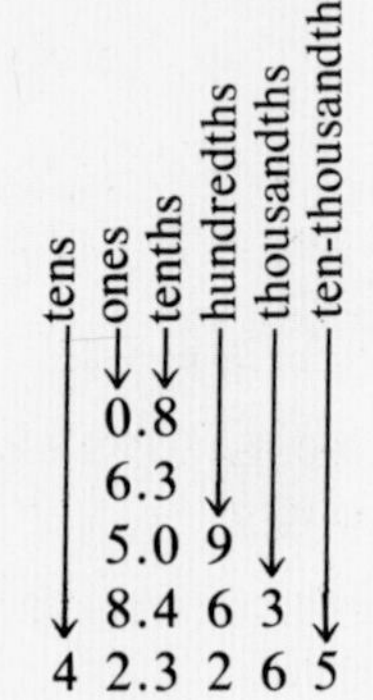

STANDARD NUMERAL	SHORT WORD-NAME
0.8	8 tenths
6.3	6 and 3 tenths
5.09	5 and 9 hundredths
8.463	8 and 463 thousandths
42.3265	42 and 3265 ten-thousandths

3. Look at the *Here's how*. To read 57.68, you say "57 and 68 [?]."

4. To read 8.463, you say "8 and 463 [?]."

EXERCISES

In what place is the last digit?

5. 16.3 *tenths* **6.** 0.357 **7.** 6.25 **8.** 0.4216 **9.** 2.069

10. 16.38 **11.** 26.9 **12.** 0.0371 **13.** 19.6421 **14.** 58.4

15. 13.005 **16.** 24.57 **17.** 8.0007 **18.** 220.68 **19.** 126.9

20. 8.594 **21.** 1206.74 **22.** 1.7241 **23.** 0.003 **24.** 468.2

Write the short word-name.

25. 3.5 *3 and 5 tenths* **26.** 12.35 **27.** 0.125 **28.** 17.003 **29.** 9.02

30. 0.025 **31.** 14.9 **32.** 3.0075 **33.** 0.0634 **34.** 253.61

35. 72.006 **36.** 0.0594 **37.** 631.74 **38.** 3.1005 **39.** 0.875

40. 3968.4 **41.** 860.2 **42.** 9002.11 **43.** 63.0004 **44.** 0.4005

45. 4216.9 **46.** 421.69 **47.** 42.169 **48.** 4.2169 **49.** 0.0062

Write the standard numeral.

50. 2 thousandths *0.002*

51. 25 and 4 tenths

52. 12 and 3 hundredths

53. 2 thousandths

54. 34 and 32 hundredths

55. 164 and 58 hundredths

56. 452 thousandths

57. 27 and 148 thousandths

58. 9 and 75 thousandths

59. 8 and 6 thousandths

60. 4275 ten-thousandths

61. 20 and 840 ten-thousandths

Speed records

Copy the numeral and place a decimal point so that the statement makes sense. *Hint: Use Bill's chart.*

62. The world speed record for a skateboard is **718** miles per hour.

63. The world speed record for a bicycle is **140525** miles per hour.

64. Top speed for roller skates is **2578** miles per hour.

Cumulative Skill Practice

Add. *(pages 6, 8)*

1. 7406 + 1629	**2.** 2917 + 2579	**3.** 824 + 5081	**4.** 1056 + 3780	**5.** 3643 + 8561
6. 53,246 + 2,107	**7.** 38,529 + 4,266	**8.** 17,329 + 54,600	**9.** 51,083 + 74,291	**10.** 38,294 + 27,461
11. 83,174 + 29,356	**12.** 71,892 + 71,892	**13.** 56,093 + 8,714	**14.** 30,005 + 6,999	**15.** 43,770 + 29,846
16. 76,391 + 28,477	**17.** 63,085 + 25,473	**18.** 69,377 + 44,293	**19.** 58,296 + 87,742	**20.** 64,888 + 59,999

21. 76 + 82 + 53
22. 374 + 29 + 659
23. 572 + 153 + 604
24. 3982 + 427 + 965
25. 428 + 3461 + 2009
26. 4721 + 3066 + 5814
27. 52,140 + 89 + 2417
28. 17 + 2573 + 43,880
29. 889 + 14 + 72,354
30. 68,613 + 19,216 + 526
31. 909 + 7326 + 27
32. 3068 + 402 + 25,162

Round to the nearest ten. *(page 12)*

33. 62	**34.** 85	**35.** 151	**36.** 438	**37.** 395	**38.** 982
39. 216	**40.** 302	**41.** 461	**42.** 285	**43.** 373	**44.** 795
45. 5675	**46.** 3502	**47.** 6296	**48.** 8743	**49.** 9608	**50.** 6304
51. 3438	**52.** 5164	**53.** 8750	**54.** 2309	**55.** 6791	**56.** 9997

Write the standard numeral. *(page 16)*

57. 9 tenths
58. 6 hundredths
59. 4 thousandths
60. 15 hundredths
61. 36 thousandths
62. 147 thousandths
63. 6 and 3 tenths
64. 22 and 81 hundredths
65. 40 and 5 hundredths
66. 36 and 235 ten-thousandths
67. 28 and 16 thousandths
68. 9 and 1374 ten-thousandths
69. 45 and 4653 ten-thousandths
70. 38 and 491 ten-thousandths

Problem solving

You have a summer job at the Lincoln Woods Mountain Slide. You sell tickets and work in the gift shop.

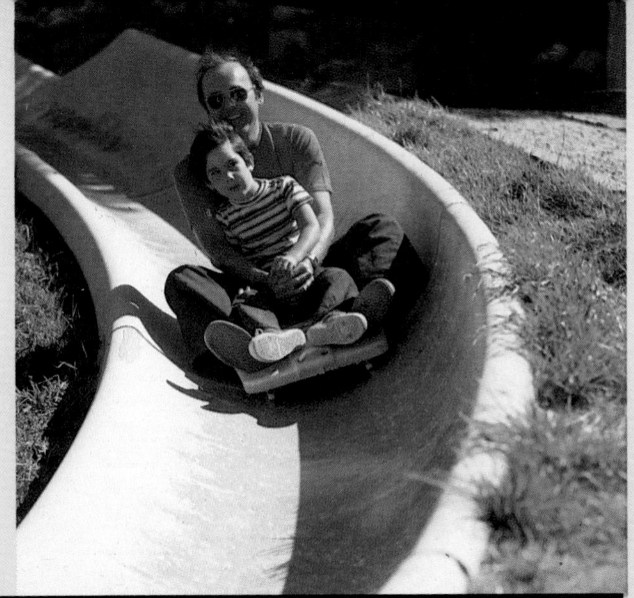

RIDE THE *SLIDE!*	TICKET PRICES
	Adult (18 and over) . . . $2.25 Student (12 to 18) . . . . . $1.50 Child (under 12) $1.00

Use the chart to answer these customers' questions.

1. *How much will 2 adult tickets cost?*

2. *How much for 2 adult tickets and 1 child's ticket?*

3. *5 students and 1 adult, please. How much do I owe you?*

4. "I have $5.00. Can I buy tickets for 2 adults and 1 child?" *Hint: Use your answer to problem 2.*

5. "Is $10.00 enough money to buy 1 adult ticket and 5 student tickets?"

6. "My sister has $4.75 and I have $3.50."

- **a.** "How much do we have altogether?"
- **b.** "Do we have enough money to buy 5 student tickets?"

7.
- **a.** "What is the total cost of 1 student ticket and 1 child's ticket?"
- **b.** "My father decided not to ride. Can we trade his adult ticket for 1 student ticket and 1 child's ticket?"

Solve.

8. Your ticket sales for today were 350 children's, 249 students', and 123 adults'.

- **a.** How many tickets did you sell in all?
- **b.** Yesterday you sold a total of 738 tickets. Did you sell at least that many tickets today?

9. Bumper-sticker sales for today were 24 *LINCOLN WOODS*, 72 *ZIPPER*, and 63 *MOUNTAIN SLIDE*.

- **a.** Which bumper sticker had the highest number of sales?
- **b.** What were the combined sales of the *ZIPPER* and the *MOUNTAIN SLIDE*?

Rounding decimals

Kitty O'Neil holds the land speed record for women. Driving her 48,000-horsepower rocket-powered car, she averaged 512.715 miles per hour. It took her over 5 miles just to stop!

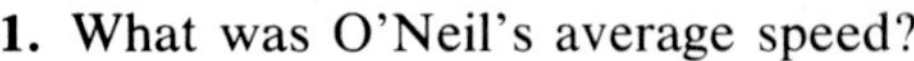

1. What was O'Neil's average speed?

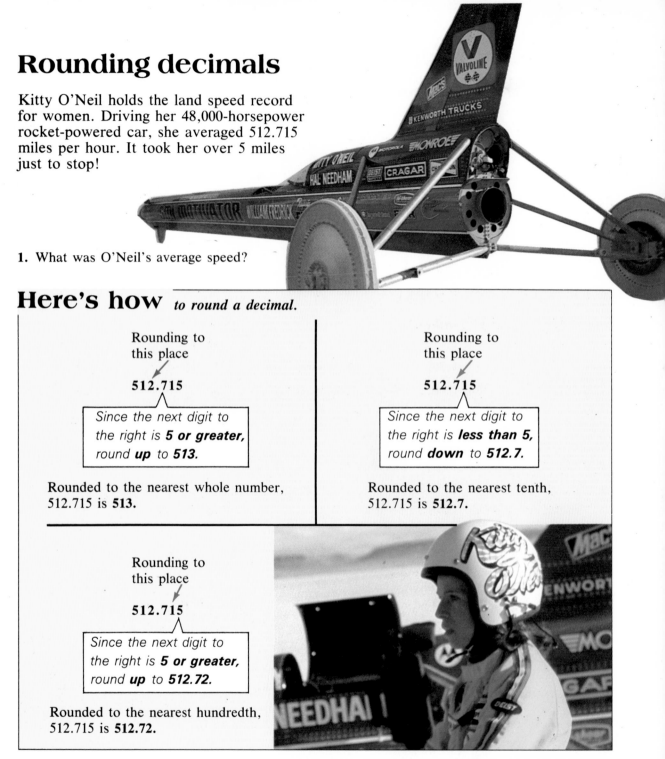

Here's how *to round a decimal.*

Rounding to this place

512.715

*Since the next digit to the right is **5 or greater,** round **up** to **513.***

Rounded to the nearest whole number, 512.715 is **513.**

Rounding to this place

512.715

*Since the next digit to the right is **less than 5,** round **down** to **512.7.***

Rounded to the nearest tenth, 512.715 is **512.7.**

Rounding to this place

512.715

*Since the next digit to the right is **5 or greater,** round **up** to **512.72.***

Rounded to the nearest hundredth, 512.715 is **512.72.**

2. Was O'Neil's speed closer to 512 miles per hour or 513 miles per hour?

EXERCISES

Round to the nearest whole number.

3. 15.7 4. 47.2 5. 0.25 6. 35.34 7. 0.95
8. 52.19 9. 28.928 10. 69.523 11. 421.073 12. 99.786
13. 215.07 14. 429.562 15. 0.895 16. 76.0125 17. 25.21
18. 97.612 19. 10.72 20. 172.26 21. 51.347 22. 0.86

Round to the nearest tenth.

23. 1.62 24. 28.108 25. 7.28 26. 0.552 27. 7.342
28. 2.460 29. 69.169 30. 31.03 31. 9.381 32. 8.1106
33. 705.49 34. 913.91 35. 0.056 36. 43.012 37. 53.299
38. 4.295 39. 0.123 40. 72.575 41. 2.107 42. 41.0086

Round to the nearest hundredth.

43. 18.216 44. 38.107 45. 2.543 46. 61.625 47. 84.612
48. 83.581 49. 4.2029 50. 0.0254 51. 8.3815 52. 0.013
53. 6.3522 54. 0.005 55. 16.949 56. 234.789 57. 13.023
58. 2.1685 59. 12.825 60. 5.201 61. 398.166 62. 4.117

Round to the nearest dollar.

63. \$7.77 64. \$14.48 65. \$234.61 66. \$67.52 67. \$24.87
68. \$35.92 69. \$35.50 70. \$129.79 71. \$99.89 72. \$3.02
73. \$179.79 74. \$42.49 75. \$2.55 76. \$34.09 77. \$48.91

You're a reporter **Using a chart**

Use the chart. Complete the story.

78. On August __?__ (date), __?__ (year), ______?______ (driver's name) in the ______?______ (car's name) set a new one-mile speed record of about 410 miles per hour.

79. On October __?__ (date), __?__ (year), ______?______ (driver's name) in the ______?______ (car's name) set a new record of nearly 540 miles per hour.

One-Mile Speed Records

DATE	DRIVER	CAR	MPH
9/3/35	Campbell	Bluebird Special	301.13
9/16/38	Eyston	Thunderbolt 1	357.5
9/16/47	Cobb	Railton-Mobil	394.2
8/5/63	Breedlove	Spirit of America	407.45
10/27/64	Arfons	Green Monster	536.71
11/15/65	Breedlove	Spirit of America	600.601
10/23/70	Gabelich	Blue Flame	622.407

Adding decimals

You are a disc jockey! You have a request to play some songs from the soundtracks of old Beatles movies. The list below shows some of the songs you plan to play.

SONG	PLAYING TIME (IN MINUTES)
A Hard Day's Night	2.47
I Am the Walrus	4.57
And I Love Her	2.45
Help!	2.28
Yellow Submarine	2.62
Let It Be	4.02
Ticket to Ride	3.10
The Long and Winding Road	3.60

1. How many minutes will it take to play *A Hard Day's Night*?
2. How many minutes will it take to play *I Am the Walrus*?
3. Would you add or subtract to find the number of minutes needed to play both songs?

Here's how *to add decimals.* *2.47 + 4.57 = ?*

Line up the decimal points.	Add hundredths and regroup.	Add tenths and regroup.	Add ones.
2.47 +4.57	1 2.47 +4.57 4	1 1 2.47 +4.57 .04	1 1 2.47 +4.57 7.04

4. Study the *Here's how*. How long will it take you to play both songs?

EXERCISES

Add. *Here are scrambled answers for the next row of exercises:*
19.6 9.1 13.4 8.7 10.7 10.4

5. 6.3 + 2.4
6. 8.5 + 0.6
7. 9.8 + 9.8
8. 8.6 + 4.8
9. 6.5 + 3.9
10. 7.2 + 3.5

11. 5.26 +3.42	**12.** 6.74 +3.19	**13.** 8.65 +4.93	**14.** 5.99 +0.86	**15.** 2.48 +0.06	**16.** 7.91 +3.14
17. 52.83 + 1.95	**18.** 73.47 + 8.61	**19.** 5.09 +34.84	**20.** 641.1 + 74.9	**21.** 63.84 + 9.66	**22.** 2.43 +1.11
23. 5.6 3.9 +8.4	**24.** 9.4 5.9 +4.3	**25.** 42.6 55.7 +62.8	**26.** 8.96 3.74 +5.09	**27.** 81.6 5.9 +17.4	**28.** 87.2 1.3 +15.2
29. 3.8 2.6 0.7 +1.5	**30.** 2.93 1.06 5.11 +4.04	**31.** 23.5 8.6 13.4 + 9.7	**32.** 23.48 9.57 14.22 + 3.08	**33.** 15.60 21.47 5.92 +11.05	**34.** 24.13 3.40 15.91 + 2.03

. 5.8 + 2.9	**36.** 9.4 + 3.7	**37.** 12.0 + 7.5
38. 19.8 + 6.5	**39.** 4.32 + 1.65	**40.** 0.83 + 9.07
41. 6.93 + 1.86	**42.** 81.3 + 26.5	**43.** 9.4 + 3.8
44. 1.16 + 3.28 + 5.36	4.07 + 0.35 + 1.68	**46.** 2.06 + 3.18 + 6.95
47. 16.3 + 0.8 + 5.7	**48.** 3.99 + 0.87 + 5.77	**49.** 2.74 + 3.95 + 6.05

Solve. Refer to the list on page 22.

50. How many minutes will it take you to play *A Hard Day's Night* and *Help!*?

51. How many minutes will it take you to play the two shortest songs on the list?

52. You play *And I Love Her*, read a 0.75-minute commercial, then play *Yellow Submarine*. How much program time do you use?

53. You have 10 minutes left in your show. Do you have time to play *Let It Be*, *Ticket to Ride*, and *The Long and Winding Road*?

54. How many minutes will be needed to play the two longest songs on the list?

55. Which four songs can you play in less than 10 minutes?

Key it in!

Find a way to push each marked key once to get the answer.

56.

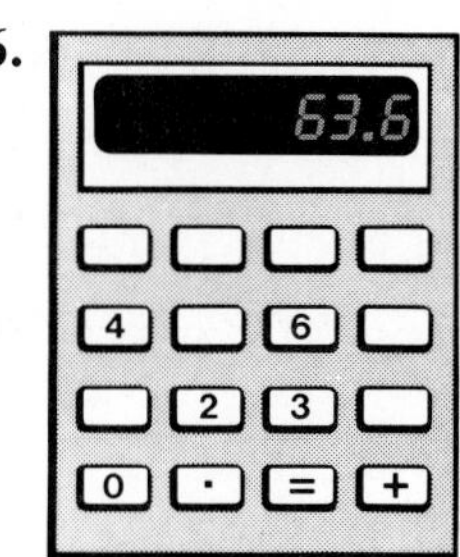

57.

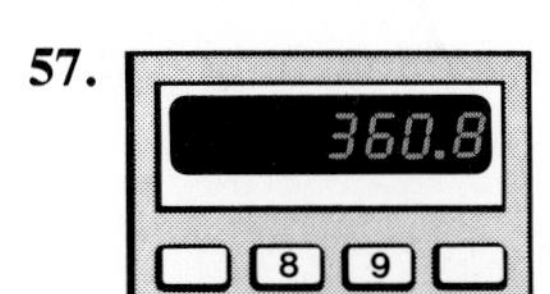

58.

More on adding decimals

MULTIMILLION–DOLLAR DEAL

Rolling Hills, KY Unicorn Acres, the largest local horse farm, made two near-record sales at yesterday's thoroughbred auction. Western Dancer was sold for \$2.835 million, and Miss Smoothy went for \$1.39 million.

Western Dancer and his new owner, Alice Logan of Saratoga, NY.

1. Read the newspaper report. What was Western Dancer's sale price?
2. What was Miss Smoothy's sale price?
3. Would you add or subtract to find the amount of the total sale in millions of dollars?

Here's how *to add decimals.* ***2.835 + 1.39 = ?***

Line up the decimal points.	Add.
2.835 +1.39	2.835 +1.39 4.225

To estimate the sum, I first round each number to the nearest whole number and then add. 3 + 1 = 4. So the total sale price was about \$4 million.

4. Look at the *Here's how*. Would \$4 million be a good estimate?

EXERCISES

5. Three of the calculator answers are wrong. Find them by estimating.

a.	58.07 + 9.784	67.854	**b.**	29.799 + 21.042	50.841
c.	8.0654 + 2.8152	10.8806	**d.**	34.968 + 12.141	69.109
e.	63.597 + 8.295	71.892	**f.**	6.9537 + 4.8806	11.8343
g.	43.952 + 14.231	58.183	**h.**	7.693 + 8.444	161.35
i.	53.809 + 20.298	94.109	**j.**	5.3975 + 0.7055	6.103

Chapter REVIEW

Here are scrambled answers for the review exercises:

4, 8, 13, 80, billion, decimal, greater, hundreds, hundredths, million, sum, tenths, thousand, thousandths

1. The short word-name for this number is 2 [?], 74 [?]. *(page 4)*

2,074,000

2. The long word-name for this number is two [?], six million, fifty-four thousand. *(page 4)*

2,006,054,000

3. The answer to an addition exercise is called the [?]. To complete this addition exercise, add the digits in the [?] place. *(page 6)*

328
+154
82

...o round this number ...e nearest hundred, ...ok at the digit in the ...ace. Since it is [?] ...round the hundreds ...o [?]. *(page 12)*

...382

5. To estimate this sum, round each amount to the nearest ten dollars. The estimated sum is [?] dollars. *(page 14)*

$54
+32

6. The short word-name for this number is 24 and 86 [?]. *(page 16)*

24.086

...is number ...hole ...uld first ...n the [?] ...ess than ...the ...e 20)

8. To do this addition exercise, first add the digits in the [?] place. *(page 22)*

5.78
+2.95

9. Round each number to the nearest whole number and estimate the sum. The estimate is [?]. To find the sum, line up the [?] points and add. *(page 24)*

2.94 + 10.2 = ?

First estimate the sum and then add.

6. 18.33 + 9.40 **7.** 19.783 + 15.95 **8.** 26.3 + 24.0 **9.** 17 + 8.56 **10.** 16.33 + 38.994

11. \$4.32 + 3.18 **12.** \$7 + 4.35 **13.** \$12.52 + 9 **14.** \$18.06 + 7.29 **15.** \$23.56 + 17

16. \$32.21 + 19 **17.** \$25 + 3.98 **18.** \$52.06 + 8.35 **19.** \$46.53 + 9.00 **20.** \$8.57 + 2

21. 3.329 + 6.437 **22.** 9.509 + 7.388 **23.** 7.4206 + 0.7835 **24.** 9.684 + 6.70 **25.** 16.942 + 9.77

26. 5.96 + 8.842 **27.** 16.543 + 8.92 **28.** 8.04 + 2.973 **29.** 16.295 + 12.03 **30.** 6.4928 + 9.653

31. 5.6 + 3.84 + 2.9 **32.** 5.72 + 3.6 + 2.89 **33.** 8 + 2.74 + 3.6 **34.** 8.07 + 4 + 3.99 **35.** 7.4 + 3.75 + 16

36. 5.18 + 4 **37.** 5 + 2.63 **38.** 1.8 + 9.38

39. 7.04 + 2.9 **40.** 8.62 + 5 **41.** 7 + 4.6

42. 4.16 + 0.379 **43.** 27.6 + 9.28 **44.** 7.88 + 0.594

45. 3.21 + 0.853 **46.** 0.174 + 6.76 **47.** 3.0683 + 1.925

48. 5.8 + 2.42 + 6.3 **49.** 19.4 + 31.6 + 8.74 **50.** 52 + 3.6 + 1.8

51. 2.5 + 17 + 0.8 **52.** 30 + 2.9 + 0.541 **53.** 2.6 + 4 + 0.75

54. 0.06 + 0.4 + 2 **55.** 0.8 + 0.36 + 0.04 **56.** 12 + 1.2 + 0.372

57. 5.36 + 0.1 + 0.4 **58.** 9 + 3.2 + 0.15 **59.** 6 + 7.2 + 9.184

And the winner is . . . Reading a chart

60. Which horse won \$1.98 million?

61. Which horse won \$1.46 million?

62. Which horse won \$1.75 million?

63. Which horse won about \$2.4 million?

64. Which horse won \$1.18 million more than Seattle Slew?

Thoroughbred Racing—Money Winners

HORSE	TOTAL WINNINGS
Spectacular Bid	**\$2,390,000**
Kelso	**1,980,000**
Forego	**1,940,000**
Round Table	**1,750,000**
Buckpasser	**1,460,000**
Seattle Slew	**1,210,000**

Cumulative Skill Practice

Round to the nearest tenth. *(page 20)*

1. 0.42 2. 8.55 3. 6.69 4. 13.42 5. 50.98
6. 2.436 7. 8.761 8. 18.250 9. 27.342 10. 71.062
11. 3.8214 12. 6.3500 13. 9.6175 14. 14.0924 15. 26.9341

Round to the nearest hundredth. *(page 20)*

16. 2.726 17. 4.634 18. 4.205 19. 2.371 20. 8.082
21. 1.0314 22. 7.2936 23. 5.1171 24. 9.0853 25. 6.6152
26. 4.5347 27. 6.0821 28. 3.6349 29. 8.5981 30. 2.7436

Add. *(page 22)*

31. 8.1 + 2.3 32. 6.7 + 2.8 33. 5.9 + 5.9 34. 7.4 + 6.8 35. 4.8 + 3.6 36. 6.2 + 9.1
37. 4.72 + 3.61 38. 5.08 + 2.74 39. 3.96 + 0.84 40. 9.72 + 1.99 41. 3.86 + 0.44 42. 4.02 + 1.77
43. 53.6 + 29.4 44. 7.38 + 2.97 45. 5.33 + 0.46 46. 9.74 + 2.38 47. 5.75 + 5.75 48. 6.03 + 6.03
49. 5.6, 2.9, + 3.4 50. 6.82, 3.74, + 2.96 51. 15.4, 38.3, + 29.7 52. 8.72, 6.91, + 4.75 53. 5.93, 8.41, + 1.09 54. 5.91, 2.33, + 1.09

Give the sum. *(page 24)*

55. 2.1 + 3.46 56. 5.78 + 2.92 57. 8.14 + 35.6
58. 2.74 + 0.635 59. 0.182 + 7.853 60. 4.0831 + 2.619
61. 6.2 + 3.14 + 7.4 62. 15.8 + 42.6 + 3.95 63. 36 + 5.4 + 2.9
64. 7.5 + 18 + 0.6 65. 50 + 4.7 + 0.184 66. 7.7 + 6 + 0.92
67. 0.05 + 0.8 + 6 68. 0.1 + 0.73 + 0.05 69. 15 + 1.5 + 0.15
70. 5 + 2.3 + 6.4 71. 5.9 + 2.7 + 5.4 72. 18 + 6.7 + 3.4
73. 9.23 + 6.04 + 5.8 74. 16 + 3.74 + 19 75. 22.8 + 3.5 + 31
76. 0.03 + 2 + 2.1 77. 6.3841 + 2.9871 + 4.0035 78. 6.281 + 3.091 + 15.26

Problem solving

COMPUTERS IN BANKING

Many banks have computers to operate machines that can be used by customers 24 hours a day. Customers can use these "24-hour tellers" to deposit and withdraw money, make payments, and check account balances. The customer follows directions that appear on the screen. The computer makes the transaction and prints a record of it.

When Justine inserts her card and enters her personal identification number, this message appears on the screen.

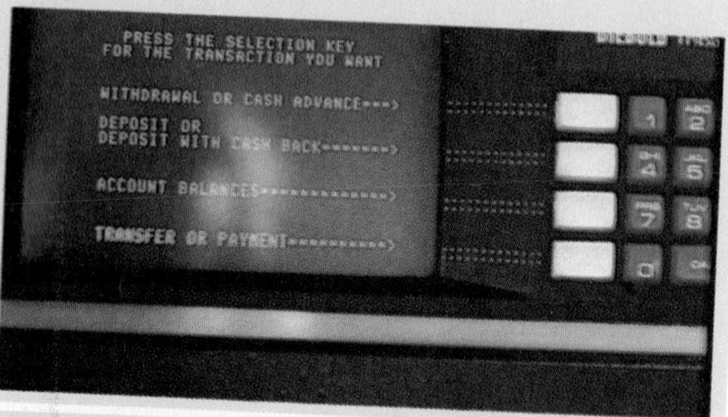

When she wants to make a withdrawal message appears.

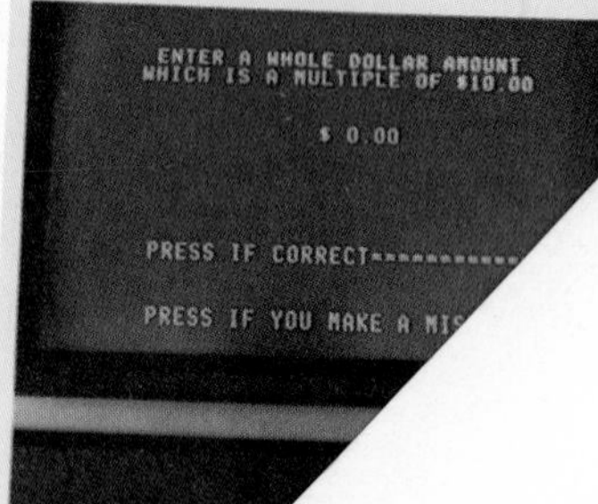

Solve.

1. If Justine needs $27, she has to withdraw $30. How much would she withdraw if she needs
   a. $18.57? b. $69.50? c. $31.95?
   d. $185.99? e. $ 5.92? f. $299.30?

2. J

3. In October Justine made these deposit her checking account:

   October 5 $78.00
   October 14 $89.00
   October 20 $65.00
   October 31 $83.00

   a. What was the amount of her la deposit in October?
   b. Did Justine deposit more than $350 in October?

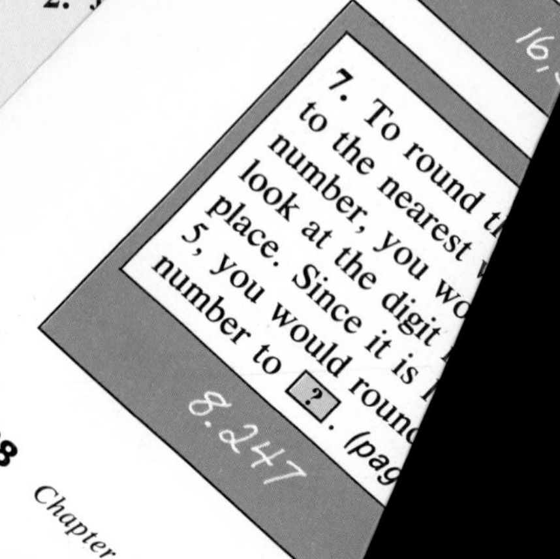

Chapter TEST

Write the short word-name. *(page 4)*

1. 25,340 **2.** 836,000 **3.** 19,046,000 **4.** 25,000,260 **5.** 6,330,000,000

Write the standard numeral. *(page 4)*

6. 9 thousand 420
7. 63 million, 75 thousand, 436
8. five hundred nine thousand
9. sixteen million, eighty-three thousand

Add. *(pages 6, 8)*

10. $\begin{array}{r} 52 \\ +36 \\ \hline \end{array}$ **11.** $\begin{array}{r} 349 \\ +142 \\ \hline \end{array}$ **12.** $\begin{array}{r} 396 \\ +158 \\ \hline \end{array}$ **13.** $\begin{array}{r} 6381 \\ +2974 \\ \hline \end{array}$ **14.** $\begin{array}{r} 26,352 \\ +\ 8,968 \\ \hline \end{array}$ **15.** $\begin{array}{r} 79,368 \\ +14,973 \\ \hline \end{array}$

16. 74 + 39 + 98 **17.** 25 + 82 + 9 **18.** 236 + 95 + 381 + 74

Round to the nearest hundred. *(page 12)*

19. 634 **20.** 850 **21.** 961 **22.** 13,439 **23.** 42,956 **24.** 908

Write the short word-name. *(page 16)*

25. 5.9 **26.** 38.06 **27.** 9.274 **28.** 0.063 **29.** 7.0865 **30.** 6.803

Write the standard numeral. *(page 16)*

31. 26 and 43 hundredths **32.** 8 and 61 thousandths **33.** 60 and 52 ten-thousandths

Round to the nearest tenth. *(page 20)*

34. 6.38 **35.** 15.43 **36.** 9.75 **37.** 8.064 **38.** 6.98 **39.** 8.87

Add. *(pages 22, 24)*

40. $\begin{array}{r} 8.4 \\ +2.3 \\ \hline \end{array}$ **41.** $\begin{array}{r} 15.9 \\ +\ 8.7 \\ \hline \end{array}$ **42.** $\begin{array}{r} 6.09 \\ +2.954 \\ \hline \end{array}$ **43.** $\begin{array}{r} 15.936 \\ +\ 8.742 \\ \hline \end{array}$ **44.** $\begin{array}{l} 3.750 \\ +8.6 \\ \hline \end{array}$ **45.** $\begin{array}{l} 6.36 \\ +1.2 \\ \hline \end{array}$

46. 8.3 + 2.9 **47.** 2.7 + 3.45 **48.** 6.01 + 8.213 **49.** 3.06 + 2.784 + 5.39

BARBARA'S KITCHEN

Vegetable Soup	$ .85
Chili	1.35
Beefburger	1.65
Grilled Cheese	1.40
Hot Dog	1.15
Milk	.45
Orange Juice	.60

Solve.

50. How much for a beefburger and milk?

51. What is the total cost of a bowl of chili, a grilled cheese sandwich, and orange juice?

You have $3.00. Can you buy 2 hot dogs and an orange juice?

Cumulative TEST Standardized Format

Choose the correct letter.

1. The short word-name for 5,060,000 is

A. 5 million, 600 thousand
B. 5 million, 6 thousand
C. 5 billion, 60 million
D. none of these

2. The standard numeral for five billion, twenty-five million is

A. 5,025,000
B. 5,000,025,000
C. 5,025,000,000
D. none of these

3. The standard numeral for thirty-two million is

A. 32,000
B. 32,000,000
C. 32,000,000,000
D. none of these

4. Add.

$$\begin{array}{r} 563 \\ 291 \\ +\ 87 \\ \hline \end{array}$$

A. 941
B. 931
C. 741
D. none of these

5. Give the sum.

327 + 84 + 219

A. 1386
B. 610
C. 630
D. none of these

6. 2895 rounded to the nearest ten is

A. 3000
B. 2890
C. 2900
D. none of these

7. The standard numeral for 15 and 34 thousandths is

A. 15.034
B. 15.34
C. 15.0034
D. none of these

8. 36.952 rounded to the nearest tenth is

A. 36.9
B. 36.95
C. 37.0
D. none of these

9. 54.0349 rounded to the nearest hundredth is

A. 54.035
B. 54.04
C. 54.03
D. none of these

10. Add.

$$\begin{array}{r} 3.82 \\ 2.09 \\ +6.57 \\ \hline \end{array}$$

A. 12.48
B. 11.38
C. 11.48
D. none of these

11. Give the sum.

36.3 + 8.09 + 5.96

A. 17.68
B. 39.25
C. 49.35
D. none of these

12. What is the total price of 2 adult tickets and 1 child's ticket?

A. $6.25　B. $8.00
C. $4.75　D. none of these

Chapter 2
Subtracting Whole Numbers and Decimals

Comparing whole numbers

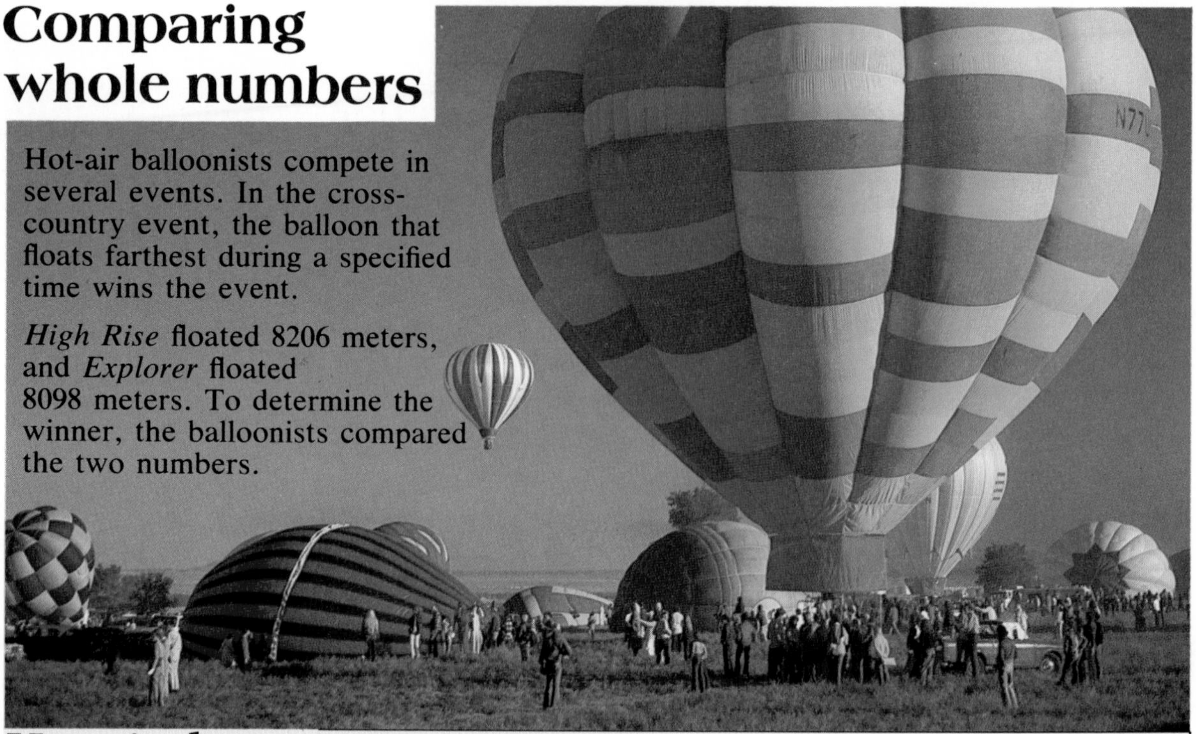

Hot-air balloonists compete in several events. In the cross-country event, the balloon that floats farthest during a specified time wins the event.

High Rise floated 8206 meters, and *Explorer* floated 8098 meters. To determine the winner, the balloonists compared the two numbers.

Here's how *to compare whole numbers.* *8206 ● 8098*

To compare two whole numbers, start at the left and compare the digits that are in the same place.

Step 1.

8206 ● 8098

same

Step 2.

8206 ● 8098

2 is greater than 0.

Step 3.

So, 8206 > 8098.
Read > as "is greater than."

1. Look at the *Here's how.* Which balloon won (floated the greater distance)?

Study these examples.

Example A.

2 is less than 5.

So, 3628 < 3659.
Read < as "is less than."

Example B.

ten thousands place ↓ 53,402 > No digit here! ↓ 6348

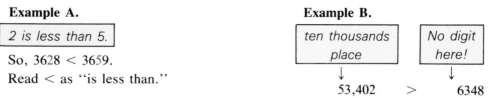

2. Look at Example B. Are the digits 5 and 6 in the same place?

EXERCISES

Less than (<) or greater than (>)?

3. 783 ● 784 **4.** 593 ● 590 **5.** 856 ● 1200 **6.** 1342 ● 819

7. 3621 ● 3514 **8.** 5834 ● 5741 **9.** 9834 ● 9843 **10.** 6519 ● 6514

11. 68,352 ● 68,411 **12.** 39,436 ● 39,400 **13.** 88,361 ● 89,000

14. 29,361 ● 30,362 **15.** 86,000 ● 85,999 **16.** 74,399 ● 74,000

17. 634,298 ● 624,298 **18.** 714,362 ● 714,459 **19.** 597,821 ● 609,375

20. 560,000 ● 559,000 **21.** 900,000 ● 879,694 **22.** 89,999 ● 900,000

Solve.

23. The results of the spot-landing event are shown in the table. The winner is the balloon that lands closest to a certain spot.

a. Which balloon came in first (landed closest to the spot)?

b. Which balloon came in last?

c. List the balloons in order of finish, from first to last.

SPOT-LANDING EVENT	
NAME OF BALLOON	METERS LANDED FROM SPOT
America	**834**
Big Apple	**929**
Easy Floater	**938**
Free Spirit	**763**
High Flier	**771**
Up and Away	**840**

24. Remember that the winner of the cross-country event is the balloon that floats the farthest.

a. Which balloon came in first?

b. Which balloon came in last?

c. List the balloons in order of finish, from first to last.

CROSS-COUNTRY EVENT	
NAME OF BALLOON	METERS TRAVELED
America	**12,642**
Big Apple	**10,837**
Easy Floater	**11,134**
Free Spirit	**11,099**
High Flier	**10,909**
Up and Away	**12,800**

Test pilots wanted

25. The first "test pilots" on a hot-air balloon were a duck, a rooster, and a sheep. The historic flight took place in the year [?]. Study these clues to find the year.

Clues:

- If you round the year to the nearest ten, you get 1780.
- If you add the digits of the year, you get 19.

Subtracting 2- and 3-digit numbers

WHAT WOULD YOU SAY?

Twelve hundred people were asked how long they listened to the radio each day. Here are the results of the survey:

LISTENING TIME	NUMBER OF PEOPLE
Less than 1 hour	240
1 hour	456
2 hours	252
3 hours	96
4 hours	84
More than 4 hours	72

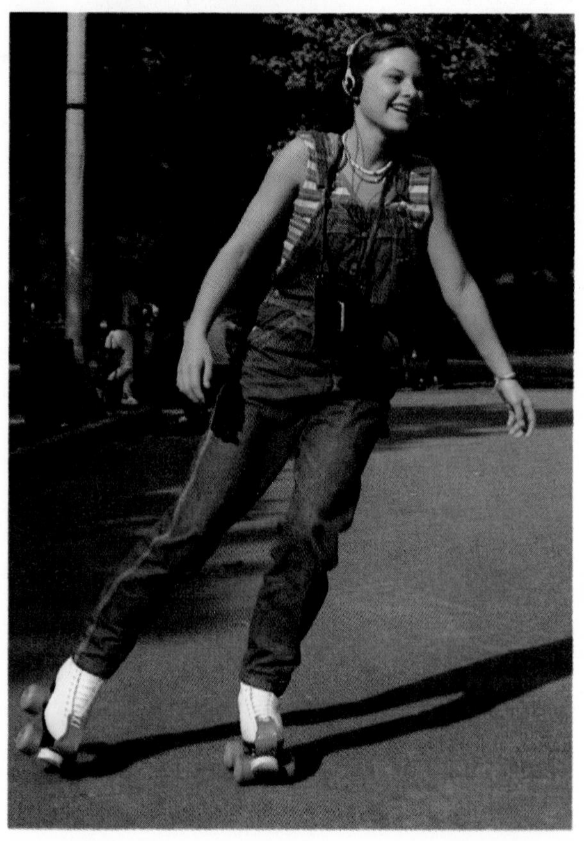

1. How many people listened 2 hours a day?
2. How many listened 3 hours?
3. Would you add or subtract to find how many more people listened 2 hours than listened 3 hours?

Here's how *to subtract whole numbers.* *252 − 96 = ?*

Line up the digits that are in the same place.	Regroup. Subtract ones.	Regroup. Subtract tens.	Subtract hundreds.
252 − 96	4 2 5̸ ¹2 − 9 6 6	1 ¹4 2̸ 5̸ ¹2 − 9 6 5 6	1 ¹4 2̸ 5̸ ¹2 − 9 6 1 5 6

The answer is called the **difference.**

4. Look at the *Here's how*. How many more people listened 2 hours than listened 3 hours?

EXERCISES

Subtract. *Here are scrambled answers for the next row of exercises: 26 13 15 21 27 54*

5. 56 − 35	**6.** 68 − 42	**7.** 42 − 15	**8.** 73 − 58	**9.** 90 − 77	**10.** 81 − 27
11. 256 − 28	**12.** 341 − 50	**13.** 722 − 65	**14.** 429 − 84	**15.** 536 − 98	**16.** 828 − 19
17. 429 − 116	**18.** 638 − 229	**19.** 514 − 152	**20.** 923 − 347	**21.** 752 − 294	**22.** 541 − 329
23. 361 − 183	**24.** 511 − 256	**25.** 837 − 389	**26.** 640 − 462	**27.** 438 − 249	**28.** 827 − 143

29. 93 − 21 **30.** 53 − 17 **31.** 60 − 28 **32.** 72 − 56

33. 243 − 30 **34.** 351 − 26 **35.** 633 − 59 **36.** 835 − 76

37. 598 − 375 **38.** 547 − 229 **39.** 743 − 256 **40.** 921 − 538

41. 418 − 179 **42.** 320 − 183 **43.** 635 − 379 **44.** 523 − 244

Solve. Use the survey information on page 34.

45. How many more people listened 1 hour than listened 2 hours?

46. How many more people listened 1 hour than listened less than 1 hour?

47. How many people listened 1 hour or less than 1 hour?

48. How many people listened 3 hours or more?

You're a program director **Reading a schedule**

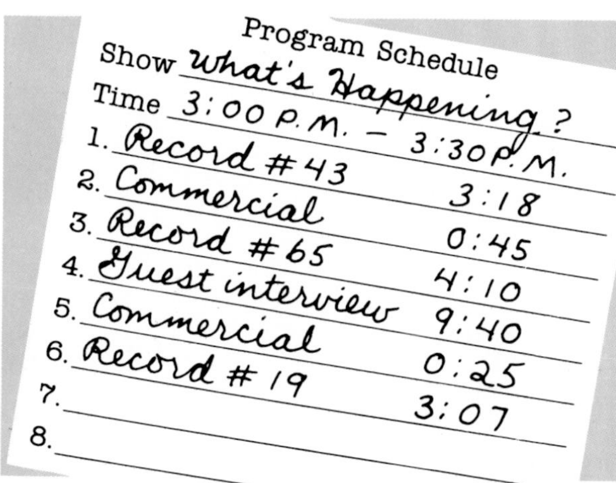

Program Schedule
Show What's Happening?
Time 3:00 P.M. – 3:30 P.M.
1. Record #43 3:18
2. Commercial 0:45
3. Record #65 4:10
4. Guest interview 9:40
5. Commercial 0:25
6. Record #19 3:07
7.
8.

49. What is the name of the show?

50. How many minutes long is the show?

51. The schedule shows that the first record will take 3 minutes and 18 seconds to play. Study the schedule. How much more time must you fill to complete the show? *Hint: 1 minute = 60 seconds.*

Subtracting 3- and 4-digit numbers

Here are some things that you probably use each day. Notice that each was invented before the beginning of the 20th century (the year 1901).

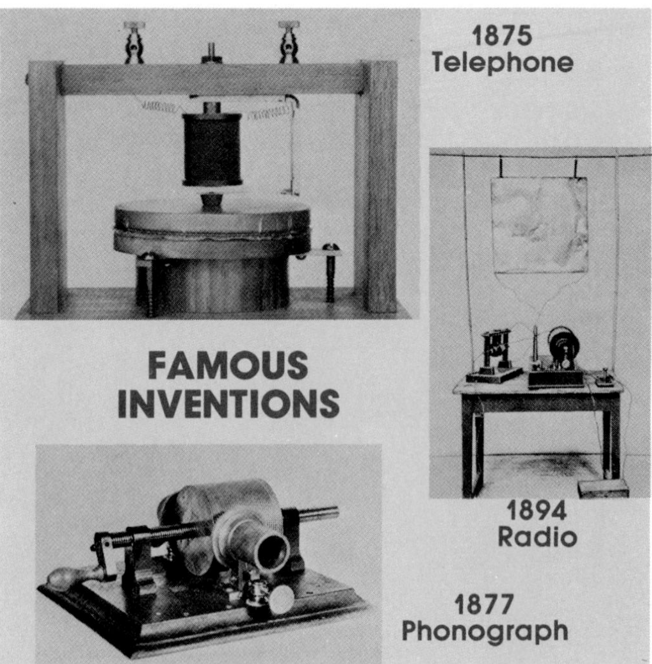

1. Which was invented first? second? third?
2. Was the telephone invented before or after the beginning of the 20th century?
3. Would you add or subtract to find how many years before the beginning of the 20th century the telephone was invented?

Here's how *to subtract whole numbers.* *1901 − 1875 = ?*

To estimate the difference, first round each number to the nearest ten and then subtract. 1900 − 1880 = 20

Line up the digits that are in the same place.	No tens! Regroup 1 hundred for 10 tens.	Regroup 1 ten for 10 ones.	Subtract.
1901 −1875	8 1 9 ¹0 1 −1875	8 9 1 9 ¹0 ¹1 −1875	8 9 1 9 ¹0 ¹1 −1875 26

4. Look at the *Here's how*. Was 20 a good estimate?
5. How many years before the beginning of the 20th century was the telephone invented?

EXERCISES

6. Three of the calculator answers are wrong. Find them by estimating.

a. 281 − 259 22	**b.** 329 − 197 132	**c.** 578 − 383 295
d. 600 − 511 89	**e.** 902 − 750 252	**f.** 800 − 311 489
g. 1249 − 993 256	**h.** 1680 − 1275 305	**i.** 2000 − 1309 691

First estimate the difference. Then subtract.

7. 802 − 238
8. 305 − 157
9. 901 − 396
10. 704 − 429
11. 806 − 638
12. 861 − 249
13. 976 − 238
14. 579 − 243
15. 701 − 455
16. 800 − 627
17. 506 − 329
18. 209 − 124
19. 1883 − 351
20. 1980 − 635
21. 1704 − 658
22. 1700 − 453
23. 1603 − 496
24. 3302 − 861
25. $35.00 − 13.94
26. $29.00 − 16.82
27. $23.02 − 13.44
28. $42.00 − 29.37
29. $96.00 − 47.01
30. $98.02 − 12.99

31. 796 − 313
32. 804 − 375
33. 900 − 493
34. 800 − 366
35. 756 − 403
36. 601 − 574
37. 1976 − 533
38. 2834 − 685
39. 5603 − 4384
40. 5600 − 2916
41. 9000 − 3817
42. 7000 − 5034
43. $37.00 − $20.59
44. $80.03 − $57.97
45. $60.00 − $38.92

Solve. Use the dates on page 36.

46. How many years after the invention of the telephone was the radio invented?

47. How many years before the beginning of the 20th century was the phonograph invented?

48. The telescope was invented 288 years before the radio. What year was that?

49. The pendulum clock was invented 221 years before the telephone. What year was that?

50. The airplane was invented 26 years after the phonograph. What year was that?

51. The thermometer was invented 7 years before the beginning of the 17th century. What year was that?

Key it in!

Find a way to push each marked key once to get the answer.

52.

53.

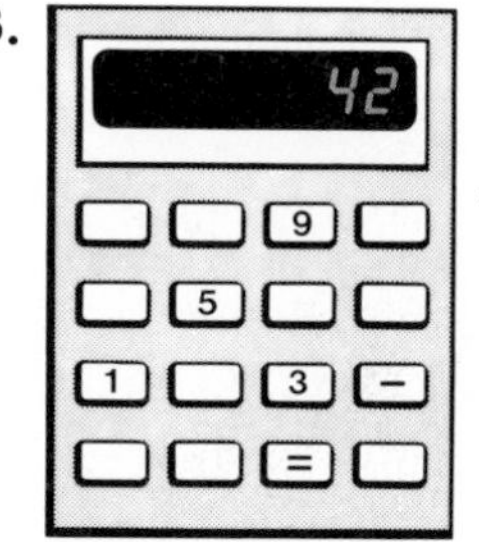

54.

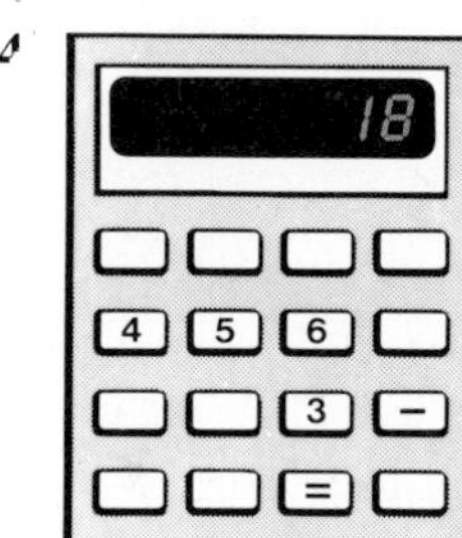

Subtracting larger numbers

IT HAPPENED IN VETERANS STADIUM!

On August 10, 1981, Pete Rose became the National League's leader in lifetime hits. Rose hit number 3631 before an over-capacity crowd of 60,561 fans.

SEATING CAPACITIES OF SOME MAJOR LEAGUE STADIUMS		
TEAM	STADIUM	SEATING CAPACITY
Braves	Atlanta Stadium	52,744
Orioles	Memorial Stadium	52,137
Cubs	Wrigley Field	37,741
Tigers	Tiger Stadium	54,220
Astros	Astrodome	45,000
Dodgers	Dodger Stadium	56,000
Yankees	Yankee Stadium	73,205
Phillies	Veterans Stadium	56,581
Rangers	Arlington Stadium	40,078

1. How many people attended the game when Pete Rose set a new record for lifetime hits?
2. What is the seating capacity of Veterans Stadium?
3. What two numbers would you use to find the number of fans that could not be seated?

Here's how *to subtract.*

First round each number to the nearest thousand and then estimate the difference:
61,000 − 57,000 = 4000

60,561 − 56,581 = ?

Subtract.	Regroup and subtract.	Regroup twice.	Subtract.
60,561 −56,581 0	(4 above 5, 1 written beside 6) 60,561 −56,581 80	(5 9 14 above, 6, 0, 5 crossed out) 60,561 −56,581 80	(5 9 14 above, 6, 0, 5 crossed out) 60,561 −56,581 3,980

4. Look at the *Here's how*. Was 4000 a good estimate?
5. How many fans could not be seated?

Here's how *to check the difference by addition.*

$$\begin{array}{r} 60{,}561 \\ -56{,}581 \\ \hline 3{,}980 \end{array} \longrightarrow \begin{array}{r} 3{,}980 \\ +56{,}581 \\ \hline 60{,}561 \end{array}$$

It checks!

EXERCISES

6. Three of the calculator answers are wrong. Find them by estimating.

a. 935 − 426	509	**b.** 883 − 201	682	**c.** 618 − 225	393
d. 1813 − 637	1176	**e.** 2490 − 678	1812	**f.** 3331 − 846	2485
g. 5823 − 1995	4828	**h.** 4993 − 3481	2512	**i.** 3603 − 1587	1016

First estimate the difference. Then subtract.

7. 7383 − 5906
8. 3826 − 1039
9. 5287 − 3240
10. 8002 − 3495
11. 6081 − 2943
12. 5960 − 2880
13. 7020 − 1930
14. 9220 − 7900
15. 8007 − 3241
16. 8063 − 1297
17. 35,110 − 8,790
18. 40,230 − 7,320
19. 53,984 − 6,216
20. 47,832 − 9,949
21. 86,142 − 1,986

Subtract. Then check by addition.

22. 19,354 − 16,258
23. 36,093 − 24,720
24. 68,391 − 26,493
25. 94,003 − 62,875
26. 36,902 − 12,118
27. 359,061 − 52,839
28. 365,291 − 64,775
29. 903,461 − 386,229
30. 806,000 − 542,600
31. 603,010 − 225,311

Solve. Use the table on page 38.

32. How many more seats does Yankee Stadium have than the Astrodome?
33. How many more seats does Dodger Stadium have than Tiger Stadium?
34. Which stadium has 15,003 more seats than Wrigley Field?
35. List the nine stadiums from greatest seating capacity to least capacity.

Won by one!

36. Study the clues to find which team won.
Clues:
- After 7 complete innings, the Dodgers were leading the Pirates 5 to 3.
- Both teams scored after the 7th inning.
- The game went extra innings.
- A total of 11 runs was scored.

Cumulative Skill Practice

Write the short word-name. *(page 4)*

1.	46220	**2.**	9337	**3.**	11835	**4.**	63201
5.	186743	**6.**	237105	**7.**	864319	**8.**	145623
9.	6723804	**10.**	5657129	**11.**	29000573	**12.**	1000235

Write the standard numeral. *(page 4)*

13. 246 thousand, 659 **14.** 34 million **15.** 57 billion

16. 28 million, 213 thousand **17.** 5 million, 18 thousand **18.** 4 million, 24 thousand, 73

19. five hundred forty-seven thousand, three hundred ninety-five

20. sixty-two thousand, two hundred fifty

21. thirty-one million, two hundred eighty-six thousand

22. thirty-one million, two hundred eighty-six

23. seventeen million, sixty-three thousand, ninety

Add. *(page 8)*

24. 5384 + 297 **25.** 4627 + 309 **26.** 6714 + 888 **27.** 5376 + 2944 **28.** 2846 + 5907 **29.** 6302 + 1984

30. 52,374 + 5,986 **31.** 92,335 + 4,618 **32.** 27,584 + 27,584 **33.** 57,319 + 65,007 **34.** 52,916 + 38,155 **35.** 71,209 + 36,142

36. 328 + 296 + 54 **37.** 927 + 58 + 629 **38.** 3942 + 567 + 8314 **39.** 2715 + 6130 + 852 **40.** 593 + 2577 + 4255 **41.** 623 + 1586 + 29

Round to the nearest hundred. *(page 12)*

42. 567 **43.** 824 **44.** 650 **45.** 471 **46.** 35 **47.** 98

48. 3607 **49.** 6532 **50.** 8880 **51.** 9050 **52.** 3982 **53.** 1924

Round to the nearest tenth. *(page 20)*

54. 3.53 **55.** 24.305 **56.** 9.67 **57.** 0.884 **58.** 1.750 **59.** 3.215

60. 52.04 **61.** 8.96 **62.** 7.390 **63.** 0.064 **64.** 27.95 **65.** 9.013

Problem solving

YOU WANT TO BUY A CAR!

You have circled the ads for seven used cars you'd like to look at.

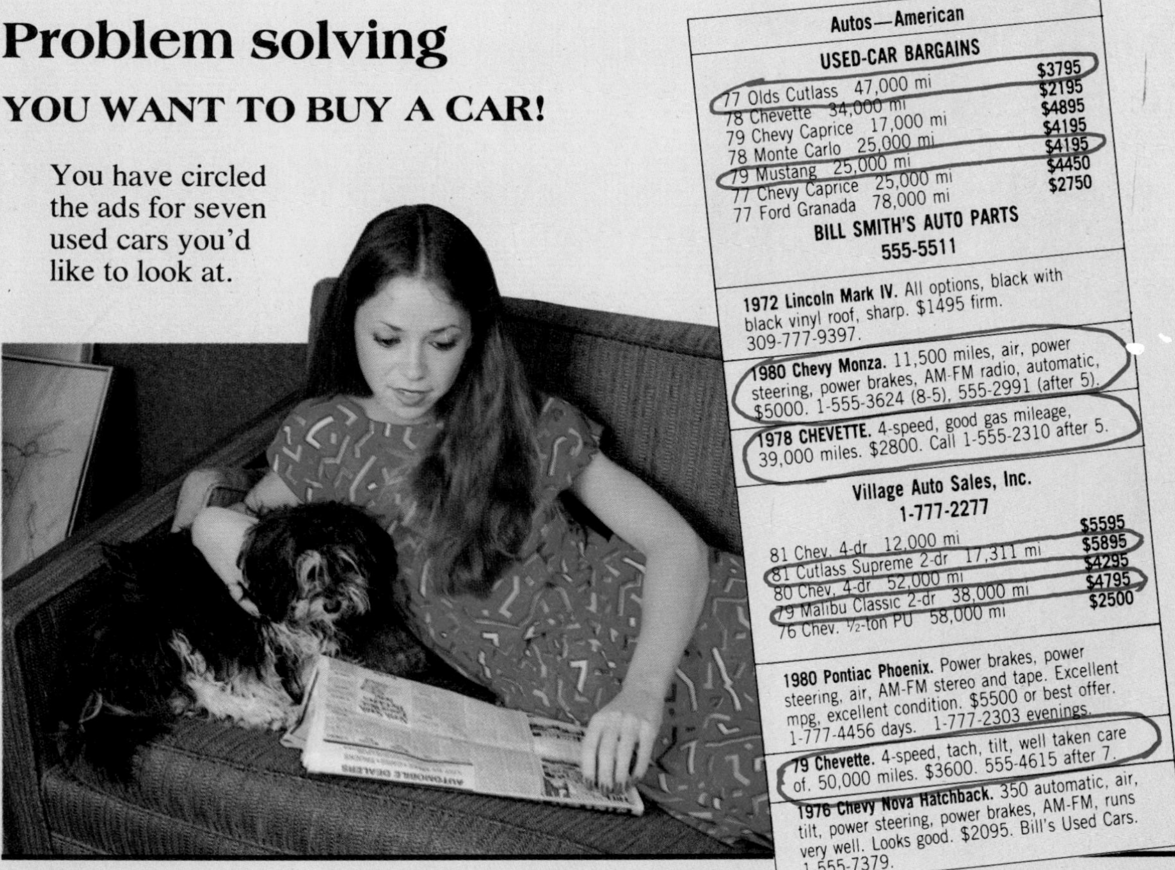

Autos—American

USED-CAR BARGAINS

77 Olds Cutlass 47,000 mi $3795
78 Chevette 34,000 mi $2195
79 Chevy Caprice 17,000 mi $4895
78 Monte Carlo 25,000 mi $4195
79 Mustang 25,000 mi $4195
77 Chevy Caprice 25,000 mi $4450
77 Ford Granada 78,000 mi $2750

BILL SMITH'S AUTO PARTS
555-5511

1972 Lincoln Mark IV. All options, black with black vinyl roof, sharp. $1495 firm. 309-777-9397.

1980 Chevy Monza. 11,500 miles, air, power steering, power brakes, AM-FM radio, automatic, $5000. 1-555-3624 (8-5), 555-2991 (after 5).

1978 CHEVETTE. 4-speed, good gas mileage, 39,000 miles. $2800. Call 1-555-2310 after 5.

Village Auto Sales, Inc.
1-777-2277

81 Chev. 4-dr 12,000 mi $5595
81 Cutlass Supreme 2-dr 17,311 mi $5895
80 Chev. 4-dr 52,000 mi $4295
79 Malibu Classic 2-dr 38,000 mi $4795
76 Chev. ½-ton PU 58,000 mi $2500

1980 Pontiac Phoenix. Power brakes, power steering, air, AM-FM stereo and tape. Excellent mpg, excellent condition. $5500 or best offer. 1-777-4456 days. 1-777-2303 evenings.

79 Chevette. 4-speed, tach, tilt, well taken care of. 50,000 miles. $3600. 555-4615 after 7.

1976 Chevy Nova Hatchback. 350 automatic, air, tilt, power steering, power brakes, AM-FM, runs very well. Looks good. $2095. Bill's Used Cars. 1-555-7379.

Use the circled ads to answer these questions.

1. Which car costs the most?
2. Which car costs the least?
3. Which car is the newest model?
4. Which car is the oldest?
5. Which car has been driven the most miles?
6. Which car has been driven the fewest miles?
7. How many more miles has the 1977 Cutlass been driven than the 1981 Cutlass?
8. What is the difference in price between the two Cutlass cars?
9. What is the difference in price between the cheapest and the most expensive 1979 model?
10. You have $1835 in one savings account and $979 in another. Do you have enough money to pay cash for the cheapest car?
11. You have $2814. How much will you need to borrow to buy the 1979 Mustang?
12. Village Auto Sales guarantees its cars for 7500 miles after the purchase. How many miles will the Cutlass have when the guarantee expires?

Comparing decimals

Can you recognize the four common objects in these close-up photos?

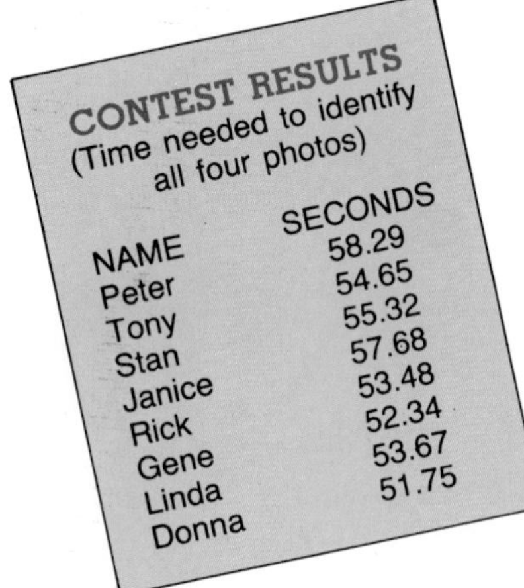

CONTEST RESULTS
(Time needed to identify all four photos)

NAME	SECONDS
Peter	58.29
Tony	54.65
Stan	55.32
Janice	57.68
Rick	53.48
Gene	52.34
Linda	53.67
Donna	51.75

Stretchers

. . . fields forever

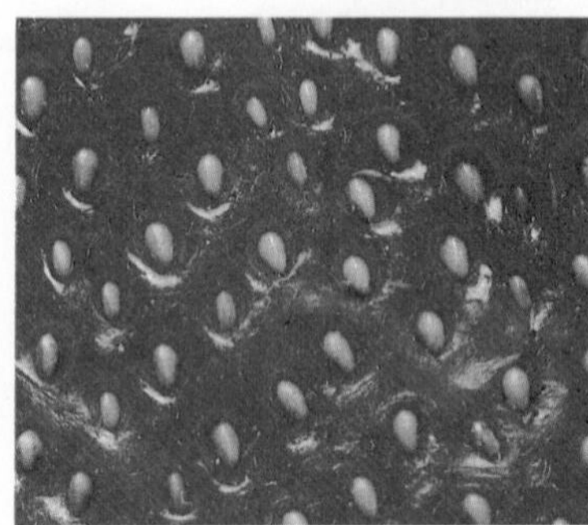

CLOSE-UP CONTEST

Draw, Pardner!

Solve this for a clean sweep

1. Who recognized all four close-up photos in 53.67 seconds?
2. Who had a time of 53.48 seconds?
3. Which two numbers would you compare to decide whether Rick or Linda had the better (shorter) time?

Here's how *to compare decimals.* ***53.48 ● 53.67***

Start at the left and compare digits that are in the same place.

Step 1. 53.48 ● 53.67 — same

Step 2. 53.48 ● 53.67 — 4 is less than 6.

Step 3. $53.48 < 53.67$

4. Look at the *Here's how*. Who had the better time, Linda or Rick?
5. Check each example. Have the decimals been compared correctly?

   a. 52.34 ● 51.68 — 2 is greater than 1.
   $52.34 > 51.68$

   b. 54.60 ● 54.65 — It helps to fill in a zero.
   $54.6 < 54.65$

EXERCISES

Less than (<) or greater than (>)?

6. 0.4 ● 0.5
7. 0.07 ● 0.06
8. 0.009 ● 0.008
9. 14.3 ● 14.1
10. 6.75 ● 6.57
11. 0.27 ● 0.2
12. 0.005 ● 0.03
13. 0.1 ● 0.02
14. 8.23 ● 8.32
15. 31.69 ● 31.7
16. 2.1 ● 1.98
17. 5.352 ● 53.52
18. 0.725 ● 1.1
19. 1.07 ● 1.007
20. 0.815 ● 0.82
21. 33.86 ● 33.87
22. 0.34 ● 0.43
23. 6.215 ● 62.16
24. 23.78 ● 21.88
25. 1.1 ● 1.08
26. 782.1 ● 783
27. 18.02 ● 18.003
28. 53.06 ● 53.2
29. 0.333 ● 0.332
30. 3.504 ● 3.54
31. 52.8 ● 8.29
32. 0.021 ● 0.12
33. 6.72 ● 6.75
34. 6.153 ● 6.2
35. 2.61 ● 2.58
36. 0.04 ● 0.006
37. 7.017 ● 7.005
38. 3.53 ● 3.55
39. 13.7 ● 13.69
40. 38.06 ● 38.7
41. 0.914 ● 0.92

Solve. Use the chart on page 42.

42. Which girl recognized the four close-up photos in less than 52 seconds?
43. Which boys took more than 55 seconds?
44. Who had the shorter time, Tony or Gene?
45. Who had the longer time, Rick or Janice?
46. Who had the better combined time, Tony and Linda or Janice and Gene?
47. **a.** List the times in order from best (shortest) to worst (longest).
    b. Who came in first?
    c. Who came in last?

More close-ups

Use the word clues to name these close-ups.

48.

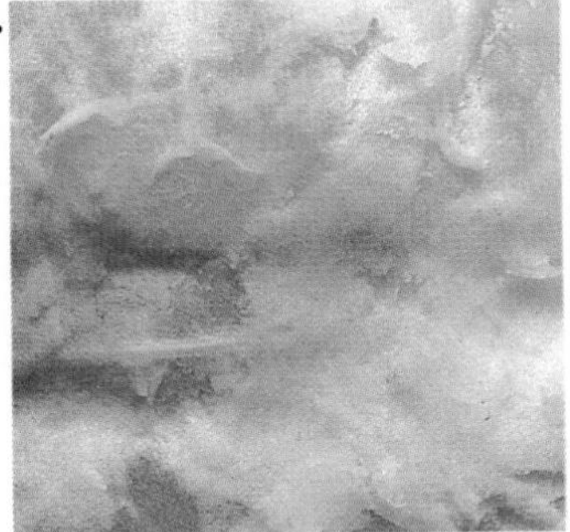

Lost appeal

49.

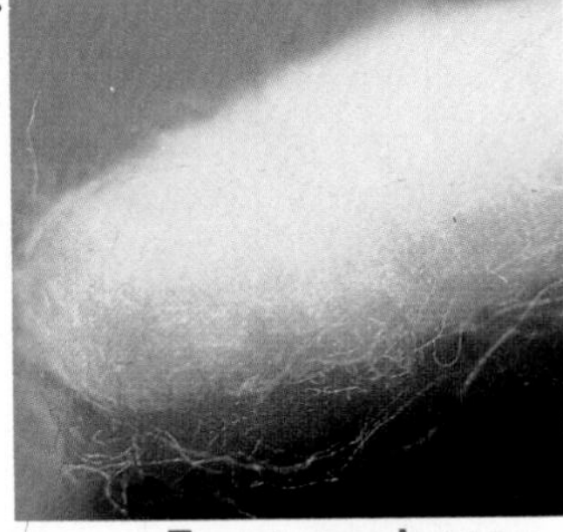

Ears to you!

50.

Rubber soul

Subtracting decimals

1890

1900

1910

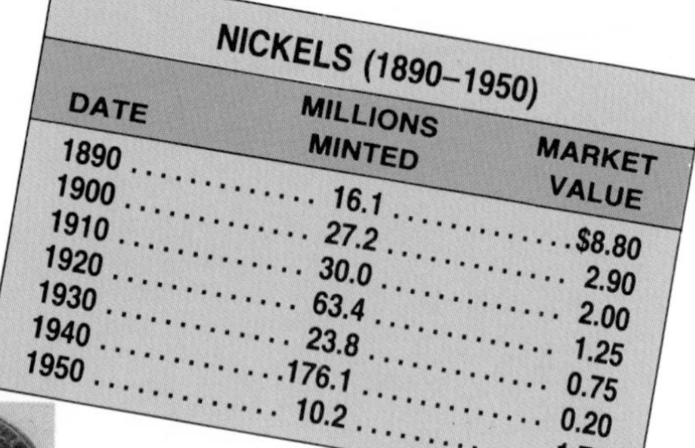

NICKELS (1890–1950)

DATE	MILLIONS MINTED	MARKET VALUE
1890	16.1	$8.80
1900	27.2	2.90
1910	30.0	2.00
1920	63.4	1.25
1930	23.8	0.75
1940	176.1	0.20
1950	10.2	1.75

1920 1930 1940

1950

1. A coin dealer will pay you $8.80 for one of these nickels. Which nickel is it?
2. Which nickel has a market value of $1.25?
3. How many million nickels were minted in 1920? in 1930?
4. Would you add or subtract to find how many more millions of nickels were minted in 1920 than in 1930?

Here's how *to subtract decimals.* *63.4 − 23.8 = ?*

Line up the decimal points.	Regroup and subtract.	Regroup and subtract.
63.4 −23.8	6$\not{3}^{2}$.^{1}4 −23.8 .6	$\not{6}^{5}\not{3}^{12}$.^{1}4 −23.8 39.6

5. Look at the *Here's how.* How many more millions of nickels were minted in 1920 than in 1930?

EXERCISES

Subtract.

Here are scrambled answers for the next row of exercises: *6.54 7.15 26.4 21.7 34.7 37.1*

6.	7.	8.	9.	10.	11.
49.6 −12.5	7.42 −0.27	42.6 − 7.9	9.18 −2.64	75.3 −48.9	43.5 −21.8

12. 0.31 −0.18	**13.** 80.2 −38.9	**14.** 6.19 −2.74	**15.** 5.91 −0.26	**16.** 72.9 − 8.7	**17.** 8.42 −3.54
18. 0.74 −0.68	**19.** 646.5 − 89.3	**20.** 6.75 −2.41	**21.** 87.3 − 1.6	**22.** 93.71 − 8.41	**23.** 104.5 − 25.6
24. \$52.40 −12.75	**25.** \$7.29 −5.36	**26.** \$7.38 − .88	**27.** \$110.60 − 85.20	**28.** \$47.35 −39.88	**29.** \$87.65 − 4.82

30. 70.2 − 6.1　**31.** 16.3 − 5.7　**32.** 80.06 − 5.14　**33.** 55.06 − 2.14

34. 59.4 − 23.7　**35.** 23.16 − 4.10　**36.** 75.4 − 44.6　**37.** 35.2 − 8.4

38. 60.49 − 33.71　**39.** 63.3 − 9.6　**40.** 70.02 − 4.16　**41.** 63.14 − 7.21

42. 0.35 − 0.22　**43.** 7.89 − 0.97　**44.** 115.4 − 53.4　**45.** 86.3 − 42.3

46. 9.4 − 2.9　**47.** 345.8 − 258.4　**48.** 8.04 − 0.56　**49.** 3.42 − 2.91

50. 8.74 − 2.06　**51.** 5.03 − 2.78　**52.** 5.0 − 2.6　**53.** 6.1 − 3.7

54. 51.0 − 29.4　**55.** 2.00 − 1.46　**56.** 18.00 − 6.93　**57.** 7.00 − 1.92

Solve. Use the chart on page 44.

58. How many million nickels were minted in
  a. 1890?
  b. 1900?
  c. 1950?

59. The number of nickels minted in 1890 written as a whole number is 16,100,000. Write the number of nickels minted in the other years as whole numbers.

60. How many more nickels were minted in 1940 than in 1930? Give the answer as a whole number.

61. How much more is the market value of a 1900 nickel than the market value of a 1920 nickel?

62. What is the total market value of a 1910, a 1940, and a 1950 nickel?

63. Why do you think a 1950 nickel has a greater market value than a 1930 nickel?

Nickel mysteries

Study the clue. Use the pictures of the coins and the chart on page 44.

64. What date is on each nickel?

a.

b.

Clue:
- The total market value of both nickels is \$4.15.

65. What date is on each nickel?

a.

b.

Clue:
- 40.2 million of these nickels were minted altogether.

More on subtracting decimals

HOW LONG IS 30 SECONDS?

Cal and Barb had a contest to see who could come closer to guessing how long 30 seconds is. Their stopwatches show the results.

CONTEST RULES

- Use a stopwatch.
- Push the Start button.
- Don't look at the display.
- When you think 30 seconds have passed, push the Stop button.
- The person whose guess is closer to 30 seconds wins.

1. Read the stopwatches. Whose guess was off by 5.67 seconds?
2. What time is shown on Barb's stopwatch?
3. Which two numbers would you use to compute how far off Barb's guess was?

Cal's guess

Barb's guess

Here's how *to subtract decimals.* *30 − 24.29 = ?*

Line up the decimal points. Write in the 0's.	Regroup.	Subtract.
30.00 −24.29	$\overset{2}{\cancel{3}}\overset{9}{\cancel{0}}.\overset{9}{\cancel{0}}\overset{10}{0}$ −24.29	$\overset{2}{\cancel{3}}\overset{9}{\cancel{0}}.\overset{9}{\cancel{0}}\overset{10}{0}$ −24.29 5.71

To estimate the difference, first round to the nearest second and then subtract:

30 − 24 = 6

4. Look at the *Here's how*. Whose guess was off by 5.71 seconds? Who won the contest, Cal or Barb?

EXERCISES

5. Four of the calculator answers are wrong. Find them by estimating.

a. 37.42 − 4.25  33.17

b. 68.12 − 29.31 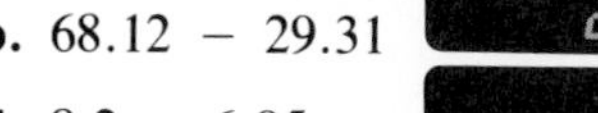 28.81

c. 5.01 − 1.99 9.02

d. 8.2 − 6.95 1.25

e. 43.8 − 2.12 4.16

f. 7.21 − 3.194  4.016

g. 53.8 − 19.926 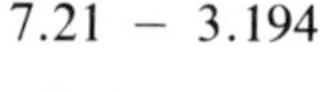 33.874

h. 4.78 − 0.8 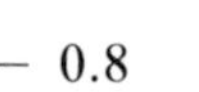 3.98

i. 29.79 − 21.046 18.744

j. 118.9 − 19.02 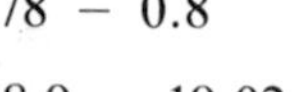 99.88

Subtract. *Here are scrambled answers for the next row of exercises:* *1.055 9.42 5.21 3.84 0.69 13.02*

6. 8.63 − 3.42
7. 9.76 − 0.34
8. 24.1 − 11.08
9. 6.3 − 5.245
10. 3.29 − 2.6
11. 6.14 − 2.3

12. 3.74 − 2.5
13. 7.3 − 0.74
14. 7.86 − 1.59
15. 6.83 − 2.7
16. 8.7 − 6.25
17. 9.61 − 2.9

18. 9.6 − 2.64
19. 28.31 − 24.7
20. 17.0 − 8.95
21. 3.781 − 0.97
22. 7.52 − 4.083
23. 8.312 − 2.77

24. $4 − 2.98
25. $5 − 1.47
26. $10 − 5.78
27. $24 − 16.43
28. $16 − 11.29
29. $6 − 3.11

30. 6 − 2.7 (6.0 − 2.7)
31. 8 − 4.2
32. 12.94 − 8.53
33. 16.4 − 5
34. 15.1 − 12.8
35. 23.4 − 2.89
36. 9.5 − 6
37. 14.5 − 12.8
38. 7 − 6.52
39. 9.72 − 0.865
40. 7.4 − 5.125
41. 123.7 − 101.4
42. 12.935 − 4.6
43. 9.323 − 1.747
44. 5.2 − 2.456
45. 25 − 8.2
46. 100 − 44.75
47. 75.25 − 16

Solve.

48. What is the difference in price between a $37 digital watch and a $29.85 alarm watch?

49. You have $17.50. How much more money do you need in order to buy a $29.95 video-game watch?

50. A customer paid for a $32.99 calculator watch with a $50 bill. How much change should she get?

51. You are the clerk. How much change should you give a customer who paid for a $27.97 stopwatch and a $24.95 alarm watch with a $100 bill?

Key it in!

Find a way to push each marked key once to get the answer.

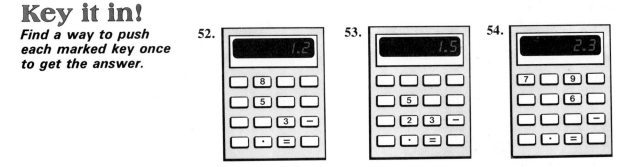

52.

53.
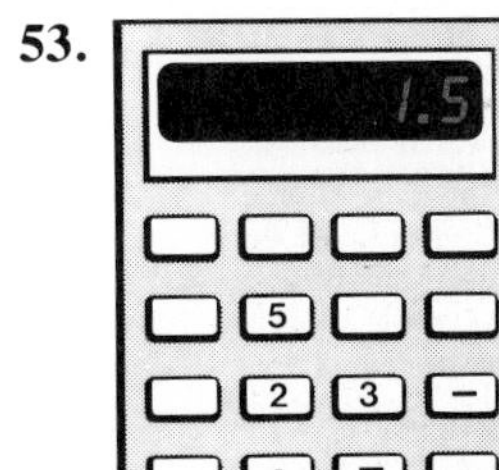

54.
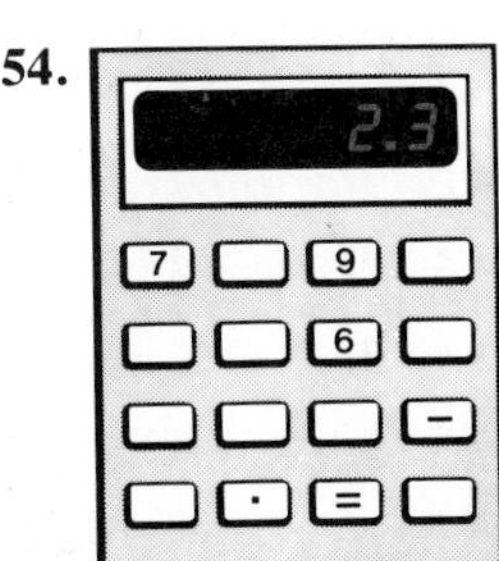

Cumulative Skill Practice

Give the sum. *(page 24)*

1. 7.6 + 0.82 + 5.3
2. 3.74 + 2.9 + 65.9
3. 39.82 + 52 + 96.5
4. 84.8 + 7.463 + 73.29
5. 7.564 + 7.3 + 68.83
6. 70.2 + 58.61 + 3.56
7. 52.14 + 0.89 + 24
8. 1.7 + 25.73 + 43.83
9. 88.9 + 14 + 72.35
10. 68.6 + 19.21 + 52.6
11. 90.9 + 73.26 + 25
12. 30.68 + 4.02 + 251.6

Less than (<) or greater than (>)? *(page 32)*

13. 593 ● 594
14. 786 ● 768
15. 599 ● 600
16. 895 ● 885
17. 960 ● 1000
18. 1501 ● 999
19. 3431 ● 3318
20. 2815 ● 3815
21. 29,361 ● 29,400
22. 40,000 ● 38,652
23. 55,399 ● 54,000
24. 4106 ● 4214

Subtract. *(page 36)*

25. 567 − 239
26. 863 − 299
27. 802 − 574
28. 901 − 732
29. 600 − 371
30. 459 − 368
31. 2634 − 256
32. 7972 − 388
33. 3174 − 570
34. 2063 − 1421
35. 3105 − 1638
36. 4986 − 2897
37. 6017 − 2842
38. 5203 − 195
39. 3800 − 695
40. 4000 − 928
41. 5000 − 1639
42. 7001 − 3542

Less than (<) or greater than (>)? *(page 42)*

43. 0.008 ● 0.007
44. 3.57 ● 3.75
45. 0.005 ● 0.03
46. 2.01 ● 2.1
47. 3.1 ● 2.97
48. 0.615 ● 0.62
49. 4.215 ● 42.15
50. 3.82 ● 3.62
51. 1.1 ● 1.07
52. 621.7 ● 622
53. 0.031 ● 0.13
54. 73.9 ● 7.39

Give the difference. *(pages 44, 46)*

55. 53.4 − 29.6
56. 30.6 − 15.8
57. 9.00 − 5.74
58. 25.41 − 3.02
59. 8.6 − 3.5
60. 10.18 − 9.54
61. 20.34 − 15.95
62. 41.08 − 23.6
63. 26 − 13.5
64. 20 − 6.34
65. 9.8 − 6.99
66. 14.32 − 4.08
67. 42.1 − 3.84
68. 9.6 − 3.74
69. 12 − 3.52
70. 83 − 52.06

Problem solving

COMPUTERS AT THE AIRPORT

You're an airline agent. You use computers to write tickets, make reservations, assign seats, check luggage, and provide arrival and departure information.

ARRIVALS
FLIGHT CITY TIME GATE
303 BOSTON 9:05 2
110 LOS ANGELES 9:20 8
65 ATLANTA 9:35 14
220 PHILADELPHIA 9:40 20
DEPARTURES
FLIGHT CITY TIME GATE
303 DENVER 9:45 2
615 DALLAS 10:10 15
110 NEW YORK 10:15 8
45 SEATTLE 10:20 12

Use the computer screen to answer these customers' questions.

1. *What time does Flight 615 leave for Dallas? From which gate?*

2. *Which flight is arriving at 9:35? Which city is it coming from?*

3. *My sister is arriving at 9:40 from Philadelphia. At which gate should I meet her?*

4. "My friend is arriving on Flight 65 and departing on Flight 45. Will he have more than a half hour between flights?"

5. "My travel agent said you start assigning seats 45 minutes before each flight leaves. Will you be assigning seats for Flight 110 at 9:00?"

Solve.

6. A first-class ticket from Atlanta to Chicago is $201. Coach fare is $32 less. What is the price of a coach ticket?

7. Airfare from Los Angeles to Chicago is $372. How much would 2 tickets cost?

8. A 727 jet liner carries 135 passengers. Your computer shows 123 coach reservations and 18 first-class reservations. Has the flight been overbooked? ("Overbooked" means there are more reservations than seats.)

9. A DC 9 has 139 passenger seats. The flight attendant counted 27 empty seats. Your computer shows you have assigned seats to 129 passengers. Are all the passengers on board?

Multiplying by multiples of 10, 100, or 1000

FRANKLIN,
HAMILTON,
OR
CLEVELAND?

Which is worth more money, 6 Hamiltons, 4 Franklins, or 3 Clevelands? *Hint: Hamilton is on the $10 bill, Franklin is on the $100 bill, and Cleveland is on the $1000 bill.*

To answer the question, you will need to multiply by 10, 100, and 1000.

Here's how ***to multiply by multiples of 10, 100, or 1000.***

6 × 10 = ?

To multiply a whole number by 10, multiply by 1 and write 1 zero.

6 × 10 = 60

Six Hamiltons are worth $60.

4 × 100 = ?

To multiply a whole number by 100, multiply by 1 and write 2 zeros.

4 × 100 = 400

Four Franklins are worth $400.

3 × 1000 = ?

To multiply a whole number by 1000, multiply by 1 and write 3 zeros.

3 × 1000 = 3000

Three Clevelands are worth $3000.

Study these examples.

a. $\begin{array}{r} 20 \\ \times 30 \\ \hline 600 \end{array}$ Use basic facts. Multiply 2 × 3. Write 2 zeros.

b. $\begin{array}{r} 500 \\ \times \ \ 70 \\ \hline 35{,}000 \end{array}$ Multiply 7 × 5. Write 3 zeros.

EXERCISES

Multiply. *Here are scrambled answers for the next row of exercises:* *800* *12,000* *120* *6000*

1. 12×10 **2.** 20×40 **3.** 60×100 **4.** 60×200

5. 83×10 **6.** 9×1000 **7.** 44×10 **8.** 60×40

9. 81×10 **10.** 30×300 **11.** 50×30 **12.** 60×400

13. 3×70 **14.** 9×200 **15.** 70×60 **16.** 4×200

17. 8×3000 **18.** 50×70 **19.** 23×100 **20.** 8×2000

21. 20×4 **22.** 800×3 **23.** 70×40 **24.** 500×3

25. 900×20 **26.** 10×30 **27.** 100×40 **28.** 8000×2

29. 70×70 **30.** 5000×50 **31.** 80×100 **32.** 70×100

33. 70×1000 **34.** 60×1000 **35.** 300×100 **36.** 5000×90

37. 400×80 **38.** 1000×600 **39.** 900×100 **40.** 600×800

41. 80×1000 **42.** 600×10 **43.** 700×100 **44.** 300×10

Use the money facts. How much money would you have if you had

45. 14 Hamiltons?

46. 40 Jeffersons?

47. 23 Franklins?

48. 60 Lincolns?

49. 7 Grants?

50. 9 Jacksons?

51. 10 Washingtons and 5 Jacksons?

52. 20 Jeffersons and 3 Grants?

MONEY FACTS

BILL	PORTRAIT
$1	Washington
$2	Jefferson
$5	Lincoln
$10	Hamilton
$20	Jackson
$50	Grant
$100	Franklin

You're the bank teller!

Answer these questions.

53. *Are 9 Hamiltons the same amount of money as 90 Washingtons?*

54. "Are 8 Grants the same amount of money as 80 Lincolns?"

55. "Are 7 Jacksons and 30 Jeffersons equal to 3 Franklins?"

56. "Would you give me 50 Hamiltons, 20 Jacksons, and 60 Grants for 15 Franklins? Why or why not?"

Multiplying by a 1-digit number

890 × 7 is about 900 × 7, or 6300.

TRY THIS PUZZLE!

Place the digits (7, 8, 9, and 0) in the boxes to get the largest possible answer.

$$\begin{array}{r} \boxed{?}\ \boxed{?}\ \boxed{?} \\ \times \quad \boxed{?} \\ \hline \end{array}$$

870 × 9 is about 900 × 9, or 8100.

Kathleen

$$\begin{array}{r} 890 \\ \times\ 7 \\ \hline \end{array}$$

David

$$\begin{array}{r} 870 \\ \times\ 9 \\ \hline \end{array}$$

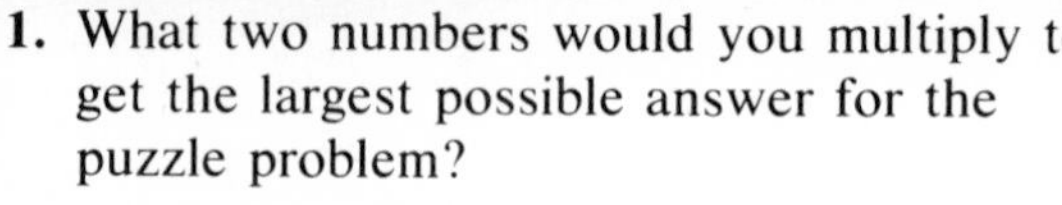

1. What two numbers would you multiply to get the largest possible answer for the puzzle problem?

Here's how *to multiply by a 1-digit number.* *870 × 9 = ?*

Multiply ones.	Multiply tens and regroup.	Multiply hundreds and add.
$\begin{array}{r} 870 \\ \times\ 9 \\ \hline 0 \end{array}$	$\begin{array}{r} ^{6} \\ 870 \\ \times\ 9 \\ \hline 30 \end{array}$	$\begin{array}{r} ^{6} \\ 870 \\ \times\ 9 \\ \hline 7830 \end{array}$

The numbers that are multiplied are called **factors.**
The answer is called the **product.**

2. Look at the *Here's how*. Was David's estimate near the actual product?
3. Check each example. Is the estimate near the product?

a. *890 × 7 = ?*
Estimate.
900 × 7 = 6300

$$\begin{array}{r} ^{6} \\ 890 \\ \times\ 7 \\ \hline 6230 \end{array}$$

b. *790 × 8 = ?*
Estimate.
800 × 8 = 6400

$$\begin{array}{r} ^{7} \\ 790 \\ \times\ 8 \\ \hline 6320 \end{array}$$

EXERCISES

4. Four of these calculator answers are wrong. Find them by estimating.

a. 89 × 9	641	b. 398 × 2	796
c. 71 × 5	355	d. 602 × 4	2408
e. 62 × 7	334	f. 707 × 9	6363
g. 59 × 6	354	h. 207 × 8	1656
i. 78 × 6	358	j. 198 × 4	592

First estimate the product. Then multiply.

5. 19 × 4
6. 81 × 6
7. 53 × 9
8. 87 × 5
9. 32 × 8
10. 44 × 8
11. 46 × 7
12. 71 × 3
13. 68 × 7
14. 90 × 6
15. 89 × 4
16. 29 × 5
17. 612 × 9
18. 797 × 6
19. 921 × 5
20. 584 × 3
21. 604 × 8
22. 201 × 8
23. 504 × 4
24. 685 × 7
25. 732 × 8
26. 493 × 5
27. 893 × 2
28. 691 × 3
29. $12.02 × 8
30. $21.93 × 3
31. $16.88 × 6
32. $43.07 × 9
33. $58.87 × 4
34. $23.81 × 5
35. 63 × 7
36. 88 × 4
37. 47 × 9
38. 31 × 6
39. 252 × 9
40. 319 × 5
41. 571 × 6
42. 487 × 8
43. 1023 × 5
44. 4216 × 4
45. 3924 × 6
46. 4879 × 3
47. 2106 × 7
48. 8135 × 9
49. 2147 × 2
50. 6627 × 8
51. 7265 × 9
52. 2140 × 5
53. 8108 × 6
54. 5479 × 3

Missing digits

Copy; then fill in the missing digits.

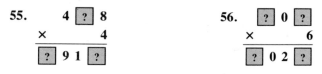

55. 4 ? 8 × 4 = ? 9 1 ?

56. ? 0 ? × 6 = ? 0 2 ?

57. 9 ? 3 × ? = 2 ? 4 9

Multiplying by a 2-digit number

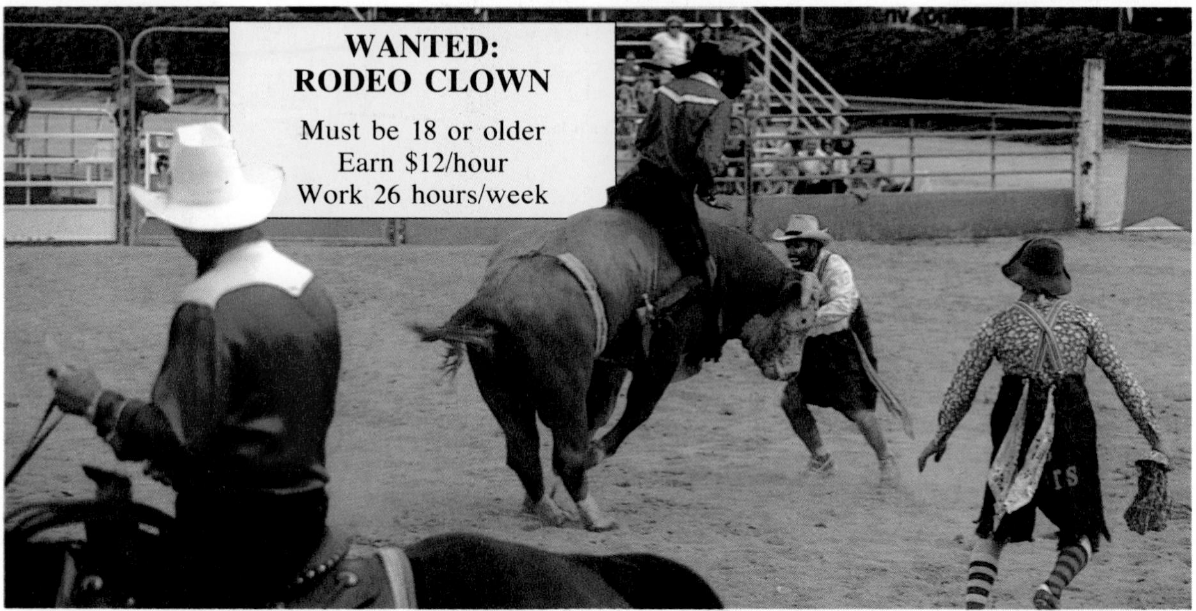
WANTED:
RODEO CLOWN
Must be 18 or older
Earn $12/hour
Work 26 hours/week

1. Which operation would you use to find how many dollars a rodeo clown is paid per week?

Here's how *to multiply by a 2-digit number.* *26 × 12 = ?*

Line up the digits. Multiply by 2.	Multiply by 10.	Add.
$\begin{array}{r} 26 \\ \times 12 \\ \hline 52 \end{array}$	$\begin{array}{r} 26 \\ \times 12 \\ \hline 52 \\ 260 \end{array}$	$\begin{array}{r} 26 \\ \times 12 \\ \hline 52 \\ 260 \\ \hline 312 \end{array}$

2. Look at the *Here's how*. How much money is a rodeo clown paid per week? Would you take the job for that much money?

3. Check each example. Is the answer correct?

a. $\begin{array}{r} 473 \\ \times 54 \\ \hline 1892 \\ 23650 \\ \hline 25{,}542 \end{array}$ **b.** $\begin{array}{r} 4936 \\ \times 63 \\ \hline 14808 \\ 296160 \\ \hline 310{,}968 \end{array}$ **c.** $\begin{array}{r} 7254 \\ \times 89 \\ \hline 65286 \\ 58032 \\ \hline 645{,}606 \end{array}$

EXERCISES

Multiply. *Here are scrambled answers for the next row of exercises:* *2576 2655 1980 1242 2176 1610*

4. 68 × 32	**5.** 59 × 45	**6.** 46 × 56	**7.** 70 × 23	**8.** 33 × 60	**9.** 27 × 46
10. 631 × 20	**11.** 168 × 52	**12.** 246 × 19	**13.** 604 × 31	**14.** 120 × 20	**15.** 403 × 15
16. 146 × 32	**17.** 487 × 51	**18.** 268 × 25	**19.** 452 × 46	**20.** 283 × 49	**21.** 765 × 43
22. 864 × 65	**23.** 398 × 56	**24.** 577 × 48	**25.** 903 × 52	**26.** 685 × 63	**27.** 492 × 53
28. 2413 × 41	**29.** 2804 × 34	**30.** 6533 × 95	**31.** 1897 × 57	**32.** 4294 × 83	**33.** 2319 × 24
34. $1.56 × 33	**35.** $4.08 × 17	**36.** $18.06 × 22	**37.** $71.24 × 95	**38.** $38.65 × 79	**39.** $42.08 × 44

Solve. Use the classified-ad information to tell which job each person is thinking about.

40. "If I took that job, I'd earn $48 a day."

41. "I would earn $440 a week doing that job."

42. "If I took that job, I would earn $75 in three days."

DISHWASHER
Mon.–Sat.
5 hours a day $5/hour

WATER-TOWER PAINTER
40-hour week $11/hour

PHOTOGRAPHER
Mon.–Wed.
6-hour day $8/hour
Must furnish own camera.

Key it in!

Find a way to push each marked key once to get the answer.

43.

44.

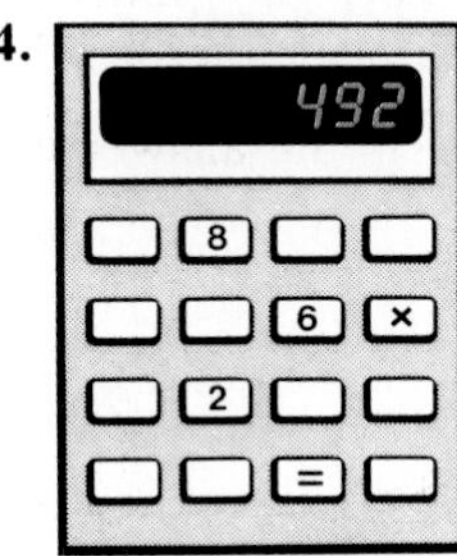

45.

490
8 9
5 ×
=

Multiplying larger numbers

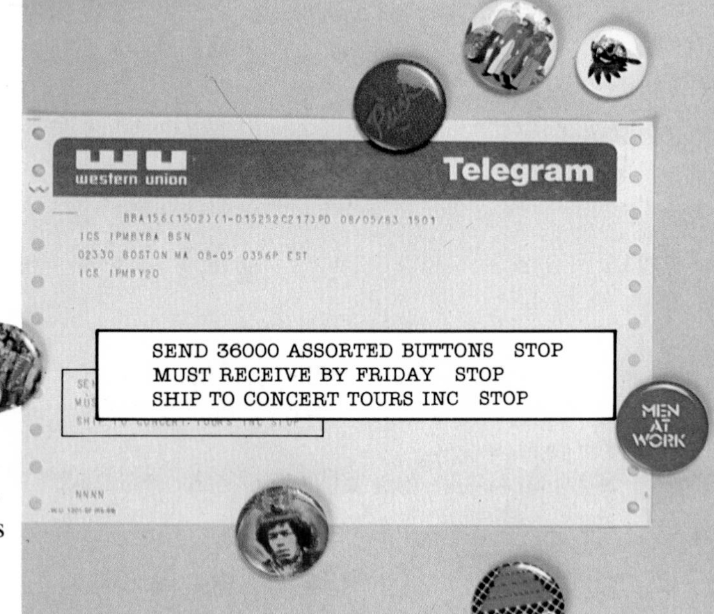

western union
Telegram
SEND 36000 ASSORTED BUTTONS STOP
MUST RECEIVE BY FRIDAY STOP
SHIP TO CONCERT TOURS INC STOP
MEN AT WORK
DEVO

You're a Shipping Clerk!

You have 246 boxes of assorted buttons. There are 144 buttons in each box.

1. How many buttons are in a box?
2. How many boxes do you have in stock?
3. What two numbers would you multiply to find out whether you have enough buttons to fill the order?

Here's how *to multiply 3-digit numbers.* ***246 × 144 = ?***

Start each product directly below the digit you are multiplying by.

```
   246
 × 144
   984
  9840
 24600
 35,424
```

You don't have to write the 0's.

Other examples:

```
   402        305
 × 103      × 750
  1206      15250
 402        2135
 41,406     228,750
```

4. Look at the *Here's how*. Do you have enough buttons to fill the order?
5. Check each example. Is the answer correct?

```
a.   372       b.   301       c.   807
   × 132          × 506          × 490
     744           1806          72630
   1116          1505           3228
   372           152,306        395,430
  49,104
```

EXERCISES.

Multiply. *Here are scrambled answers for the next row of exercises: 122,990 81,315 81,432 52,204 146,784 124,982*

6. 348×234 7. 695×117 8. 834×176 9. 502×245 10. 506×247 11. 421×124

12. 523×402 13. 938×136 14. 734×274 15. 608×403 16. 909×123 17. 707×246

18. 1839×256 19. 1265×329 20. 2576×395 21. 8152×406 22. 6805×203 23. 7304×155

24. 1652×330 25. 3728×250 26. 9162×407 27. 8610×720 28. 1785×909 29. 8042×105

30. $65.23 × 200 31. $13.75 × 400 32. $17.06 × 600 33. $86.10 × 500 34. $75.69 × 300 35. $42.30 × 200

36. 546 × 324 37. 603 × 425 38. 582 × 515 39. 497 × 305
40. 1252 × 213 41. 8260 × 206 42. 1175 × 225 43. 1063 × 215
44. 8606 × 400 45. 7625 × 900 46. 5403 × 700 47. 9302 × 200

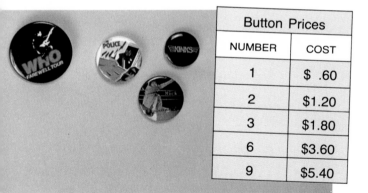

Button Prices	
NUMBER	COST
1	$ .60
2	$1.20
3	$1.80
6	$3.60
9	$5.40

Solve. Use the price list.

48. How many buttons can you buy for $1.20?
49. What is the cost of 6 buttons?
50. How many buttons can you buy for $5.40?
51. What is the cost of 10 buttons?
52. You gave the clerk a $10 bill for 9 buttons. How much change should you receive?

Make the change

53. Carlo made a $1.43 purchase. He gave the clerk $2. What 5 coins did he get in change?

54. Sandy made an $8.79 purchase. She gave the clerk $10.04. What coin and bill did Sandy receive as change?

Cumulative Skill Practice

Add. *(page 6)*

1. 395 + 21	**2.** 267 + 38	**3.** 409 + 126	**4.** 536 + 342	**5.** 658 + 591	**6.** 796 + 384
7. 246 138 + 52	**8.** 506 74 + 382	**9.** 921 274 + 136	**10.** 729 635 + 347	**11.** 911 555 + 426	**12.** 687 42 + 394
13. 462 329 83 + 114	**14.** 632 95 377 + 216	**15.** 536 291 432 + 51	**16.** 329 416 238 + 627	**17.** 513 753 916 + 742	**18.** 457 365 21 + 914

Round to the nearest hundred. *(page 12)*

19. 478 **20.** 609 **21.** 746 **22.** 250 **23.** 963

24. 2748 **25.** 3290 **26.** 8062 **27.** 5555 **28.** 6350

Write the standard numeral. *(page 16)*

29. 6 tenths

30. 29 hundredths

31. 7 hundredths

32. 15 thousandths

33. 3 and 9 tenths

34. 8 and 32 hundredths

35. 15 and 4 hundredths

36. 7 and 26 thousandths

37. 9 and 3 thousandths

38. 24 and 396 ten-thousandths

Round to the nearest hundredth. *(page 20)*

39. 0.296 **40.** 0.275 **41.** 3.6081 **42.** 4.002 **43.** 2.7450

44. 3.4382 **45.** 8.297 **46.** 9.3841 **47.** 7.5004 **48.** 6.8296

Give the sum. *(page 24)*

49. 3.28 + 0.56

50. 4.381 + 2.743

51. 15.829 + 6.542

52. 9.1 + 3.06

53. 17.2 + 23.4

54. 26.71 + 8.5

55. 6 + 3.7 + 2.94

56. 0.18 + 1.6 + 3

57. 52.5 + 6.21 + 7

58. 0.06 + 2.432 + 1.5

59. 7.5 + 6.37 + 0.057

60. 6.91 + 4.283 + 9.71

61. 2.4 + 1.65 + 4

62. 25.5 + 1.26 + 10

63. 8.1 + 16 + 0.3

Problem solving

You are a sales clerk at the Quick Print Photo Shop. The shop is running a sale on film and photo finishing.

Big Holiday Sale!

FILM SHOP Color Film			PHOTO FINISHING Color Prints	
SIZE	EXPOSURES	PRICE		
135	36	$3.00	Any negative	25¢
135	20	$2.15	Each additional print	15¢
126	20	$2.05	5 x 7 enlargement	99¢
110	12	$1.49	8 x 10 enlargement	$2.59

What questions would you have to ask each customer before you could complete the sale?

1. *I'd like a print of this negative for each person in my family.*

2. *I'd like a roll of size 135 film for my camera.*

3. *My mother wants an enlargement of this picture of Niagara Falls. How much will it cost?*

4. "I have $15. Can I buy 6 rolls of film for my camera?"

5. "I'd like to have a 5 x 7 enlargement made from each of these negatives. How much will they cost?"

Solve. Use the sale prices.

6. Garret had $7.50. He bought a roll of 20-exposure size 135 film. How much money did he have left?

7. Jenny bought a roll of film. She got $7.95 change from a $10 bill. What size film did she buy?

8. Mrs. Fisher bought 2 rolls of film. She spent $5.15. How many pictures will she be able to take?

9. How much more does an 8 x 10 enlargement cost than a 5 x 7 enlargement?

10. How many pictures will a customer be able to take if she buys 3 rolls of 36-exposure size 135 film?

11. Mr. Wilson wants 5 negatives made into color prints. How much will they cost?

Multiplying decimals

DID YOU KNOW . . . The height that you can jump depends on the force of gravity. Since the force of gravity varies from planet to planet, you would jump different heights on different planets.

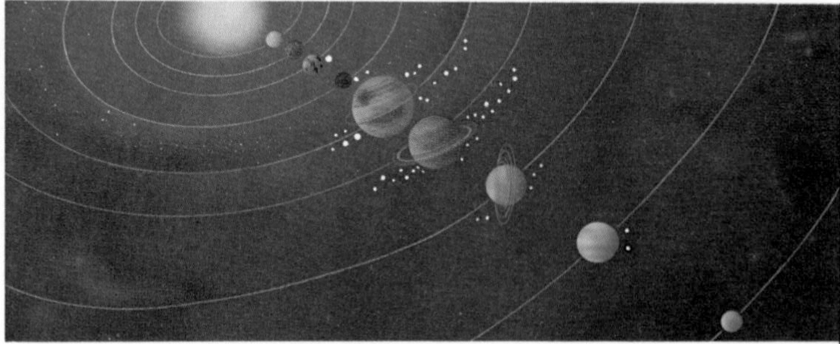

PLANET	HIGH-JUMP FACTOR
Earth	1.00
Mercury	3.57
Venus	1.16
Mars	2.63
Jupiter	0.38
Saturn	0.83
Uranus	1.09
Neptune	0.91
Pluto	1.43

1. What is the high-jump factor for the planet Mercury?
2. Suppose that you high-jumped 1.63 m (meters) on the planet Earth. You could multiply 1.63 by the high-jump factor of Venus to find how high the jump would have been on Venus. What two numbers would you multiply to find how many meters you would have jumped on Venus?

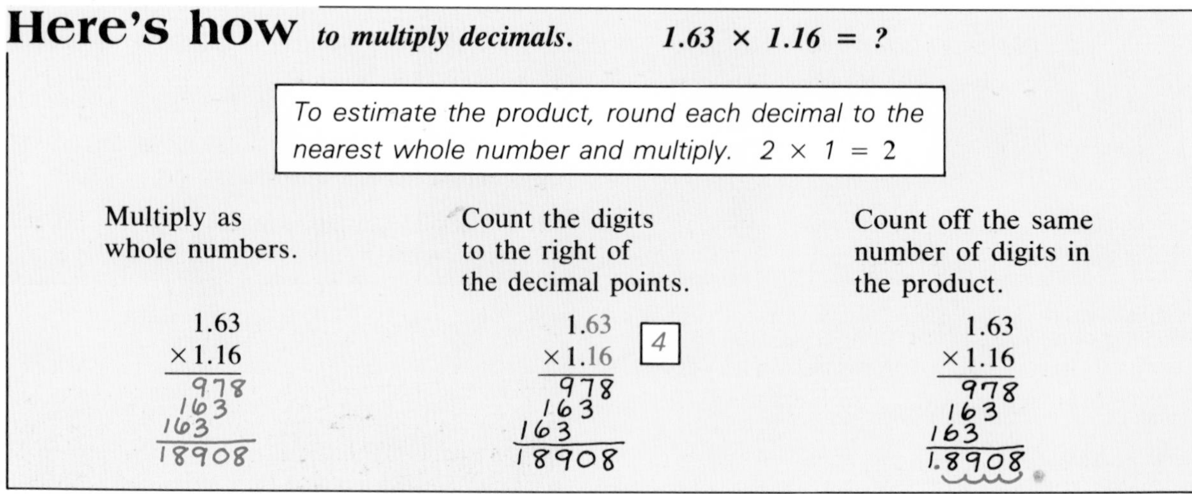

Here's how *to multiply decimals.* *1.63 × 1.16 = ?*

To estimate the product, round each decimal to the nearest whole number and multiply. 2 × 1 = 2

Multiply as whole numbers.	Count the digits to the right of the decimal points.	Count off the same number of digits in the product.
1.63 ×1.16 978 163 163 18908	1.63 ×1.16 [4] 978 163 163 18908	1.63 ×1.16 978 163 163 1.8908

3. Look at the *Here's how*. How high would you have jumped on Venus? Was 2 meters a good estimate?
4. Check each example. Is the answer correct?

a. 4.6 × 2 = 9.2

b. 3.46 × 0.02 = 0.0692 — *You have to write a zero here to place the decimal point.*

c. 65 × 0.3 = 19.5

EXERCISES

Multiply. *Here are scrambled answers for the next row of exercises: 0.0231 11.97 2.914 2.635 26.22 4.8*

5. 3.8 × 6.9	**6.** 5.7 × 2.1	**7.** 2.4 × 2	**8.** 0.31 × 9.4	**9.** 2.31 × 0.01	**10.** 4.25 × 0.62
11. 1.8 × 56	**12.** 7.4 × 10	**13.** 0.05 × 0.7	**14.** 0.85 × 16	**15.** 0.44 × 6.6	**16.** 321 × 8.4
17. 3.28 × 3.5	**18.** 7.46 × 6.1	**19.** 5.26 × 4.2	**20.** 0.06 × 0.44	**21.** 8.52 × 0.65	**22.** 4.16 × 0.06
23. \$7.52 × 89	**24.** \$5.47 × 33	**25.** \$2.83 × 17	**26.** \$7.53 × 62	**27.** \$3.91 × 53	**28.** \$8.74 × 21

29. 5.7 × 0.42
30. 3.5 × 0.57
31. 0.29 × 0.05
32. 2.4 × 0.6
33. 39 × 6.3
34. 0.51 × 8.2
35. 65 × 0.39
36. 77 × 1.4
37. 368 × 2.7
38. 4.06 × 10
39. 0.08 × 0.4
40. 0.25 × 0.3
41. 5.83 × 0.95
42. 0.01 × 0.5
43. 79.5 × 0.36
44. 4.62 × 9.5

Solve. Use the table on page 64.

45. If you high-jumped 1.63 meters on Earth, how high would you have jumped on Pluto?

46. If you high-jumped 1.56 meters on Earth, how high would you have jumped on Mercury? Round the answer to the nearest hundredth of a meter.

47. On which planet would you jump the lowest? the highest?

48. On which planets would you jump higher than on the planet Earth? On which planets would you jump lower?

49. Suppose that you could jump 1.54 meters on Earth. How much higher could you jump on Uranus than on Neptune?

50. Solve problem 49 in another way.

Moon meet

51. Study the clues to determine the high-jump factor for the moon.

Clues:
- There are two places to the right of the decimal point.
- If you round it to the nearest tenth, you get 5.9.
- It has two digits that are the same.
- The sum of the digits is odd.

Simplifying expressions

You are a mail-order clerk for the Wee Forest Folk Gift Shop. Your job is to compute the total cost of the gifts you pack and ship.

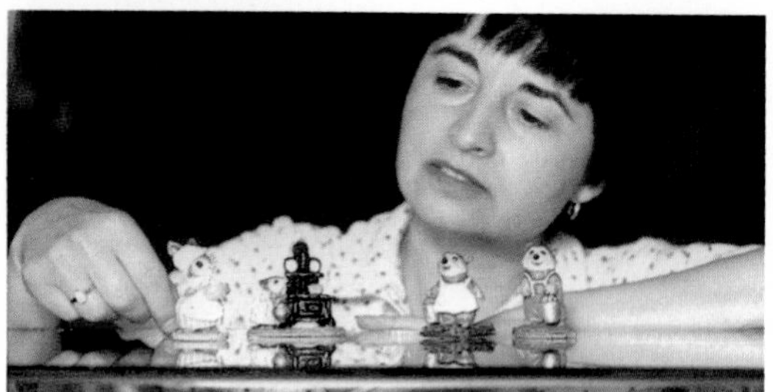

Wee Forest Folk Gifts

1. What is the cost of an Office Mouse?
2. What is the cost of a Graduate Owl?
3. To find the total cost of 3 Graduate Owls and an Office Mouse, you would first multiply 3 times [?] and then add $24.79.

Here's how *to simplify the expression (3 × $29.79) + $24.79.*

If you estimate before you calculate, you will know whether your answer makes sense.

Estimate this way:
$(3 \times 30) + 25 = ?$
$90 + 25 = 115$

Remember to work inside the grouping symbols first.

(3 × $29.79) + $24.79 = ?

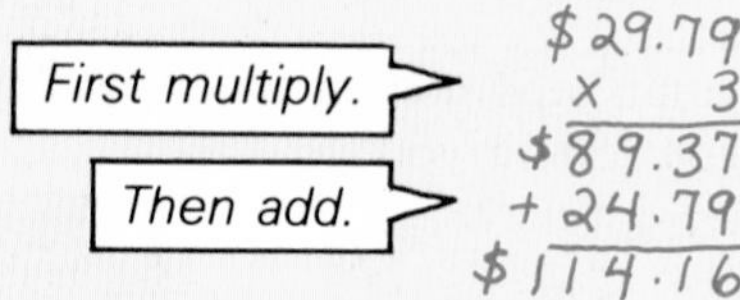

$29.79
× 3
$89.37
+ 24.79
$114.16

4. Look at the *Here's how.* What is the total cost of 3 Graduate Owls and an Office Mouse? Was the estimate near the answer?
5. Check each example. Which answer cannot be correct?
Hint: Estimate by rounding each decimal to the nearest whole number.

[80 − (25 + 30)]
a. 79.78 − (24.79 + 29.79) = 25.20

[(30 + 40) × 4]
b. (29.79 + 39.89) × 4 = 73.68

EXERCISES

6. Two of these calculator answers are wrong. Find them by estimating.
Hint: Remember to work inside the grouping symbols first.

(82 + 60) − 10		9 − (6 + 2)	
a. (82.3 + 59.7) − 9.8	132.2	b. 9.3 − (6.2 + 1.9)	1.2
c. 29.7 + (19.8 × 3)	198.5	d. (24.8 + 35.3) + 40.1	100.2
e. (59.2 − 10.9) + 21.8	70.1	f. 20 − (5.8 × 2.1)	51.06
g. (3.1 + 5.8) × 2.1	18.69	h. 3.1 + (5.8 × 2.1)	15.28

Simplify. *Here are scrambled answers for the next row of exercises: 2.2 12.4 74.4*

7. 5.2 + (2.4 × 3)
8. 10 − (4.6 + 3.2)
9. 9.3 × (4.8 + 3.2)
10. (15 × 0.6) + 3.25
11. (0.3 × 4) + 1.45
12. 6 − (3.5 + 2.5)
13. (4.8 − 3.5) × 5
14. (2.8 + 4.2) + 5.9
15. 2.4 + (2.65 × 4)
16. 14.6 + (9.2 − 3.1)
17. 35 − (3.6 × 8)
18. (3.4 × 6) − 8.2
19. (9.15 + 6.45) − 12
20. (9.1 × 2) + 4.6
21. 8 − (1.5 × 3)
22. 1.45 + (2.15 × 3)
23. (7.7 + 5.2) − 6
24. 15 − (2.5 × 4)
25. (7.2 + 8.4) − 5.9
26. 2.8 + (6 × 5.4)
27. (6 × 2.5) − 7
28. 8.5 − (4.4 + 1.8)
29. (7.5 × 4) − 12
30. 22.25 − (5.25 × 3)

You decide!

Use the prices on page 66. Decide whether expression A, B, C, or D would be used to solve the problem. Then solve the problem.

Expression A: \$39.89 + (3 × \$24.79)
Expression B: \$100 − (3 × \$29.79)
Expression C: (3 × \$39.89) − \$100
Expression D: \$24.79 + (3 × \$39.89)

31. *What's the total cost for an Office Mouse and 3 Travelin' Bears?*

32. What is the total cost for a Travelin' Bear and 3 Office Mice?

33. A customer paid for 3 Graduate Owls with a \$100 bill. How much change should the customer receive?

34. How much more money would a customer need in order to buy 3 Travelin' Bears if the customer had a \$100 gift certificate?

Multiplying decimals by 10, 100, or 1000

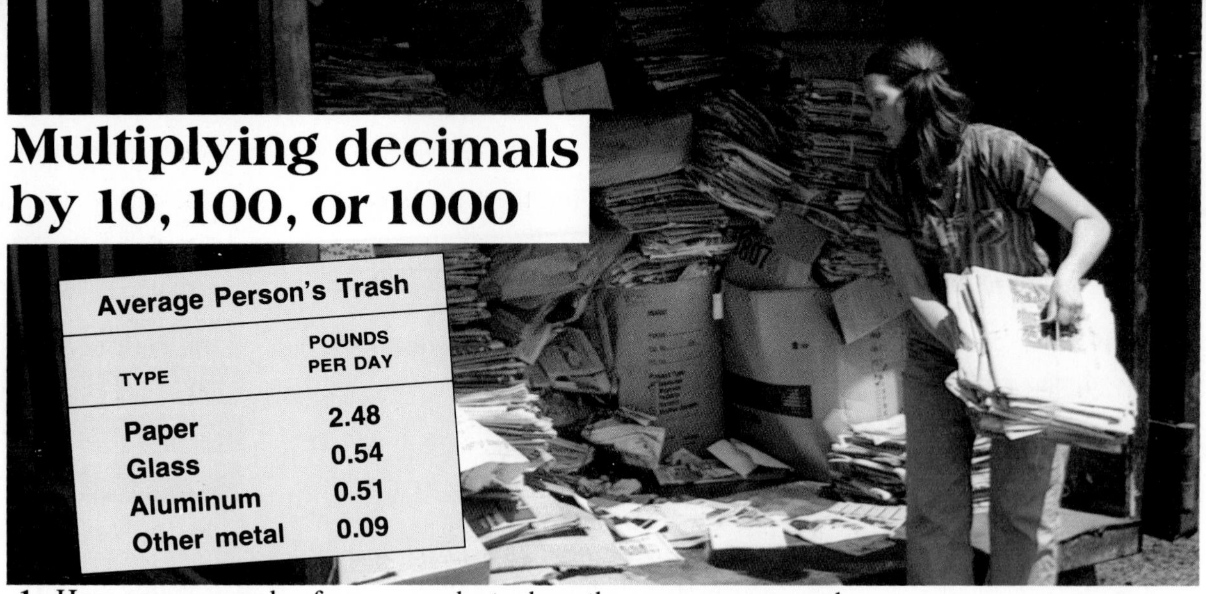

Average Person's Trash

TYPE	POUNDS PER DAY
Paper	2.48
Glass	0.54
Aluminum	0.51
Other metal	0.09

1. How many pounds of paper products does the average person throw away each day?

2. What two numbers would you multiply to find how many pounds of paper products the average person throws away in 10 days? 100 days? 1000 days?

Here's how *to multiply by 10, 100, or 1000.*

When you multiply a number by 10, 100, or 1000, the product is greater than the number.

$2.48 \times 10 = ?$

Multiplying by 10 moves the decimal point 1 place to the right.

$$\begin{array}{r} 2.48 \\ \times \quad 10 \\ \hline 24.80 \end{array}$$

$2.48 \times 10 =$ 24.8

$2.48 \times 100 = ?$

Multiplying by 100 moves the decimal point 2 places.

$2.48 \times 100 =$ 248.

$2.48 \times 1000 = ?$

Multiplying by 1000 moves the decimal point 3 places.

$2.48 \times 1000 =$ 2480.

3. Look at the *Here's how*. How many pounds of paper products does the average person throw away in 10 days? 100 days? 1000 days?

EXERCISES

Give the product. *Here are scrambled answers for the next two rows of exercises: 53,600 680 42 420 536 5360 4.2 6800*

4. 4.2×10	**5.** 42×10	**6.** 0.42×10	**7.** 5.36×100
8. 536×100	**9.** 5.36×1000	**10.** 6.8×1000	**11.** 0.68×1000
12. 68×1000	**13.** 0.396×1000	**14.** 3.96×10	**15.** 3.96×100

16. 3.96 × 1000 **17.** 15.3 × 10 **18.** 15.3 × 100 **19.** 15.3 × 1000

20. 4900 × 10 **21.** 4900 × 100 **22.** 4900 × 1000 **23.** 490 × 100

24. 38 × 10 **25.** 38 × 100 **26.** 38 × 1000 **27.** 380 × 100

28. 0.67 × 1000 **29.** 0.67 × 100 **30.** 0.67 × 10 **31.** 6.7 × 1000

32. 0.08 × 1000 **33.** 0.08 × 100 **34.** 0.08 × 10 **35.** 0.8 × 10

36. 142 × 10 **37.** 142 × 1000 **38.** 142 × 100 **39.** 1.42 × 100

40. 346 × 100 **41.** 346 × 10 **42.** 346 × 1000 **43.** 34.6 × 1000

44. 7.46 × 1000 **45.** 7.46 × 10 **46.** 7.46 × 100 **47.** 746 × 100

48. 0.006 × 100 **49.** 0.006 × 1000 **50.** 0.006 × 10 **51.** 0.06 × 10

52. 6.088 × 1000 **53.** 6.088 × 100 **54.** 6.088 × 10 **55.** 60.88 × 10

Solve. Use the table on page 68. Assume that your trash is the average amount.

56. How many pounds of glass would you throw away in 10 days?

57. How many pounds of aluminum would you throw away in 100 days?

58. What is the total number of pounds of trash that you throw away each day?

59. How many pounds of non-paper trash would you throw away in 100 days?

60. Suppose you save glass instead of throwing it away. How many pounds would you save for recycling in 100 days?

61. How many pounds of aluminum would you save for the recycling center in 100 days?

62. The recycling center pays $.02 a pound for paper products. How much would you earn if you sold 100 days' worth of paper products?

63. The price for recycled aluminum is $.15 per pound. How much would you earn if you recycled 100 days' worth of aluminum?

Check the products

64. Find and correct the two wrong answers.

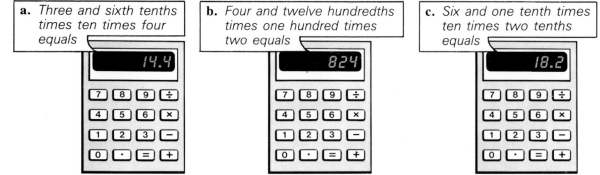

a. *Three and sixth tenths times ten times four equals*

14.4

b. *Four and twelve hundredths times one hundred times two equals*

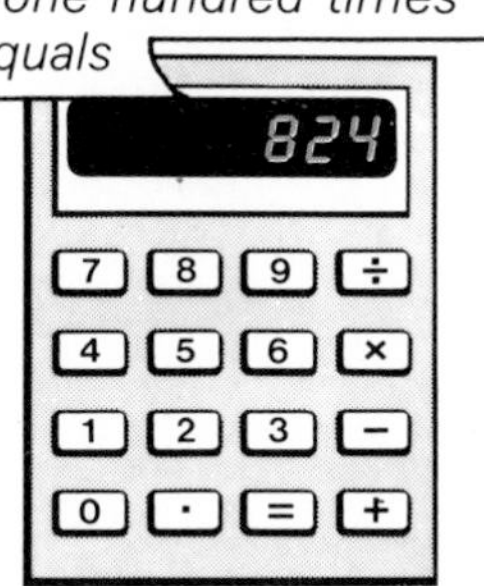

c. *Six and one tenth times ten times two tenths equals*

Cumulative Skill Practice

Subtract. *(page 36)*

1. 3897 − 142	**2.** 6351 − 248	**3.** 7293 − 1526	**4.** 8374 − 2987	**5.** 5328 − 1479	**6.** 9742 − 2836
7. 2384 − 1527	**8.** 6635 − 558	**9.** 4981 − 3465	**10.** 9310 − 2852	**11.** 7611 − 3629	**12.** 4280 − 1066
13. 6034 − 351	**14.** 5901 − 529	**15.** 4077 − 1384	**16.** 8300 − 564	**17.** 6700 − 1387	**18.** 3040 − 1264

Less than (<) or greater than (>)? *(page 42)*

19. 0.6 ● 0.5 **20.** 0.03 ● 0.04 **21.** 12.8 ● 12.7

22. 0.1 ● 0.03 **23.** 3.05 ● 3.005 **24.** 2.6 ● 2.599

25. 4.206 ● 4.26 **26.** 1 ● 0.99 **27.** 0.034 ● 0.34

Give the difference. *(page 46)*

28. 74.3 − 38.5 **29.** 26.3 − 14.9 **30.** 6.00 − 3.81

31. 9.4 − 3.8 **32.** 20.15 − 6.83 **33.** 48.06 − 3.57

34. 29 − 15.8 **35.** 30 − 7.42 **36.** 6.3 − 5.88

Multiply. *(page 60)*

37. 223 × 115	**38.** 402 × 321	**39.** 336 × 152	**40.** 538 × 226	**41.** 629 × 427	**42.** 745 × 281
43. 592 × 206	**44.** 380 × 305	**45.** 635 × 530	**46.** 706 × 290	**47.** 832 × 308	**48.** 434 × 267

Give the product. *(page 64)*

49. 3.2 × 0.8 **50.** 4.6 × 0.31 **51.** 0.55 × 0.4

52. 28 × 1.4 **53.** 0.56 × 8.3 **54.** 4.21 × 1.3

55. 6.54 × 18 **56.** 26.8 × 7.3 **57.** 46.3 × 0.84

Simplify. *(page 66)*

58. 3.5 + (2.1 × 4) **59.** 26 − (8.3 + 2.6) **60.** (8.3 − 6) + 2.6

61. (9.4 × 0.5) − 1.4 **62.** (7.2 − 3.81) × 5 **63.** 4.6 + (4.2 × 3)

64. (5.4 + 3.86) × 2 **65.** 5.4 + (3.86 × 2) **66.** (7.5 − 4.1) × 0.7

Problem solving

COMPUTERIZED CASH REGISTERS

Many cafeterias use computerized cash registers. The computer is programmed to calculate and display the total cost when the cashier keys in an order. When the cashier keys in the amount rendered (the amount the customer uses to pay), the computer will calculate the amount of change.

MENU
DINNERS
BAKED HAM $3.25
ROAST BEEF 2.75
FRIED CHICKEN 2.50
TUNA PLATE 2.25
SALADS
TOSSED GREEN .55
FRUIT .65
CHEF 2.85
DRINKS
MILK .40
JUICE .80
COFFEE OR TEA .30

Use the information on the menu and the cash register to answer these questions.

1. *My last customer ordered a dinner and a salad. What keys did I push?*
2. *He paid with a $5 bill. I gave him 4 coins and a bill for change. What were the coins?*

3. What total does the computer display when these keys are pushed?

4. What coins and bills would you use to make change for these purchases? (Assume each customer paid with a $10 bill. Use the fewest coins possible.)

   a. TOTAL 6.90

   b. TOTAL 3.80

   c. TOTAL 3.55

5. Each of these customers bought a dinner, a salad, and a drink. What did each customer order?

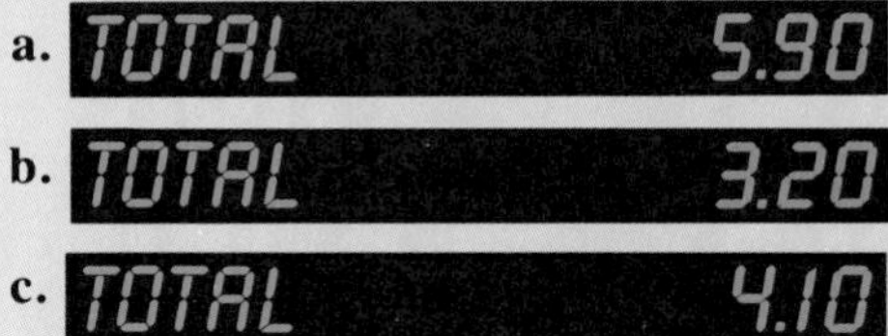

6. Each of these customers bought two items and paid with a $5 bill. What did each customer buy?

   a. CHANGE 2.45

   b. CHANGE .95

   c. CHANGE .25

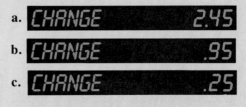

Chapter REVIEW

Here are scrambled answers for the review exercises:

3	5	12	add	right	zeros
4	7	80	product	whole	

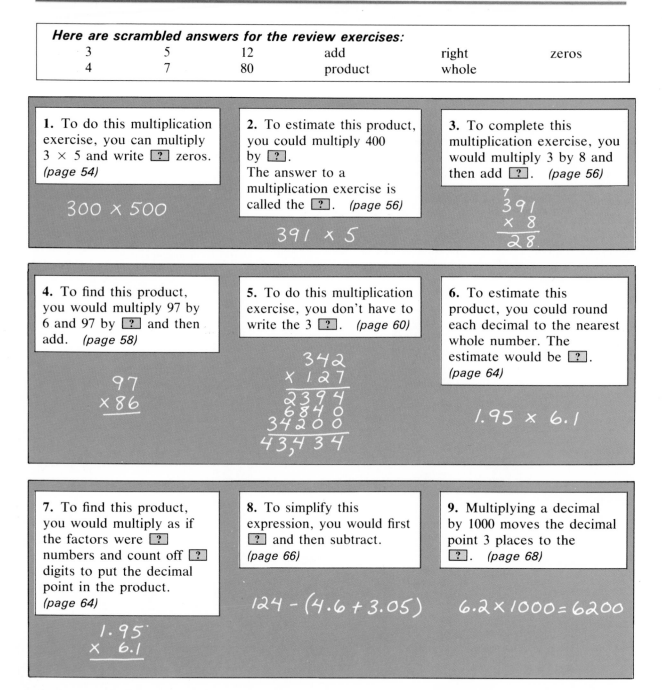

1. To do this multiplication exercise, you can multiply 3 × 5 and write [?] zeros. *(page 54)*

300 × 500

2. To estimate this product, you could multiply 400 by [?].
The answer to a multiplication exercise is called the [?]. *(page 56)*

391 × 5

3. To complete this multiplication exercise, you would multiply 3 by 8 and then add [?]. *(page 56)*

```
  7
 391
×  8
 ---
  28
```

4. To find this product, you would multiply 97 by 6 and 97 by [?] and then add. *(page 58)*

```
  97
 ×86
 ---
```

5. To do this multiplication exercise, you don't have to write the 3 [?]. *(page 60)*

```
   342
 × 127
 -----
  2394
  6840
 34200
 -----
43,434
```

6. To estimate this product, you could round each decimal to the nearest whole number. The estimate would be [?]. *(page 64)*

1.95 × 6.1

7. To find this product, you would multiply as if the factors were [?] numbers and count off [?] digits to put the decimal point in the product. *(page 64)*

```
  1.95
 × 6.1
 -----
```

8. To simplify this expression, you would first [?] and then subtract. *(page 66)*

124 − (4.6 + 3.05)

9. Multiplying a decimal by 1000 moves the decimal point 3 places to the [?]. *(page 68)*

6.2 × 1000 = 6200

Chapter TEST

Multiply. *(pages 54, 56)*

1. 6×10 **2.** 9×100 **3.** 8×1000 **4.** 30×30 **5.** 23×100

6. 60×40 **7.** 18×100 **8.** 30×500 **9.** 700×800 **10.** 5000×90

11. 32×3 **12.** 76×8 **13.** 256×5 **14.** 3906×6 **15.** 487×8

Multiply. *(pages 58, 60)*

16. 24×12 **17.** 78×27 **18.** 139×35 **19.** 420×64 **20.** 268×25 **21.** 685×63

22. 326×153 **23.** 439×540 **24.** 3561×209 **25.** 4298×753 **26.** 6533×95 **27.** 1806×22

Multiply. *(page 64)*

28. 3.4×1.5 **29.** 6.3×1.4 **30.** 0.84×0.6 **31.** 53.7×4.6 **32.** 0.06×0.44 **33.** 3.28×3.5

34. 0.39×2.8 **35.** 0.12×6 **36.** 9.44×1.05 **37.** 82.1×0.7

Simplify. *(page 66)*

38. $2.41 + (0.04 \times 0.2)$ **39.** $(31.5 - 4.6) + 8.9$ **40.** $(5.7 + 3.2) \times 4.6$

41. $10.42 - (8.63 - 2.48)$ **42.** $(60 - 5.4) \times 5.6$ **43.** $4 - (1.63 \times 1.5)$

Multiply. *(page 68)*

44. 27×10 **45.** 3.49×10 **46.** 5.4×100 **47.** 0.67×1000

48. 0.08×100 **49.** 15.6×1000 **50.** 0.04×1000 **51.** 2.0312×100

Solve.

52. What is the total price of 1 pound of macaroni salad and 1 pound of Bar-B-Q beef ribs?

53. How much will 1.5 pounds of honey-cured ham cost?

54. How much will 2.25 pounds of cheddar cheese cost? Round the answer to the nearest cent.

55. What is the total price of 1.5 pounds of beef ribs and 1.75 pounds of ham?

DAVID'S DELI

Fresh and Creamy
Macaroni Salad .... pound 99¢

Fresh Sliced
Honey-cured Ham .... pound $4.48

Bar-B-Q Beef Ribs .... pound $2.98

Fresh Sliced
Cheddar Cheese .... pound $2.89

Cumulative TEST Standardized Format

Choose the correct letter.

1. Add.

$$\begin{array}{r} 326 \\ 435 \\ 284 \\ +175 \\ \hline \end{array}$$

A. 1220
B. 1000
C. 1200
D. none of these

2. 4950 rounded to the nearest hundred is

A. 4950
B. 4900
C. 5000
D. none of these

3. The standard numeral for 3 and 48 thousandths is

A. 3.48
B. 3.0048
C. 3.048
D. none of these

4. 8.954 rounded to the nearest hundredth is

A. 9.0
B. 8.95
C. 8.75
D. none of these

5. Give the sum.

31.4 + 3.89 + 4

A. 39.29
B. 38.29
C. 70.7
D. none of these

6. Subtract.

$$\begin{array}{r} 4600 \\ -\ 235 \\ \hline \end{array}$$

A. 4375
B. 4365
C. 4435
D. none of these

7. Which number is less than 0.89?

A. 0.98
B. 0.089
C. 1
D. none of these

8. Give the difference.

35.2 − 1.84

A. 16.8
B. 33.44
C. 33.36
D. none of these

9. Multiply.

$$\begin{array}{r} 374 \\ \times 106 \\ \hline \end{array}$$

A. 39,644
B. 5984
C. 5564
D. none of these

10. Give the product.

6.25 × 1.8

A. 112.50
B. 1125.0
C. 5.625
D. none of these

11. Simplify.

26.3 − (4.6 × 3.8)

A. 35.12
B. 8.82
C. 82.46
D. none of these

12. You're on a 10-mile hike. You hike 2.5 miles during the first hour. How many miles do you have left to hike?

A. 7.5
B. 6.5
C. 4.5
D. none of these

Chapter 4
Dividing Whole Numbers and Decimals

Dividing by a 1-digit number

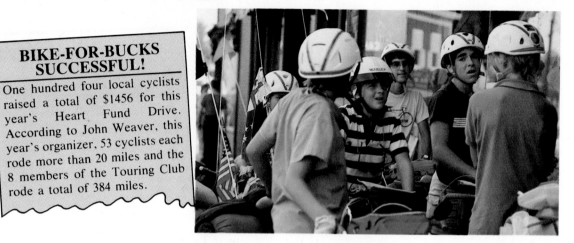

BIKE-FOR-BUCKS SUCCESSFUL!

One hundred four local cyclists raised a total of $1456 for this year's Heart Fund Drive. According to John Weaver, this year's organizer, 53 cyclists each rode more than 20 miles and the 8 members of the Touring Club rode a total of 384 miles.

1. How many members of the Touring Club rode a total of 384 miles?
2. What two numbers would you use to compute the average number of miles ridden by the Touring Club members?
3. Would you multiply or divide to compute the average?

Here's how *to divide by a 1-digit number.* ***384 ÷ 8 = ?***

Not enough hundreds. Think 38 tens.	Divide tens. Subtract.	Think 64 ones.	Divide ones. Subtract.
$8\overline{)384}$	$\begin{array}{r} 4 \\ 8\overline{)384} \\ -32 \\ \hline 6 \end{array}$	$\begin{array}{r} 4 \\ 8\overline{)384} \\ -32 \\ \hline 64 \end{array}$	$\begin{array}{r} 48 \\ 8\overline{)384} \\ -32 \\ \hline 64 \\ -64 \\ \hline 0 \end{array}$

The answer is called the **quotient.**

4. Look at the *Here's how.* What was the average distance ridden by the Touring Club members?

EXERCISES

Divide. *Here are scrambled answers for the next row of exercises:* 22 21 24 14 13 29

5. $2\overline{)48}$	**6.** $3\overline{)39}$	**7.** $4\overline{)56}$	**8.** $3\overline{)63}$	**9.** $4\overline{)88}$	**10.** $2\overline{)58}$
11. $2\overline{)38}$	**12.** $2\overline{)86}$	**13.** $5\overline{)75}$	**14.** $6\overline{)96}$	**15.** $2\overline{)66}$	**16.** $3\overline{)72}$

17. $8\overline{)96}$	**18.** $4\overline{)92}$	**19.** $7\overline{)91}$	**20.** $2\overline{)96}$	**21.** $4\overline{)60}$	**22.** $5\overline{)65}$
23. $3\overline{)81}$	**24.** $5\overline{)85}$	**25.** $4\overline{)72}$	**26.** $2\overline{)84}$	**27.** $6\overline{)72}$	**28.** $4\overline{)96}$
29. $7\overline{)84}$	**30.** $9\overline{)99}$	**31.** $5\overline{)70}$	**32.** $3\overline{)75}$	**33.** $5\overline{)90}$	**34.** $7\overline{)77}$
35. $2\overline{)426}$	**36.** $4\overline{)484}$	**37.** $3\overline{)693}$	**38.** $5\overline{)555}$	**39.** $4\overline{)848}$	**40.** $6\overline{)456}$
41. $3\overline{)537}$	**42.** $6\overline{)738}$	**43.** $3\overline{)432}$	**44.** $7\overline{)994}$	**45.** $3\overline{)735}$	**46.** $8\overline{)432}$
47. $2\overline{)536}$	**48.** $9\overline{)396}$	**49.** $6\overline{)438}$	**50.** $8\overline{)752}$	**51.** $4\overline{)636}$	**52.** $2\overline{)348}$
53. $7\overline{)658}$	**54.** $5\overline{)735}$	**55.** $5\overline{)360}$	**56.** $4\overline{)676}$	**57.** $2\overline{)174}$	**58.** $9\overline{)531}$
59. $8\overline{)656}$	**60.** $9\overline{)846}$	**61.** $5\overline{)235}$	**62.** $7\overline{)595}$	**63.** $6\overline{)858}$	**64.** $4\overline{)932}$
65. $4\overline{)792}$	**66.** $7\overline{)434}$	**67.** $9\overline{)621}$	**68.** $6\overline{)534}$	**69.** $8\overline{)792}$	**70.** $5\overline{)965}$

71. $84 \div 6$	**72.** $60 \div 5$	**73.** $84 \div 3$	**74.** $78 \div 6$	**75.** $896 \div 8$
76. $267 \div 3$	**77.** $216 \div 9$	**78.** $725 \div 5$	**79.** $896 \div 7$	**80.** $844 \div 4$
81. $732 \div 6$	**82.** $592 \div 8$	**83.** $684 \div 9$	**84.** $679 \div 7$	**85.** $745 \div 5$

Solve.

86. One cyclist had 4 pledges. They were \$.60, \$.85, \$1.25, and \$.55 per mile. What was her total pledge per mile?

87. The best time for a 68-mile course was 4 hours. How many miles per hour did the cyclist average?

88. One cyclist had a total pledge of \$3.17 per mile. He rode 53 miles. How much money did he raise?

89. One Touring Club member had a total pledge of \$3.35 per mile and another had a total pledge of \$2.92 per mile. They both rode 56 miles. What was the difference in the amounts they raised?

An awesome average!

90. In 1973, Dr. Allan Abbot set a speed record for a bicycle. He rode behind a special windshield mounted on a car. Over a 1-mile course he averaged [?] miles per hour.

To find [?], write the number that has

8 ones	3 tens
7 hundredths	6 tenths
4 thousandths	1 hundred

More on dividing by a 1-digit number

". . . BUY A HOME COMPUTER.
PAY NO MONEY DOWN.
PAY $615 IN THREE EQUAL
MONTHLY PAYMENTS . . ."

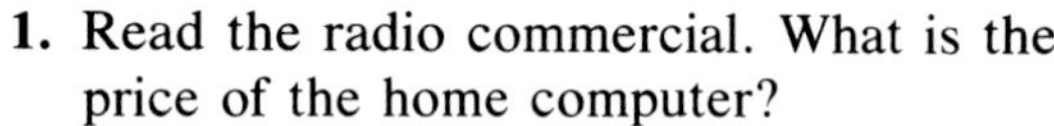

1. Read the radio commercial. What is the price of the home computer?

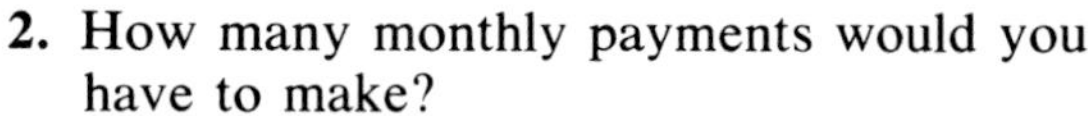

2. How many monthly payments would you have to make?

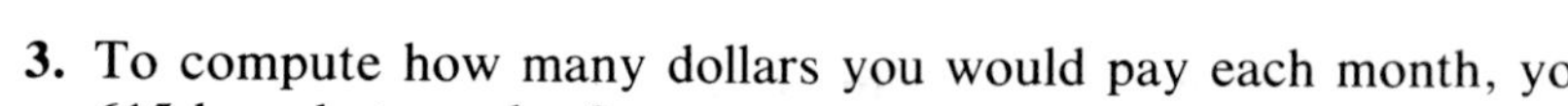

3. To compute how many dollars you would pay each month, you would divide 615 by what number?

Here's how *to divide by a 1-digit number.* *615 ÷ 3 = ?*

To estimate the quotient, find the first digit in the quotient.

$$3\overline{)615} \quad \text{quotient: } 2$$

Then write 0's in the remaining places.

$$3\overline{)615} \quad \text{quotient: } 200$$

Divide hundreds.

$$\begin{array}{r} 2 \\ 3\overline{)615} \\ -6 \end{array}$$

Not enough tens. Think 15 ones.

$$\begin{array}{r} 20 \\ 3\overline{)615} \\ -6 \\ 15 \end{array}$$

Don't forget the zero!

Divide ones.

$$\begin{array}{r} 205 \\ 3\overline{)615} \\ -6 \\ 15 \\ -15 \\ 0 \end{array}$$

4. Look at the *Here's how.* Is $200 a good estimate for the monthly payment?

5. How much is the monthly payment?

6. Find the missing quotient. Use an estimate to check your answer.

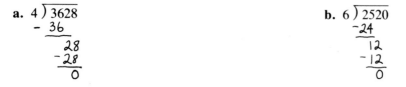

a.
$$\begin{array}{r} 4\overline{)3628} \\ -36 \\ 28 \\ -28 \\ 0 \end{array}$$

b.
$$\begin{array}{r} 6\overline{)2520} \\ -24 \\ 12 \\ -12 \\ 0 \end{array}$$

EXERCISES

7. Three of the calculator answers are wrong. Find them by estimating.

a. $3\overline{)6243}$ 2081	b. $4\overline{)832}$ 208	c. $5\overline{)1020}$ 24
d. $6\overline{)6456}$ 176	e. $9\overline{)873}$ 97	f. $4\overline{)1624}$ 46
g. $7\overline{)2961}$ 423	h. $8\overline{)5608}$ 701	i. $6\overline{)3792}$ 632

Divide. *Here are scrambled answers for the next row of exercises:* *31 2077 412 405 302*

8. $5\overline{)2025}$	9. $8\overline{)248}$	10. $7\overline{)2884}$	11. $6\overline{)1812}$	12. $4\overline{)8308}$
13. $3\overline{)597}$	14. $7\overline{)217}$	15. $9\overline{)450}$	16. $5\overline{)355}$	17. $6\overline{)2934}$
18. $2\overline{)4132}$	19. $6\overline{)3672}$	20. $9\overline{)6390}$	21. $7\overline{)5621}$	22. $3\overline{)525}$
23. $4\overline{)732}$	24. $6\overline{)240}$	25. $5\overline{)2965}$	26. $7\overline{)4263}$	27. $9\overline{)207}$
28. $5\overline{)405}$	29. $8\overline{)744}$	30. $3\overline{)3648}$	31. $6\overline{)1266}$	32. $5\overline{)365}$
33. $782 \div 2$	34. $592 \div 4$	35. $480 \div 3$	36. $1248 \div 6$	37. $830 \div 5$
38. $945 \div 9$	39. $1640 \div 2$	40. $405 \div 5$	41. $450 \div 9$	42. $1896 \div 4$

Solve. Use the information in the ad.

43. What was the regular price of the radio?

44. How much would you save if you bought the radio on sale?

45. After you made the first monthly payment, how much would you have left to pay on the radio?

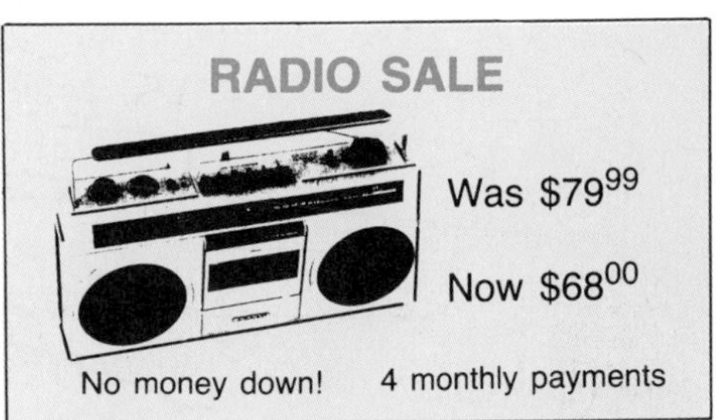

RADIO SALE
Was $79.99
Now $68.00
No money down!
4 monthly payments

Which statement is correct?

Disc jockeys play your favorite records, present the news, and read commercials.

46. The air time for the commercials a D.J. reads costs $480 per minute. Which statement is correct?

   a. A 30-second commercial costs $240.

   b. A 30-second commercial costs $300.

Dividing by a 2-digit number

You can predict your adult height by first multiplying your present height (in inches) by 100 and then dividing the answer by the growth factor found in the table.

1. On his 12th birthday, John was 57 inches tall. To predict his adult height, you would first multiply 57 by what number?
2. Which number in the table is the growth factor for John?
3. To predict John's adult height, you would divide what number by 82?

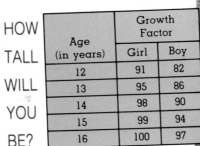

HOW TALL WILL YOU BE?

Age (in years)	Growth Factor	
	Girl	Boy
12	91	82
13	95	86
14	98	90
15	99	94
16	100	97

Here's how *to divide by a 2-digit number.*

5700 ÷ 82 = ?

Step 1. Think about dividing 57 by 8. So, try 7.

82 × 7 = 574

$$\begin{array}{r} 7 \\ 82\,\overline{)\,5700} \\ -574 \end{array}$$

574 is too large.

Step 2. Try 6.

82 × 6 = 492

$$\begin{array}{r} 6 \\ 82\,\overline{)\,5700} \\ -492 \\ \hline 78 \end{array}$$

Step 3. Think about dividing 78 by 8. Try 9.

82 × 9 = 738

$$\begin{array}{r} 69 \text{ R}42 \\ 82\,\overline{)\,5700} \\ -492 \\ \hline 780 \\ -738 \\ \hline 42 \end{array}$$

*Notice that the division did not come out even. The **quotient** is 69 and the **remainder** is 42.*

Here's how to check the division.

$$\begin{array}{r} 69 \\ \times\ 82 \\ \hline 138 \\ 552 \\ \hline 5658 \\ +\ \ 42 \\ \hline 5700 \end{array}$$

69 ← quotient; 42 ← remainder

4. Look at the *Here's how*. John's adult height would be between 69 and [?] inches.

EXERCISES

Divide and check.

5. $43\overline{)1333}$ 6. $51\overline{)1337}$ 7. $34\overline{)1620}$ 8. $60\overline{)1690}$ 9. $63\overline{)1638}$

10. $81\overline{)2703}$ 11. $38\overline{)2812}$ 12. $41\overline{)2500}$ 13. $54\overline{)2916}$ 14. $73\overline{)2835}$

15. $66\overline{)3823}$ 16. $92\overline{)3700}$ 17. $83\overline{)3206}$ 18. $71\overline{)3408}$ 19. $46\overline{)3642}$

Divide. *Here are scrambled answers for the next row of exercises:* *24 R37 36 25 44 R25 26*

20. $63\overline{)1575}$ 21. $56\overline{)1381}$ 22. $92\overline{)4073}$ 23. $58\overline{)1508}$ 24. $78\overline{)2808}$

25. $12\overline{)5400}$ 26. $39\overline{)4263}$ 27. $53\overline{)2204}$ 28. $61\overline{)1323}$ 29. $57\overline{)4640}$

30. $58\overline{)74{,}693}$ 31. $94\overline{)63{,}941}$ 32. $78\overline{)15{,}825}$ 33. $42\overline{)75{,}061}$ 34. $44\overline{)23{,}561}$

35. $1596 \div 38$ 36. $2974 \div 24$ 37. $2624 \div 82$ 38. $3806 \div 17$

39. $50{,}000 \div 72$ 40. $89{,}216 \div 82$ 41. $53{,}819 \div 25$ 42. $74{,}281 \div 31$

Solve. Use the table on page 80.

43. A 13-year-old girl is 60 inches tall. Her adult height (in inches) should be between which two whole numbers?

44. A 15-year-old boy is 64 inches tall. His adult height (in inches) should be between which two whole numbers?

45. a. What is your height to the nearest inch?
    b. What is your growth factor?

46. Your adult height (in inches) should be between what two whole numbers?

47. At what age do girls usually attain their adult height?

48. Do boys usually attain their adult height earlier or later than girls?

49. Who should be the taller adult, a 12-year-old girl who is 56 inches tall or a 13-year-old girl who is 58 inches tall?

50. Who should be the taller adult, a 15-year-old girl who is 66 inches tall or a 15-year-old boy who is 65 inches tall?

Key it in!

Find a way to push each marked key once to get the answer.

51.

52.

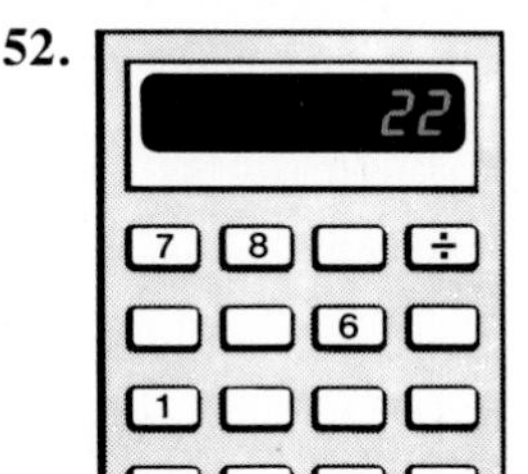

53.

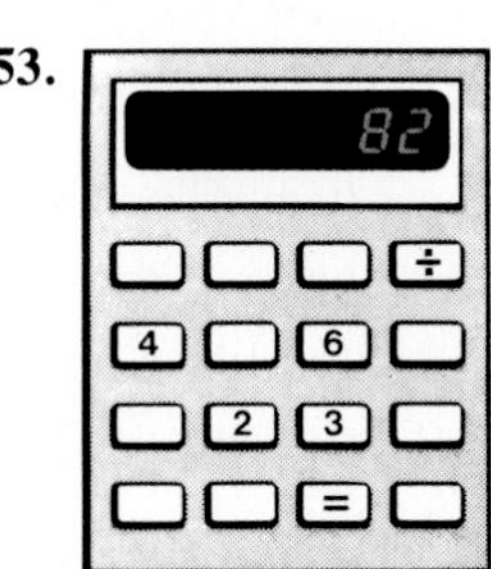

Cumulative Skill Practice

Write the short word-name. *(page 4)*

1. 26338	**2.** 9057	**3.** 36401	**4.** 23104
5. 419853	**6.** 64083	**7.** 250036	**8.** 100003
9. 9961240	**10.** 344082129	**11.** 31650000	**12.** 261418
13. 68000125	**14.** 5643088	**15.** 83000000	**16.** 10000000

Add. *(page 8)*

17. 6217 + 435	**18.** 8107 + 399	**19.** 5628 + 529	**20.** 7436 + 289	**21.** 3054 + 729
22. 58,237 + 3,916	**23.** 36,051 + 5,471	**24.** 44,729 + 3,821	**25.** 6,508 + 19,261	**26.** 1,994 + 37,306
27. 21,345 + 18,466	**28.** 85,841 + 23,509	**29.** 11,295 + 27,832	**30.** 38,451 + 56,009	**31.** 93,816 + 26,957
32. $9.25 .63 + .25	**33.** $7.63 1.25 + .18	**34.** $5.94 3.29 + 1.36	**35.** $8.32 4.73 + 5.19	**36.** $5.99 5.99 + 6.14
37. $21.32 18.56 + 9.27	**38.** $16.53 6.74 + 29.07	**39.** $12.34 12.34 + 12.34	**40.** $47.35 62.00 + 73.65	**41.** $56.00 37.52 + 83.36

Give the sum. *(page 24)*

42. 8.3 + 2.6	**43.** 5.74 + 3.96	**44.** 0.82 + 1.74
45. 3.521 + 2.806	**46.** 4.333 + 9.074	**47.** 12.02 + 9.08
48. 6 + 3.4	**49.** 8.2 + 9	**50.** 15 + 7.68
51. 2.6 + 3 + 8.04	**52.** 5 + 6.71 + 3.0	**53.** 0.83 + 2.7 + 6
54. 0.92 + 2.7 + 8.6	**55.** 9.34 + 21.6 + 9.8	**56.** 15.21 + 16 + 21.5
57. 3.471 + 2.05 + 6.4	**58.** 4.21 + 3 + 7.813	**59.** 6.2 + 3.816 + 7.55
60. 8.64 + 2.009 + 7.5	**61.** 3.004 + 0.06 + 0.5	**62.** 8.32 + 6.1 + 0.008
63. 4 + 2.38 + 9.6	**64.** 5.07 + 2.452 + 8.1	**65.** 3.96 + 2.74 + 5.3

Problem solving

Use the chart to answer these truckers' questions.

1. *I know it's 802 miles from New York to Chicago. How far is it from New York to Denver?*

2. *How far is it from New York to Los Angeles?*

MILEAGE CHART	Baltimore	Chicago	Cleveland	Denver	Houston	Los Angeles	New York
Baltimore		668	343	1621	1412	2636	196
Chicago	668		335	996	1067	2054	802
Cleveland	343	335		1321	1273	2367	473
Denver	1621	996	1321		1019	1059	1771
Houston	1412	1067	1273	1019		1538	1608
Los Angeles	2636	2054	2367	1059	1538		2786
New York	196	802	473	1771	1608	2786	

3. "I first drive from Chicago to Denver and then from Denver to Los Angeles. What is the total mileage?"

4. "What is the total mileage of a Houston–Denver–Los Angeles run?"

5. "How much farther is Cleveland from Baltimore than from Chicago?"

6. "I have driven the first 195 miles of a Houston–Cleveland run. How much farther do I have to go?"

7. "I am 380 miles from Chicago on a Baltimore–Chicago run. How many miles have I driven?"

8. "I leave Cleveland and plan to drive 55 miles per hour. Will I be in Baltimore in 7 hours?"

9. "I want to drive from Chicago to Baltimore in less than 10 hours. Can I do it by traveling at 50 miles per hour?"

10. "I leave Chicago at 8:00 A.M. and plan to drive 50 miles per hour on a run to Cleveland. Will I reach Cleveland by 3:00 P.M.?"

11. "My truck holds 100 gallons of diesel fuel. If it averages 4.5 miles per gallon, can I drive from Denver to Cleveland without stopping for fuel?"

12. "My truck gets about 5 miles per gallon of diesel fuel. How many gallons of fuel will I need to get from Chicago to Cleveland?"

Dividing by a 3-digit number

Suppose that an eccentric millionaire asked you to enter this contest.

CARRY-THE-CASH CONTEST

1. Before touching any of the bags, choose a bag of money.
2. If you can carry the bag of money for 1 mile without resting, the money is yours.

Note: Each bag contains only $1 bills.

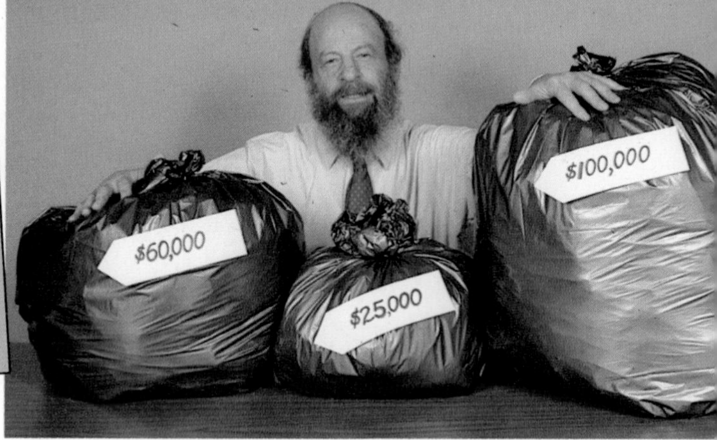

WHICH WOULD YOU CHOOSE?

1. How many $1 bills are in the largest bag?
2. The weight of 454 $1 bills is one pound. Suppose that you choose the $100,000 bag. To find the number of pounds that you would have to carry you would divide 100,000 by [?].

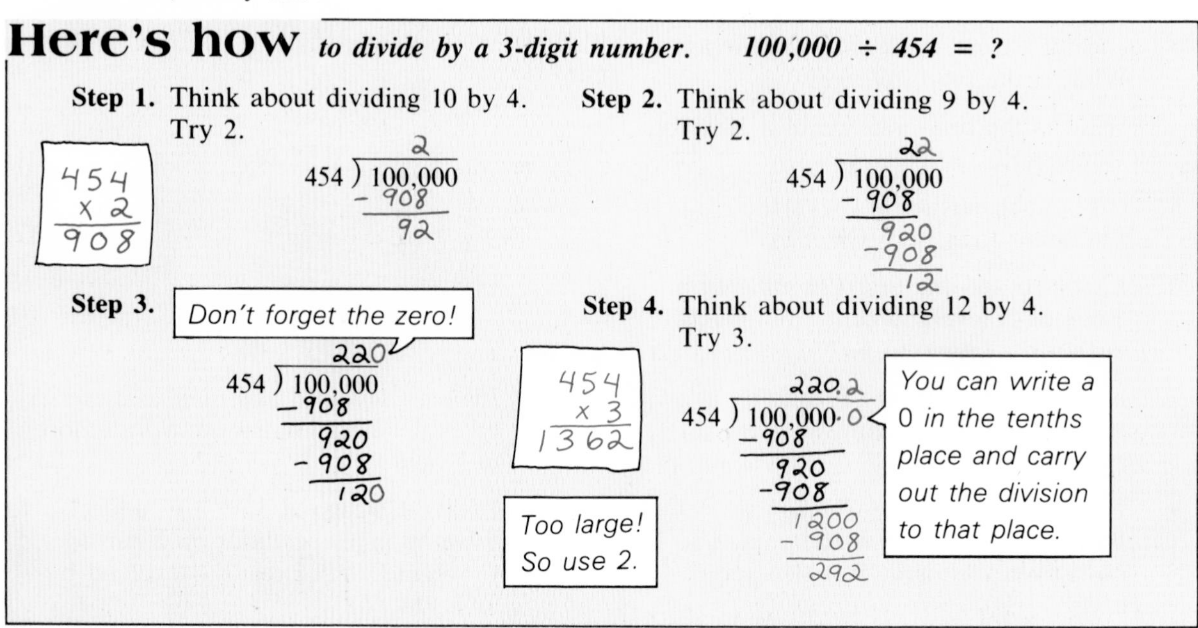

3. Look at the *Here's how*. How many pounds would the $100,000 weigh? Round the answer to the nearest whole pound.
4. Could you have carried the $100,000 for a mile?

EXERCISES

Divide. Use the multiplication facts.

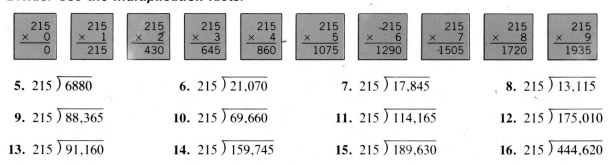

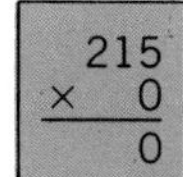

215 × 0	215 × 1	215 × 2	215 × 3	215 × 4	215 × 5	215 × 6	215 × 7	215 × 8	215 × 9
0	215	430	645	860	1075	1290	1505	1720	1935

5. 215) 6880 **6.** 215) 21,070 **7.** 215) 17,845 **8.** 215) 13,115

9. 215) 88,365 **10.** 215) 69,660 **11.** 215) 114,165 **12.** 215) 175,010

13. 215) 91,160 **14.** 215) 159,745 **15.** 215) 189,630 **16.** 215) 444,620

First carry out the division to the tenths place.
Then round the quotient to the nearest whole number.
Here are scrambled answers for the next row of exercises: 139 82 43 101

17. 7) 299 **18.** 9) 741 **19.** 6) 604 **20.** 4) 555

21. 3) 811 **22.** 8) 507 **23.** 2) 731 **24.** 9) 847

25. 8) 3421 **26.** 6) 6539 **27.** 7) 9603 **28.** 5) 5702

29. 12) 593 **30.** 15) 974 **31.** 18) 800 **32.** 16) 777

33. 23) 5012 **34.** 35) 2906 **35.** 40) 3582 **36.** 56) 4711

37. 123) 53,061 **38.** 130) 29,438 **39.** 146) 42,111 **40.** 193) 70,629

41. 625) 139,528 **42.** 834) 374,200 **43.** 935) 561,348 **44.** 753) 829,005

Solve. Use the information on page 84.

45. How many pounds would the $60,000 bag weigh? Round the answer to the nearest whole number.

46. How many pounds would the $25,000 bag weigh? Round the answer to the nearest whole number.

47. Suppose that you could carry 48 pounds for 1 mile. How many $1 bills would that be?

Million-dollar weigh-in

48. How much would 1 million dollars in $100 bills weigh? Round the answer to the nearest whole number.

49. Could you carry 1 million dollars in $100 bills?

Order of operations

David, Carla, and Jane take pictures for their school's yearbook. In checking the film supply, David found a roll of 36 and 2 rolls of 24. Here is how he wrote the number of pictures that they could take:

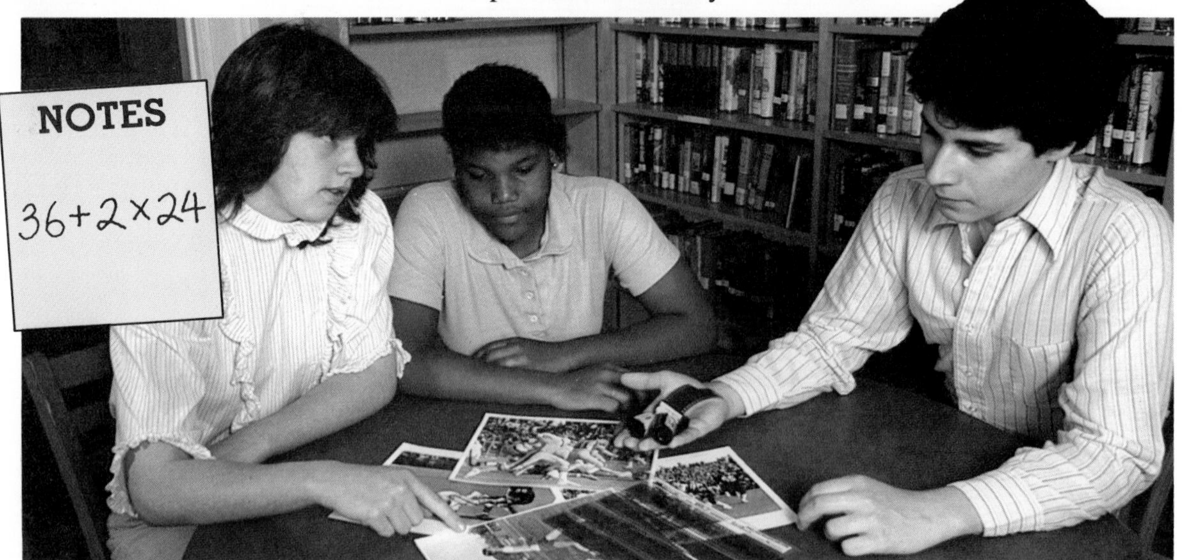

1. When Carla saw the note, she claimed that they could take 912 pictures. How did she get 912?
2. When Jane saw the note, she claimed that they could take 84 pictures. How did she get 84?
3. They got different answers because they did the operations in different orders. Who added first and then multiplied?
4. Which operation did Jane do first?

Here's how *to simplify expressions having more than one kind of operation.*

So that an expression has only one value, we use these rules for the **order of operations:**

Rule 1. First do the operations within the grouping symbols.

Rule 2. Next, work from left to right doing any multiplication and division.

Rule 3. Last, work from left to right doing any addition and subtraction.

5. Study the rules. Who was right, Carla or Jane?

EXERCISES

Simplify each expression.
Hint: The order of operations is shown by the numbered arrows.

6. $8 \overset{1}{\div} 4 \overset{2}{\times} 2$

7. $10 \overset{1}{-} 6 \overset{2}{+} 3$

8. $7 \overset{2}{+} 3 \overset{1}{\times} 8 \overset{3}{-} 4$

9. $4 \overset{1}{\times} 2 \overset{3}{+} 20 \overset{2}{\div} 2$

10. $5 \overset{3}{+} (6 \overset{1}{+} 2) \overset{2}{\div} 4$

11. $(7 \overset{1}{+} 6) \overset{2}{\times} 2 \overset{3}{-} 10$

12. $20 \div 5 - 1$

13. $5 \times 6 - 3$

14. $18 \times 3 \div 3$

15. $50 - 10 - 4$

16. $20 + 16 \div 4$

17. $16 + 8 \div 4$

18. $36 \div 9 \times 2$

19. $43 + 17 - 20$

20. $23 - 9 + 6$

21. $(96 + 24) \div 6$

22. $72 \times (8 - 2)$

23. $16 \times (15 - 5)$

24. $24 + 8 \div 4 + 4$

25. $(24 + 8) \div 4 + 4$

26. $24 + 8 \div (4 + 4)$

27. $18 + 12 \times 6 - 1$

28. $(18 + 12) \times 6 - 1$

29. $18 + 12 \times (6 - 1)$

30. $15 \times 3 + 5 \times 3$

31. $(15 + 5) \times 3$

32. $15 \times (3 + 5) \times 3$

33. $24 - (14 + 4) \div 2$

34. $24 - 14 + 4 \div 2$

35. $(24 - 14) + 4 \div 2$

36. $36 \div (2 + 4) \times 4 - 2$

37. $36 \div 2 + 4 \times 4 - 2$

38. $36 \div 2 + 4 \times (4 - 2)$

Write an expression for the number of pictures that can be taken with

39. 3 rolls of 24.

40. 5 rolls of 36 and 12 on another roll.

41. 4 rolls of 24 with 7 pictures already taken on one of the rolls.

42. 2 rolls of 24 and 3 rolls of 36.

Clip 'n' save

43. Two of these statements are false. Which two are they?

- **a.** With this coupon you can buy 6 rolls of film and get 2 rolls free.
- **b.** This coupon is good on the third Monday in March.
- **c.** The regular price for 4 rolls of film is \$15.96.
- **d.** With this coupon you get 4 rolls of film for less than \$10.

STORE COUPON

BUY 3 rolls of film and get 1 roll FREE.

COLOR FILM FOR PRINTS
Heathcofilm Inc. 36 exp

Reg. \$3.99 a roll

Limit: 1 free roll per coupon

Coupon expires March 22.

Dividing a decimal by a whole number

HOW FAST CAN YOU REACT?

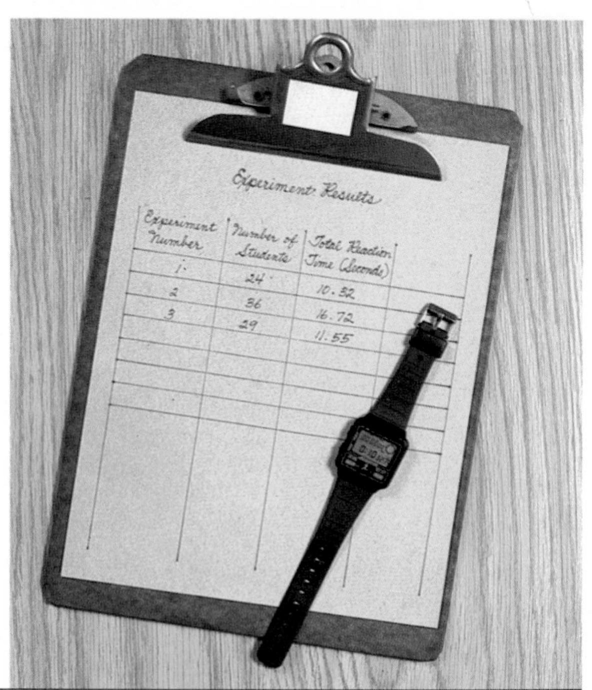

Here is how some students answered the question. First they formed a circle by grasping hands. Then with their eyes closed, they "passed a hand squeeze" around the circle as quickly as possible. Their teacher timed how long it took for the squeeze to go around the circle.

1. How many students were in Experiment 1?
2. How long did it take the hand squeeze to go around the circle (the Total Reaction Time)?
3. For Experiment 1, what would you do to compute the average reaction time per student?

Here's how ***to divide a decimal by a whole number.*** ***10.32 ÷ 24 = ?***

Place the decimal point in the quotient.

$$24\overline{)10.32}$$

Divide as you would whole numbers.

```
     0.43
24 ) 10.32
    - 9 6
       72
     - 72
        0
```

4. Look at the *Here's How*. What is the average reaction time for Experiment 1?
5. Study these examples. Round each quotient to the nearest hundredth.

a.

```
    0.023
7 ) 0.161
   - 14
      21
    - 21
       0
```

You have to write a zero here.

b.

```
    0.541
6 ) 3.250
  - 30
     25
    -24
      10
     - 6
       4
```

Sometimes the division does not come out even. You can write a zero here and carry out the division to the next place.

EXERCISES

Divide. *Here are scrambled answers for the next row of exercises:* *6.5 0.94 1.76 0.346*

6. $8\overline{)14.08}$ **7.** $12\overline{)11.28}$ **8.** $6\overline{)2.076}$ **9.** $25\overline{)162.5}$

10. $34\overline{)0.714}$ **11.** $41\overline{)108.65}$ **12.** $7\overline{)2.492}$ **13.** $53\overline{)331.25}$

14. $78\overline{)\$82.68}$ **15.** $81\overline{)\$286.74}$ **16.** $66\overline{)\$162.36}$ **17.** $35\overline{)\$368.55}$

18. $90\overline{)367.20}$ **19.** $9\overline{)165.33}$ **20.** $87\overline{)3036.3}$ **21.** $8\overline{)821.6}$

First carry out the division to the thousandths place. Then round the quotient to the nearest hundredth.

22. $7\overline{)4.100}$ (handwritten: $0.585 \approx 0.59$; -35, 60, -56, 40, -35, 5) **23.** $12\overline{)8}$ **24.** $18\overline{)42.16}$ **25.** $64\overline{)38.45}$

26. $11\overline{)6}$ **27.** $62\overline{)74.08}$ **28.** $23\overline{)4.278}$

29. $56.92 \div 25$ **30.** $7.34 \div 14$ **31.** $3.64 \div 90$

32. $0.891 \div 8$ **33.** $7.53 \div 38$ **34.** $2.96 \div 26$

35. $4.82 \div 68$ **36.** $3.11 \div 42$ **37.** $89.1 \div 94$

38. $3.8 \div 9$ **39.** $4.64 \div 12$ **40.** $8.42 \div 15$

41. $9.25 \div 13$ **42.** $8.42 \div 15$ **43.** $9.9 \div 24$

Solve. Use the experiments on page 88.

44. What was the average reaction time for Experiment 2? Round the answer to the nearest hundredth of a second.

45. What was the average reaction time for Experiment 3? Round the answer to the nearest hundredth of a second.

46. In which experiment was the reaction time the fastest?

47. What was the difference between the fastest and slowest average reaction times? Work with times rounded to the nearest hundredth of a second.

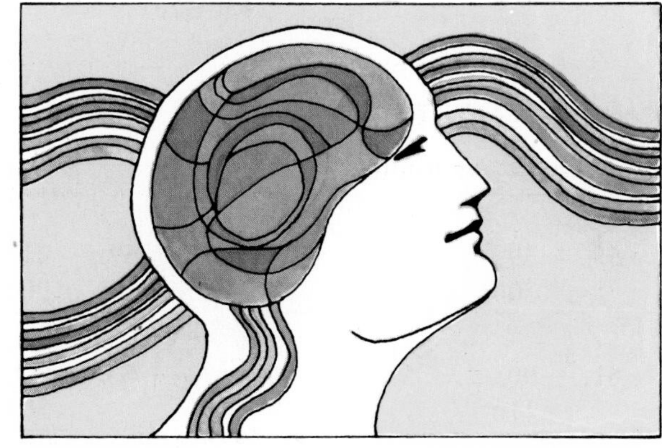

Muscle messages

48. Impulses from your brain control the muscles in all parts of your body. Certain impulses can travel through your body at the rate of 300 feet per second. Change the rate to miles per hour by multiplying by 3600 and dividing the answer by 5280.

Cumulative Skill Practice

Subtract. *(page 38)*

1. 4897 − 2235	**2.** 6271 − 5004	**3.** 7829 − 374	**4.** 9652 − 836	**5.** 5834 − 1297
6. 3902 − 1755	**7.** 7301 − 879	**8.** 5026 − 3477	**9.** 6085 − 392	**10.** 5004 − 1679
11. 86,294 − 7,381	**12.** 72,855 − 6,974	**13.** 68,302 − 9,756	**14.** 29,001 − 17,362	**15.** 30,047 − 18,492

Less than (<) or greater than (>)? *(page 42)*

16. 0.5 ● 0.6	**17.** 0.08 ● 0.07	**18.** 0.008 ● 0.007
19. 16.1 ● 16.0	**20.** 7.86 ● 7.68	**21.** 0.38 ● 0.3
22. 42.79 ● 42.8	**23.** 3.1 ● 2.97	**24.** 6.347 ● 63.4
25. 0.852 ● 1.2	**26.** 1.3 ● 1.03	**27.** 529.6 ● 530
28. 14.006 ● 14.06	**29.** 73.02 ● 72.03	**30.** 0.021 ● 0.21

Give the difference. *(page 46)*

31. 5.9 − 3.6	**32.** 8.42 − 3.76	**33.** 5.02 − 3.44
34. 72.3 − 2.59	**35.** 29.7 − 15.92	**36.** 74.36 − 2.1
37. 26.083 − 7.461	**38.** 74.4 − 3.88	**39.** 65.0 − 42.5
40. 12 − 3.7	**41.** 52 − 9.64	**42.** 29.4 − 2.94
43. 56.7 − 8.821	**44.** 37.4 − 18	**45.** 45.6 − 2.735

Multiply. *(page 60)*

46. 538 × 132	**47.** 603 × 115	**48.** 492 × 236	**49.** 871 × 382	**50.** 729 × 533	**51.** 821 × 364
52. 666 × 240	**53.** 434 × 320	**54.** 921 × 402	**55.** 399 × 306	**56.** 671 × 580	**57.** 214 × 200
58. 738 × 426	**59.** 521 × 180	**60.** 426 × 253	**61.** 903 × 116	**62.** 800 × 204	**63.** 900 × 305

Problem solving

This calculator only does addition.

This one only does subtraction.

Multiplication is the only operation this one will do.

Division only on this one.

Whose calculator solved it? Name the two people who worked together to solve each problem.

1. **Names** ? ?

My friend delivers 35 papers 6 days a week. She also delivers 48 Sunday papers. How many papers does she deliver each week?

Answer: 258 papers

2. **Names** ? ?

We bought some $3 records. We gave the cashier $20 and got $8 in change. How many records did we buy?

Answer: 4 records

3. **Names** ? ?

My friend and I earned $27.50 yesterday and $15.40 today. We shared the money equally. How much money did I get?

Answer: $21.45

4. **Names** ? ?

I bought 4 frozen pizzas at $2.90 each. How much change should I get from a $20 bill?

Answer: $8.40

Name the two people who should work together to solve each problem. Then solve each problem.

5. **Names** ? ?

After 5 friends each ate 4 tacos, there were 3 tacos left. How many tacos were there to start with?

Answer: ?

6. **Names** ? ?

I bought 5 hockey tickets. I gave the cashier $20 and got $2.50 in change. What was the price of each ticket?

Answer: ?

7. **Names** ? ?

At my school, 106 girls and 92 boys signed up to play volleyball. A total of 18 teams were formed. How many players were on each team?

Answer: ?

8. **Names** ? ?

We bought a 14.5-pound watermelon at $.08 per pound and a $2.98 bag of oranges. What was the total cost?

Answer: ?

Dividing by 10, 100, or 1000

The banker can fill in these missing numbers in 5 seconds. How fast can you do it?

> *8000 \$1 bills equals [?] \$10 bills, [?] \$100 bills, or [?] \$1000 bills.*

The banker knows that if you divide a number by 10, 100, or 1000, the quotient is less than the number. So, she moves the decimal point to the left.

Here's how *to divide by 10, 100, or 1000.*

8000 ÷ 10 = 800.0 or 800	Dividing by 10 moves the decimal point 1 place to the left.
8000 ÷ 100 = 80.00 or 80	Dividing by 100 moves the decimal point 2 places to the left.
8000 ÷ 1000 = 8.000 or 8	Dividing by 1000 moves the decimal point 3 places to the left.

Other examples:
Dividing by

10	23.25 ÷ 10 = 2.325
100	6.1 ÷ 100 = 0.061
1000	9.75 ÷ 1000 = 0.00975

> *Some zeros had to be written before the decimal point could be placed in the quotient.*

EXERCISES

Divide. *Here are scrambled answers for the next two rows of exercises:* *0.536 6.7 0.067 3.62 36.2 5.36 0.0536 0.67*

1. 36.2 ÷ 10	**2.** 362 ÷ 10	**3.** 53.6 ÷ 100	**4.** 53.6 ÷ 1000
5. 536 ÷ 100	**6.** 67 ÷ 1000	**7.** 6700 ÷ 1000	**8.** 67 ÷ 100
9. 712.2 ÷ 10	**10.** 712.2 ÷ 100	**11.** 712.2 ÷ 1000	**12.** 71.22 ÷ 10
13. 18.6 ÷ 1000	**14.** 18.6 ÷ 100	**15.** 18.6 ÷ 10	**16.** 0.186 ÷ 10

17. 60 ÷ 10	**18.** 60 ÷ 100	**19.** 60 ÷ 1000	**20.** 600 ÷ 10
21. 14.32 ÷ 10	**22.** 14.32 ÷ 100	**23.** 14.32 ÷ 1000	**24.** 143.2 ÷ 100
25. 486 ÷ 1000	**26.** 486 ÷ 100	**27.** 486 ÷ 10	**28.** 4.86 ÷ 10
29. 421.9 ÷ 1000	**30.** 421.9 ÷ 100	**31.** 421.9 ÷ 10	**32.** 42.19 ÷ 1000
33. 242 ÷ 10	**34.** 242 ÷ 1000	**35.** 242 ÷ 100	**36.** 24.2 ÷ 1000
37. 81.5 ÷ 100	**38.** 81.5 ÷ 10	**39.** 81.5 ÷ 1000	**40.** 815 ÷ 10
41. 7 ÷ 1000	**42.** 7 ÷ 10	**43.** 7 ÷ 100	**44.** 70 ÷ 100
45. 9.3 ÷ 100	**46.** 9.3 ÷ 1000	**47.** 9.3 ÷ 10	**48.** 93 ÷ 1000
49. 2.03 ÷ 10	**50.** 2.03 ÷ 1000	**51.** 2.03 ÷ 100	**52.** 20.3 ÷ 10
53. 765 ÷ 1000	**54.** 765 ÷ 10	**55.** 765 ÷ 100	**56.** 76.5 ÷ 10
57. 0.6 ÷ 100	**58.** 0.6 ÷ 1000	**59.** 0.6 ÷ 10	**60.** 60 ÷ 1000

Solve. Use the money facts.

61. What is the height of $50,000 in
- **a.** $10 bills?
- **b.** $100 bills?
- **c.** $1000 bills?
- **d.** $1 bills?

62. What is the weight of $50,000 in
- **a.** $10 bills?
- **b.** $100 bills?
- **c.** $1000 bills?
- **d.** $1 bills?

MONEY FACTS

$50,000 in $10 bills is 20 inches high.

$50,000 in $10 bills weighs 11 pounds.

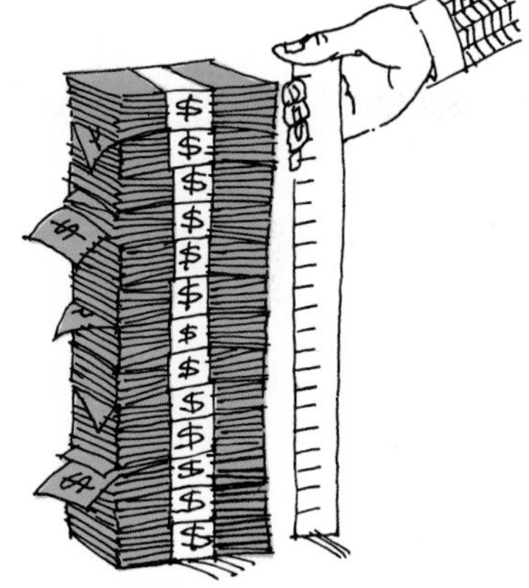

Make your money stretch

63. a. Suppose you have 1 million dollars in $1 bills. If you laid the bills end-to-end, how many miles of money would you have? To find the number of miles, write a
- *5* in the hundredths place
- *7* in the ones place
- *8* in the tenths place
- *9* in the tens place

b. Suppose that you have 1 billion dollars in $1 bills. If you laid the bills end-to-end, how many miles of money would you have? *Hints: 1000 million is 1 billion. Use your answer from part a.*

Dividing a decimal by a decimal

> **ONION TEARS**
>
> Skip Gilligan's attempt at setting a new onion-peeling record ended in tears. After 3.5 minutes and 31.5 pounds of peeled onions, Gilligan was forced to stop due to eye discomfort. With tears in his eyes, the 28-year-old cafeteria worker said he would be back for another shot at the record.

1. Read the newspaper article. How many pounds of onions did Gilligan peel in 3.5 minutes?
2. To compute how many pounds of onions he peeled per minute, you would divide 31.5 by what number?

Here's how *to divide a decimal by a decimal.* *31.5 ÷ 3.5 = ?*

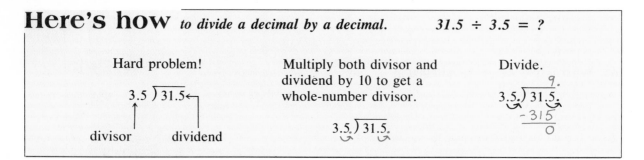

Hard problem!	Multiply both divisor and dividend by 10 to get a whole-number divisor.	Divide.
$3.5\,\overline{)\,31.5}$ (divisor: 3.5; dividend: 31.5)	$3.5.\,\overline{)\,31.5.}$	$3.5.\,\overline{)\,31.5.}$ = 9. − 315 0

3. Look at the *Here's how*. To get a whole-number divisor, both decimal points were moved [?] place(s) to the right.
4. How many pounds of onions did Gilligan peel per minute?
5. Check these examples. Are the answers correct?

   a. 8.32 ÷ 0.32

   $0.32.\,\overline{)\,8.32.}$ = 26.
   − 64
   192
   − 192
   0

   Move both decimal points 2 places to the right.

   b. 0.9856 ÷ 0.004

   $0.004.\,\overline{)\,0.985.6}$ = 246.4
   − 8
   18
   − 16
   25
   − 24
   16
   − 16
   0

   Move both decimal points 3 places to the right.

EXERCISES

Divide. *Here are scrambled answers for the next row of exercises: 3.6 6.8 6.5 38*

6. $0.2\overline{)1.36}$	**7.** $0.5\overline{)3.25}$	**8.** $0.4\overline{)1.44}$	**9.** $0.02\overline{)0.76}$
10. $0.07\overline{)4.62}$	**11.** $0.02\overline{)2.12}$	**12.** $0.005\overline{)0.515}$	**13.** $0.007\overline{)7.280}$
14. $0.6\overline{)1.5}$	**15.** $0.8\overline{)2.56}$	**16.** $0.03\overline{)1.26}$	**17.** $0.005\overline{)0.485}$
18. $0.2\overline{)5.46}$	**19.** $4.5\overline{)22.5}$	**20.** $0.05\overline{)0.075}$	**21.** $0.08\overline{)1.016}$
22. $0.4\overline{)2.488}$	**23.** $0.3\overline{)0.06}$	**24.** $0.05\overline{)0.75}$	**25.** $0.008\overline{)0.512}$
26. $1.2\overline{)31.2}$	**27.** $0.15\overline{)0.57}$	**28.** $3.4\overline{)3.57}$	**29.** $0.26\overline{)0.884}$
30. $7.4\overline{)40.7}$	**31.** $5.9\overline{)21.24}$	**32.** $0.81\overline{)49.41}$	**33.** $0.94\overline{)10.528}$
34. $9.3\overline{)6.045}$	**35.** $0.66\overline{)0.3366}$	**36.** $5.2\overline{)21.164}$	**37.** $0.48\overline{)1.5216}$
38. $4.5 \div 0.3$	**39.** $12.6 \div 0.2$	**40.** $56.84 \div 0.7$	**41.** $4.32 \div 0.4$
42. $1.684 \div 0.02$	**43.** $0.7085 \div 0.05$	**44.** $0.1128 \div 0.08$	**45.** $0.567 \div 0.09$
46. $0.341 \div 0.11$	**47.** $1.875 \div 0.25$	**48.** $26.22 \div 5.7$	**49.** $23.24 \div 2.8$
50. $4.14 \div 1.8$	**51.** $8.4 \div 2.1$	**52.** $1.56 \div 0.12$	**53.** $1.260 \div 0.12$
54. $43.2 \div 0.24$	**55.** $0.522 \div 0.036$	**56.** $1.6254 \div 3.01$	**57.** $43.594 \div 0.71$

Solve.

58. Calvin set out to break the onion-peeling record. He peeled 12.6 pounds in 1.5 minutes. Did he peel more or less than 9 pounds per minute? *Hint: Divide to get the answer.*

59. In 1979, a team of 57 men pushed a baby carriage 345.25 miles in 24 hours. How many miles did they average per hour? Round the answer to the nearest hundredth of a mile.

60. Fourteen students leapfrogged for 148 hours at the average rate of 3.75 miles per hour. How many miles did they leapfrog?

61. The record for treading water is 80 hours. How many minutes is that?

Just for the record

62. In 1981, Norman Johnson sliced a 12-inch cucumber into 22 slices per inch. It took him 19.11 seconds. What was his average time per slice? Round the answer to the nearest hundredth.

More on dividing a decimal by a decimal

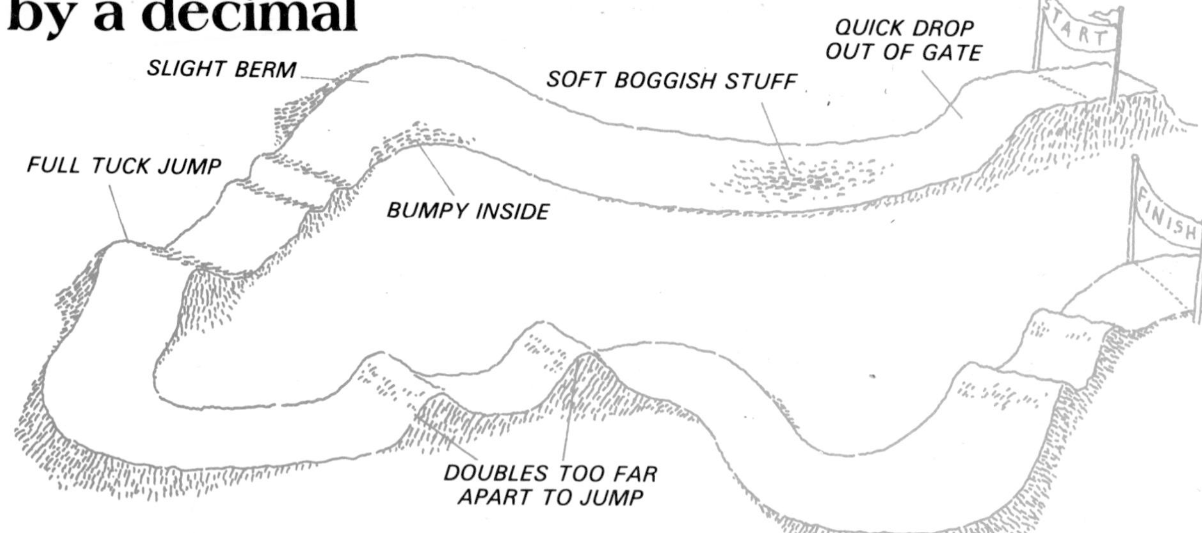

1. What distance did each rider travel?
2. Which rider completed the race in 32.4 seconds?
3. What was LeDuc's time in hours?
4. To compute LeDuc's average speed in miles per hour, you would divide 0.2 (miles traveled) by what number?

BMX RACING			
Rider	Distance in miles	Time	
		in seconds	*in hours*
LeDuc	0.2	32.4	0.009
Elliott	0.2	39.6	0.011

Here's how *to divide a decimal by a decimal.*

0.2 ÷ 0.009 = ?

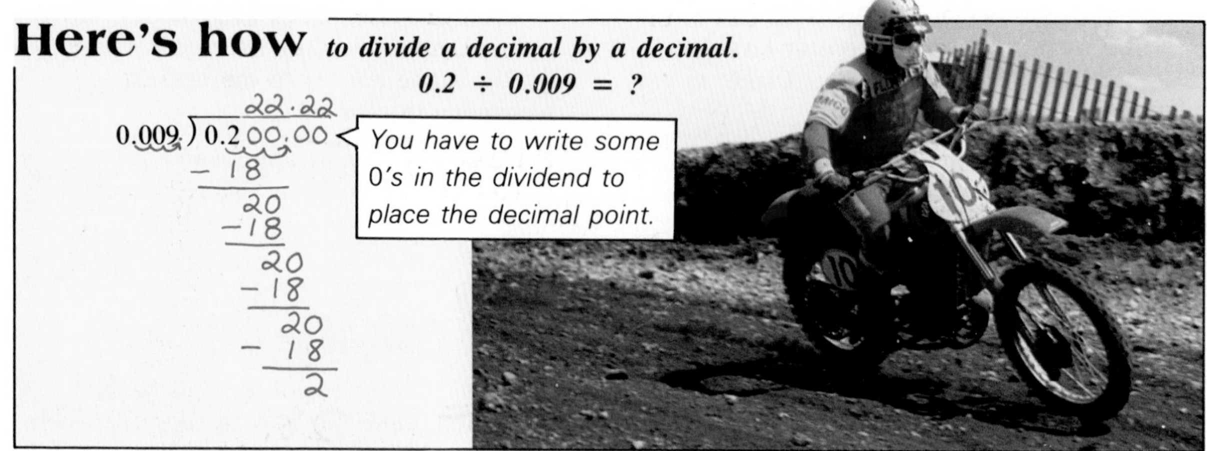

22.22
0.009) 0.200.00
− 18
20
− 18
20
− 18
20
− 18
2
You have to write some 0's in the dividend to place the decimal point.

5. Look at the *Here's how*. Notice that the division will never come out even. What is LeDuc's average speed rounded to the nearest tenth?

EXERCISES

Divide. *Hint: You will need to write some zeros.*
Here are scrambled answers for the next row of exercises: 5.5 5 7.2 7.5

6. $0.5\overline{)3.6}$ **7.** $0.2\overline{)1.1}$ **8.** $0.06\overline{)0.3}$ **9.** $0.4\overline{)3}$

10. $0.8\overline{)56}$ **11.** $0.4\overline{)1.4}$ **12.** $0.02\overline{)7}$ **13.** $0.005\overline{)0.047}$

14. $0.2\overline{).01}$ **15.** $0.4\overline{)0.26}$ **16.** $0.08\overline{)1.24}$ **17.** $0.006\overline{)0.285}$

18. $1.2\overline{)4.2}$ **19.** $2.5\overline{)0.55}$ **20.** $3.1\overline{)124}$ **21.** $4.2\overline{)6.3}$

Divide. Round each quotient to the nearest tenth.
Here are scrambled answers for the next row of exercises: 0.4 2.3 0.2 4.7

22. $0.3\overline{)1.4}$ **23.** $0.6\overline{)0.14}$ **24.** $1.4\overline{)0.528}$ **25.** $2.2\overline{)4.98}$

26. $2.5\overline{)6.1}$ **27.** $3.1\overline{)7.5}$ **28.** $0.06\overline{)0.5}$ **29.** $1.2\overline{)0.54}$

30. $7.5\overline{)62.91}$ **31.** $3.9\overline{)7.503}$ **32.** $2.6\overline{)7.4}$ **33.** $0.31\overline{)0.09}$

34. $12.1\overline{)156.3}$ **35.** $1.84\overline{)192.6}$ **36.** $23.5\overline{)6.843}$ **37.** $3.41\overline{)18.5}$

Solve. Refer to the chart and drawing on page 96.

38. Was Elliott's average speed more or less than 20 miles per hour? *Hint: Divide to answer the question.*

39. How many seconds faster did LeDuc ride the 0.2-mile track than Elliott?

40. From the starting line to the full tuck jump is 0.09 mile. How far is it from the full tuck jump to the finish line?

41. LeDuc's riding time from start to the full tuck jump was 14.7 seconds. How many seconds did it take LeDuc to ride from the full tuck jump to the finish line?

Who's ahead?

As the winner crosses the finish line,
Cherie is 4 feet ahead of Eric.
Kenny is 2 feet behind Justin.
Eric is 6 feet ahead of Kenny.

42. Who is the winner?

43. Who is last?

44. How many feet separate the first and last racers?

Draw a picture like this one. It will help you solve the problems.
←?ft— ?ft— 4ft→
? ? Eric Cherie

Cumulative Skill Practice

Give the product. *(page 64)*

1. 2.6×0.9 **2.** 3.98×0.6 **3.** 27.5×0.8 **4.** 2.9×0.7

5. 6.2×0.59 **6.** 0.38×1.5 **7.** 36×0.42 **8.** 3.1×0.2

9. 206×4.3 **10.** 8.36×19 **11.** 0.35×50 **12.** 14.6×82

13. 8.32×5.6 **14.** 7.42×3.9 **15.** 5.66×0.41 **16.** 3.12×4.15

17. 4.63×2.06 **18.** 3.05×71 **19.** 6.09×5.51 **20.** 6.2×1.93

21. 3.2×2.81 **22.** 4.5×30 **23.** 6.41×62 **24.** 9.8×1.34

Divide. If the division does not come out even, round the quotient to the nearest whole number. *(pages 80, 84)*

25. $24\overline{)864}$ **26.** $24\overline{)2328}$ **27.** $24\overline{)2160}$ **28.** $24\overline{)2472}$ **29.** $24\overline{)5016}$

30. $28\overline{)1932}$ **31.** $39\overline{)3042}$ **32.** $15\overline{)1470}$ **33.** $62\overline{)1426}$ **34.** $17\overline{)1003}$

35. $12\overline{)10,446}$ **36.** $56\overline{)69,454}$ **37.** $36\overline{)20,882}$ **38.** $41\overline{)35,867}$ **39.** $48\overline{)31,200}$

40. $117\overline{)72,594}$ **41.** $117\overline{)70,551}$ **42.** $117\overline{)24,687}$ **43.** $400\overline{)14,400}$ **44.** $504\overline{)16,128}$

45. $221\overline{)21,658}$ **46.** $221\overline{)67,184}$ **47.** $221\overline{)35,426}$ **48.** $109\overline{)34,989}$ **49.** $109\overline{)98,142}$

Simplify. *(page 86)*

50. $24 \div 4 + 2$ **51.** $30 - 5 + 7$ **52.** $8 \times 4 - 1$

53. $36 \div 6 \div 3$ **54.** $14 \times 5 \div 5$ **55.** $18 + 8 \div 2$

56. $(25 + 25) \div 10$ **57.** $16 \times (7 - 3)$ **58.** $20 \times (10 - 4)$

59. $36 + 12 \div 4 + 2$ **60.** $(36 + 12) \div 4 + 2$ **61.** $36 + 12 \div (4 + 2)$

62. $32 \times 8 - 8 + 4$ **63.** $32 \times (8 - 8) + 4$ **64.** $32 \times 8 - (8 + 4)$

Give the quotient. Round the quotient to the nearest tenth. *(pages 94, 96)*

65. $16.4 \div 0.6$ **66.** $3.74 \div 0.2$ **67.** $9.05 \div 0.05$

68. $28.7 \div 0.3$ **69.** $4.38 \div 0.04$ **70.** $8.4 \div 0.08$

71. $6.15 \div 1.2$ **72.** $2.038 \div 2.4$ **73.** $4.06 \div 0.25$

74. $12.063 \div 0.33$ **75.** $5.008 \div 0.61$ **76.** $6.42 \div 6.2$

77. $5.38 \div 5.04$ **78.** $2.971 \div 3.7$ **79.** $23.4 \div 8.07$

Problem solving

COMPUTERS IN SCHOOLS

Schools use computers to store student data. In the Franklin School District, a computer assigns each student an identification number.

FRANKLIN SCHOOL DISTRICT

Carol Hanson
Student

16
Homeroom

A. Collier
Advisor

185–72–335

Year of birth (72) **Code for birthday** (335)

Look at Carol's identification number. The middle two digits of the number tell Carol's year of birth. The last three digits tell her birthday.

To find her birthday, divide the last 3-digit number by 31. The whole number in the quotient is her month of birth, and the remainder is the day of the month.

$$\begin{array}{r} 10 \\ 31\overline{)335} \\ -31 \\ \hline 25 \end{array}$$

10 ← month

25 ← day of month

Carol was born on October 25, 1972.

Use the information on the computer printout to answer these questions.

1. *My name is Chris Harris. What is my date of birth?*

NAME	I.D. NUMBER	HOME ROOM	ADVISOR
Hanson, Carol	185-72-335	16	Collier
Harris, Chris	204-74-239	16	Vandegrift
Holmes, Brian	133-73-133	29	Collier
Holway, Amy	218-74-326	34	Vandegrift
Hull, Jack	199-73-185	34	Haver
Hurst, Mary	306-75-223	16	Collier
Heinbrough, Karen	156-76-121	16	Haver
Hernandez, Ralph	254-73-144	29	Collier
Hirai, George	314-76-289	34	Vandegrift

2. Give the birthday for each student.
- **a.** Amy Holway
- **b.** Mary Hurst
- **c.** Jack Hull

3. Mr. Haver's birthday is March 28. Which student on the list has the same birthday as Mr. Haver?

4. Who is the youngest student on the list?

5. How many students on the list have birthdays during the school year?

Solve.

6. Brian Ogel was born on March 25, 1976. What are the last 5 digits of his student ID number?

7. Suppose you registered in the Franklin School District. What would be the last 5 digits of your student ID number?

Chapter REVIEW

Here are scrambled answers for the review exercises:

1	3	6	26	divide	left	quotient	zeros
2	5	7	140	add	multiply	subtract	

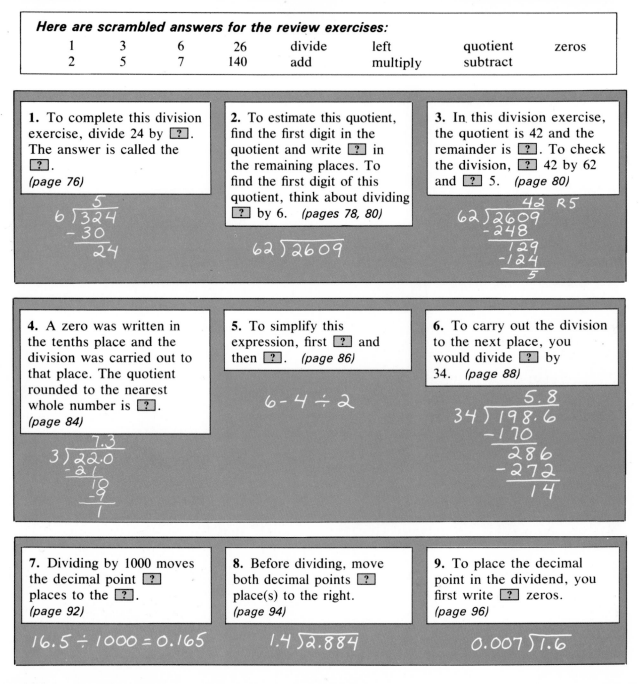

1. To complete this division exercise, divide 24 by [?]. The answer is called the [?]. *(page 76)*

$$\begin{array}{r} 5 \\ 6\overline{)324} \\ -30 \\ \hline 24 \end{array}$$

2. To estimate this quotient, find the first digit in the quotient and write [?] in the remaining places. To find the first digit of this quotient, think about dividing [?] by 6. *(pages 78, 80)*

$$62\overline{)2609}$$

3. In this division exercise, the quotient is 42 and the remainder is [?]. To check the division, [?] 42 by 62 and [?] 5. *(page 80)*

$$\begin{array}{r} 42 \text{ R5} \\ 62\overline{)2609} \\ -248 \\ \hline 129 \\ -124 \\ \hline 5 \end{array}$$

4. A zero was written in the tenths place and the division was carried out to that place. The quotient rounded to the nearest whole number is [?]. *(page 84)*

$$\begin{array}{r} 7.3 \\ 3\overline{)22.0} \\ -21 \\ \hline 10 \\ -9 \\ \hline 1 \end{array}$$

5. To simplify this expression, first [?] and then [?]. *(page 86)*

$$6 - 4 \div 2$$

6. To carry out the division to the next place, you would divide [?] by 34. *(page 88)*

$$\begin{array}{r} 5.8 \\ 34\overline{)198.6} \\ -170 \\ \hline 286 \\ -272 \\ \hline 14 \end{array}$$

7. Dividing by 1000 moves the decimal point [?] places to the [?]. *(page 92)*

$$16.5 \div 1000 = 0.165$$

8. Before dividing, move both decimal points [?] place(s) to the right. *(page 94)*

$$1.4\overline{)2.884}$$

9. To place the decimal point in the dividend, you first write [?] zeros. *(page 96)*

$$0.007\overline{)1.6}$$

Chapter TEST

Divide. *(pages 76, 78)*

1. $3\overline{)93}$ **2.** $5\overline{)85}$ **3.** $9\overline{)198}$ **4.** $6\overline{)738}$ **5.** $8\overline{)816}$

6. $2\overline{)608}$ **7.** $4\overline{)1624}$ **8.** $7\overline{)4235}$ **9.** $8\overline{)6424}$ **10.** $5\overline{)4195}$

Divide. If the division does not come out even, round the quotient to the nearest whole number. *(pages 80, 84)*

11. $24\overline{)888}$ **12.** $18\overline{)1098}$ **13.** $30\overline{)2734}$ **14.** $56\overline{)8365}$

15. $53{,}216 \div 500$ **16.** $38{,}296 \div 213$ **17.** $71{,}025 \div 432$ **18.** $67{,}055 \div 621$

Simplify. *(page 86)*

19. $8 - 4 + 2$ **20.** $7 \times 5 - 3$ **21.** $20 + 8 \div 4$ **22.** $3 + 9 \div 3$

23. $5 + 8 \div 4 + 9$ **24.** $(16 + 8) \div 4 + 2$ **25.** $16 + 8 \div 4 + 2$ **26.** $8 + 4 \times 2 - 1$

Divide. *(pages 88, 92)*

27. $19.2 \div 8$ **28.** $118.4 \div 4$ **29.** $109.62 \div 9$ **30.** $6.45 \div 5$

31. $558.7 \div 37$ **32.** $99.84 \div 48$ **33.** $1483.2 \div 72$ **34.** $205.44 \div 32$

35. $364 \div 10$ **36.** $528 \div 100$ **37.** $327 \div 1000$ **38.** $326 \div 100$

39. $123.9 \div 100$ **40.** $682.3 \div 10$ **41.** $529.64 \div 100$ **42.** $65.2 \div 100$

Divide. Round each quotient to the nearest tenth. *(pages 94, 96)*

43. $0.5\overline{)4.8}$ **44.** $0.6\overline{)31.26}$ **45.** $0.9\overline{)4.32}$ **46.** $1.6\overline{)35}$

47. $1.1\overline{)5.73}$ **48.** $3.6\overline{)7.039}$ **49.** $0.64\overline{)15.3}$ **50.** $3.2\overline{)6.84}$

Solve.

51. How much will it cost to have a roll of 12 and a roll of 24 printed?

52. How much will it cost to have 3 rolls of 15 printed?

53. How much does each print cost for a roll of 36? Round your answer to the nearest cent.

54. You had 2 rolls of 12 and 1 roll of 24 printed. You gave the clerk \$20. How much change should you have received?

PHOTO FINISHING	
12 EXPOSURES	\$2.39
15 EXPOSURES	2.72
24 EXPOSURES	3.71
36 EXPOSURES	5.03

Cumulative TEST Standardized Format

Choose the correct letter.

1. The short word-name for 8,020,000 is
   - A. 8 billion, 20 million
   - B. 8 million, 20 thousand
   - C. 8 million, 2 thousand
   - D. none of these

2. Add. $\begin{array}{r} 56{,}394 \\ +26{,}748 \\ \hline \end{array}$
   - A. 83,142
   - B. 72,032
   - C. 72,042
   - D. none of these

3. Give the sum.

   $14.6 + 31.5 + 2.06$
   - A. 66.7
   - B. 47.16
   - C. 481.6
   - D. none of these

4. Subtract. $\begin{array}{r} 35{,}064 \\ -13{,}297 \\ \hline \end{array}$
   - A. 22,233
   - B. 21,767
   - C. 22,767
   - D. none of these

5. Which number is greater than 0.06?
   - A. 0.5
   - B. 0.04
   - C. 0.059
   - D. none of these

6. Give the difference.

   $424.7 - 38.46$
   - A. 40.1
   - B. 382.36
   - C. 386.24
   - D. none of these

7. Multiply. $\begin{array}{r} 629 \\ \times 240 \\ \hline \end{array}$
   - A. 15,096
   - B. 150,960
   - C. 149,660
   - D. none of these

8. Give the product.

   3.62×1.7
   - A. 5.774
   - B. 61.54
   - C. 6.154
   - D. none of these

9. Divide. $68\overline{)7140}$
   - A. 105
   - B. 15
   - C. 106
   - D. none of these

10. Simplify.

    $20 - 8 \div 4 \times 2$
    - A. 6
    - B. 19
    - C. 36
    - D. none of these

11. Give the quotient rounded to the nearest tenth.

    $4.615 \div 0.3$
    - A. 15.3
    - B. 15.4
    - C. 1.5
    - D. none of these

12. You can buy a car for $325 down and 12 payments of $48.75 each. What is the total cost?
    - A. $910
    - B. $373.75
    - C. $260
    - D. none of these

Chapter 5
Graphs and Statistics

Organizing data

A group of students took the road-sign quiz. Their scores are listed on this card.

National Road-Sign Quiz
Choose the correct answer.

a. Slippery when wet
b. Road curves
c. Steep hill

a. Housing
b. Youth hostel
c. Hospital

a. No passing
b. No parking
c. No pedestrians

a. Zoo
b. Hunting area
c. Deer crossing

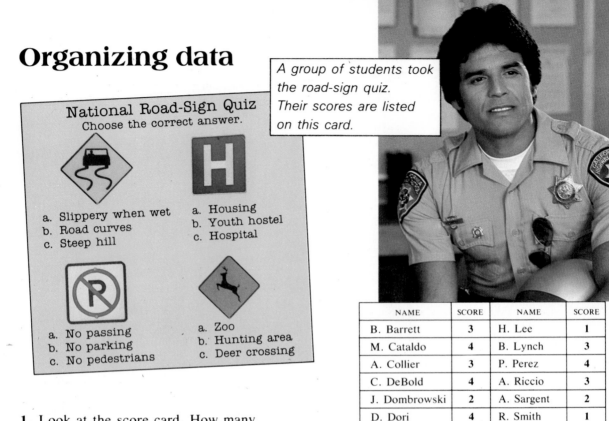

NAME	SCORE	NAME	SCORE
B. Barrett	3	H. Lee	1
M. Cataldo	4	B. Lynch	3
A. Collier	3	P. Perez	4
C. DeBold	4	A. Riccio	3
J. Dombrowski	2	A. Sargent	2
D. Dori	4	R. Smith	1
J. Goldman	2	G. Summers	3
V. Hawkins	3	J. Vandegrift	3
A. Jacobson	1	S. Vlahach	4
K. Kennedy	2	C. Werner	0

1. Look at the score card. How many students had a score of 4?
2. How many students had a score of 3?

To help answer questions like these, you can make a frequency table.

Here's how *to organize the data (quiz scores) in a frequency table.*

A tally mark shows each time a score occurred. The frequency column shows the total number of times each score occurred.

Frequency Table for Quiz Scores

SCORE	NUMBER OF TIMES SCORE OCCURRED	
	TALLY	FREQUENCY
4	~~||||~~	5
3	~~||||~~ ||	7
2	||||	4
1	|||	3
0	|	1

3. How many students had a score less than 4?
4. How many had a score greater than 2?
5. What was the highest score? lowest score?
6. Which score occurred most often? least often?
7. How many students took the quiz?

EXERCISES

Use the frequency tables to answer the questions.

8. What was the highest score on the engine-repair exam?
9. Which score occurred most often?
10. How many students scored 13 or less?
11. How many students took the exam?
12. What was the difference between the highest and lowest scores?
13. A score of 14 or better is an A. How many students received an A?

Frequency Table for Engine-Repair Exam Scores

SCORE	NUMBER OF OCCURRENCES	
	TALLY	FREQUENCY
15	|||	**3**
14	||||	**4**
13	𝍸 𝍸 ||	**12**
12	𝍸		**6**
11		**0**
10	||	**2**

14. How many families in the survey have 3 cars?
15. How many families have 2 or more cars?
16. How many families have at least 1 car?
17. What is the most common number of cars per family?
18. How many families were in the survey?

Frequency Table for Cars per Family

CARS PER FAMILY	NUMBER OF FAMILIES	
	TALLY	FREQUENCY
4	||	**2**
3	𝍸 ||	**7**
2	𝍸 𝍸 𝍸		**16**
1	𝍸 𝍸 𝍸 𝍸 ||	**22**
0	|||	**3**

Try it yourself! Organizing information

19. Make a frequency table for the driver's-license information on the map.
20. In how many states can you obtain a driver's license before age 16?

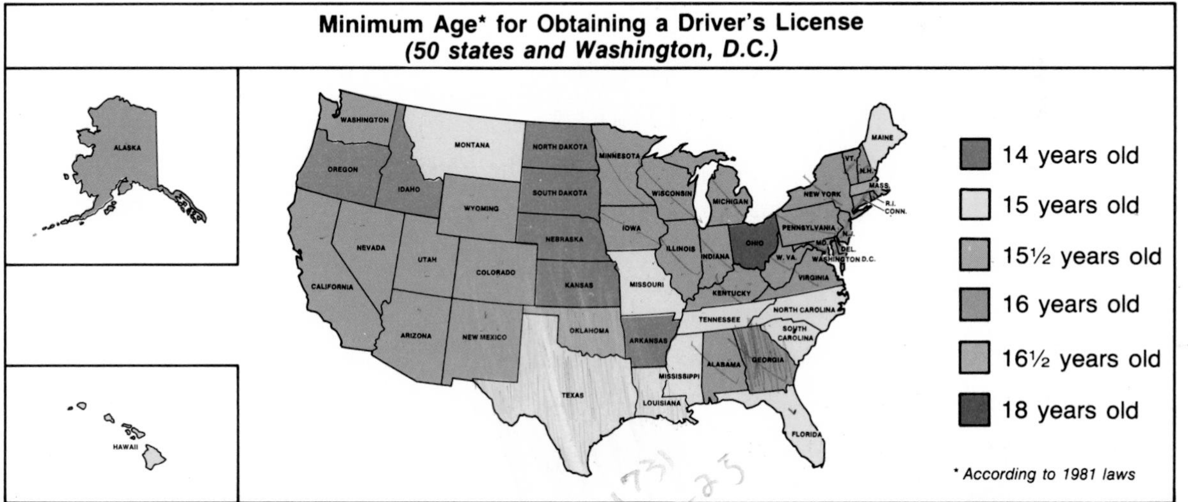

Using bar graphs

Fifty people took part in a TV trivia survey. In Part 1 of the survey, each person was asked to name these situation comedy characters.

WHO ARE THESE CHARACTERS?

The results of Part 1 of the survey are shown in this **bar graph.**

Results:

Character: Lucy Ricardo, Oscar Madison, The Fonz, Shirley Feeney

Number of People: 0, 5, 10, 15, 20, 25, 30, 35, 40, 45, 50

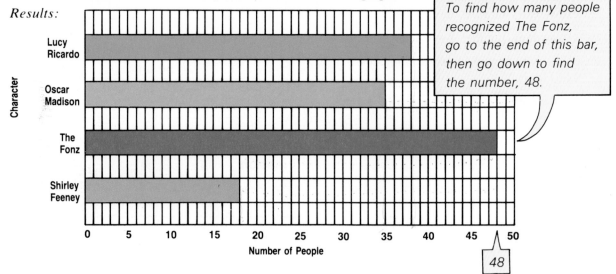

To find how many people recognized The Fonz, go to the end of this bar, then go down to find the number, 48.

48

1. Read the bar graph. How many people recognized The Fonz?
2. How many recognized Shirley Feeney?
3. How many knew Oscar Madison?
4. How many knew Lucy Ricardo?
5. Which character was recognized by the most people? the fewest people?
6. How many more people recognized The Fonz than Shirley Feeney?
7. How many of the 50 people surveyed did not recognize Oscar Madison?

EXERCISES

Use the bar graphs to answer the questions.

In Part 2 of the survey, each person was asked to name the TV show in which the character appeared.

8. How many people knew that Shirley appeared in *Laverne and Shirley*?
9. How many knew that Oscar appeared in *The Odd Couple*?
10. How many more people knew the name of the TV show The Fonz appeared in than knew the TV show Oscar appeared in?

Results:

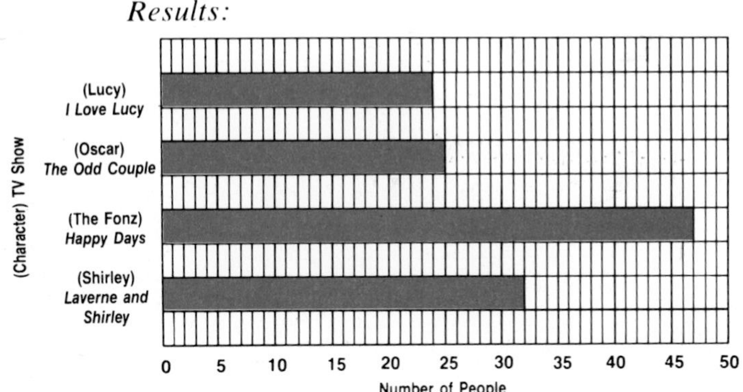

In Part 3 each person was asked to name the actor or actress that played the character.

11. Which actor or actress was identified by the most people? the fewest people?
12. How many people identified Lucille Ball?
13. How many people identified Jack Klugman?
14. How many more people identified Henry Winkler than identified Cindy Williams?

Results:

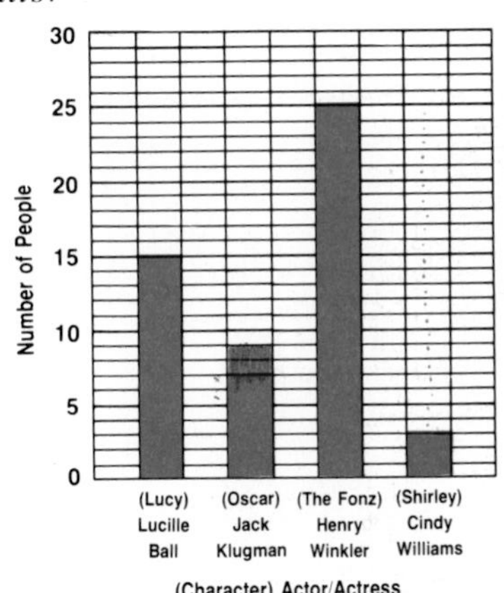

You're the reporter

Use the bar graph. Complete the story.

15. The price of a movie ticket in [?] was $1.50. A movie ticket in 1980 cost [?].
16. Between 1975 and [?], the price of a ticket increased $1.00, from $1.50 to [?].
17. In 1975, 4 tickets cost [?]. The cost of [?] tickets in 1980 was $10.00.

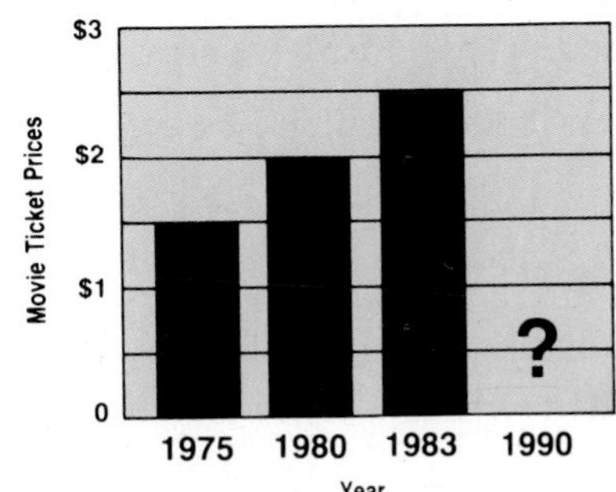

Using line graphs

Livestock that are raised to be shown at fairs receive special care and attention. Feed is controlled and growth is measured monthly. The **line graph** shows Zella's weight increase.

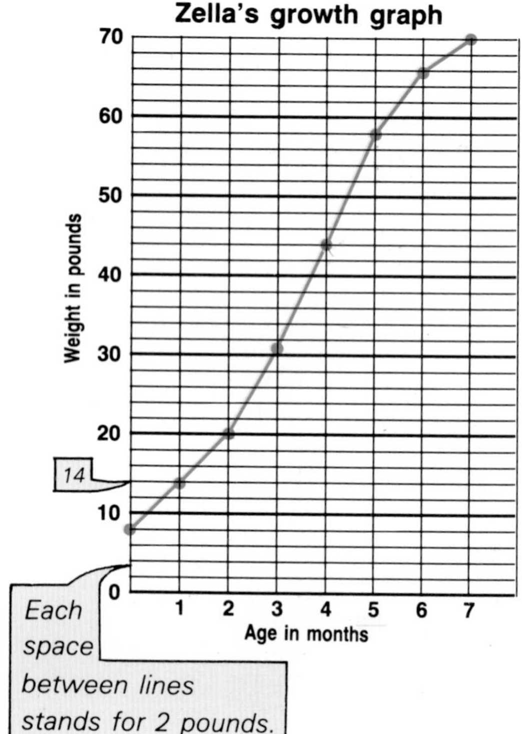

ZELLA WINS THE BLUE!

LANCASTER, N.H. This year's Grand Champion Lamb is Zella. Zella is 7 months old and weighs 70 pounds.

This year's Mason County Grand Champion Lamb with her owner, Julie Eastman.

To find Zella's weight when she was 1 month old, look up along the 1-month line, then look left to find her weight, 14 pounds.

1. Read the line graph. How much did Zella weigh at
   a. 4 months? **b.** 5 months? **c.** 7 months?
2. How old was Zella when she weighed
   a. 20 pounds? **b.** 31 pounds? **c.** 66 pounds?
3. How many pounds did Zella gain during the first two months?
4. How much more did Zella weigh at 3 months than she did at 1 month?
5. When did Zella gain more, in the third month or in the sixth month?
6. During which 3-month period did Zella gain the most weight?

EXERCISES

Use the line graphs to answer the questions.

7. What was the fair attendance at
   - a. 10 A.M.?
   - b. noon?
   - c. 6 P.M.?
   - d. 10 P.M.?

8. What was the approximate time when the attendance reached
   - a. 1200 people?
   - b. 1800 people?
   - c. 2500 people?
   - d. 2700 people?

9. Fair officials predicted that 3000 people would be in attendance opening day, September 1. How far off was their prediction?

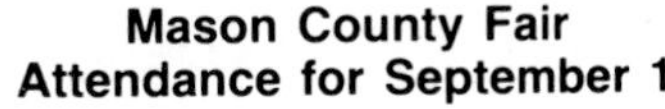

Mason County Fair
Attendance for September 1

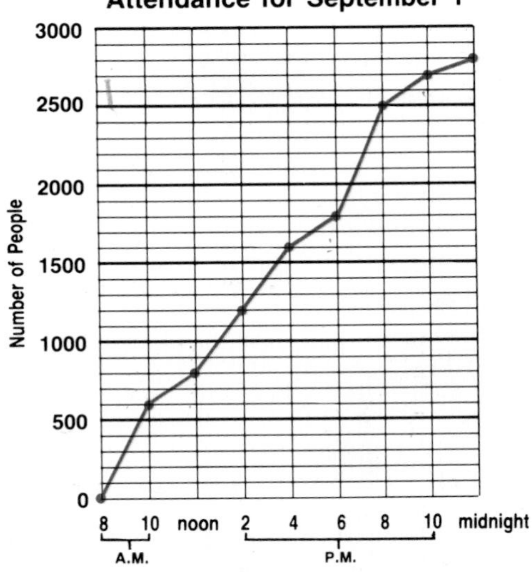

10. Workers at the booth worked 4-hour shifts. The first shift took in $150. How much did the second shift take in?

11. How much money did the Lancaster Booster Club take in between 8 P.M. and midnight?

12. The shift Carmen worked took in $500. What time did she get off work?

13. The Booster Club charged $5 for each hat. About how many hats did the club sell on September 1?

Lancaster Booster Club
Hat Sales Booth
Receipts for September 1

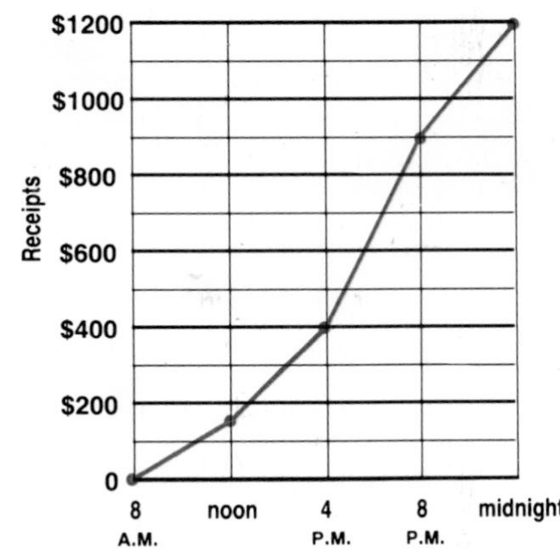

Don't be fooled! Interpreting data

14. Each bar graph compares attendance at the Mason County Fair. One of the two graphs has been drawn to mislead people. Which graph is misleading? How is it misleading?

a.

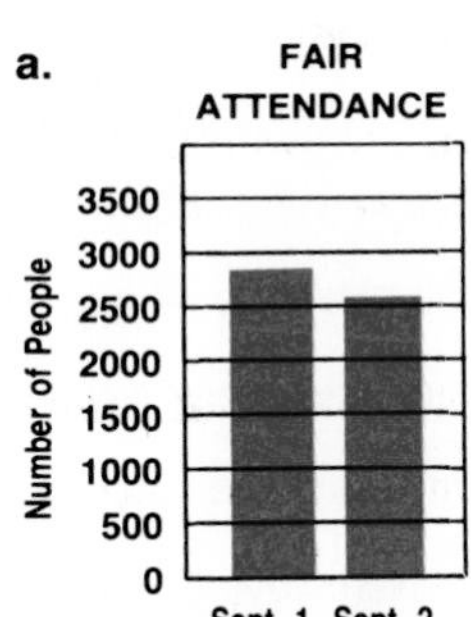

b.

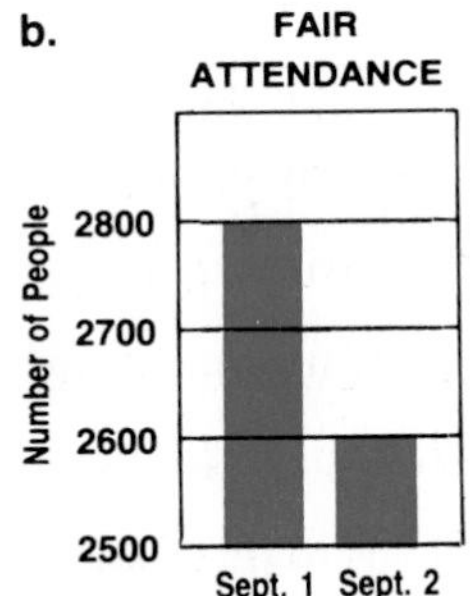

Reading circle graphs and picture graphs

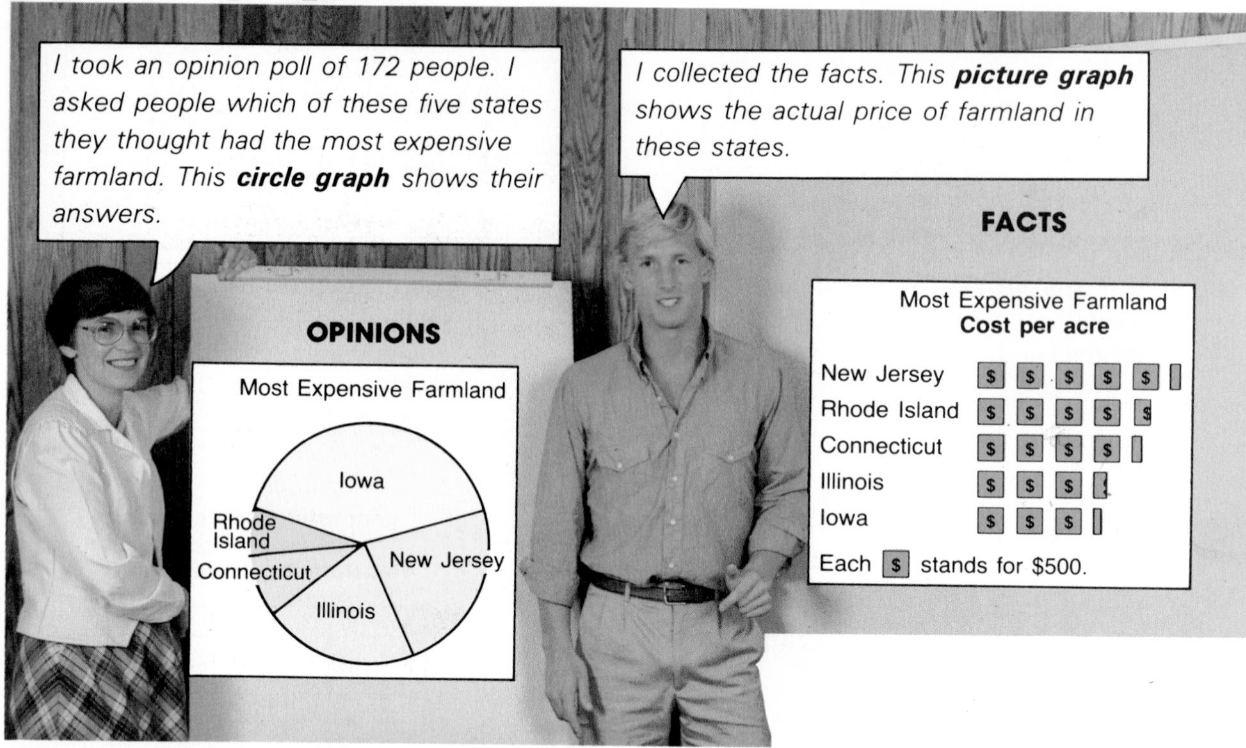

I took an opinion poll of 172 people. I asked people which of these five states they thought had the most expensive farmland. This **circle graph** shows their answers.
I collected the facts. This **picture graph** shows the actual price of farmland in these states.
OPINIONS
Most Expensive Farmland
Iowa
Rhode Island
Connecticut
Illinois
New Jersey
FACTS
Most Expensive Farmland
Cost per acre
New Jersey
Rhode Island
Connecticut
Illinois
Iowa
Each $ stands for $500.

Use the circle graph to answer these questions.

1. Which state was picked by the most people?

2. Which state was picked by the fewest people?

3. Did more people pick Illinois than picked Connecticut?

4. Did more people pick New Jersey than picked Iowa?

Use the picture graph to answer these questions.

5. Which state has the most expensive farmland?

6. Which state's farmland averages about $1800 an acre? About $2700 an acre?

7. How many [$] would be used to show $1500-an-acre farmland?

8. How many [$] would be used to show $1250-an-acre farmland?

9. Does Connecticut's farmland average more or less than $2000 an acre?

10. Which state's farmland costs about $500 per acre more than Connecticut's?

EXERCISES

Use the circle graph to answer the questions.

11. How many people thought Alaska had the least expensive farmland?

12. Which state was picked by 42 people?

13. Which state was picked by the fewest people?

14. Which two states were picked by a total of 128 people?

15. Which three states were picked by a total of 75 people?

Least Expensive Farmland
According to an Opinion Poll

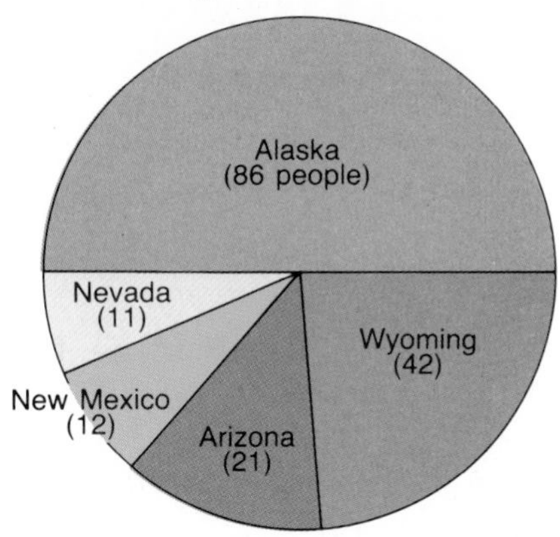

Use the picture graph to answer the questions.

16. Which state's farmland costs about
   a. \$109 per acre?
   b. \$191 per acre?
   c. \$195 per acre?
   d. \$146 per acre?

17. Which state's farmland costs about \$90 per acre more than Alaska's?

18. Does New Mexico's farmland cost more or less than \$150 per acre?

19. How many (\$) would be used to show \$260-per-acre land?

Least Expensive Farmland
(based on U.S. Census Bureau averages)

Alaska	(\$) (\$) (\$) (\$) (\$) ◖
Wyoming	(\$) (\$) (\$) (\$) (\$) (\$) (\$) ◖
New Mexico	(\$) (\$) (\$) (\$) (\$) (\$) (\$) ◖
Nevada	(\$) (\$) (\$) (\$) (\$) (\$) (\$) (\$) (\$) ◖
Arizona	(\$) (\$) (\$) (\$) (\$) (\$) (\$) (\$) (\$) ◖

Each (\$) stands for \$20 per acre.

Make a picture graph

20. Use the information in the chart to make a picture graph. You may choose any symbol to represent pounds of fruit. Draw one symbol for each 4 pounds. Be sure to label your graph.

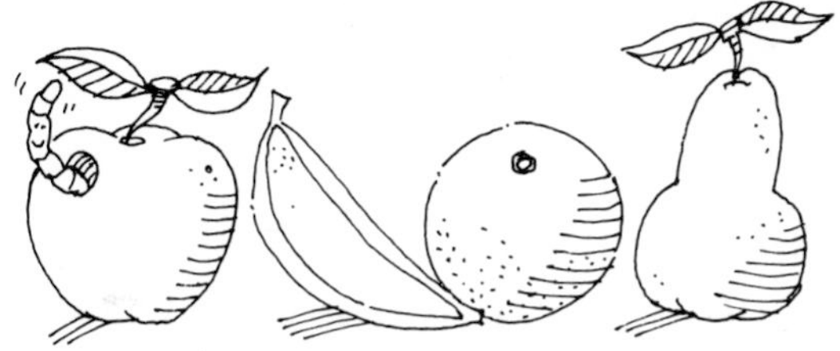

Yearly Consumption of Fruit
by the Average American

TYPE	NUMBER OF POUNDS
Fresh	80
Canned	36
Frozen	12
Dried	4

Cumulative Skill Practice

Write the standard numeral. *(page 4)*

1. 26 thousand, 429
2. 18 thousand, 92
3. 238 thousand, 164
4. 37 million
5. 259 million
6. 3 million, 375 thousand
7. 38 million, 61
8. 9 billion
9. 7 billion, 293 million
10. two hundred twenty-five thousand, four hundred seven
11. sixty thousand, ninety-one
12. thirty-three million, eight hundred seventy-three thousand
13. five million, thirty thousand, two hundred eight
14. six billion, one hundred ninety-three million, four hundred thousand

Round to the nearest ten thousand. *(page 12)*

15. 28,192
16. 56,700
17. 74,825
18. 59,600
19. 76,501
20. 48,400
21. 74,391
22. 93,866
23. 356,200
24. 635,000
25. 824,999
26. 544,099

Write the standard numeral. *(page 16)*

27. 5 hundredths
28. 36 thousandths
29. 12 and 5 tenths
30. 59 and 74 hundredths
31. 74 and 18 thousandths
32. 3951 ten-thousandths
33. 8 and 7 ten-thousandths
34. 15 and 235 thousandths
35. 41 and 72 ten-thousandths

Round to the nearest hundredth. *(page 20)*

36. 8.316
37. 22.207
38. 8.530
39. 60.845
40. 74.573
41. 6.3048
42. 0.0659
43. 5.3625
44. 9.3511
45. 0.005
46. 13.949
47. 372.678

Give the sum. *(page 24)*

48. 7.4 + 2.2
49. 6.83 + 2.59
50. 0.73 + 2.88
51. 2.793 + 3.899
52. 5.466 + 1.805
53. 18.05 + 8.03
54. 0.84 + 5.96 + 7.6
55. 56.4 + 1.82 + 6.6
56. 7 + 3.85 + 6.8

Give the difference. *(page 46)*

57. 7.8 − 3.1
58. 9.63 − 2.08
59. 8.03 − 6.55
60. 54.5 − 4.56
61. 32.6 − 19.38
62. 45.61 − 3.8
63. 22 − 5.9
64. 9 − 0.748
65. 6.1 − 3.045

Problem solving

Andy and Sarah Wallace have just completed a 5-day motorcycle trip. They started in Dallas, rode to Houston, and spent the night with friends. They spent the next three nights in San Antonio, Lubbock, and Amarillo, and returned to Dallas on the fifth day.

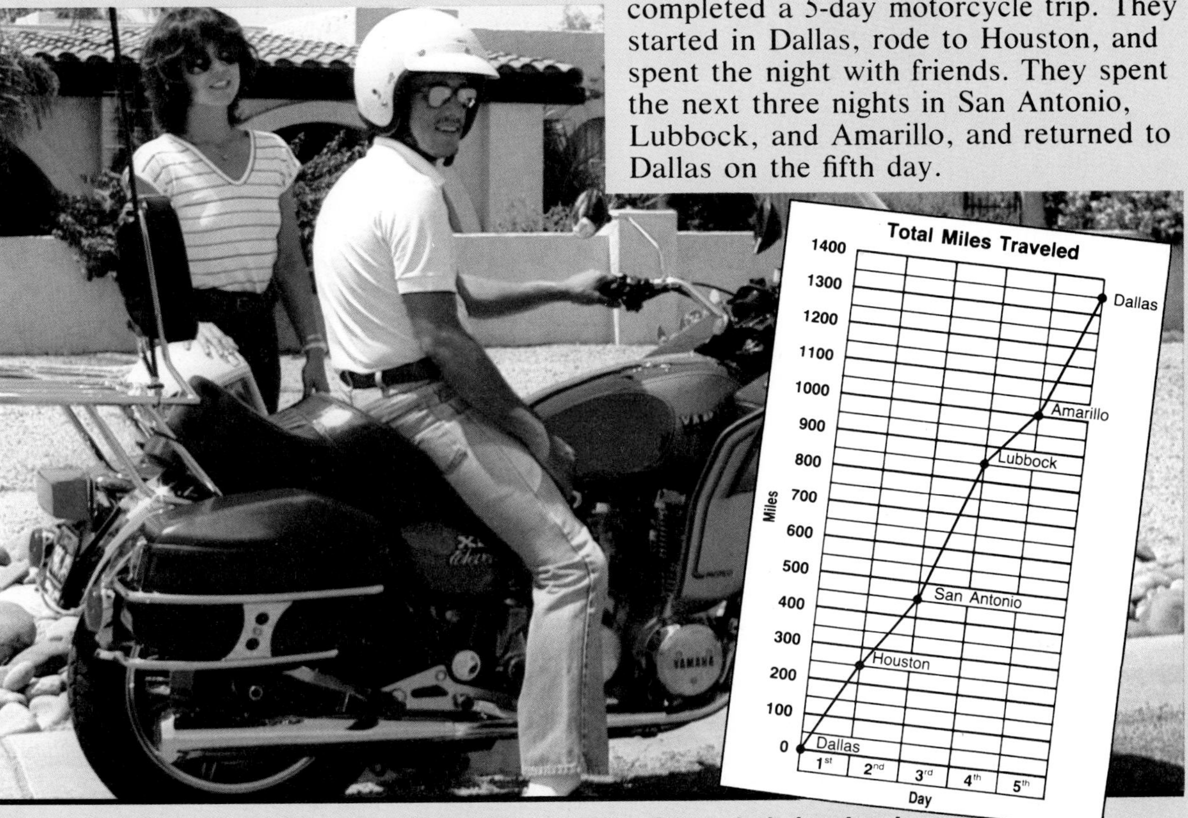

Sarah made the line graph using the information from their log book. Use the graph to answer these questions.

1. The log book says they were in San Antonio the second night. How many miles is it from Dallas to San Antonio?
2. How many miles is it from San Antonio to Lubbock?
3. How far is it from Lubbock to Amarillo?
4. On which day did they travel 150 miles?
5. On which day did they travel the most miles? How many miles did they travel that day?
6. The log book shows that they traveled 4 hours on the second day. How many miles per hour did they average the second day?
7. During which day did their trip mileage reach a total of 1000 miles?
8. They were between what two cities when their trip was half over? *Hint: Divide the total distance by 2 and use the graph.*
9. One day they drove 10 hours and averaged 40 miles per hour. They were between what cities?
10. Could they have completed the trip in 4 days if they had driven 50 miles per hour for 6 hours each day?

Analyzing data—finding the mean

Nine students in a psychology class conducted an experiment on hand-eye coordination. Each student was asked to stack 50 pennies as quickly as possible.

The results are shown in the chart.

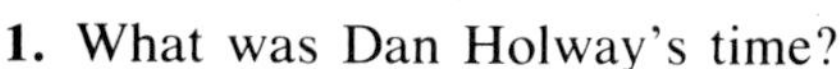

1. What was Dan Holway's time?
2. Who stacked the coins in 44.2 seconds?
3. Who had the shortest time? the longest time?
4. The average of a set of numbers is called the **mean.** Whose time do you think is closer to the mean time, Ed Dorr's or Polly Smith's?

STUDENT	TIME (SECONDS)
Dan Holway	43.3
Julia Belmore	38.2
Charlie Allen	56.1
Ed Dorr	45.4
Judy Conrey	44.2
Tracy McDonald	45.2
Polly Smith	37.1
José Rivera	52.8
Angelo Robinson	46.3

Here's how *to find the mean.*

Find the sum of the times.

$$\begin{array}{r} 43.3 \\ 38.2 \\ 56.1 \\ 45.4 \\ 44.2 \\ 45.2 \\ 37.1 \\ 52.8 \\ +46.3 \\ \hline 408.6 \end{array}$$

Divide the sum by the number of students.

$$\begin{array}{r} 45.4 \\ 9\,\overline{)\,408.6} \\ -36 \\ \hline 48 \\ -45 \\ \hline 36 \\ -36 \\ \hline 0 \end{array}$$

The mean time is 45.4 seconds.

5. Look at the *Here's how*. Who had a time that was the same as the mean time?
6. Which students had a time longer than the mean time?
7. Which students had a time shorter than the mean time?

EXERCISES

Find the mean. Round each answer to the nearest tenth.

Here are scrambled answers for the next two rows of exercises: 182.6 32.3 9.8 264.6

8. 12 4 14 9

9. 35 39 27 28

10. 195 176 183 178 181

11. 253 276 248 281 265

12. 361 375 392 386 379

13. 432 481 467 429 450

14. 18.6 19.4 21.6

15. 13.5 14.8 14.2

16. 29.6 32.7 31.9 28.7

17. 46.8 48.9 43.7 41.2

18. 112.2 114.7 116.3

19. 129.6 128.7 126.3

20. 18 28 16 32 14 26 10

21. 15 21 18 24 31 27 19

22. 28 31 19 42 37 16 12

23. 19 29 17 33 15 27 11

Use the chart on page 114 to answer the questions.

24. Who stacked the coins in a shorter time, Ed Dorr or Julia Belmore?

25. Which student had a time that was 1.2 seconds less than the mean time?

26. Who stacked the coins 2.1 seconds faster than Ed Dorr?

27. Who stacked the coins 1.1 seconds slower than Tracy McDonald?

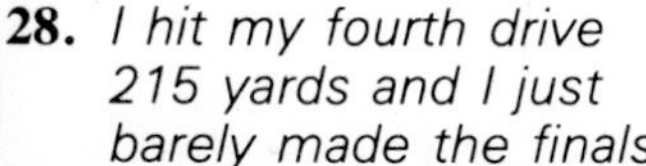

Tee time! Analyzing data

To qualify for the finals in the Heavy Hitters Golf Ball Driving Contest, golfers must have a mean distance of 205 yards on 4 drives.

GOLFER	LENGTH OF DRIVE (YARDS)			
	1	2	3	4
Ann	195	210	200	?
Jan	205	195	200	?
Nan	198	205	218	?

Use the clues to name each golfer.

28. *I hit my fourth drive 215 yards and I just barely made the finals!*

29. *I made the finals with a fourth drive of 200 yards.*

30. *I never made the finals.*

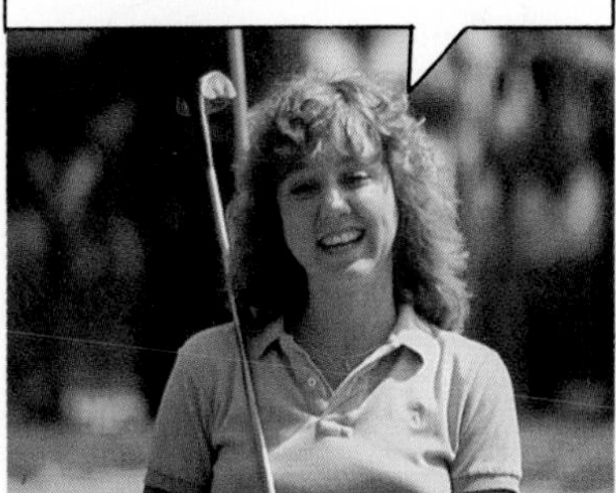

Hint: To make the finals, what must the four drives total?

Analyzing data—finding the median, mode, and range

FAMOUS-FACES QUIZ Whose famous face is in the picture?

Cartoonist (*10 points*)	**Tennis player** (*8 points*)	**U.S. President** (*5 points*)	**Singer** (*7 points*)
a. Johnny Hart	**a.** Tracy Austin	**a.** Harry Truman	**a.** Juice Newton
b. Walt Disney	**b.** Chris Evert-Lloyd	**b.** John F. Kennedy	**b.** Barbra Streisand
c. Charles Schulz	**c.** Pam Shriver	**c.** Abraham Lincoln	**c.** Donna Summer

Fifteen high school students took the Famous-Faces Quiz. Their scores are shown in the chart.

NAME	SCORE	NAME	SCORE	NAME	SCORE
T. Coyle	5	A. Milan	20	C. Sanford	13
L. Cummings	13	M. Olsen	18	A. Travers	17
F. Epstein	15	K. Panetta	7	L. Vita	5
J. Kenney	12	J. Perry	13	K. Wong	23
J. Lubell	15	J. Quiroga	22	M. Young	25

1. What would be your score if you knew the cartoonist and the singer?

2. What is the lowest score shown on the chart? the highest score?

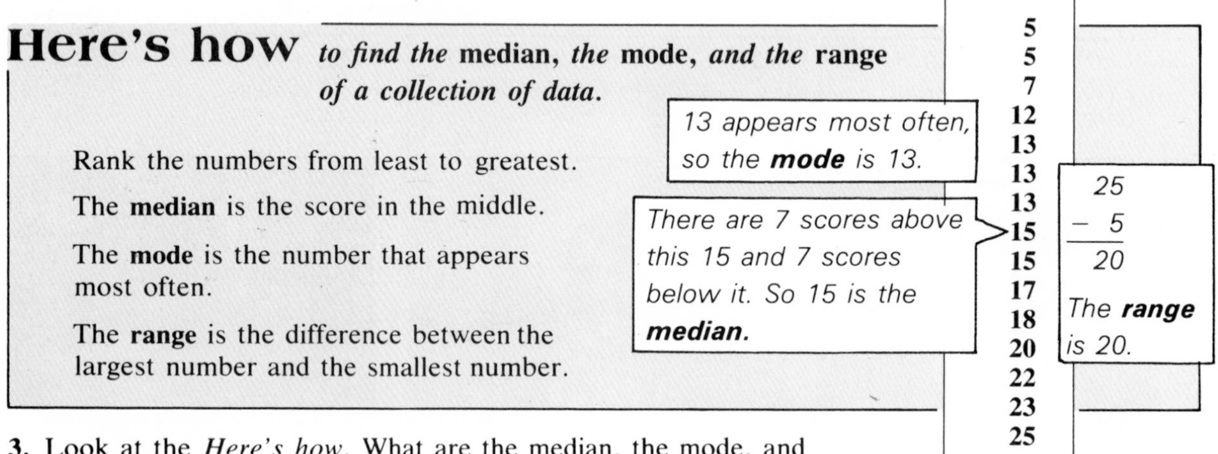

Here's how to find the median, the mode, and the range of a collection of data.
Rank the numbers from least to greatest.
The median is the score in the middle.
The mode is the number that appears most often.
The range is the difference between the largest number and the smallest number.
13 appears most often, so the mode is 13.
There are 7 scores above this 15 and 7 scores below it. So 15 is the median.
5
5
7
12
13
13
13
15
15
17
18
20
22
23
25
25
− 5
20
The range is 20.

3. Look at the *Here's how*. What are the median, the mode, and the range of the Famous-Faces Quiz scores?

EXERCISES

Find the median.

> *Hint: Average the two middle numbers, 10 and 11.*

4. 13, 12, 11, 6, 7, 12, 9

5. 12, 9, 8, 14, 10, 11

6. 14, 7, 12, 7, 7, 10, 13

7. 13, 14, 9, 11, 13, 10, 9

8. 183, 182, 183, 180, 187, 182

9. 12, 15, 13, 19, 13, 15, 13

10. 1243, 1245, 1301, 1248, 1256, 1276, 1287, 1308, 1299

11. 6797, 6785, 6897, 6579, 6057, 6896, 6570, 6075, 6597, 6895, 6579, 6719, 6852

Find the mode and range. (It is possible for a list to have more than one mode.)

12. 5, 7, 9, 7, 5, 9, 7

13. 11, 15, 12, 15, 10, 14, 15

14. 20, 27, 22, 23, 21, 24, 22

15. 66, 82, 69, 73, 68, 66, 76, 66

16. 16, 19, 21, 16, 18, 19, 23

17. 43, 39, 47, 43, 48, 41, 38, 43

18. 104, 108, 103, 106, 103, 107, 101, 103, 108, 104, 100, 110

19. 506, 511, 508, 503, 500, 503, 505, 508, 505, 503, 514, 501, 505, 509

Solve. Refer to the data on page 116.

20. Whose scores were greater than the median?

21. Did any student know all four famous people?

22. What is the mean rounded to the nearest tenth?

23. Is the mean greater than or less than the median?

You're the reporter **Math on the job**

Copy and complete the chart. Then complete the story.

Larry Bird's 7-Game Point Production			
TEAM	FG	FT	TOTAL POINTS
Knicks	10	8	?
Nets	12	6	?
76ers	9	11	?
Bucks	14	6	?
Pacers	8	3	?
Bulls	10	8	?
Lakers	7	7	?
FG Field Goal—2 points each			
FT Free Throw—1 point each			

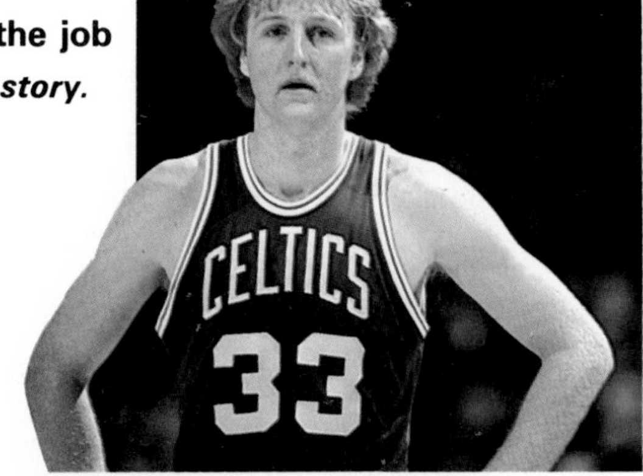

24. Larry Bird of the Boston Celtics averaged [?] points per game for these seven games.

25. His lowest scoring effort during the seven games was against the [?], when he only scored [?] points.

26. On his best scoring night he scored [?] points above his mean score for the seven games.

Presenting data—constructing graphs

The Haydon High School Band sold bumper stickers to raise money for new uniforms. Five different bumper stickers were offered. The table shows the distribution of the first 100 bumper stickers sold.

Frequency Table for Bumper-Sticker Sales (First 100)

Bumper sticker	Number sold	
	TALLY	FREQUENCY
DRAGON POWER!	𝍸 𝍸 𝍸 𝍸 𝍸 𝍸 𝍸 𝍸	40
Big Green Machine	𝍸 𝍸 𝍸 𝍸	20
Haydon High is #1	𝍸	5
MEAN AND GREEN	𝍸 𝍸	10
Go for it, Dragons	𝍸 𝍸 𝍸 𝍸 𝍸	25

Answer these questions to see how you would fill in the missing information on the graphs.

Look at the bar graph and the frequency table.

1. What bumper sticker does the longest bar represent?
2. What number is represented by H? A? B? J?
3. The shortest bar represents what bumper sticker?
4. What bumper sticker is represented by a? b? c? d? e?

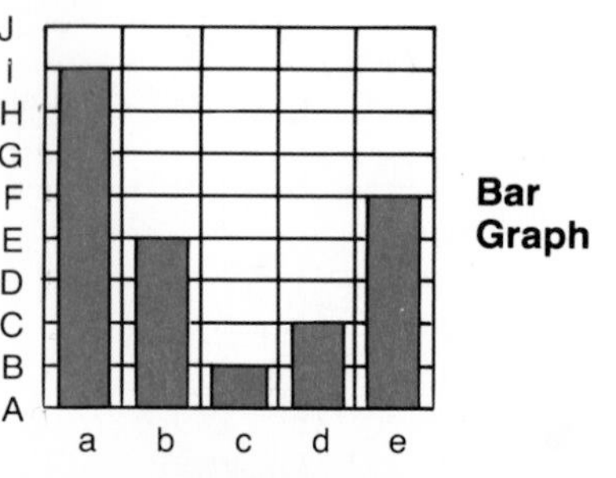

Bar Graph

Look at the circle graph and the frequency table.

5. What number does each color represent?
6. The blue sector represents sales of which bumper sticker?
7. Which graph do you think allows you to compare the sales more accurately?

BUMPER-STICKER SALES (First 100)

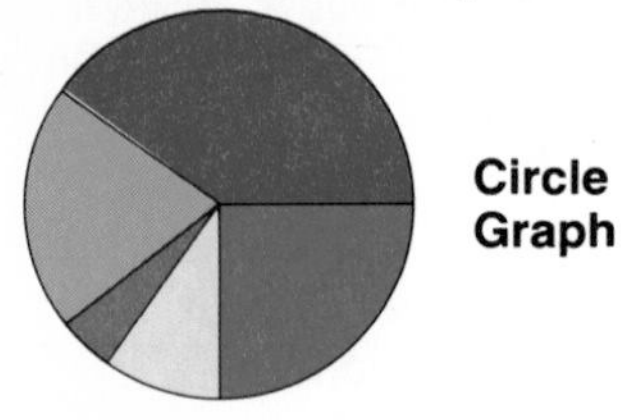

Circle Graph

EXERCISES

Solve.

8. Look at the sales chart and the picture graph.
   a. How many ▪ were used to show the first week's sales?
   b. What does each ▪ represent?
9. Look at the sales chart and the line graph.
   a. Sales for the first week were \$150. What number is represented by C? A? L?
   b. The total sales goal was \$500. Did the band reach this goal?
10. Look at both graphs. Which one do you think shows total sales better? Why?
11. Which of the two graphs do you think looks more interesting? Why?

SALES— FIRST 4 WEEKS

Sales Chart

Week	Sales
1	\$150
2	\$185
3	\$135
4	\$ 70

Line Graph

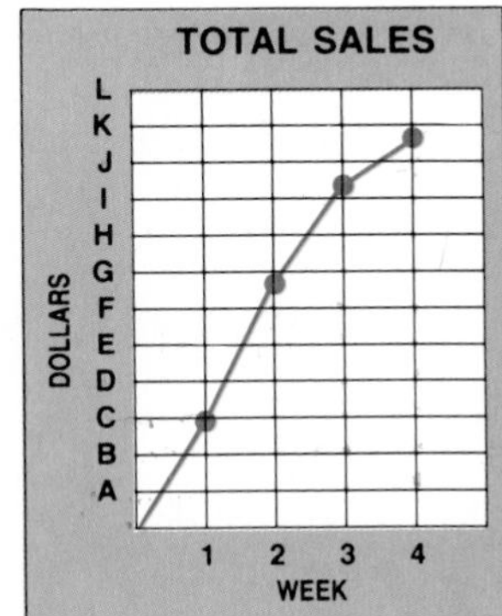

Picture Graph

WEEKLY SALES
Week 1
Week 2
Week 3
Week 4

Join the band

12. The Haydon High School Band has 66 members. Complete the frequency table and make a bar or picture graph showing the distribution of instruments in the band.

INSTRUMENT	TALLY	FREQUENCY
Baritone	||	?
Bassoon	||	?
Clarinet	𝍸 𝍸 𝍸	?
Flute	𝍸 𝍸	?
French horn	||||	?
Oboe	||	?
Percussion	𝍸 |	?
Piccolo	|	?
Saxophone	𝍸	?
Trombone	𝍸	?
Trumpet	𝍸 𝍸 ||	?
Tuba	||	?

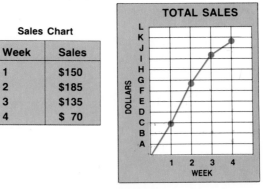

Cumulative Skill Practice

Give the product. *(page 64)*

1. 3.4 × 0.8 **2.** 5.61 × 0.9 **3.** 32.4 × 0.4
4. 8.4 × 0.44 **5.** 0.47 × 0.16 **6.** 36 × 0.52
7. 305 × 5.8 **8.** 9.63 × 17 **9** 0.33 × 40
10. 7.41 × 6.5 **11.** 8.53 × 2.6 **12.** 0.05 × 0.29
13. 3.51 × 2.08 **14.** 4.07 × 71 **15.** 0.02 × 1.03

Give the product. *(page 68)*

16. 18.4 × 10 **17.** 18.4 × 100 **18.** 18.4 × 1000
19. 39 × 10 **20.** 39 × 100 **21.** 39 × 1000
22. 2.07 × 100 **23.** 2.07 × 1000 **24.** 2.07 × 10
25. 0.007 × 10 **26.** 0.007 × 1000 **27.** 0.007 × 100
28. 16.49 × 100 **29.** 16.49 × 1000 **30.** 16.49 × 10

Give the quotient. *(page 92)*

31. 234 ÷ 10 **32.** 234 ÷ 100 **33.** 234 ÷ 1000
34. 36.4 ÷ 10 **35.** 36.4 ÷ 100 **36.** 36.4 ÷ 1000
37. 8 ÷ 100 **38.** 8 ÷ 10 **39.** 8 ÷ 1000
40. 83.07 ÷ 1000 **41.** 83.07 ÷ 10 **42.** 83.07 ÷ 100
43. 9.73 ÷ 100 **44.** 9.73 ÷ 1000 **45.** 9.73 ÷ 10

Give the quotient rounded to the nearest tenth. *(pages 94, 96)*

46. 13.5 ÷ 0.6 **47.** 2.81 ÷ 0.3 **48.** 5.08 ÷ 0.05
49. 35.7 ÷ 0.3 **50.** 2.76 ÷ 0.04 **51.** 6.3 ÷ 0.03
52. 6.34 ÷ 1.4 **53.** 2.059 ÷ 2.5 **54.** 5.07 ÷ 0.12
55. 15.082 ÷ 0.33 **56.** 4.006 ÷ 0.52 **57.** 4.21 ÷ 4.1
58. 7.49 ÷ 5.11 **59.** 3.716 ÷ 2.9 **60.** 38.2 ÷ 6.05

Find the mean. *(page 114)*

61. 124, 117, 131 **62.** 243, 257, 232 **63.** 706, 599, 639
64. 18, 27, 15, 24 **65.** 58, 40, 63, 46 **66.** 163, 174, 150, 157
67. 16, 23, 15, 20, 18 **68.** 43, 81, 49, 58, 74 **69.** 93, 85, 90, 93, 87

Problem solving

USING COMPUTER GRAPHICS

Lori Adriano is the Fine Arts Coordinator for Lincoln High School. She uses a personal computer to store data about students who participate in school-sponsored fine-arts activities. A special **software** package helped her produce these graphs.

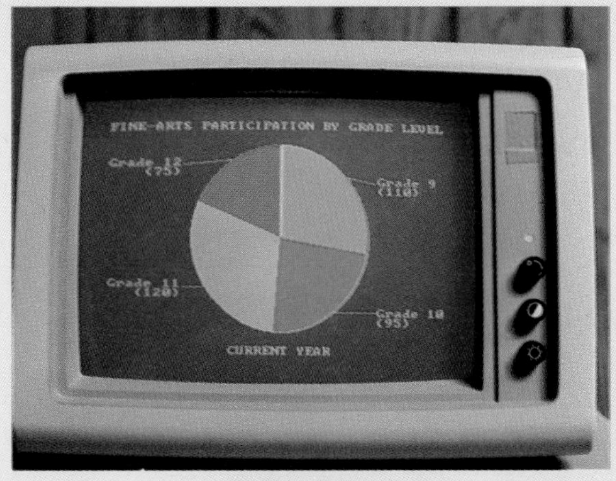

GRAPH 1

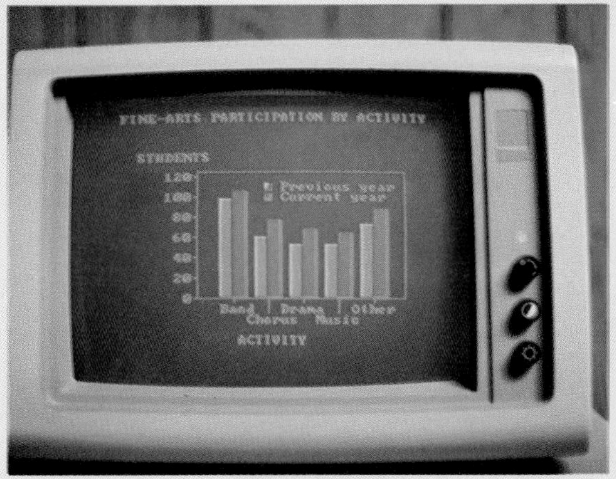

GRAPH 2

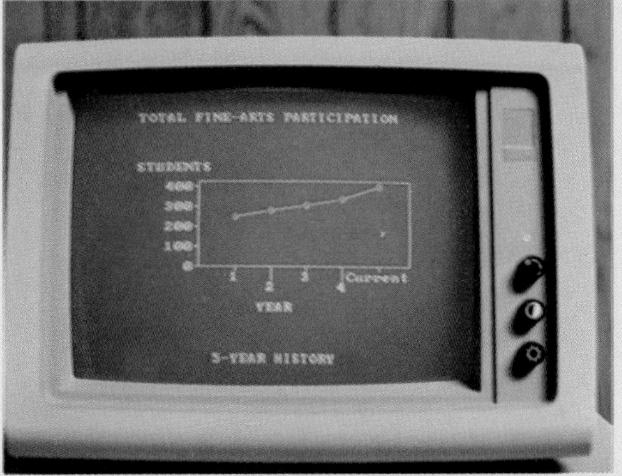

GRAPH 3

Decide which graph or graphs Ms. Adriano could use to answer the question. Then write a reasonable answer.

1. Parent: "Which fine-arts activity is the most popular?"

2. School Board Member: "Are the school's fine-arts activities as popular with seniors as they are with freshmen?"

3. Taxpayer: "How many students are enrolled in fine-arts activities anyway?"

4. Parent: "Is participation in fine-arts activities increasing or decreasing?"

5. School Board Member: "Our costs have gone up nearly 25% over the past 5 years. How do you account for this?"

6. Taxpayer: "I read in the paper that 50 players tried out for football this year. Why doesn't the school do more for non-athletes?"

Chapter REVIEW

Here are scrambled answers for the review exercises:

1	200	500	circle	mean	mode	range
4	300	bar	line	median	picture	

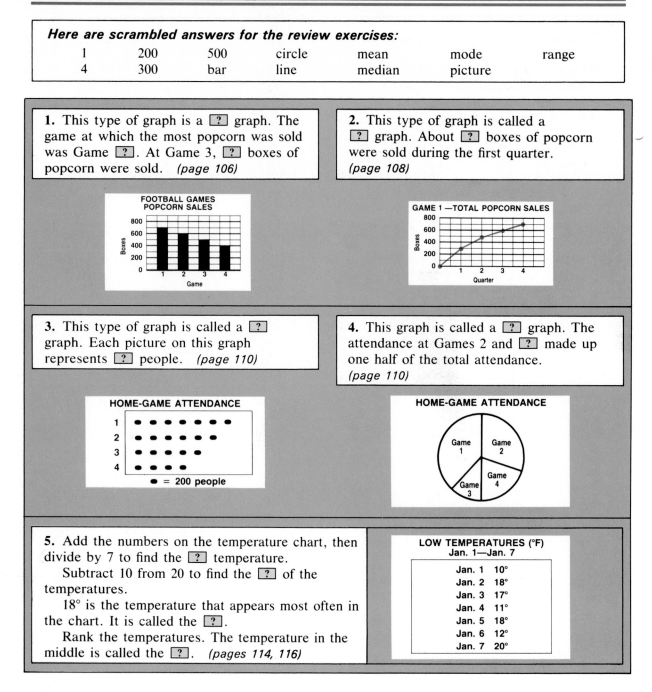

1. This type of graph is a [?] graph. The game at which the most popcorn was sold was Game [?]. At Game 3, [?] boxes of popcorn were sold. *(page 106)*

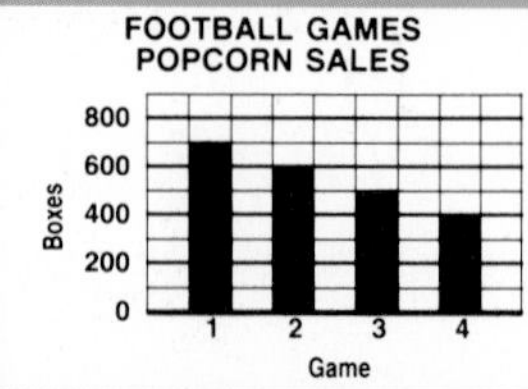

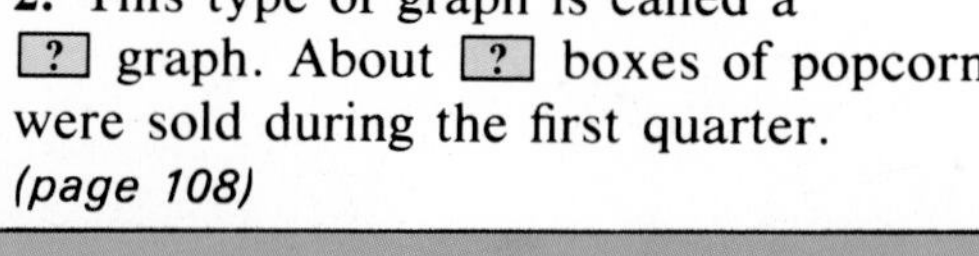

2. This type of graph is called a [?] graph. About [?] boxes of popcorn were sold during the first quarter. *(page 108)*

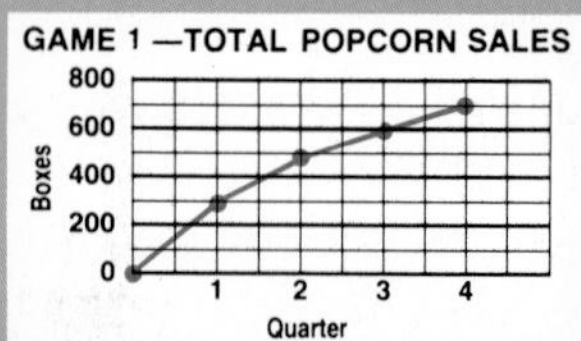

3. This type of graph is called a [?] graph. Each picture on this graph represents [?] people. *(page 110)*

HOME-GAME ATTENDANCE

1	● ● ● ● ● ● ●
2	● ● ● ● ● ●
3	● ● ● ● ●
4	● ● ● ●

● = 200 people

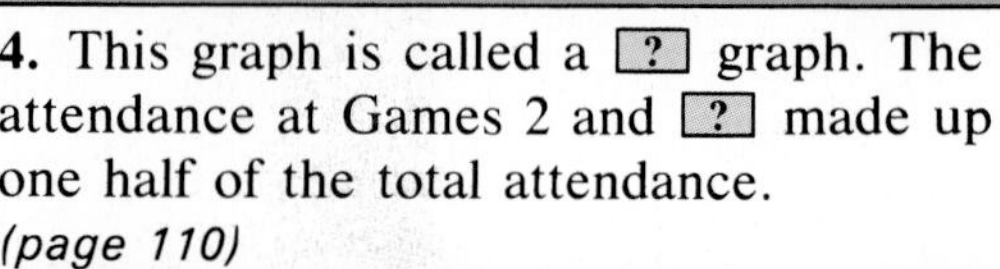

4. This graph is called a [?] graph. The attendance at Games 2 and [?] made up one half of the total attendance. *(page 110)*

5. Add the numbers on the temperature chart, then divide by 7 to find the [?] temperature.

Subtract 10 from 20 to find the [?] of the temperatures.

18° is the temperature that appears most often in the chart. It is called the [?].

Rank the temperatures. The temperature in the middle is called the [?]. *(pages 114, 116)*

LOW TEMPERATURES (°F)
Jan. 1—Jan. 7

Jan. 1	10°
Jan. 2	18°
Jan. 3	17°
Jan. 4	11°
Jan. 5	18°
Jan. 6	12°
Jan. 7	20°

Chapter TEST

Use the frequency table to answer each question.
(page 104)

1. How many students saw 3 movies last month?
2. How many didn't go to a movie?
3. How many saw 2 or fewer movies?
4. How many students were in the survey?

NUMBER OF MOVIES ATTENDED LAST MONTH

Number of Movies	Number of Students	
	TALLY	FREQUENCY
4	|||	3
3	~~||||~~ |	6
2	~~||||~~ ~~||||~~ ||	12
1	||	2
0	|||	3

Use the bar graph to answer each question.
(page 106)

5. Who spent the most time doing homework?
6. How many hours did David spend doing homework?
7. How many hours did Jan spend doing homework?
8. How many more hours did Kim spend doing homework than Gayle?

HOMEWORK DURING THE WEEK

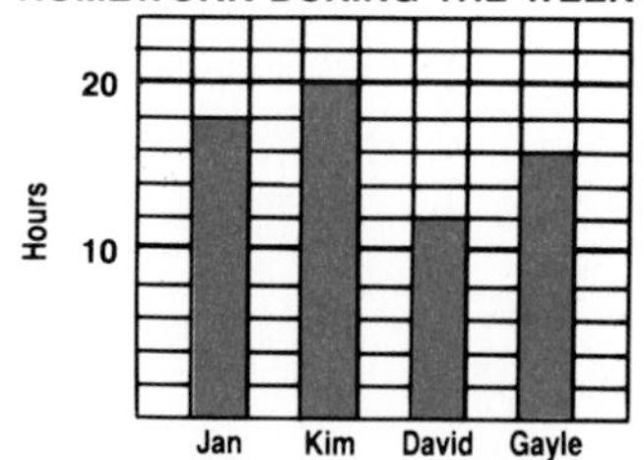

Use the line graph to answer each question.
(page 108)

9. By the end of the second week, Anne had saved \$8. How much had she saved by the end of the third week?
10. During which week did Anne save the most?
11. How much did Anne save during the six weeks?

ANNE'S TOTAL SAVINGS

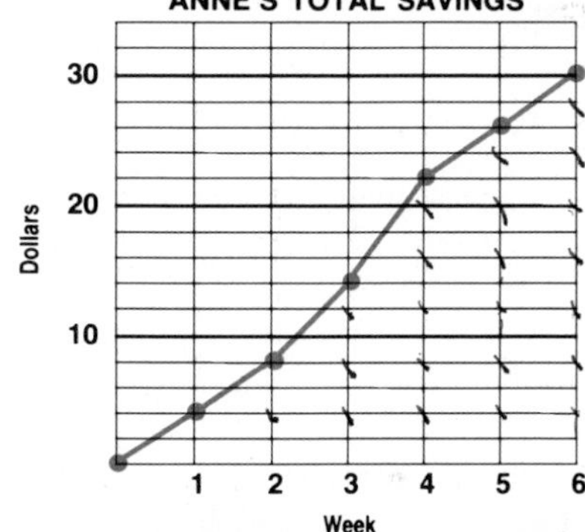

Use the picture graph to answer each question.
(page 110)

12. Who has the most records? the fewest?
13. How many records does Bob have?
14. How many records does Loni have?
15. How many records do Carl and Randy have together?

NUMBER OF RECORDS IN COLLECTION	
Bob	● ● ● ● ● ● ●
Carl	● ● ● ● ◖
Loni	● ● ● ● ● ◔
Randy	● ● ● ◕
Each ● stands for 4 records.	

Use the list of scores to answer each question.
(pages 114, 116)

16. What is the mean of Kathleen's math test scores?
17. What is the median?
18. What is the mode?
19. What is the range of her math test scores?

KATHLEEN'S MATH TEST SCORES
83 77 79 77 84

Cumulative TEST Standardized Format

Choose the correct letter.

1. The standard numeral for 3 billion, 32 thousand is

   A. 3,032,000
   B. 3,320,000
   C. 3,032,000,000
   D. none of these

2. 253,599 rounded to the nearest ten thousand is

   A. 300,000
   B. 254,000
   C. 250,000
   D. none of these

3. The standard numeral for 16 and 64 thousandths is

   A. 16.64
   B. 16.064
   C. 16.0064
   D. none of these

4. 7.695 rounded to the nearest hundredth is

   A. 7.60
   B. 7.69
   C. 7.70
   D. none of these

5. Give the sum.

   $6.4 + 0.65 + 12.9$

   A. 19.95
   B. 25.8
   C. 18.95
   D. none of these

6. Give the difference.

   $19.7 - 1.93$

   A. 0.04
   B. 17.77
   C. 17.83
   D. none of these

7. Give the product.

   23.6×1.09

   A. 4.484
   B. 25.474
   C. 25.724
   D. none of these

8. Give the product.

   5.772×1000

   A. 577.2
   B. 5772
   C. 57,720
   D. none of these

9. Give the quotient.

   $2.41 \div 100$

   A. 241
   B. 24.1
   C. 0.241
   D. none of these

10. Give the quotient rounded to the nearest tenth.

    $3.609 \div 3.4$

    A. 1.1
    B. 1.6
    C. 1.06
    D. none of these

11. The mean of 80, 83, 87, 88, and 92 is

    A. 9
    B. 87
    C. 86
    D. none of these

12. You bought 4 adult tickets for \$2.75 each and 3 children's tickets for \$1.25 each. How much did you spend?

    A. \$14.75
    B. \$13.25
    C. \$14.25
    D. none of these

Chapter 6
Fractions, Mixed Numbers, and Decimals

Equivalent fractions

Jan traded school pictures with her close friends. Here is her picture collection.

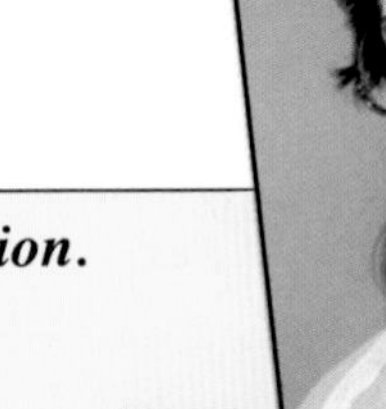

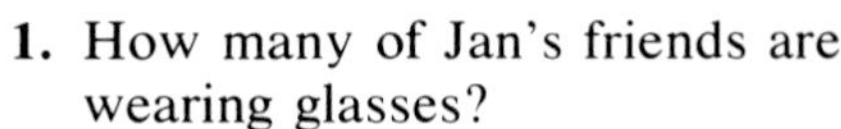

1. How many of Jan's friends are wearing glasses?
2. How many friends are pictured?
3. What fraction of her close friends are wearing glasses?
4. $\frac{2}{8}$, or $\frac{1}{4}$, of Jan's close friends are boys. Do you agree or disagree with this statement?

Here's how *to change a fraction to an equivalent fraction.*

To change a fraction to an equivalent fraction, multiply or divide both numerator and denominator by the same whole number (not 0).

numerator →
denominator →

$$\frac{1}{4} = \frac{2}{8} \quad (\times 2 \text{ numerator and denominator})$$

$$\frac{2}{8} = \frac{1}{4} \quad (\div 2 \text{ numerator and denominator})$$

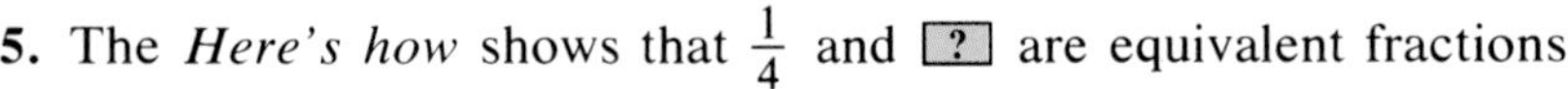

5. The *Here's how* shows that $\frac{1}{4}$ and [?] are equivalent fractions.
6. Complete these equivalent fractions.

a. $\frac{6}{5} = \frac{?}{15}$ (× 3, × 3)

You multiply 5 by 3 to get 15. So multiply 6 by 3 to find the missing numerator.

b. $\frac{15}{10} = \frac{?}{2}$ (÷ 5, ÷ 5)

You have to divide 10 by 5 to get 2. So divide 15 by 5 to find the missing numerator.

EXERCISES

Complete to get an equivalent fraction.

7. $\frac{2}{5} = \frac{?}{15}$ (× 3 above and below)

8. $\frac{4}{3} = \frac{?}{6}$ (× 2 above and below)

9. $\frac{10}{12} = \frac{?}{6}$ (÷ 2 above and below)

10. $\frac{9}{15} = \frac{?}{5}$ (÷ 3 above and below)

11. $\frac{6}{24} = \frac{?}{4}$ (÷ 6 above and below)

12. $\frac{1}{2} = \frac{?}{10}$ (× 5 above and below)

13. $\frac{3}{8} = \frac{?}{16}$ (× 2 above and below)

14. $\frac{12}{16} = \frac{?}{4}$ (÷ 4 above and below)

15. $\frac{6}{9} = \frac{?}{3}$ (÷ 3 above and below)

16. $\frac{7}{8} = \frac{?}{24}$ (× 3 above and below)

17. $\frac{1}{8} = \frac{?}{16}$

18. $\frac{5}{2} = \frac{?}{10}$

19. $\frac{4}{9} = \frac{?}{27}$

20. $\frac{6}{8} = \frac{?}{4}$

21. $\frac{5}{6} = \frac{?}{18}$

22. $\frac{16}{10} = \frac{?}{5}$

23. $\frac{9}{12} = \frac{?}{4}$

24. $\frac{8}{12} = \frac{?}{3}$

25. $\frac{4}{7} = \frac{?}{21}$

26. $\frac{3}{18} = \frac{?}{6}$

27. $\frac{10}{9} = \frac{?}{90}$

28. $\frac{24}{30} = \frac{?}{15}$

29. $\frac{25}{75} = \frac{?}{15}$

30. $\frac{2}{9} = \frac{?}{45}$

31. $\frac{30}{50} = \frac{?}{5}$

Give the "next" three equivalent fractions.

32. $\frac{1}{2}, \frac{2}{4}, \frac{3}{6}$, ?, ?, ?

33. $\frac{2}{3}, \frac{4}{6}, \frac{6}{9}$, ?, ?, ?

34. $\frac{1}{4}, \frac{2}{8}, \frac{3}{12}$, ?, ?, ?

35. $\frac{1}{5}, \frac{2}{10}$, ?, ?, ?

36. $\frac{3}{4}, \frac{6}{8}$, ?, ?, ?

37. $\frac{4}{5}, \frac{8}{10}$, ?, ?, ?

38. $\frac{1}{6}$, ?, ?, ?

39. $\frac{3}{8}$, ?, ?, ?

40. $\frac{6}{5}$, ?, ?, ?

Solve. Use the collection of pictures on page 126.

41. What fraction of the pictures have been autographed?

42. What fraction of the pictures have not been autographed?

43. What fraction of those pictured are girls? Give two equivalent fractions.

44. What fraction of the girls pictured wear glasses? Give two equivalent fractions.

Smile!

45. Study the clues to find in what year this photograph was taken.

Clues:

- The year rounded to the nearest ten is 1900.
- The sum of the digits is 12.

Writing fractions in lowest terms

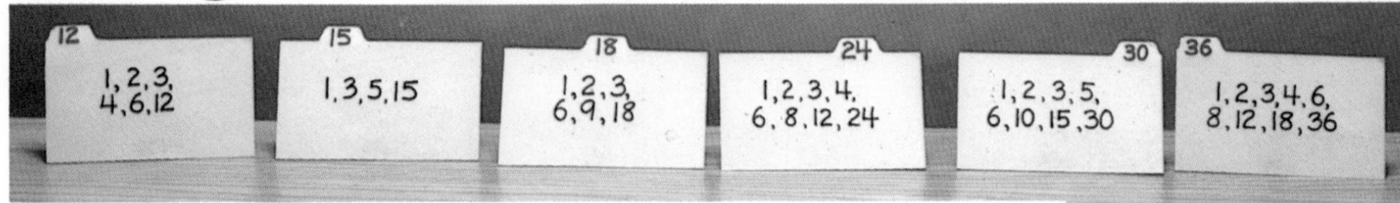

DIVISOR CARDS

1. Look at the divisor card for 12. Are 1, 2, 3, 4, 6, and 12 divisors of 12?
2. What are the divisors of 18?
3. What are the common divisors of 12 and 18 (divisors that divide both 12 and 18)?
4. What are the common divisors of 15 and 24?
5. What are the common divisors of 30 and 36?

Here's how *to write a fraction in* **lower terms.**

To write a fraction in **lower terms**, divide both terms (the numerator and the denominator) by a common divisor greater than 1.

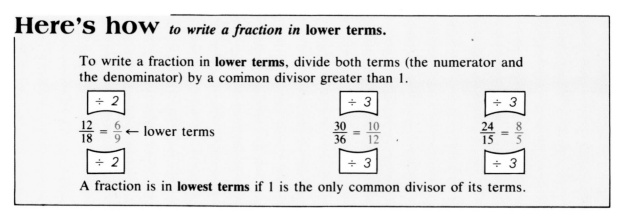

÷ 2: $\frac{12}{18} = \frac{6}{9}$ ← lower terms

÷ 3: $\frac{30}{36} = \frac{10}{12}$

÷ 3: $\frac{24}{15} = \frac{8}{5}$

A fraction is in **lowest terms** if 1 is the only common divisor of its terms.

6. Which fraction written above is in lowest terms?

Here's how *to write a fraction in* **lowest terms.**

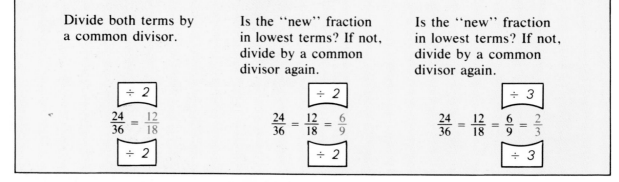

Divide both terms by a common divisor.

÷ 2: $\frac{24}{36} = \frac{12}{18}$

Is the "new" fraction in lowest terms? If not, divide by a common divisor again.

÷ 2: $\frac{24}{36} = \frac{12}{18} = \frac{6}{9}$

Is the "new" fraction in lowest terms? If not, divide by a common divisor again.

÷ 3: $\frac{24}{36} = \frac{12}{18} = \frac{6}{9} = \frac{2}{3}$

7. Look at the *Here's how*. $\frac{24}{36}$ written in lowest terms is **?**.

EXERCISES

Is the "new" fraction in lowest terms? If not, write it in lowest terms.

8. $\frac{2}{8} = \frac{1}{4}$ **9.** $\frac{16}{4} = \frac{8}{2}$ **10.** $\frac{8}{12} = \frac{2}{3}$ **11.** $\frac{24}{16} = \frac{3}{2}$ **12.** $\frac{6}{18} = \frac{2}{6}$

13. $\frac{6}{4} = \frac{3}{2}$ **14.** $\frac{18}{27} = \frac{2}{3}$ **15.** $\frac{12}{20} = \frac{6}{10}$ **16.** $\frac{27}{45} = \frac{9}{15}$ **17.** $\frac{6}{9} = \frac{2}{3}$

18. $\frac{7}{21} = \frac{1}{3}$ **19.** $\frac{20}{12} = \frac{10}{6}$ **20.** $\frac{15}{12} = \frac{5}{4}$ **21.** $\frac{24}{48} = \frac{2}{4}$ **22.** $\frac{36}{18} = \frac{18}{9}$

Write each fraction in lowest terms.

Here are scrambled answers for the next row of exercises: $\frac{3}{5}$ $\frac{4}{5}$ $\frac{1}{2}$ $\frac{3}{4}$ $\frac{3}{1}$ $\frac{5}{8}$ $\frac{4}{9}$

23. $\frac{9}{12}$ **24.** $\frac{36}{12}$ **25.** $\frac{18}{30}$ **26.** $\frac{24}{30}$ **27.** $\frac{15}{24}$ **28.** $\frac{15}{30}$ **29.** $\frac{20}{45}$

30. $\frac{6}{8}$ **31.** $\frac{3}{9}$ **32.** $\frac{2}{6}$ **33.** $\frac{3}{12}$ **34.** $\frac{10}{30}$ **35.** $\frac{30}{36}$ **36.** $\frac{14}{42}$

37. $\frac{5}{15}$ **38.** $\frac{4}{6}$ **39.** $\frac{18}{15}$ **40.** $\frac{9}{6}$ **41.** $\frac{4}{12}$ **42.** $\frac{10}{15}$ **43.** $\frac{25}{10}$

44. $\frac{24}{8}$ **45.** $\frac{15}{10}$ **46.** $\frac{20}{50}$ **47.** $\frac{40}{50}$ **48.** $\frac{14}{24}$ **49.** $\frac{15}{25}$ **50.** $\frac{9}{24}$

51. $\frac{18}{14}$ **52.** $\frac{18}{6}$ **53.** $\frac{15}{45}$ **54.** $\frac{40}{30}$ **55.** $\frac{11}{22}$ **56.** $\frac{20}{24}$ **57.** $\frac{22}{33}$

58. $\frac{24}{32}$ **59.** $\frac{14}{16}$ **60.** $\frac{25}{15}$ **61.** $\frac{14}{6}$ **62.** $\frac{10}{40}$ **63.** $\frac{15}{20}$ **64.** $\frac{20}{40}$

65. $\frac{10}{24}$ **66.** $\frac{12}{18}$ **67.** $\frac{20}{32}$ **68.** $\frac{25}{20}$ **69.** $\frac{12}{24}$ **70.** $\frac{30}{20}$ **71.** $\frac{18}{21}$

72. $\frac{24}{18}$ **73.** $\frac{18}{36}$ **74.** $\frac{8}{24}$ **75.** $\frac{30}{18}$ **76.** $\frac{24}{36}$ **77.** $\frac{30}{24}$ **78.** $\frac{75}{100}$

No bones about it

Did you know there is only one bone in your skull that can move? It is the one in your lower jaw, which permits you to talk, laugh, and chew food!

79. How many bones are in your skull?
Clues:

- There are more than 12 but less than 30 bones.
- 11 is a divisor of the number of bones.

Least common denominator

1. Look at the multiple strips for 3 and 4.
   a. Are 3, 6, 9, 12, 15, 18, 21, and 24 multiples of 3?
   b. Are 4, 8, 12, 16, 20, 24, 28, and 32 multiples of 4?
   c. Are 12 and 24 common multiples of 3 and 4?
   d. Is 12 the least common multiple of 3 and 4?
2. What is the least common multiple of 4 and 6?
3. What is the least common multiple of 5 and 6?

Multiple Strips

2	3	4	5	6	7	8
4	6	8	10	12	14	16
6	9	12	15	18	21	24
8	12	16	20	24	28	32
10	15	20	25	30	35	40
12	18	24	30	36	42	48
14	21	28	35	42	49	56
16	24	32				
18						

Here's how *to find the* **least common denominator** *of* $\frac{2}{3}$ *and* $\frac{1}{4}$.

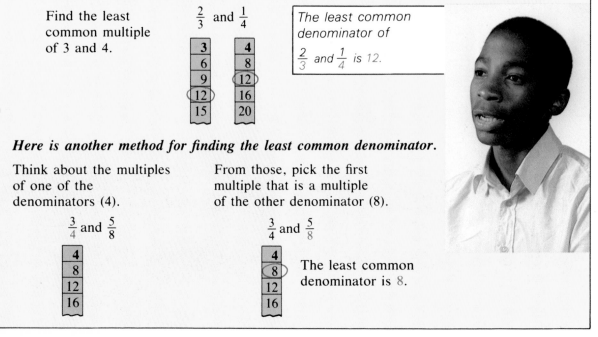

To find the **least common denominator** of two fractions, find the least common multiple of the denominators.

Find the least common multiple of 3 and 4.

$\frac{2}{3}$ and $\frac{1}{4}$

3	4
6	8
9	(12)
(12)	16
15	20

The least common denominator of $\frac{2}{3}$ and $\frac{1}{4}$ is 12.

Here is another method for finding the least common denominator.

Think about the multiples of one of the denominators (4).

$\frac{3}{4}$ and $\frac{5}{8}$

From those, pick the first multiple that is a multiple of the other denominator (8).

$\frac{3}{4}$ and $\frac{5}{8}$

The least common denominator is 8.

4. Look at the *Here's how*. What is the least common denominator of $\frac{3}{4}$ and $\frac{5}{8}$?

EXERCISES

Find the least common denominator.

Here are scrambled answers for the next row of exercises: 9 18 20 4 24

5. $\frac{1}{2}$ $\frac{3}{4}$ 6. $\frac{2}{9}$ $\frac{1}{3}$ 7. $\frac{1}{4}$ $\frac{3}{10}$ 8. $\frac{1}{2}$ $\frac{5}{9}$ 9. $\frac{1}{8}$ $\frac{1}{6}$

10. $\frac{1}{5}$ $\frac{1}{6}$ 11. $\frac{2}{5}$ $\frac{1}{10}$ 12. $\frac{2}{3}$ $\frac{4}{9}$ 13. $\frac{4}{3}$ $\frac{1}{8}$ 14. $\frac{5}{6}$ $\frac{4}{3}$

15. $\frac{5}{6}$ $\frac{3}{4}$ 16. $\frac{3}{4}$ $\frac{5}{12}$ 17. $\frac{3}{7}$ $\frac{1}{2}$ 18. $\frac{2}{3}$ $\frac{1}{12}$ 19. $\frac{4}{5}$ $\frac{1}{10}$

20. $\frac{4}{7}$ $\frac{1}{4}$ 21. $\frac{2}{9}$ $\frac{1}{5}$ 22. $\frac{3}{5}$ $\frac{1}{4}$ 23. $\frac{1}{8}$ $\frac{2}{5}$ 24. $\frac{1}{6}$ $\frac{3}{7}$

25. $\frac{1}{3}$ $\frac{1}{6}$ 26. $\frac{2}{5}$ $\frac{3}{2}$ 27. $\frac{1}{3}$ $\frac{5}{12}$ 28. $\frac{4}{3}$ $\frac{3}{8}$ 29. $\frac{1}{8}$ $\frac{1}{12}$

30. $\frac{1}{2}$ $\frac{3}{20}$ 31. $\frac{1}{12}$ $\frac{7}{8}$ 32. $\frac{3}{4}$ $\frac{7}{6}$ 33. $\frac{5}{9}$ $\frac{7}{6}$ 34. $\frac{1}{10}$ $\frac{2}{15}$

35. $\frac{4}{5}$ $\frac{1}{6}$ 36. $\frac{3}{8}$ $\frac{1}{6}$ 37. $\frac{3}{4}$ $\frac{9}{10}$ 38. $\frac{1}{8}$ $\frac{7}{10}$ 39. $\frac{1}{7}$ $\frac{1}{3}$

40. $\frac{1}{7}$ $\frac{3}{8}$ 41. $\frac{2}{5}$ $\frac{3}{4}$ 42. $\frac{3}{7}$ $\frac{1}{5}$ 43. $\frac{1}{9}$ $\frac{3}{8}$ 44. $\frac{2}{15}$ $\frac{1}{30}$

45. $\frac{1}{20}$ $\frac{3}{40}$ 46. $\frac{2}{11}$ $\frac{1}{33}$ 47. $\frac{1}{15}$ $\frac{5}{6}$ 48. $\frac{7}{3}$ $\frac{2}{11}$ 49. $\frac{4}{9}$ $\frac{1}{8}$

50. $\frac{4}{5}$ $\frac{1}{3}$ 51. $\frac{5}{4}$ $\frac{2}{9}$ 52. $\frac{3}{4}$ $\frac{1}{12}$ 53. $\frac{1}{3}$ $\frac{7}{24}$ 54. $\frac{6}{7}$ $\frac{1}{4}$

55. $\frac{2}{3}$ $\frac{1}{36}$ 56. $\frac{1}{10}$ $\frac{1}{100}$ 57. $\frac{3}{10}$ $\frac{1}{25}$ 58. $\frac{1}{8}$ $\frac{1}{80}$ 59. $\frac{2}{25}$ $\frac{7}{30}$

Credit cutting

Credit-card companies suggest that expired cards be destroyed. With 3 straight cuts, this credit card was cut into 7 pieces.

60. What is the greatest number of pieces you can get with 5 straight cuts? *Hints: Draw a diagram. Use the clues to check your answer.*

    Clues:
    - There are more than 10 but less than 20 pieces.
    - The number of pieces is a multiple of 8.

Comparing fractions

MOUNT RUSHMORE RECALL

A group of high school students were asked to name one of the presidents whose face is carved into Mount Rushmore. The circle graph shows the results of the poll.

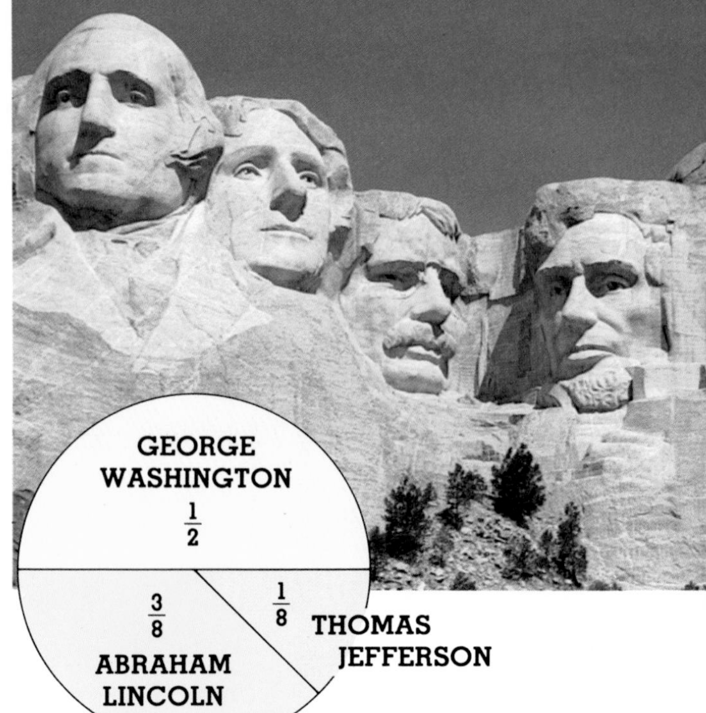

1. What fraction of the students named Abraham Lincoln?

2. Thomas Jefferson was named by what fraction of the students?

3. What two fractions would you compare to decide whether more students named Lincoln than named Jefferson?

Here's how *to compare two fractions with a common denominator.* $\frac{3}{8} \bullet \frac{1}{8}$

To compare fractions with a common denominator, compare the numerators.

$\frac{3}{8} > \frac{1}{8}$

3 is greater than 1. So $\frac{3}{8}$ is greater than $\frac{1}{8}$.

4. Which president, Abraham Lincoln or Thomas Jefferson, did more students name?

Here's how *to compare two fractions with different denominators.* $\frac{3}{8} \bullet \frac{1}{2}$

To compare fractions with different denominators, compare equivalent fractions with the same denominator.

Find the least common denominator.	Write equivalent fractions.	Compare.	
$\frac{3}{8} \bullet \frac{1}{2}$	$\frac{3}{8} \bullet \frac{1}{2}$	$\frac{3}{8} \bullet \frac{1}{2}$	
8	$\frac{3}{8}$ $\frac{4}{8}$	$\frac{3}{8} < \frac{4}{8}$	So $\frac{3}{8}$ is less than $\frac{1}{2}$.

5. Which president, Abraham Lincoln or George Washington, did more students name?

EXERCISES

$<$ or $>$?

6. $\frac{2}{5} \bullet \frac{3}{5}$ **7.** $\frac{5}{4} \bullet \frac{7}{4}$ **8.** $\frac{5}{7} \bullet \frac{3}{7}$ **9.** $\frac{5}{9} \bullet \frac{4}{9}$ **10.** $\frac{3}{8} \bullet \frac{0}{8}$

11. $\frac{4}{4} \bullet \frac{5}{4}$ **12.** $\frac{6}{5} \bullet \frac{7}{5}$ **13.** $\frac{7}{8} \bullet \frac{5}{8}$ **14.** $\frac{0}{6} \bullet \frac{1}{6}$ **15.** $\frac{7}{4} \bullet \frac{8}{4}$

16. $\frac{5}{3} \bullet \frac{3}{3}$ **17.** $\frac{3}{8} \bullet \frac{2}{8}$ **18.** $\frac{7}{9} \bullet \frac{4}{9}$ **19.** $\frac{11}{10} \bullet \frac{13}{10}$ **20.** $\frac{0}{5} \bullet \frac{1}{5}$

$<$, $>$, or $=$? Hint: First write equivalent fractions with the same denominator.

21. $\frac{1}{4} \bullet \frac{3}{8}$ ($\frac{2}{8}$, $\frac{3}{8}$) **22.** $\frac{5}{6} \bullet \frac{2}{3}$ ($\frac{5}{6}$, $\frac{4}{6}$) **23.** $\frac{1}{3} \bullet \frac{2}{7}$ ($\frac{7}{21}$, $\frac{6}{21}$) **24.** $\frac{1}{3} \bullet \frac{1}{4}$ ($\frac{?}{12}$, $\frac{?}{12}$) **25.** $\frac{3}{2} \bullet \frac{5}{4}$ ($\frac{?}{4}$, $\frac{?}{4}$)

26. $\frac{1}{3} \bullet \frac{3}{10}$ **27.** $\frac{3}{8} \bullet \frac{3}{4}$ **28.** $\frac{1}{6} \bullet \frac{1}{8}$ **29.** $\frac{2}{9} \bullet \frac{4}{18}$ **30.** $\frac{2}{5} \bullet \frac{1}{4}$

31. $\frac{3}{4} \bullet \frac{2}{3}$ **32.** $\frac{5}{6} \bullet \frac{3}{4}$ **33.** $\frac{3}{4} \bullet \frac{3}{5}$ **34.** $\frac{2}{3} \bullet \frac{7}{9}$ **35.** $\frac{0}{3} \bullet \frac{0}{7}$

36. $\frac{3}{7} \bullet \frac{9}{21}$ **37.** $\frac{9}{16} \bullet \frac{5}{8}$ **38.** $\frac{4}{7} \bullet \frac{5}{8}$ **39.** $\frac{7}{8} \bullet \frac{8}{9}$ **40.** $\frac{15}{12} \bullet \frac{5}{4}$

41. $\frac{7}{10} \bullet \frac{69}{100}$ **42.** $\frac{6}{100} \bullet \frac{55}{1000}$ **43.** $\frac{9}{1000} \bullet \frac{1}{10}$ **44.** $\frac{49}{1000} \bullet \frac{4}{100}$ **45.** $\frac{7}{10} \bullet \frac{73}{100}$

Solve.

46. On the day that Marcia visited Mount Rushmore, $\frac{1}{12}$ of the visitors were from Texas and $\frac{1}{8}$ were from California. From which state were there more visitors?

47. On another day, $\frac{1}{4}$ of the visitors were from North Dakota and $\frac{7}{20}$ of the visitors were from Nebraska. Were there more visitors from North Dakota or Nebraska?

You're the statistical clerk!

Statistical clerks gather information from surveys and records. Business people depend on statistical clerks to help them make decisions.

48. Which statement is correct?
  a. A greater fraction of girls knew the location of Mount Rushmore.
  b. A greater fraction of boys knew the location of Mount Rushmore.

SURVEY FINDINGS
8 out of 15 boys knew that Mount Rushmore was located in South Dakota.
7 out of 12 girls knew its location.

Cumulative Skill Practice

Write the short word-name. *(page 16)*

1. 8.4 2. 16.3 3. 0.451 4. 9.86 5. 0.03

6. 7.5 7. 7.05 8. 7.005 9. 21.4 10. 13.001

11. 5.036 12. 0.29 13. 3.8352 14. 0.308 15. 10.61

16. 112.74 17. 11.274 18. 1.1274 19. 16.02 20. 31.301

Give the sum. *(page 24)*

21. 8.24 + 6.59 **22.** 59.2 + 36.4 **23.** 6.095 + 4.968

24. 4.03 + 6.9 **25.** 5.74 + 3.692 **26.** 9 + 3.97

27. 4.7 + 3.52 **28.** 18.3 + 31 **29.** 0.368 + 0.44

30. 6.09 + 4.196 **31.** 15 + 12.9 **32.** 8.6 + 3.36

33. 2.3 + 4 + 5.8 **34.** 18 + 5.6 + 10 **35.** 8.4 + 6 + 5.9

36. 4.7 + 3.52 + 7.4 **37.** 18.3 + 31.9 + 7.53 **38.** 2.74 + 5.9 + 18

39. 16.34 + 21.7 + 32.5 **40.** 45.6 + 38 + 0.79 **41.** 56.7 + 42.3 + 87

<, >, or =? *(page 42)*

42. 0.6 ● 0.4 **43.** 0.05 ● 0.06 **44.** 0.008 ● 0.007

45. 24.3 ● 24.2 **46.** 9.63 ● 9.635 **47.** 0.32 ● 0.3

48. 52.58 ● 52.6 **49.** 3.060 ● 3.06 **50.** 0.914 ● 0.9

51. 17.1 ● 17.08 **52.** 0.034 ● 0.34 **53.** 6.804 ● 6.84

54. 28.24 ● 2.842 **55.** 2.0 ● 1.99 **56.** 3.008 ● 3.8

Give the difference. *(page 46)*

57. 9.8 − 3.4 **58.** 6.54 − 2.39 **59.** 12.346 − 7.591

60. 26.0 − 8.4 **61.** 16.02 − 5.88 **62.** 28.103 − 9.617

63. 8 − 3.4 **64.** 6.7 − 2.93 **65.** 5.467 − 2.18

66. 17 − 9.04 **67.** 18.3 − 2.67 **68.** 33.4 − 1.839

69. 5.43 − 2.976 **70.** 42.3 − 9.9 **71.** 100 − 2.46

72. 6.9 − 5.708 **73.** 227.9 − 34.88 **74.** 500.7 − 138.9

75. 36.8 − 8.37 **76.** 59 − 8.75 **77.** 1 − 0.399

Problem solving

Use the ad to answer these questions.

Apartments—Furnished

EFFICIENCY APARTMENT
New carpet, spotless. Bus at door, all shopping half block away. **ALL UTILITIES PAID BY LANDLORD.** $195 per month. Call 999-1668.

2 or 3 bedrooms, $350 per month, all utilities paid. 104 E. Green. 999-4457. 999-4688.

Quiet 2-bedroom second-floor apartment in private home. Close to downtown. References, deposit, and lease. $275 per month plus electricity. After 5 P.M.: 999-8923.

NEW BUILDING
Now Leasing
New furniture & appliances. 3-bedroom apartments have dishwashers.
3 bedrooms—$395 per month
Efficiencies—$215 per month
999-5046 or 999-3689

Unfurnished 2-bedroom apartment. Maximum 3 persons. $250 per month. Phone: Hodges Real Estate, 999-5126.

One-bedroom furnished apartment. Available immediately. $200 per month. 1-888-3355 days.

1. *How much would I spend per year for the first apartment listed?*

2. *My "take-home" pay is $830 each month. How much would I have left after paying the rent on the second apartment listed?*

3. Look at the third apartment listed. If the average cost of electricity is $74.50 per month, how much would you spend a year for rent and electricity?

4. Suppose that you and 2 of your friends decided to rent the next-to-the-last apartment listed. What would your share of the rent be each month? Round your answer to the nearest cent.

5. Suppose that your "take-home" pay is $724 per month and that you rented the third apartment listed. If the electric bill was $89.76 the first month, how much would you have left after paying the rent and electric bill?

6. You decided that you could pay a maximum of $340 a month for rent and utilities. The monthly utilities for the efficiency apartment in the new building are estimated to be $76 for heat and $68 for electricity. Should you rent the apartment?

7. According to a tenant of the last apartment listed, the total amount paid for the apartment and utilities for last year was $3762. How much did the utilities cost if the rent was the same last year as this year?

8. Suppose that you and 4 of your friends rented a 3-bedroom apartment in the new building. How much would each of you pay in a year for rent?

9. The estimated total rent and utilities for a 3-bedroom apartment in the new building is $6480 per year. What is the estimated average monthly utility bill?

Writing whole numbers and mixed numbers as fractions

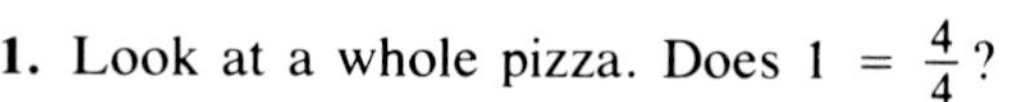

1. Look at a whole pizza. Does $1 = \frac{4}{4}$?

2. Look at 2 whole pizzas. Does $2 = \frac{8}{4}$?

Here's how *to change a whole number to a fraction.* $2 = \frac{?}{4}$

Write the whole number over the denominator 1.

$$\frac{2}{1}$$

Multiply the numerator and denominator by the same whole number (not 0).

$$\frac{2 \times 4}{1 \times 4} = \frac{8}{4}$$

There are 8 fourths in 2.

3. What would you have to multiply the numerator and denominator by to change $\frac{2}{1}$ to eighths?

4. Look at the pizzas. There are 2 whole pizzas plus [?] fourths.
   The mixed number $2\frac{3}{4}$ is read as "2 and $\frac{3}{4}$."

Here's how *to change a mixed number to a fraction.* $2\frac{3}{4} = ?$

Multiply the denominator by the whole number. (This gives the number of fourths in 2.)

$$2\frac{3}{4} \quad (4 \times 2)$$

Add the numerator. (This gives the number of fourths in $2\frac{3}{4}$.)

$$2\frac{3}{4} = \frac{11}{4} \quad (4 \times 2 + 3)$$

There are 11 fourths in $2\frac{3}{4}$.

5. Look at the pizzas. Does $2\frac{3}{4} = \frac{11}{4}$?

6. Check these examples. Are they correct?

   a. $3 = \frac{6}{2}$ b. $4 = \frac{12}{3}$ c. $1\frac{1}{2} = \frac{3}{2}$ d. $2\frac{2}{3} = \frac{8}{3}$

EXERCISES

Change to thirds.

Here are scrambled answers for the next row of exercises: $\frac{21}{3}$ $\frac{27}{3}$ $\frac{30}{3}$ $\frac{3}{3}$ $\frac{9}{3}$ $\frac{6}{3}$ $\frac{42}{3}$

7. 2 **8.** 9 **9.** 3 **10.** 1 **11.** 7 **12.** 10 **13.** 14

14. 6 **15.** 12 **16.** 4 **17.** 11 **18.** 5 **19.** 8 **20.** 15

Change to fifths.

21. 5 **22.** 1 **23.** 6 **24.** 2 **25.** 10 **26.** 7 **27.** 13

28. 4 **29.** 12 **30.** 9 **31.** 8 **32.** 3 **33.** 11 **34.** 15

Change each mixed number to a fraction.

35. $1\frac{1}{3}$ **36.** $1\frac{1}{2}$ **37.** $2\frac{1}{2}$ **38.** $2\frac{1}{3}$ **39.** $1\frac{1}{4}$ **40.** $3\frac{1}{4}$ **41.** $7\frac{3}{4}$

42. $1\frac{2}{3}$ **43.** $2\frac{3}{4}$ **44.** $4\frac{1}{3}$ **45.** $3\frac{2}{3}$ **46.** $2\frac{2}{5}$ **47.** $3\frac{4}{5}$ **48.** $9\frac{1}{6}$

49. $4\frac{3}{4}$ **50.** $4\frac{1}{6}$ **51.** $5\frac{3}{4}$ **52.** $4\frac{3}{5}$ **53.** $5\frac{5}{6}$ **54.** $2\frac{3}{8}$ **55.** $11\frac{1}{8}$

56. $6\frac{3}{8}$ **57.** $3\frac{5}{8}$ **58.** $6\frac{3}{10}$ **59.** $8\frac{7}{8}$ **60.** $4\frac{9}{10}$ **61.** $5\frac{5}{8}$ **62.** $7\frac{4}{5}$

63. $6\frac{1}{2}$ **64.** $3\frac{5}{6}$ **65.** $4\frac{7}{8}$ **66.** $4\frac{2}{3}$ **67.** $5\frac{4}{5}$ **68.** $2\frac{3}{5}$ **69.** $9\frac{2}{3}$

70. $2\frac{7}{8}$ **71.** $2\frac{1}{6}$ **72.** $6\frac{2}{3}$ **73.** $7\frac{5}{6}$ **74.** $3\frac{3}{4}$ **75.** $9\frac{3}{8}$ **76.** $13\frac{1}{4}$

77. $10\frac{3}{5}$ **78.** $12\frac{1}{2}$ **79.** $11\frac{2}{3}$ **80.** $15\frac{1}{2}$ **81.** $12\frac{3}{4}$ **82.** $10\frac{3}{8}$ **83.** $11\frac{1}{4}$

Pizza puzzle

84. Beth, Maria, and John ate one sausage and one bacon pizza. Study the clues to find what each person ate.

Clues:

- Each pizza was cut into fifths.
- Maria didn't eat bacon pizza.
- Maria ate 3 pieces.
- Beth didn't eat sausage pizza.
- Beth ate 1 more piece than John.

Hint: Draw a picture.

Writing fractions as whole numbers or as mixed numbers

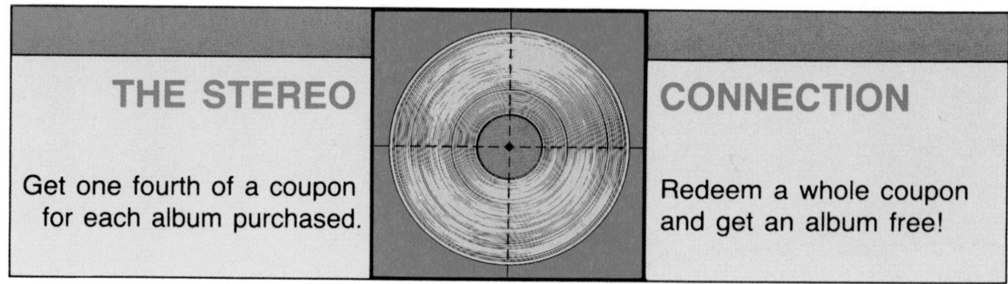

THE STEREO
CONNECTION
Get one fourth of a coupon for each album purchased.
Redeem a whole coupon and get an album free!

1. How many fourths do you need to make a whole coupon?
2. If you have 8 fourths, how many whole coupons do you have?

Here's how *to change $\frac{8}{4}$ to a whole number.*

To change a fraction to a whole number, divide the numerator by the denominator.

number of fourths in one → $4\overline{)8}$ with quotient 2 ← number of fourths in all

So $\frac{8}{4} = 2$

3. $\frac{20}{4}$ is equal to what whole number?

Here's how *to change $\frac{11}{4}$ to a mixed number.*

To change a fraction to a mixed number, divide the numerator by the denominator.

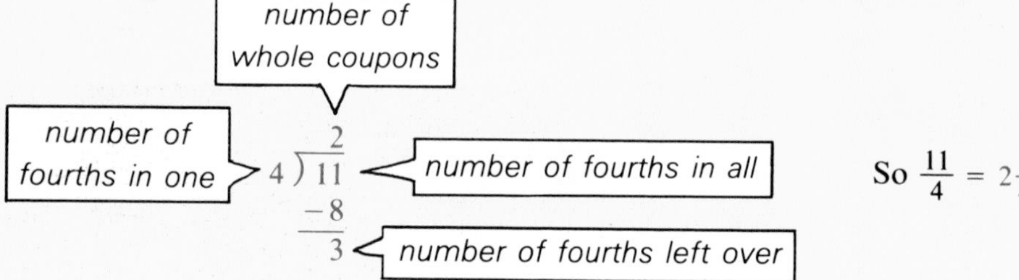

So $\frac{11}{4} = 2\frac{3}{4}$

4. $\frac{21}{4}$ is equal to what mixed number?
5. A fraction can be changed to a whole number or mixed number if the denominator is $\underset{\text{less than/greater than}}{\underline{\quad ? \quad}}$ the numerator.

EXERCISES

Change each fraction to a whole number.
Here are scrambled answers for the next row of exercises: 5 4 2 1 8 6 3

6. $\frac{9}{3}$ 7. $\frac{10}{5}$ 8. $\frac{16}{2}$ 9. $\frac{6}{6}$ 10. $\frac{16}{4}$ 11. $\frac{18}{3}$ 12. $\frac{25}{5}$

13. $\frac{15}{5}$ 14. $\frac{10}{2}$ 15. $\frac{3}{3}$ 16. $\frac{12}{4}$ 17. $\frac{16}{8}$ 18. $\frac{12}{6}$ 19. $\frac{24}{3}$

20. $\frac{20}{10}$ 21. $\frac{24}{6}$ 22. $\frac{18}{2}$ 23. $\frac{24}{8}$ 24. $\frac{5}{5}$ 25. $\frac{12}{3}$ 26. $\frac{50}{25}$

Change each fraction to a whole number or a mixed number.
Here are scrambled answers for the next row of exercises: 3 $1\frac{5}{6}$ $1\frac{1}{2}$ 2 $1\frac{1}{4}$ $2\frac{3}{5}$ 9

27. $\frac{3}{2}$ 28. $\frac{5}{4}$ 29. $\frac{9}{3}$ 30. $\frac{13}{5}$ 31. $\frac{11}{6}$ 32. $\frac{16}{8}$ 33. $\frac{81}{9}$

34. $\frac{13}{10}$ 35. $\frac{16}{4}$ 36. $\frac{5}{2}$ 37. $\frac{7}{4}$ 38. $\frac{17}{8}$ 39. $\frac{10}{3}$ 40. $\frac{11}{9}$

41. $\frac{19}{5}$ 42. $\frac{14}{3}$ 43. $\frac{15}{4}$ 44. $\frac{27}{10}$ 45. $\frac{11}{2}$ 46. $\frac{18}{3}$ 47. $\frac{27}{7}$

48. $\frac{35}{5}$ 49. $\frac{25}{3}$ 50. $\frac{30}{6}$ 51. $\frac{35}{2}$ 52. $\frac{29}{6}$ 53. $\frac{36}{4}$ 54. $\frac{36}{6}$

55. $\frac{20}{5}$ 56. $\frac{13}{6}$ 57. $\frac{37}{10}$ 58. $\frac{20}{3}$ 59. $\frac{19}{6}$ 60. $\frac{42}{5}$ 61. $\frac{21}{7}$

62. $\frac{28}{3}$ 63. $\frac{14}{14}$ 64. $\frac{8}{5}$ 65. $\frac{50}{5}$ 66. $\frac{29}{3}$ 67. $\frac{15}{3}$ 68. $\frac{19}{8}$

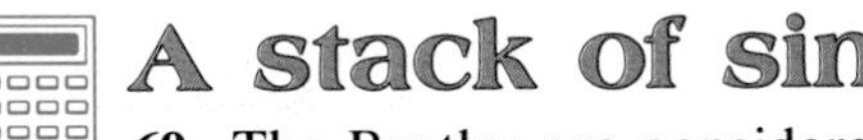

A stack of singles!

69. The Beatles are considered the most successful recording group. If you stacked the single records that they sold between 1963 and 1973 in one stack, it would be [?] feet high.

To find [?], write a
- 0 in the ones place.
- 5 in the hundreds place.
- 4 in the hundred thousands place.
- 9 in both the tens place and the ten thousands place.
- 3 in both the millions place and the thousands place.

70. About how many miles high would the stack be? *Hint: There are 5280 feet in a mile.*

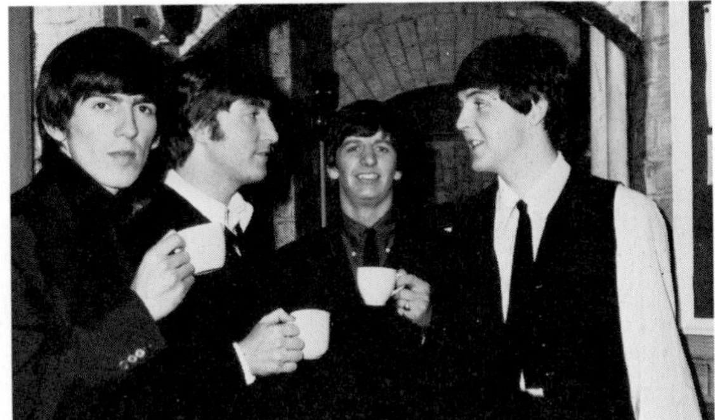

Writing fractions and mixed numbers in simplest form

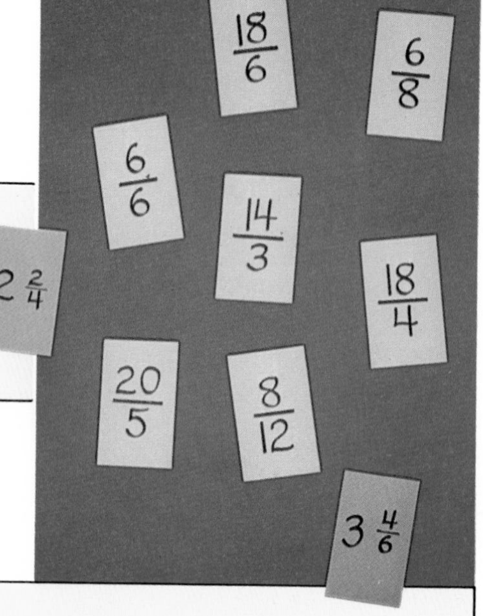

1. Look at the yellow cards. Which two fractions have numerators less than their denominators? Are these fractions less than or greater than 1?

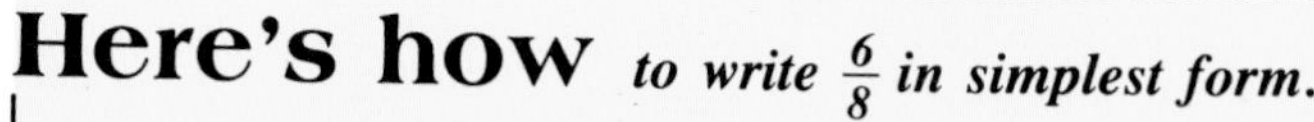

Here's how *to write $\frac{6}{8}$ in simplest form.*

Write fractions less than 1 in lowest terms.

$\frac{6}{8} = \frac{3}{4}$ ← simplest form

2. How would you write $\frac{8}{12}$ in simplest form?
3. What two mixed numbers are written on the cards?

Here's how *to write $2\frac{2}{4}$ in simplest form.*

Write mixed numbers with the fraction part less than 1 *and* in lowest terms.

$2\frac{2}{4} = 2\frac{1}{2}$ ← simplest form

4. How would you write $3\frac{4}{6}$ in simplest form?
5. Look at the yellow cards. Which fractions are greater than or equal to 1?

Here's how *to write $\frac{20}{5}$ and $\frac{14}{3}$ in simplest form.*

Write fractions that are greater than or equal to 1 as a whole number or as a mixed number in simplest form.

$\frac{20}{5} = 4$ ← simplest form $\qquad \frac{14}{3} = 4\frac{2}{3}$ ← simplest form

6. Write each fraction in simplest form.

 a. $\frac{18}{6}$ b. $\frac{18}{4}$ c. $\frac{6}{6}$

EXERCISES

Write in simplest form.

Here are scrambled answers for the next row of exercises: $\frac{3}{5}$ $\frac{1}{2}$ $\frac{3}{4}$ $\frac{5}{6}$ $\frac{1}{6}$ $\frac{2}{3}$ $\frac{4}{5}$

7. $\frac{6}{10}$ **8.** $\frac{2}{12}$ **9.** $\frac{5}{10}$ **10.** $\frac{6}{8}$ **11.** $\frac{4}{6}$ **12.** $\frac{15}{18}$ **13.** $\frac{20}{25}$

14. $\frac{6}{18}$ **15.** $\frac{8}{14}$ **16.** $\frac{10}{12}$ **17.** $\frac{5}{20}$ **18.** $\frac{16}{24}$ **19.** $\frac{14}{16}$ **20.** $\frac{6}{9}$

Write in simplest form.

21. $2\frac{2}{4}$ **22.** $4\frac{2}{8}$ **23.** $3\frac{4}{6}$ **24.** $5\frac{2}{6}$ **25.** $4\frac{6}{8}$ **26.** $6\frac{10}{12}$ **27.** $7\frac{4}{16}$

28. $4\frac{3}{12}$ **29.** $8\frac{5}{10}$ **30.** $3\frac{3}{9}$ **31.** $12\frac{10}{15}$ **32.** $5\frac{9}{12}$ **33.** $10\frac{8}{10}$ **34.** $1\frac{9}{15}$

35. $6\frac{4}{8}$ **36.** $3\frac{8}{24}$ **37.** $2\frac{15}{30}$ **38.** $5\frac{10}{18}$ **39.** $4\frac{5}{15}$ **40.** $1\frac{7}{14}$ **41.** $10\frac{8}{64}$

Write in simplest form.

42. $\frac{6}{3}$ **43.** $\frac{10}{2}$ **44.** $\frac{12}{4}$ **45.** $\frac{20}{4}$ **46.** $\frac{36}{3}$ **47.** $\frac{24}{8}$ **48.** $\frac{14}{7}$

49. $\frac{9}{2}$ **50.** $\frac{8}{3}$ **51.** $\frac{7}{4}$ **52.** $\frac{9}{5}$ **53.** $\frac{10}{3}$ **54.** $\frac{11}{4}$ **55.** $\frac{6}{1}$

56. $\frac{17}{3}$ **57.** $\frac{15}{4}$ **58.** $\frac{12}{8}$ **59.** $\frac{15}{10}$ **60.** $\frac{16}{12}$ **61.** $\frac{18}{12}$ **62.** $\frac{34}{11}$

63. $\frac{8}{10}$ **64.** $\frac{10}{8}$ **65.** $\frac{16}{3}$ **66.** $\frac{3}{6}$ **67.** $\frac{9}{8}$ **68.** $\frac{16}{14}$ **69.** $\frac{35}{30}$

70. $\frac{33}{6}$ **71.** $\frac{36}{5}$ **72.** $\frac{24}{36}$ **73.** $\frac{18}{5}$ **74.** $\frac{22}{16}$ **75.** $\frac{28}{6}$ **76.** $\frac{31}{7}$

77. $\frac{8}{12}$ **78.** $\frac{6}{24}$ **79.** $\frac{8}{1}$ **80.** $\frac{10}{25}$ **81.** $\frac{25}{10}$ **82.** $\frac{18}{36}$ **83.** $\frac{35}{15}$

84. $\frac{42}{6}$ **85.** $\frac{6}{42}$ **86.** $\frac{25}{8}$ **87.** $\frac{16}{18}$ **88.** $\frac{24}{32}$ **89.** $\frac{32}{24}$ **90.** $\frac{13}{11}$

Face fact

91. Study the clues to find how many muscles you use to smile and how many muscles you use to frown.

Clues:

- It takes more muscles to frown.
- If you add the numbers, you get 60.
- If you subtract the numbers, you get 26.

Writing quotients as mixed numbers

1. How many photos can be mounted on one page of the album?
2. To find how many pages would be needed to mount 100 photos, you would divide 100 by what number?

Here's how *to write a quotient as a mixed number.* *100 ÷ 6 = ?*

Step 1. Divide.

$$\begin{array}{r} 16 \\ 6\overline{)100} \\ -6 \\ \hline 40 \\ -36 \\ \hline 4 \end{array}$$

16: number of full pages

4: number of photos remaining

Step 2. Write the quotient as a mixed number.

$$\begin{array}{r} 16\frac{4}{6} \\ 6\overline{)100} \\ -6 \\ \hline 40 \\ -36 \\ \hline 4 \end{array}$$

Write the remainder over the divisor.

Step 3. Write the mixed number in simplest form.

$$\begin{array}{r} 16\frac{4}{6} = 16\frac{2}{3} \\ 6\overline{)100} \\ -6 \\ \hline 40 \\ -36 \\ \hline 4 \end{array}$$

3. Look at the first step in the *Here's how*. After 16 pages of the album were filled, how many photos would be left to be mounted?
4. Look at the last step of the *Here's how*. It would take 16 and [?] pages to mount all the photos.
5. Check these examples. Are they correct?

a. $$\begin{array}{r} 24\frac{3}{5} \\ 5\overline{)123} \\ -10 \\ \hline 23 \\ -20 \\ \hline 3 \end{array}$$

b. $$\begin{array}{r} 17\frac{6}{8} = 17\frac{3}{4} \\ 8\overline{)142} \\ -8 \\ \hline 62 \\ -56 \\ \hline 6 \end{array}$$

c. $$\begin{array}{r} 16\frac{7}{18} \\ 18\overline{)295} \\ -18 \\ \hline 115 \\ -108 \\ \hline 7 \end{array}$$

d. $$\begin{array}{r} 25\frac{7}{21} = 25\frac{1}{3} \\ 21\overline{)532} \\ -42 \\ \hline 112 \\ -105 \\ \hline 7 \end{array}$$

EXERCISES

Divide. Write each quotient as a mixed number in simplest form.

Here are scrambled answers for the next row of exercises: $14\frac{2}{3}$ $5\frac{1}{3}$ $8\frac{1}{3}$ $4\frac{1}{2}$ $8\frac{2}{5}$

6. $4\overline{)18}$	**7.** $3\overline{)44}$	**8.** $6\overline{)50}$	**9.** $5\overline{)42}$	**10.** $9\overline{)48}$
11. $7\overline{)45}$	**12.** $8\overline{)75}$	**13.** $6\overline{)74}$	**14.** $4\overline{)90}$	**15.** $9\overline{)78}$
16. $5\overline{)162}$	**17.** $7\overline{)253}$	**18.** $8\overline{)153}$	**19.** $9\overline{)124}$	**20.** $3\overline{)124}$
21. $12\overline{)283}$	**22.** $15\overline{)406}$	**23.** $21\overline{)592}$	**24.** $25\overline{)685}$	**25.** $18\overline{)665}$
26. $24\overline{)862}$	**27.** $28\overline{)906}$	**28.** $32\overline{)900}$	**29.** $30\overline{)820}$	**30.** $36\overline{)912}$
31. $44\overline{)2688}$	**32.** $42\overline{)2324}$	**33.** $48\overline{)3996}$	**34.** $60\overline{)2565}$	**35.** $40\overline{)2420}$

36. $1450 \div 30$	**37.** $1480 \div 16$	**38.** $1850 \div 26$	**39.** $2187 \div 36$
40. $3136 \div 42$	**41.** $2440 \div 60$	**42.** $2691 \div 72$	**43.** $3570 \div 64$
44. $3475 \div 50$	**45.** $3396 \div 48$	**46.** $2282 \div 84$	**47.** $3660 \div 80$
48. $4526 \div 30$	**49.** $4586 \div 15$	**50.** $8452 \div 12$	**51.** $6881 \div 17$
52. $3146 \div 27$	**53.** $9107 \div 23$	**54.** $3106 \div 94$	**55.** $3524 \div 15$

Solve.

56. You bought 2 rolls of film for $2.48 a roll. How much did you spend for the film?

57. You had 2 rolls of 24 developed for $6.79 a roll and 1 roll of 36 developed for $8.11. What was the total cost?

58. You can take 36 pictures on a large roll of film. If a large roll costs $3.69, how much does the film cost for each picture? Round the answer to the nearest cent.

59. You have 68 photos to put in an album. If you put 6 photos on each page, how many pages will you need? Give the answer as a mixed number in simplest form.

Photo count!

60. Study these clues to find how many pictures are in the pile.

Clues:

- There are fewer than 50.
- If you put 8 on a page, you will have 2 left over.
- If you put 9 on a page, you will have 6 left over.

Cumulative Skill Practice

Give the product. *(page 64)*

1. 2.5 × 3
2. 4.2 × 2
3. 3.3 × 5
4. 2.74 × 7
5. 3.82 × 6
6. 7.23 × 9
7. 7.4 × 0.5
8. 9.24 × 0.2
9. 8.03 × 0.7
10. 6.84 × 0.6
11. 31.5 × 0.004
12. 0.98 × 0.09
13. 24.96 × 12
14. 35.8 × 2.4
15. 2.694 × 5.1
16. 5.07 × 38
17. 3.81 × 5.31
18. 0.064 × 4.5
19. 283.4 × 1.38
20. 215 × 9.7
21. 4.003 × 21.8

Give the product. *(page 68)*

22. 42 × 10
23. 42 × 100
24. 42 × 1000
25. 125 × 100
26. 74 × 10
27. 52 × 1000
28. 0.563 × 100
29. 0.563 × 10
30. 0.563 × 1000
31. 0.64 × 100
32. 0.64 × 10
33. 0.64 × 1000
34. 7.4 × 1000
35. 7.4 × 10
36. 7.4 × 100
37. 56.39 × 10
38. 56.39 × 100
39. 56.39 × 1000
40. 12.87 × 100
41. 12.87 × 10
42. 12.87 × 1000

Give the quotient rounded to the nearest tenth. *(page 96)*

43. 3.8 ÷ 0.3
44. 7.4 ÷ 0.6
45. 9.1 ÷ 0.9
46. 9.4 ÷ 0.6
47. 8.3 ÷ 0.3
48. 2.73 ÷ 0.7
49. 5.64 ÷ 0.5
50. 8.422 ÷ 0.04
51. 5.75 ÷ 0.07
52. 34.32 ÷ 0.003
53. 56.5 ÷ 6
54. 19.4 ÷ 0.09
55. 42 ÷ 1.1
56. 6.38 ÷ 2.4
57. 74.26 ÷ 0.36
58. 96.32 ÷ 9.3
59. 6.389 ÷ 0.56
60. 9.62 ÷ 0.45
61. 0.084 ÷ 0.42
62. 0.9465 ÷ 8.3
63. 70.04 ÷ 5.2

Find the median. *(page 116)*

64. 93, 97, 58, 83, 86
65. 59, 63, 57, 55, 61
66. 39, 40, 40, 37, 35
67. 28, 27, 26, 30
68. 92, 96, 90, 89
69. 215, 217, 218, 216
70. 74, 70, 68, 75, 76
71. 23, 27, 24, 18
72. 53, 51, 47, 59
73. 308, 306, 312, 304
74. 66, 65, 68, 72
75. 71, 71, 75, 78, 73

Problem solving

The red numbers show the miles. The blue numbers show the driving time in hours and minutes. You decide to take the trip shown in yellow.

Solve.

1. How many miles is it from Los Angeles to Barstow?
2. What is the driving time from Barstow to Death Valley?
3. You leave Death Valley at 8:00 A.M. If you plan two 15-minute rest stops and an hour for lunch, at what time should you arrive in Yosemite?
4. Your fuel tank will hold 14.7 gallons. In San Francisco it takes 10.8 gallons to fill the tank. How many gallons were in the tank when you reached San Francisco?
5. If the fuel costs \$1.32 per gallon, how much should you have paid for 10.8 gallons?
6. If you want to arrive at Monterey by noon, by what time should you leave San Francisco?
7. On your way to Sequoia National Park, you fill the fuel tank. If the tank holds 14.7 gallons and your car gets 28.5 miles per gallon, how far can you drive before running out of fuel?
8. You leave Sequoia and average 52.5 miles per hour for the first 2.5 hours. How far do you travel during this time?
9. You plan to leave Sequoia and drive no more than 6 hours today. Can you reach Los Angeles today?
10. Suppose that it takes 16.5¢ per mile to operate your car. What would be the total car expense for your trip?

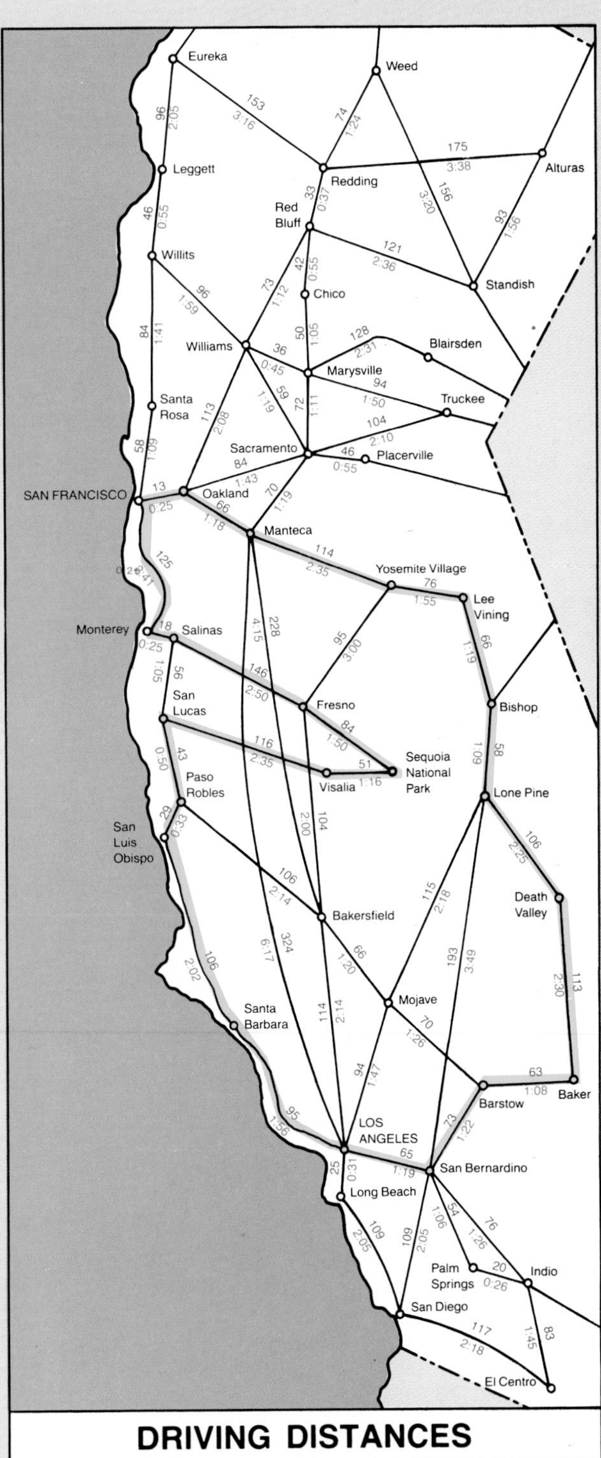

Writing fractions and mixed numbers as decimals

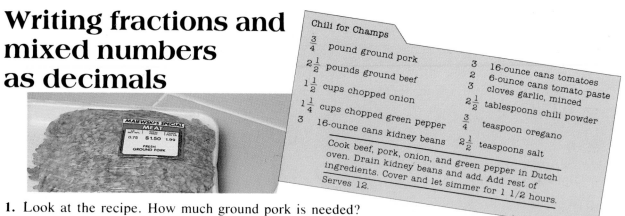

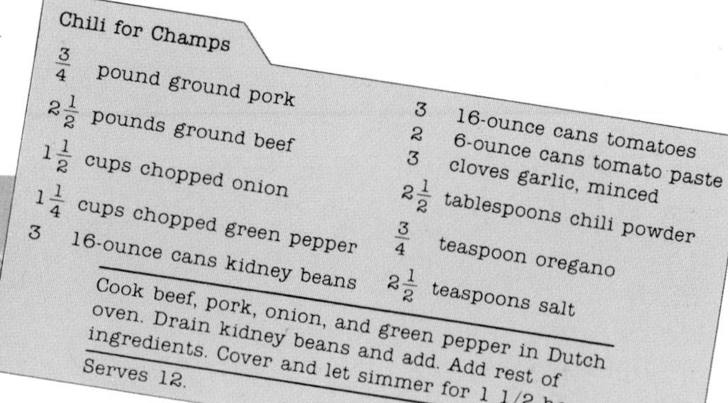

Chili for Champs
$\frac{3}{4}$ pound ground pork
$2\frac{1}{2}$ pounds ground beef
$1\frac{1}{2}$ cups chopped onion
$1\frac{1}{4}$ cups chopped green pepper
3 16-ounce cans kidney beans
3 16-ounce cans tomatoes
2 6-ounce cans tomato paste
3 cloves garlic, minced
$2\frac{1}{2}$ tablespoons chili powder
$\frac{3}{4}$ teaspoon oregano
$2\frac{1}{2}$ teaspoons salt
Cook beef, pork, onion, and green pepper in Dutch oven. Drain kidney beans and add. Add rest of ingredients. Cover and let simmer for 1 1/2 hours.
Serves 12.

1. Look at the recipe. How much ground pork is needed?
2. How much ground pork is in the package? To decide whether the package contains the proper amount of ground pork for the recipe, you can change $\frac{3}{4}$ to a decimal.

Here's how *to change $\frac{3}{4}$ to a decimal.*

To change a fraction to a decimal, divide the numerator by the denominator.

$$\begin{array}{r} 0.75 \\ 4\overline{)3.00} \\ -28 \\ \hline 20 \\ -20 \\ \hline 0 \end{array}$$

So $\frac{3}{4} = 0.75$

3. Look at the *Here's how*. Is $\frac{3}{4}$ pound the same as 0.75 pound?
4. Does the package contain the proper amount of ground pork?
5. Look at the recipe. How much ground beef is needed?

   Study this example.

$$\begin{array}{r} 0.666 \\ 3\overline{)2.000} \\ -18 \\ \hline 20 \\ -18 \\ \hline 20 \\ -18 \\ \hline 2 \end{array}$$

If the division does not end, round the quotient.

So $\frac{2}{3} \approx 0.67$

Read $\approx$ as "is approximately equal to."

6. To what place was the decimal rounded?

EXERCISES

Change each fraction to a decimal. *Here are scrambled answers for the next row of exercises: 0.2 0.25 0.4 0.75 0.3 0.625 0.375*

7. $\frac{1}{5}$ 8. $\frac{3}{10}$ 9. $\frac{1}{4}$ 10. $\frac{3}{4}$ 11. $\frac{2}{5}$ 12. $\frac{5}{8}$ 13. $\frac{3}{8}$

14. $\frac{1}{16}$ 15. $\frac{3}{16}$ 16. $\frac{9}{20}$ 17. $\frac{7}{16}$ 18. $\frac{5}{16}$ 19. $\frac{12}{25}$ 20. $\frac{15}{5}$

21. $\frac{9}{8}$ 22. $\frac{12}{5}$ 23. $\frac{15}{4}$ 24. $\frac{25}{8}$ 25. $\frac{9}{16}$ 26. $\frac{13}{10}$ 27. $\frac{3}{20}$

Change each mixed number to a decimal.

28. $2\frac{1}{2}$

$2\frac{1}{2} = 2 + \frac{1}{2}$

$\frac{1}{2} = 0.5$

$2\frac{1}{2} = 2.5$

29. $2\frac{3}{8}$ 30. $3\frac{1}{2}$ 31. $1\frac{1}{8}$ 32. $4\frac{3}{5}$ 33. $9\frac{1}{4}$

34. $2\frac{1}{4}$ 35. $3\frac{4}{5}$ 36. $4\frac{2}{5}$ 37. $2\frac{5}{8}$ 38. $3\frac{3}{16}$

39. $7\frac{7}{8}$ 40. $5\frac{3}{8}$ 41. $4\frac{3}{4}$ 42. $3\frac{3}{8}$ 43. $6\frac{1}{5}$ 44. $4\frac{3}{10}$ 45. $5\frac{5}{8}$

Change to a decimal rounded to the nearest hundredth.

46. $\frac{1}{3}$ 47. $\frac{1}{6}$ 48. $\frac{2}{3}$ 49. $\frac{1}{9}$ 50. $\frac{5}{6}$ 51. $\frac{5}{9}$ 52. $\frac{3}{14}$

53. $\frac{5}{7}$ 54. $\frac{13}{3}$ 55. $\frac{1}{12}$ 56. $\frac{11}{6}$ 57. $\frac{17}{12}$ 58. $\frac{15}{6}$ 59. $\frac{7}{22}$

60. $\frac{4}{9}$ 61. $\frac{5}{3}$ 62. $\frac{13}{6}$ 63. $\frac{5}{12}$ 64. $\frac{20}{3}$ 65. $\frac{17}{6}$ 66. $\frac{4}{7}$

Solve. Use the recipe on page 146.

67. Ground beef costs $1.50 a pound. How much will the ground beef cost for the recipe?

68. A 6-ounce can of tomato paste costs $.48 and a 16-ounce can of tomatoes costs $.59. What will be the total cost of these ingredients for the recipe?

Can you spot it?

Divide. Find the fraction that does not belong in each group.

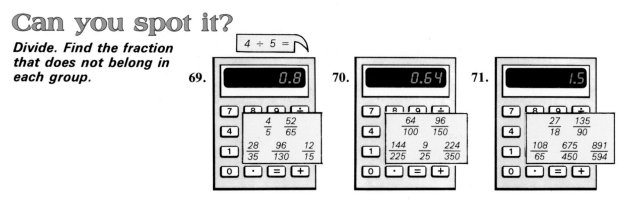

69.

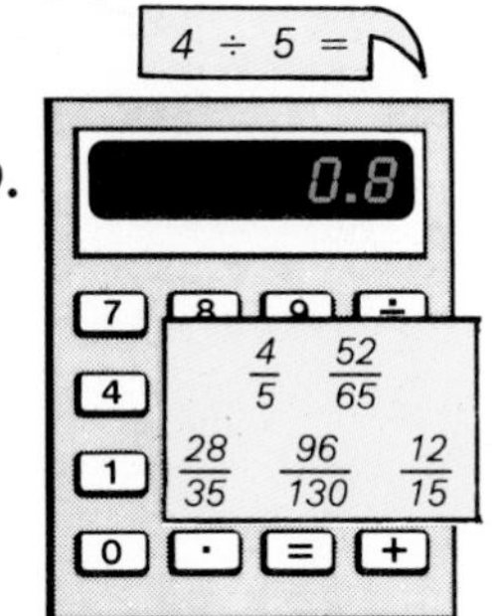

70.

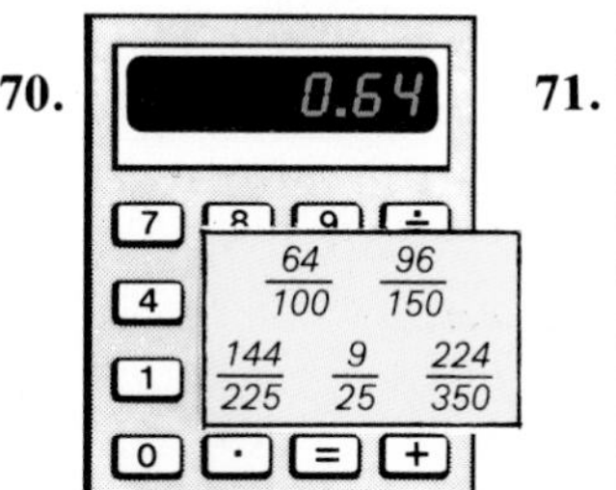

71.

1.5

$\frac{27}{18}$ $\frac{135}{90}$

$\frac{108}{65}$ $\frac{675}{450}$ $\frac{891}{594}$

Writing decimals as fractions or mixed numbers

1. What decimal is shown on this calculator?
2. Is the decimal less than or greater than 1?

Here's how *to change a decimal (less than 1) to a fraction in simplest form.* $0.75 = ?$

Read the decimal.	Write as a fraction.	Write in simplest form.
0.75 *75 hundredths*	$0.75 = \frac{75}{100}$	$0.75 = \frac{75}{100}$ $= \frac{3}{4}$

3. What decimal is shown on this calculator?
4. When 2.6 is changed to a mixed number, what should the whole-number part be?

Here's how *to change a decimal (greater than 1) to a mixed number in simplest form.* $2.6 = ?$

Read the decimal.	Write as a mixed number.	Write in simplest form.
2.6 *2 and 6 tenths*	$2.6 = 2\frac{6}{10}$	$2.6 = 2\frac{6}{10}$ $= 2\frac{3}{5}$

EXERCISES

Change to a fraction in simplest form. *Here are scrambled answers for the next row of exercises:* $\frac{3}{4}$ $\frac{1}{4}$ $\frac{1}{8}$ $\frac{3}{5}$ $\frac{1}{2}$

5. 0.6	**6.** 0.25	**7.** 0.5	**8.** 0.75	**9.** 0.125
10. 0.8	**11.** 0.24	**12.** 0.48	**13.** 0.9	**14.** 0.150
15. 0.35	**16.** 0.375	**17.** 0.72	**18.** 0.4	**19.** 0.16
20. 0.36	**21.** 0.65	**22.** 0.875	**23.** 0.45	**24.** 0.05

Change to a mixed number in simplest form.

25. 2.25	**26.** 1.4	**27.** 2.400	**28.** 5.5	**29.** 9.35
30. 7.8	**31.** 3.75	**32.** 6.08	**33.** 12.375	**34.** 4.04
35. 6.28	**36.** 8.44	**37.** 6.85	**38.** 4.50	**39.** 3.6
40. 8.52	**41.** 3.875	**42.** 10.350	**43.** 6.15	**44.** 5.625

<, =, or >?

45. $\frac{1}{4}$ ● 0.2	**46.** 0.3 ● $\frac{1}{4}$	**47.** 0.1 ● $\frac{1}{10}$	**48.** $\frac{2}{3}$ ● 0.3
49. $\frac{1}{5}$ ● 0.25	**50.** $\frac{2}{5}$ ● 0.4	**51.** $\frac{1}{2}$ ● 0.6	**52.** $1\frac{3}{8}$ ● 1.38
53. 0.375 ● $\frac{2}{5}$	**54.** $\frac{3}{5}$ ● 0.625	**55.** $\frac{3}{4}$ ● 0.80	**56.** 0.62 ● $\frac{31}{50}$
57. 1.5 ● $1\frac{1}{2}$	**58.** $2\frac{3}{4}$ ● 2.7	**59.** $1\frac{7}{8}$ ● 1.85	**60.** $\frac{3}{4}$ ● 0.075
61. 3.4 ● $3\frac{3}{8}$	**62.** 2.08 ● $2\frac{1}{10}$	**63.** 3.625 ● $3\frac{5}{8}$	**64.** 1.05 ● $1\frac{1}{20}$
65. 2.5 ● $2\frac{1}{2}$	**66.** 3.15 ● $3\frac{3}{20}$	**67.** 2.66 ● $2\frac{2}{5}$	**68.** 4.77 ● $4\frac{3}{4}$

Four fun

69. Use the digit 4 four times to build each of the numbers from 1 through 10. You may add, subtract, multiply, and/or divide. Here are two examples:

$$44 \div 44 = 1$$

$$4 \times (4 - 4) + 4 = 4$$

Cumulative Skill Practice

<, =, or >? *(page 132)*

1. $\frac{2}{5}$ ● $\frac{3}{5}$ 2. $\frac{5}{8}$ ● $\frac{3}{8}$ 3. $\frac{7}{10}$ ● $\frac{9}{10}$ 4. $\frac{5}{9}$ ● $\frac{4}{9}$ 5. $\frac{1}{6}$ ● $\frac{5}{6}$

6. $\frac{1}{2}$ ● $\frac{3}{4}$ 7. $\frac{2}{3}$ ● $\frac{5}{6}$ 8. $\frac{2}{4}$ ● $\frac{1}{2}$ 9. $\frac{1}{4}$ ● $\frac{1}{3}$ 10. $\frac{3}{8}$ ● $\frac{6}{16}$

11. $\frac{10}{15}$ ● $\frac{2}{3}$ 12. $\frac{3}{10}$ ● $\frac{1}{3}$ 13. $\frac{5}{12}$ ● $\frac{1}{4}$ 14. $\frac{3}{4}$ ● $\frac{3}{8}$ 15. $\frac{2}{3}$ ● $\frac{6}{9}$

16. $\frac{3}{2}$ ● $\frac{5}{2}$ 17. $\frac{2}{5}$ ● $\frac{1}{4}$ 18. $\frac{3}{4}$ ● $\frac{5}{6}$ 19. $\frac{9}{4}$ ● $\frac{3}{2}$ 20. $\frac{3}{4}$ ● $\frac{3}{5}$

Write in simplest form. *(page 140)*

21. $\frac{6}{8}$ 22. $\frac{9}{3}$ 23. $5\frac{4}{6}$ 24. $\frac{10}{3}$ 25. $\frac{6}{36}$ 26. $3\frac{2}{4}$ 27. $\frac{17}{34}$

28. $\frac{12}{5}$ 29. $\frac{5}{20}$ 30. $4\frac{5}{10}$ 31. $\frac{18}{24}$ 32. $3\frac{6}{10}$ 33. $1\frac{10}{12}$ 34. $1\frac{8}{14}$

35. $\frac{33}{5}$ 36. $\frac{12}{16}$ 37. $\frac{18}{7}$ 38. $\frac{10}{2}$ 39. $2\frac{3}{9}$ 40. $\frac{8}{10}$ 41. $3\frac{7}{14}$

42. $5\frac{3}{12}$ 43. $\frac{25}{10}$ 44. $\frac{4}{16}$ 45. $\frac{15}{12}$ 46. $7\frac{6}{8}$ 47. $\frac{10}{12}$ 48. $\frac{29}{12}$

Change to a decimal. *(page 146)*

49. $\frac{1}{2}$ 50. $1\frac{1}{5}$ 51. $\frac{9}{10}$ 52. $\frac{1}{4}$ 53. $\frac{1}{16}$ 54. $1\frac{1}{8}$ 55. $1\frac{3}{10}$

56. $2\frac{2}{5}$ 57. $\frac{3}{8}$ 58. $\frac{3}{4}$ 59. $\frac{5}{2}$ 60. $\frac{13}{10}$ 61. $3\frac{3}{5}$ 62. $\frac{25}{16}$

63. $1\frac{3}{16}$ 64. $\frac{9}{2}$ 65. $\frac{7}{10}$ 66. $4\frac{7}{8}$ 67. $\frac{9}{4}$ 68. $\frac{5}{16}$ 69. $\frac{9}{8}$

70. $\frac{12}{5}$ 71. $6\frac{5}{8}$ 72. $\frac{4}{5}$ 73. $\frac{7}{4}$ 74. $\frac{9}{5}$ 75. $\frac{11}{2}$ 76. $2\frac{4}{5}$

Change to a decimal rounded to the nearest hundredth. *(page 146)*

77. $\frac{1}{3}$ 78. $\frac{1}{6}$ 79. $\frac{1}{12}$ 80. $\frac{2}{3}$ 81. $\frac{1}{9}$ 82. $\frac{5}{3}$ 83. $\frac{4}{7}$

84. $\frac{7}{12}$ 85. $\frac{11}{6}$ 86. $\frac{4}{9}$ 87. $\frac{5}{12}$ 88. $\frac{10}{9}$ 89. $\frac{7}{6}$ 90. $\frac{15}{9}$

91. $\frac{5}{6}$ 92. $\frac{4}{3}$ 93. $\frac{2}{9}$ 94. $\frac{13}{6}$ 95. $\frac{7}{3}$ 96. $\frac{11}{12}$ 97. $\frac{3}{11}$

Problem solving

COMPUTERS IN STORES

Most items sold in stores are marked with light and dark bands called the Universal Product Code (UPC).

An optical scanner reads and sends the code to a computer. The computer uses the code to search its memory for the price of the item. The price is then printed on a cash-register receipt.

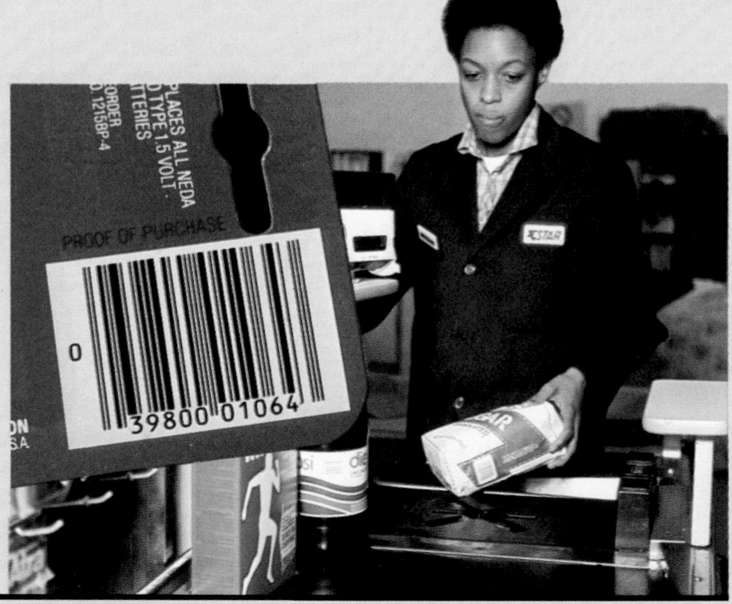

Solve. Use the information on the receipt.

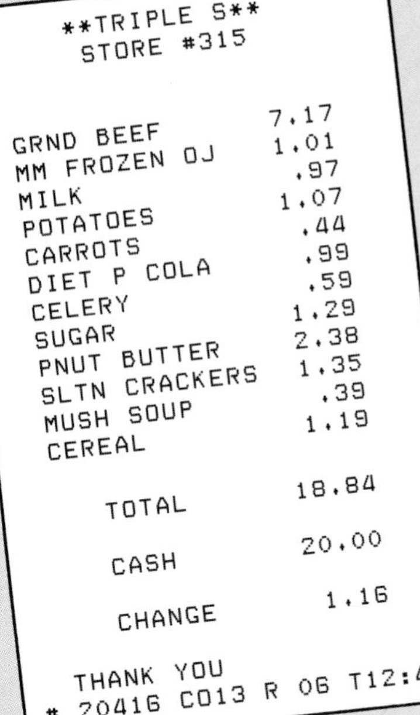

TRIPLE S
STORE #315

GRND BEEF	7.17
MM FROZEN OJ	1.01
MILK	.97
POTATOES	1.07
CARROTS	.44
DIET P COLA	.99
CELERY	.59
SUGAR	1.29
PNUT BUTTER	2.38
SLTN CRACKERS	1.35
MUSH SOUP	.39
CEREAL	1.19
TOTAL	18.84
CASH	20.00
CHANGE	1.16

THANK YOU
\# 20416 C013 R 06 T12:40

1. What was the total cost of the vegetables?
2. Did the meat item cost more than 3 times as much as the vegetables?
3. This purchase was made by 3 friends who share an apartment. What was each person's share of the cost?
4. The amount of this purchase is about $\frac{1}{5}$ of their weekly food allowance. About how much do they spend each week for food?
5. The ground beef will be used to prepare a meat loaf to serve 5 people. What is the average cost per serving? (Round to the nearest cent.)
6. What is the least number of coins that could be given in change?
7. Each of these UPCs is from an item printed on the receipt. Decide which item each code is on.

costs 28¢ more than

costs twice as much as

Chapter REVIEW

Here are scrambled answers for the review exercises:

1	3	5	100	divisor	lowest	remainder
2	4	8	common	greater	mixed	tenth

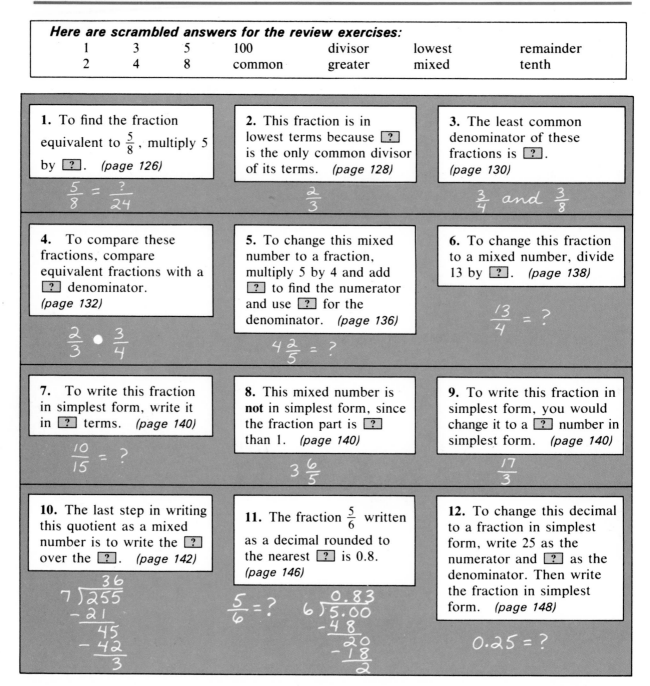

1. To find the fraction equivalent to $\frac{5}{8}$, multiply 5 by [?]. *(page 126)*

$\frac{5}{8} = \frac{?}{24}$

2. This fraction is in lowest terms because [?] is the only common divisor of its terms. *(page 128)*

$\frac{2}{3}$

3. The least common denominator of these fractions is [?]. *(page 130)*

$\frac{3}{4}$ and $\frac{3}{8}$

4. To compare these fractions, compare equivalent fractions with a [?] denominator. *(page 132)*

$\frac{2}{3} \bullet \frac{3}{4}$

5. To change this mixed number to a fraction, multiply 5 by 4 and add [?] to find the numerator and use [?] for the denominator. *(page 136)*

$4\frac{2}{5} = ?$

6. To change this fraction to a mixed number, divide 13 by [?]. *(page 138)*

$\frac{13}{4} = ?$

7. To write this fraction in simplest form, write it in [?] terms. *(page 140)*

$\frac{10}{15} = ?$

8. This mixed number is **not** in simplest form, since the fraction part is [?] than 1. *(page 140)*

$3\frac{6}{5}$

9. To write this fraction in simplest form, you would change it to a [?] number in simplest form. *(page 140)*

$\frac{17}{3}$

10. The last step in writing this quotient as a mixed number is to write the [?] over the [?]. *(page 142)*

$$\begin{array}{r} 36 \\ 7\overline{)255} \\ -21 \\ \hline 45 \\ -42 \\ \hline 3 \end{array}$$

11. The fraction $\frac{5}{6}$ written as a decimal rounded to the nearest [?] is 0.8. *(page 146)*

$\frac{5}{6} = ?$

$$\begin{array}{r} 0.83 \\ 6\overline{)5.00} \\ -48 \\ \hline 20 \\ -18 \\ \hline 2 \end{array}$$

12. To change this decimal to a fraction in simplest form, write 25 as the numerator and [?] as the denominator. Then write the fraction in simplest form. *(page 148)*

$0.25 = ?$

Chapter TEST

Complete to get an equivalent fraction. *(page 126)*

1. $\frac{1}{4} = \frac{?}{8}$ 2. $\frac{1}{3} = \frac{?}{12}$ 3. $\frac{2}{3} = \frac{?}{9}$ 4. $\frac{5}{8} = \frac{?}{24}$ 5. $\frac{8}{14} = \frac{?}{7}$

6. $\frac{12}{16} = \frac{?}{4}$ 7. $\frac{5}{10} = \frac{?}{2}$ 8. $\frac{16}{24} = \frac{?}{3}$ 9. $\frac{12}{28} = \frac{?}{7}$ 10. $\frac{3}{9} = \frac{?}{3}$

Write each fraction in lowest terms. *(page 128)*

11. $\frac{6}{12}$ 12. $\frac{6}{9}$ 13. $\frac{9}{6}$ 14. $\frac{6}{18}$ 15. $\frac{20}{15}$ 16. $\frac{21}{24}$ 17. $\frac{50}{25}$

Find the least common denominator. *(page 130)*

18. $\frac{3}{4}$ $\frac{1}{2}$ 19. $\frac{3}{10}$ $\frac{2}{5}$ 20. $\frac{1}{2}$ $\frac{1}{3}$ 21. $\frac{1}{3}$ $\frac{3}{8}$ 22. $\frac{5}{6}$ $\frac{2}{9}$

<, =, or >? *(page 132)*

23. $\frac{3}{8}$ ● $\frac{1}{4}$ 24. $\frac{2}{3}$ ● $\frac{5}{6}$ 25. $\frac{1}{3}$ ● $\frac{1}{4}$ 26. $\frac{1}{3}$ ● $\frac{5}{12}$ 27. $\frac{4}{5}$ ● $\frac{5}{6}$

Change each mixed number to a fraction. *(page 136)*

28. $1\frac{1}{2}$ 29. $3\frac{1}{4}$ 30. $2\frac{2}{3}$ 31. $4\frac{3}{4}$ 32. $2\frac{7}{8}$ 33. $3\frac{5}{6}$ 34. $7\frac{4}{5}$

Change each fraction to a whole number or a mixed number. *(page 138)*

35. $\frac{5}{2}$ 36. $\frac{8}{2}$ 37. $\frac{11}{4}$ 38. $\frac{12}{5}$ 39. $\frac{15}{3}$ 40. $\frac{23}{6}$ 41. $\frac{25}{8}$

Write in simplest form. *(page 140)*

42. $\frac{6}{8}$ 43. $\frac{8}{2}$ 44. $\frac{3}{2}$ 45. $\frac{5}{10}$ 46. $2\frac{4}{8}$ 47. $\frac{16}{4}$ 48. $11\frac{11}{22}$

49. $4\frac{2}{6}$ 50. $\frac{8}{12}$ 51. $\frac{20}{6}$ 52. $\frac{9}{3}$ 53. $\frac{10}{15}$ 54. $3\frac{6}{9}$ 55. $\frac{13}{4}$

Divide. Write each quotient as a mixed number in simplest form. *(page 142)*

56. $3\overline{)127}$ 57. $4\overline{)925}$ 58. $9\overline{)384}$ 59. $12\overline{)7023}$ 60. $15\overline{)4316}$ 61. $28\overline{)2970}$

Change to a decimal. *(page 146)*

62. $\frac{1}{4}$ 63. $6\frac{7}{10}$ 64. $6\frac{7}{8}$ 65. $\frac{1}{16}$ 66. $\frac{9}{10}$ 67. $\frac{7}{8}$ 68. $3\frac{1}{10}$

69. $3\frac{1}{20}$ 70. $2\frac{1}{4}$ 71. $2\frac{2}{5}$ 72. $5\frac{3}{8}$ 73. $2\frac{3}{4}$ 74. $4\frac{3}{100}$ 75. $\frac{4}{5}$

Change to a fraction or mixed number in simplest form. *(page 148)*

76. 0.6 77. 0.25 78. 0.2 79. 0.75 80. 0.375 81. 0.450 82. 1.42

83. 1.4 84. 2.8 85. 1.50 86. 3.08 87. 4.300 88. 3.625 89. 6.02

Cumulative TEST Standardized Format

Choose the correct letter.

1. The short word-name for 50.012 is

   A. 50 and 12 hundredths
   B. 50 and 12 thousandths
   C. 50 and 12 tenths
   D. none of these

2. Give the sum.

   $36.09 + 14.8 + 321.7$

   A. 372.59
   B. 69.74
   C. 83.06
   D. none of these

3. Which number is less than 0.04?

   A. 0.3
   B. 0.05
   C. 0.041
   D. none of these

4. Give the difference.

   $52.46 - 3.521$

   A. 17.25
   B. 48.941
   C. 48.938
   D. none of these

5. Give the product.

   4.03×4.6

   A. 185.38
   B. 18.538
   C. 18.428
   D. none of these

6. Give the product.

   10.463×100

   A. 0.10463
   B. 104.63
   C. 1046.3
   D. none of these

7. Give the quotient rounded to the nearest tenth.

   $3.742 \div 1.9$

   A. 2.0
   B. 1.9
   C. 0.2
   D. none of these

8. The median of 38, 42, 36, 36, and 43 is

   A. 38
   B. 36
   C. 39
   D. none of these

9. $\frac{1}{3} < ?$

   A. $\frac{1}{4}$
   B. $\frac{3}{10}$
   C. $\frac{3}{8}$
   D. none of these

10. $\frac{24}{16}$ in simplest form is

    A. $\frac{3}{2}$
    B. $1\frac{8}{16}$
    C. $1\frac{1}{2}$
    D. none of these

11. Change to a decimal rounded to the nearest hundredth.

    $\frac{5}{6} = ?$

    A. 0.83
    B. 0.84
    C. 1.20
    D. none of these

12. 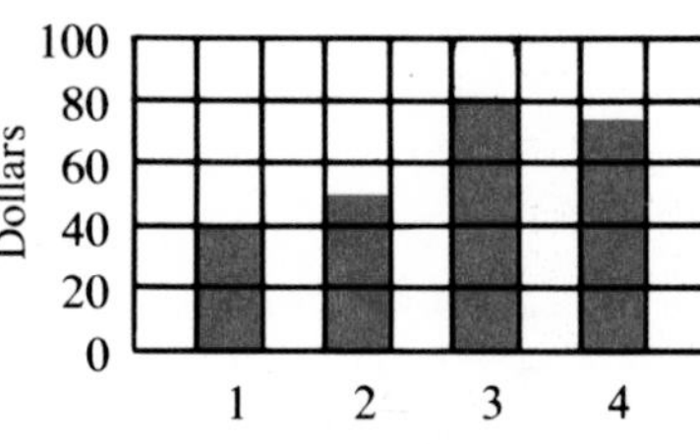

    Sal's total earnings were

    A. $80
    B. $70
    C. $130
    D. none of these

Chapter 7

Adding and Subtracting Fractions and Mixed Numbers

Adding fractions with common denominators

1. What is the weight of a nickel?
2. Which coin weighs $\frac{2}{28}$ ounce?
3. You have 3 coins that are worth 35¢. What three fractions would you add to find how many ounces they weigh?

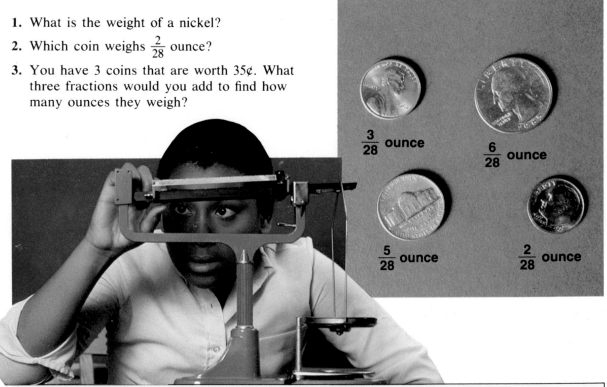

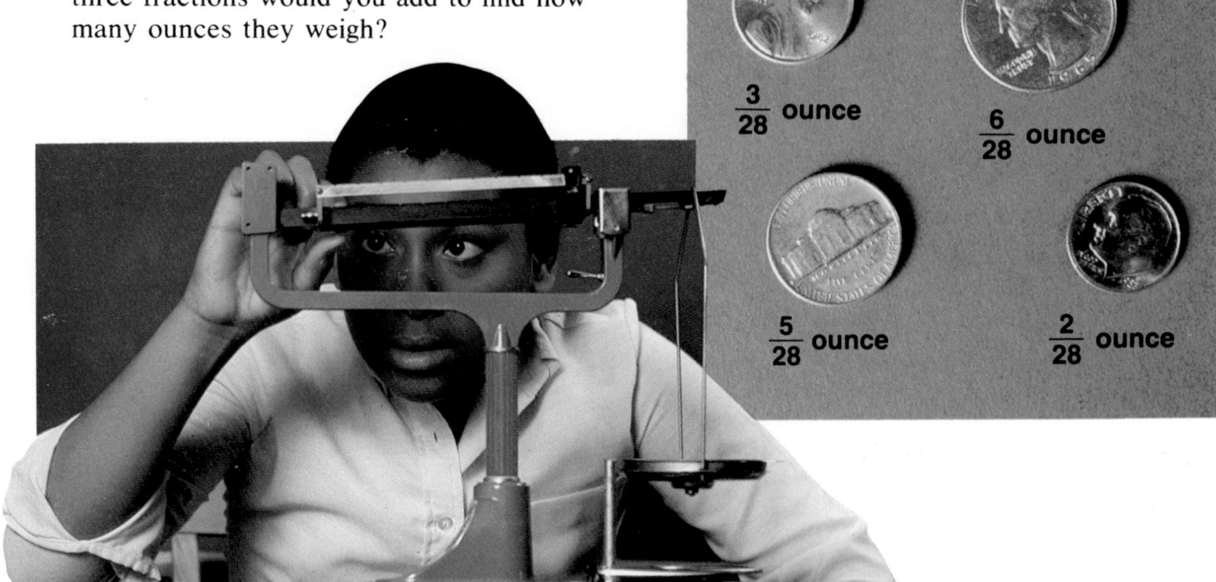

Here's how ***to add fractions with common denominators.*** $\frac{5}{28} + \frac{5}{28} + \frac{6}{28} = ?$

Add the numerators and use the common denominator.

nickel ↓ , **nickel** ↓ , **quarter** ↓

$$\frac{5}{28} + \frac{5}{28} + \frac{6}{28} = \frac{16}{28}$$

$$= \frac{4}{7}$$

4. Look at the *Here's how*. What is the total weight of the 3 coins?
5. Check these examples. Give each sum in simplest form.

a. $\frac{3}{28} + \frac{5}{28} = \frac{8}{28}$
$= ?$

b. $\frac{2}{3} + \frac{1}{3} = \frac{3}{3}$
$= ?$

c. $\frac{4}{5} + \frac{2}{5} + \frac{3}{5} = \frac{9}{5}$
$= ?$

EXERCISES

Add. Write the sum in simplest form.

Here are scrambled answers for the next row of exercises: $1\frac{1}{4}$ $\frac{5}{7}$ $\frac{2}{5}$ $\frac{1}{2}$ 1

6. $\frac{3}{8} + \frac{1}{8}$ **7.** $\frac{3}{10} + \frac{1}{10}$ **8.** $\frac{2}{7} + \frac{3}{7}$ **9.** $\frac{3}{8} + \frac{7}{8}$ **10.** $\frac{1}{3} + \frac{2}{3}$

11. $\frac{5}{9} + \frac{1}{9}$ **12.** $\frac{1}{5} + \frac{2}{5}$ **13.** $\frac{5}{12} + \frac{3}{12}$ **14.** $\frac{2}{5} + \frac{3}{5}$ **15.** $\frac{1}{6} + \frac{5}{6}$

16. $\frac{3}{10} + \frac{2}{10}$ **17.** $\frac{7}{12} + \frac{7}{12}$ **18.** $\frac{5}{8} + \frac{7}{8}$ **19.** $\frac{1}{4} + \frac{3}{4}$ **20.** $\frac{3}{5} + \frac{4}{5}$

21. $\frac{4}{15} + \frac{1}{15}$ **22.** $\frac{31}{50} + \frac{9}{50}$ **23.** $\frac{17}{100} + \frac{33}{100}$ **24.** $\frac{5}{16} + \frac{7}{16}$ **25.** $\frac{7}{10} + \frac{9}{10}$

26. $\frac{3}{10} + \frac{1}{10} + \frac{2}{10}$ **27.** $\frac{1}{6} + \frac{1}{6} + \frac{5}{6}$ **28.** $\frac{1}{12} + \frac{5}{12} + \frac{3}{12}$ **29.** $\frac{1}{8} + \frac{3}{8} + \frac{5}{8}$

30. $\frac{1}{5} + \frac{2}{5} + \frac{4}{5}$ **31.** $\frac{2}{5} + \frac{1}{5} + \frac{1}{5}$ **32.** $\frac{6}{7} + \frac{3}{7} + \frac{2}{7}$ **33.** $\frac{5}{9} + \frac{2}{9} + \frac{5}{9}$

Solve. Use the coin facts on page 156.

34. What coins are worth 40¢ and weigh $\frac{13}{28}$ ounce?

35. What coins are worth 15¢ and weigh $\frac{15}{28}$ ounce?

36. What coins are worth 15¢ and weigh $\frac{17}{28}$ ounce?

37. What coins are worth 50¢ and weigh $\frac{15}{28}$ ounce?

38. What coins are worth 60¢ and weigh $\frac{1}{2}$ ounce?

39. What coins are worth 30¢ and weigh $\frac{3}{4}$ ounce?

Change, please

40. How many ways can you make change for a nickel?

41. How many ways can you make change for a dime? *Hint: The answer is not 2.*

42. How many ways can you make change for a quarter? *Hint: Make a list.*

43. How many ways can you make change for a half-dollar?

Adding fractions with different denominators

This map shows the distance between scenic points on a hiking trail.

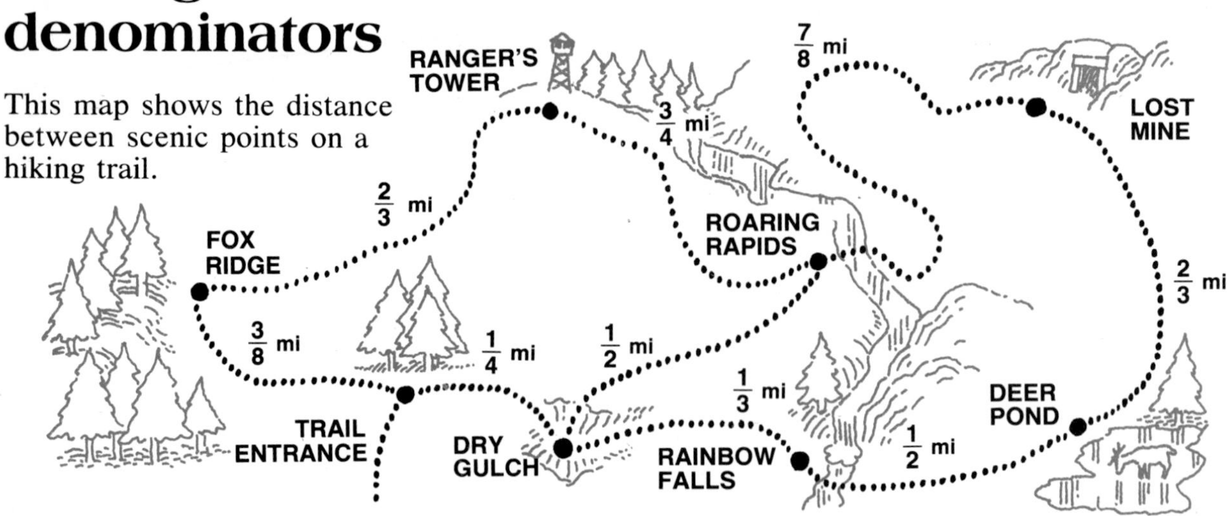

1. What is the shortest hiking distance from the Trail Entrance to Dry Gulch?
2. What two fractions would you add to compute the distance in miles from Rainbow Falls through Deer Pond to Lost Mine?

Here's how *to add fractions with different denominators.* $\frac{1}{2} + \frac{2}{3} = ?$

Find the least common denominator.

$$\begin{array}{r} \frac{1}{2} \\ +\frac{2}{3} \\ \hline \end{array} \quad \boxed{6}$$

Change to equivalent fractions.

$$\begin{array}{rcr} \frac{1}{2} & = & \frac{3}{6} \\ +\frac{2}{3} & = & +\frac{4}{6} \\ \hline \end{array}$$

Add. Write the sum in simplest form.

$$\begin{array}{rcr} \frac{1}{2} & = & \frac{3}{6} \\ +\frac{2}{3} & = & +\frac{4}{6} \\ \hline \frac{2}{3} & & \frac{7}{6} = 1\frac{1}{6} \end{array}$$

3. Look at the *Here's how*. How far is it from Rainbow Falls to Lost Mine?
4. Check these examples. Give each sum in simplest form.

a. $\frac{1}{2} + \frac{3}{4} = \frac{2}{4} + \frac{3}{4}$
$= \frac{5}{4}$
$= ?$

b. $\frac{1}{4} + \frac{1}{3} + \frac{1}{2} = \frac{3}{12} + \frac{4}{12} + \frac{6}{12}$
$= \frac{13}{12}$
$= ?$

EXERCISES

Add. Give the sum in simplest form.

Here are scrambled answers for the next row of exercises: $\frac{5}{8}$ $1\frac{1}{8}$ $\frac{7}{24}$ $1\frac{5}{24}$ $\frac{3}{5}$ $\frac{3}{4}$ 1

5. $\frac{1}{2} + \frac{1}{4}$ **6.** $\frac{1}{6} + \frac{1}{8}$ **7.** $\frac{3}{8} + \frac{1}{4}$ **8.** $\frac{3}{10} + \frac{7}{10}$ **9.** $\frac{2}{5} + \frac{1}{5}$ **10.** $\frac{5}{8} + \frac{1}{2}$ **11.** $\frac{5}{6} + \frac{3}{8}$

12. $\frac{7}{16} + \frac{1}{4}$ **13.** $\frac{1}{3} + \frac{5}{9}$ **14.** $\frac{5}{12} + \frac{2}{3}$ **15.** $\frac{5}{6} + \frac{1}{4}$ **16.** $\frac{3}{10} + \frac{1}{2}$ **17.** $\frac{2}{3} + \frac{3}{4}$ **18.** $\frac{5}{9} + \frac{5}{6}$

19. $\frac{1}{3} + \frac{1}{6}$ **20.** $\frac{3}{4} + \frac{1}{8}$ **21.** $\frac{3}{5} + \frac{7}{10}$ **22.** $\frac{5}{8} + \frac{1}{2}$ **23.** $\frac{1}{3} + \frac{1}{4}$ **24.** $\frac{1}{5} + \frac{3}{10}$ **25.** $\frac{2}{3} + \frac{2}{3}$

26. $\frac{2}{3} + \frac{1}{5}$ **27.** $\frac{1}{2} + \frac{11}{16}$ **28.** $\frac{2}{5} + \frac{1}{4}$ **29.** $\frac{5}{8} + \frac{1}{6}$ **30.** $\frac{9}{16} + \frac{1}{2}$ **31.** $\frac{2}{5} + \frac{3}{10}$ **32.** $\frac{5}{9} + \frac{1}{6}$

33. $\frac{1}{2} + \frac{1}{4} + \frac{1}{8}$ **34.** $\frac{3}{4} + \frac{3}{8} + \frac{1}{2}$ **35.** $\frac{1}{16} + \frac{3}{8} + \frac{1}{4}$ **36.** $\frac{1}{8} + \frac{5}{16} + \frac{3}{4}$

Solve. Use the map on page 158.

37. What is the shortest hiking distance from the Trail Entrance to Roaring Rapids?

38. What is the shortest hiking distance from Lost Mine to the Ranger's Tower?

39. If you hiked at 1 mile per hour, could you hike from the Trail Entrance to Lost Mine in less than $1\frac{1}{2}$ hours?

40. Which is the shorter route from the Trail Entrance to Ranger's Tower, over Fox Ridge or through Dry Gulch and past Roaring Rapids?

Where are you? Reading a map

Use the map. At which scenic points would you find these trail signs?

41.

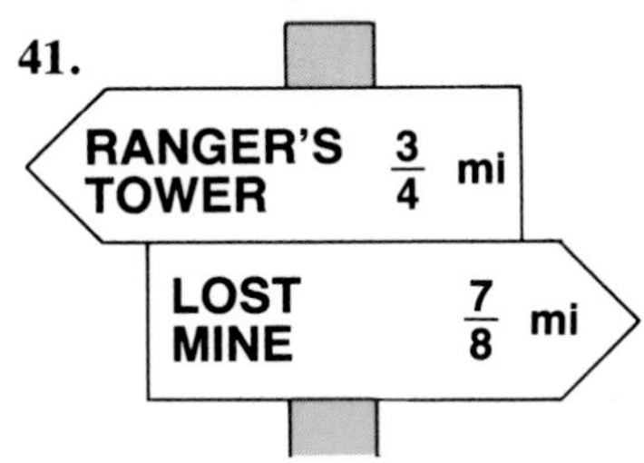

42.

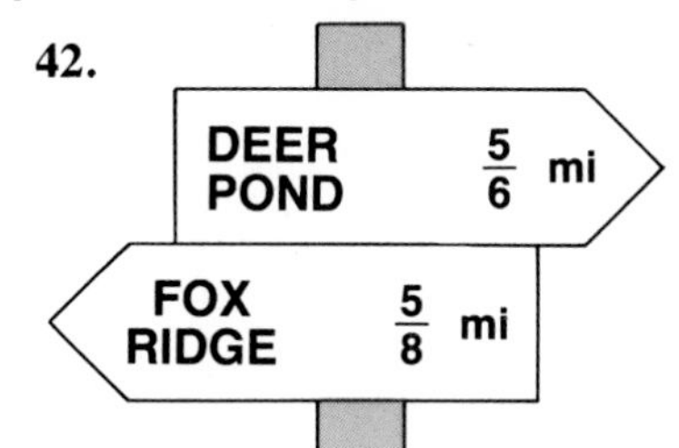

43.

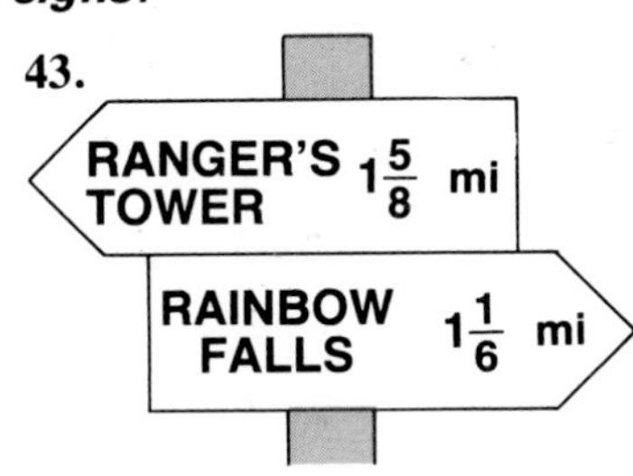

Adding mixed numbers

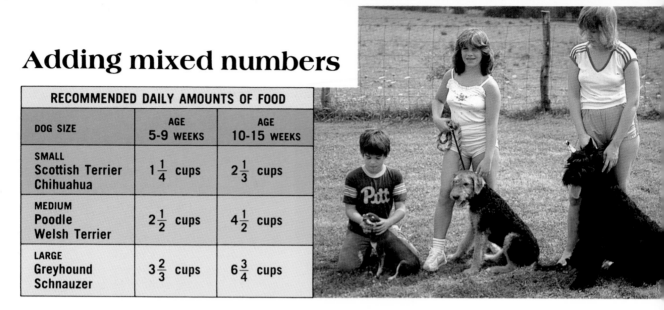

RECOMMENDED DAILY AMOUNTS OF FOOD		
DOG SIZE	AGE 5-9 WEEKS	AGE 10-15 WEEKS
SMALL Scottish Terrier Chihuahua	$1\frac{1}{4}$ cups	$2\frac{1}{3}$ cups
MEDIUM Poodle Welsh Terrier	$2\frac{1}{2}$ cups	$4\frac{1}{2}$ cups
LARGE Greyhound Schnauzer	$3\frac{2}{3}$ cups	$6\frac{3}{4}$ cups

1. How many cups of food should you feed an 8-week-old poodle each day?
2. How much daily food is recommended for a 13-week-old schnauzer?
3. You have a 6-week-old greyhound and a 12-week-old poodle. What two mixed numbers would you add to find the total number of cups of food you should feed them each day?

Here's how *to add mixed numbers.* $3\frac{2}{3} + 4\frac{1}{2} = ?$

Write equivalent fractions with a common denominator.

$$\begin{array}{rcr} 3\frac{2}{3} & = & 3\frac{4}{6} \\ +4\frac{1}{2} & = & +4\frac{3}{6} \\ \hline \end{array}$$

Add the fractions. Since the sum is greater than 1, regroup.

$$\begin{array}{rcr} 3\frac{2}{3} & = & \overset{1}{3}\frac{4}{6} \\ +4\frac{1}{2} & = & +4\frac{3}{6} \\ \hline & & \frac{1}{6} \end{array} \qquad \boxed{\frac{7}{6} = 1\frac{1}{6}}$$

Add the whole numbers.

$$\begin{array}{rcr} 3\frac{2}{3} & = & \overset{1}{3}\frac{4}{6} \\ +4\frac{1}{2} & = & +4\frac{3}{6} \\ \hline & & 8\frac{1}{6} \end{array}$$

4. Look at the *Here's how.* How many cups of food should you feed your 6-week-old greyhound and 12-week-old poodle each day?
5. Copy and complete these examples.

a. $\begin{array}{r} 3\frac{2}{3} \\ +2\frac{1}{3} \\ \hline \end{array}$ $\boxed{\frac{3}{3} = 1}$

b. $\begin{array}{rcr} 2\frac{1}{2} & = & 2\frac{2}{4} \\ +6\frac{3}{4} & = & +6\frac{3}{4} \\ \hline \end{array}$ $\boxed{\frac{5}{4} = 1\frac{1}{4}}$

c. $\begin{array}{rcr} 4\frac{5}{6} & = & 4\frac{20}{24} \\ +4\frac{3}{8} & = & +4\frac{9}{24} \\ \hline \end{array}$ $\boxed{\frac{29}{24}}$

EXERCISES

Add. Write the sum in simplest form.

Here are scrambled answers for the next row of exercises: $8\frac{7}{8}$ $10\frac{1}{8}$ $8\frac{1}{4}$ $7\frac{3}{4}$ $9\frac{1}{8}$ $6\frac{1}{6}$

6. $3\frac{1}{2} + 4\frac{1}{4}$ **7.** $5\frac{3}{4} + 2\frac{1}{2}$ **8.** $3\frac{1}{8} + 5\frac{3}{4}$ **9.** $6\frac{3}{4} + 2\frac{3}{8}$ **10.** $3\frac{1}{2} + 6\frac{5}{8}$ **11.** $4\frac{2}{3} + 1\frac{1}{2}$

12. $7\frac{3}{4} + 3\frac{1}{4}$ **13.** $8\frac{1}{6} + 4\frac{1}{9}$ **14.** $9\frac{5}{6} + 5\frac{1}{4}$ **15.** $8 + 8\frac{3}{4}$ **16.** $5\frac{1}{2} + 6\frac{7}{8}$ **17.** $4\frac{2}{5} + 1\frac{1}{2}$

18. $4\frac{2}{3} + 9\frac{5}{6}$ **19.** $8\frac{5}{12} + 6\frac{7}{8}$ **20.** $5 + 5\frac{3}{8}$ **21.** $7\frac{3}{8} + 9\frac{7}{12}$ **22.** $9\frac{3}{5} + 8\frac{2}{5}$ **23.** $6\frac{1}{3} + 4\frac{2}{3}$

24. $9\frac{4}{5} + 5\frac{3}{10}$ **25.** $7\frac{5}{12} + 4\frac{1}{3}$ **26.** $6\frac{1}{2} + 5\frac{3}{10}$ **27.** $9\frac{1}{10} + 3\frac{1}{2}$ **28.** $1\frac{1}{5} + 3\frac{3}{10}$

29. $3\frac{5}{12} + 2\frac{1}{2}$ **30.** $6\frac{1}{2} + 2\frac{1}{3}$ **31.** $1\frac{1}{4} + 3\frac{2}{5}$ **32.** $2\frac{7}{8} + 1\frac{1}{2}$ **33.** $4\frac{1}{6} + 2\frac{2}{3}$

Solve. Use the chart on page 160.

34. Is $4\frac{5}{6}$ cups of food enough food for a 6-week-old Welsh terrier and a 14-week-old Chihuahua?

35. Is $9\frac{5}{12}$ cups of food enough food for a 7-week-old greyhound and a 14-week-old schnauzer?

Check the sums

36. Find and correct the two wrong answers.

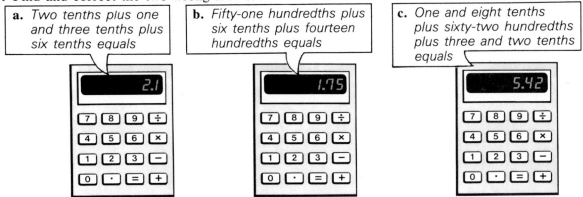

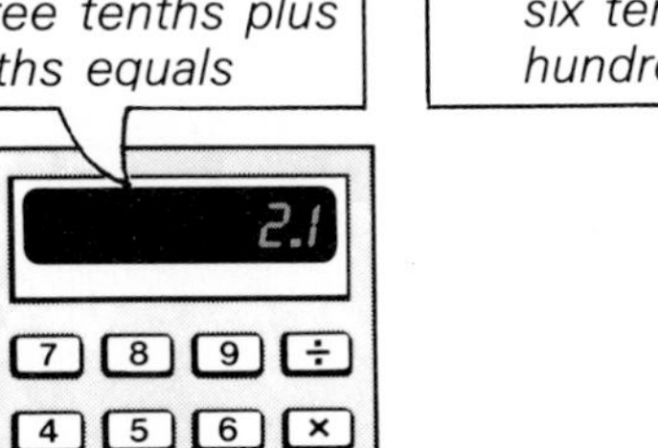

a. *Two tenths plus one and three tenths plus six tenths equals*

b. *Fifty-one hundredths plus six tenths plus fourteen hundredths equals*
1.75

c. *One and eight tenths plus sixty-two hundredths plus three and two tenths equals*

5.42

Cumulative Skill Practice

Give the sum. *(page 24)*

1. 3.4 + 4.56
2. 6.87 + 3.9
3. 7.24 + 45.6
4. 3.24 + 6.2 + 8.4
5. 25.6 + 52.5 + 2.85
6. 36 + 5.3 + 1.8
7. 0.25 + 0.6 + 3
8. 6.7 + 5 + 0.92
9. 13 + 2.5 + 0.35
10. 0.39 + 7 + 4.215
11. 3.7 + 24 + 0.146
12. 7.5 + 0.01 + 0.461

Give the difference. *(page 46)*

13. 63.5 − 49.7
14. 20.7 − 13.8
15. 8.00 − 4.47
16. 8.7 − 5.99
17. 30 − 7.24
18. 43.2 − 3.64
19. 8.6 − 2.73
20. 13 − 4.53
21. 10.18 − 8.45
22. 4.5 − 3.06
23. 17 − 3.205
24. 6 − 3.91

Give the product. *(page 64)*

25. 3.7 × 0.8
26. 2.97 × 0.6
27. 47.5 × 0.5
28. 5.2 × 0.68
29. 0.28 × 1.3
30. 24 × 0.41
31. 3.62 × 3.06
32. 2.05 × 61
33. 7.03 × 4.41
34. 4.3 × 2.04
35. 5.1 × 32
36. 2.1 × 3.05

Give the quotient. *(page 92)*

37. 63 ÷ 10
38. 534.2 ÷ 100
39. 629.8 ÷ 1000
40. 242 ÷ 100
41. 71.5 ÷ 1000
42. 6 ÷ 100
43. 3.03 ÷ 10
44. 4.29 ÷ 100
45. 7042 ÷ 1000
46. 7.34 ÷ 100
47. 2.09 ÷ 10
48. 346 ÷ 1000
49. 5.14 ÷ 10
50. 3.6 ÷ 100
51. 4.9 ÷ 100

Give the quotient rounded to the nearest hundredth. *(page 96)*

52. $0.3\overline{)1.4}$
53. $0.7\overline{)0.52}$
54. $1.2\overline{)6.4}$
55. $2.6\overline{)3.24}$
56. $0.06\overline{)0.5}$
57. $2.2\overline{)4.96}$
58. $0.006\overline{)0.04}$
59. $0.12\overline{)0.5}$
60. $3.2\overline{)7.5}$
61. $0.04\overline{)2.93}$
62. $0.7\overline{)3.4}$
63. $2.1\overline{)3.43}$
64. $4.5\overline{)2.8}$
65. $6.2\overline{)3.52}$
66. $1.7\overline{)3.96}$
67. $2.3\overline{)3.85}$

Problem solving

YOU'RE THE TRAIL GUIDE!

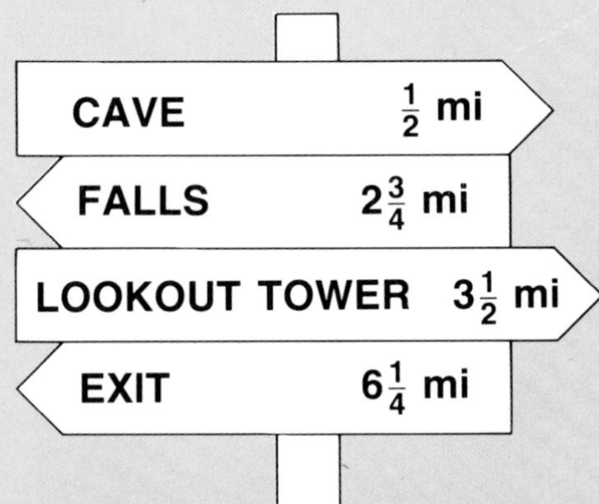

Draw a picture like this one. It will help you solve the problems.
Exit
Falls
Cave
Lookout Tower
you are here.

Use the picture to answer these hikers' questions.

1. *How many miles is it from the cave to the falls?*

2. *When I get to the lookout tower, how far will I be from the exit?*

3. "How many miles is it from the falls to the lookout tower?"

4. "How far is it from the cave to the exit?"

5. "When I'm at the cave, how far is it to the lookout tower?"

6. "Which is closer to the cave, the falls or the lookout tower?"

Draw another picture to solve these problems.

7. How many miles is the round trip from the entrance to the scenic view and back again?

8. Suppose you started at the entrance and hiked 7 miles toward the pond. How far are you from the scenic view?

9. When you are halfway between the scenic view and the pond, how far are you from the entrance?

10. Is the ledge closer to the pond or to the scenic view? How much closer?

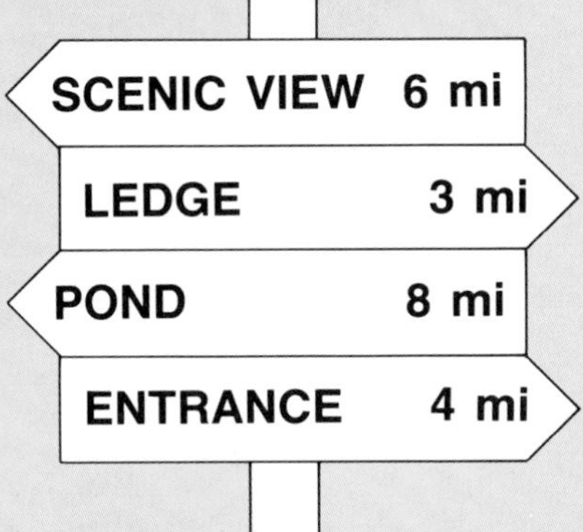

Subtracting fractions with common denominators

You won first prize at a sports-car rally.

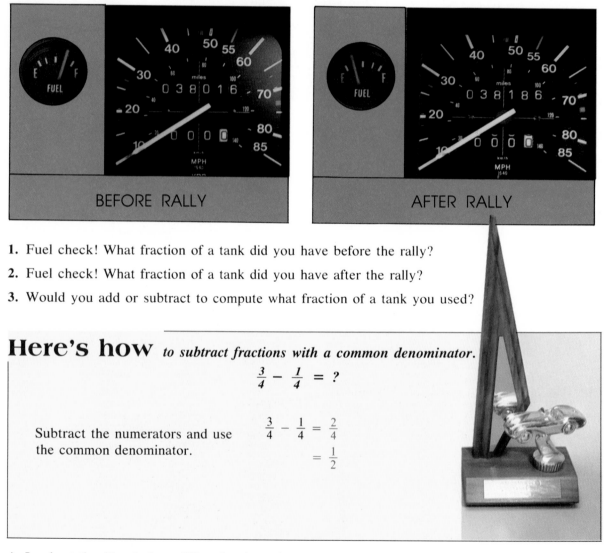

1. Fuel check! What fraction of a tank did you have before the rally?
2. Fuel check! What fraction of a tank did you have after the rally?
3. Would you add or subtract to compute what fraction of a tank you used?

Here's how *to subtract fractions with a common denominator.*

$$\frac{3}{4} - \frac{1}{4} = ?$$

Subtract the numerators and use the common denominator.

$$\frac{3}{4} - \frac{1}{4} = \frac{2}{4}$$
$$= \frac{1}{2}$$

4. Look at the *Here's how*. What fraction of a tank did you use on the rally?
5. Check these examples. Give each difference in simplest form.

a. $\frac{7}{8} - \frac{3}{8} = \frac{4}{8}$
$= ?$

b. $\frac{5}{12} - \frac{1}{12} = \frac{4}{12}$
$= ?$

c. $\frac{5}{2} - \frac{2}{2} = \frac{3}{2}$
$= ?$

EXERCISES

Subtract. Write the difference in simplest form.

Here are scrambled answers for the next row of exercises: $\frac{5}{6}$ $\frac{1}{4}$ $\frac{1}{6}$ $\frac{1}{2}$ 0 $\frac{2}{5}$

6. $\frac{3}{5} - \frac{1}{5}$	**7.** $\frac{2}{4} - \frac{1}{4}$	**8.** $\frac{6}{6} - \frac{1}{6}$	**9.** $\frac{4}{6} - \frac{3}{6}$	**10.** $\frac{5}{8} - \frac{1}{8}$	**11.** $\frac{3}{8} - \frac{3}{8}$
12. $\frac{5}{8} - \frac{3}{8}$	**13.** $\frac{5}{9} - \frac{0}{9}$	**14.** $\frac{5}{4} - \frac{1}{4}$	**15.** $\frac{7}{6} - \frac{3}{6}$	**16.** $\frac{5}{6} - \frac{1}{6}$	**17.** $\frac{6}{4} - \frac{2}{4}$
18. $\frac{3}{5} - \frac{0}{5}$	**19.** $\frac{11}{8} - \frac{5}{8}$	**20.** $\frac{5}{9} - \frac{2}{9}$	**21.** $\frac{12}{8} - \frac{6}{8}$	**22.** $\frac{11}{4} - \frac{3}{4}$	**23.** $\frac{7}{4} - \frac{4}{4}$
24. $\frac{9}{4} - \frac{3}{4}$	**25.** $\frac{5}{8} - \frac{4}{8}$	**26.** $\frac{8}{6} - \frac{2}{6}$	**27.** $\frac{5}{3} - \frac{2}{3}$	**28.** $\frac{7}{6} - \frac{2}{6}$	**29.** $\frac{10}{9} - \frac{4}{9}$
30. $\frac{12}{4} - \frac{3}{4}$	**31.** $\frac{7}{8} - \frac{3}{8}$	**32.** $\frac{13}{4} - \frac{3}{4}$	**33.** $\frac{10}{8} - \frac{2}{8}$	**34.** $\frac{9}{6} - \frac{6}{6}$	**35.** $\frac{10}{4} - \frac{2}{4}$
36. $\frac{2}{3} - \frac{2}{3}$	**37.** $\frac{7}{4} - \frac{3}{4}$	**38.** $\frac{8}{9} - \frac{3}{9}$	**39.** $\frac{4}{5} - \frac{2}{5}$	**40.** $\frac{9}{8} - \frac{3}{8}$	**41.** $\frac{13}{7} - \frac{8}{7}$
42. $\frac{12}{10} - \frac{7}{10}$	**43.** $\frac{7}{8} - \frac{4}{8}$	**44.** $\frac{6}{4} - \frac{2}{4}$	**45.** $\frac{5}{6} - \frac{5}{6}$	**46.** $\frac{6}{5} - \frac{3}{5}$	**47.** $\frac{5}{6} - \frac{3}{6}$

Solve. Look at the top of page 164.

48. How many miles had your car been driven before the rally?

49. How many miles had your car been driven after the rally?

50. How many miles was the rally? *Hint: Use your answers to problems 48 and 49.*

51. If you used 7.8 gallons of gasoline on the rally, how many miles did you average per gallon? Round the answer to the nearest tenth.

Where are they? **Making a sketch**

52. Study the clues to find out how far Carol and Joe are from the checkpoint at Clara's Corner. *Hint: Make a sketch.*

Clues:

- They left Bruskville and drove 18.6 miles east to Clara's Corner.
- They turned right on Highway 26 and drove 13.9 miles to the second checkpoint at Harold's Hollow.
- They drove 6.4 miles beyond Harold's Hollow.
- They turned around and started back for Clara's Corner. They drove 10.4 miles toward Clara's Corner.

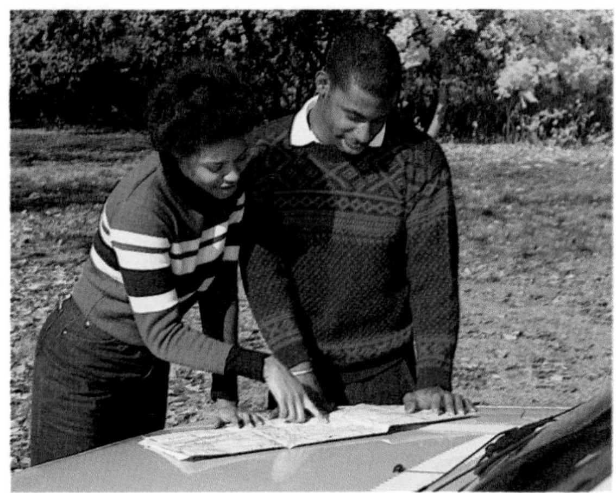

Subtracting fractions with different denominators

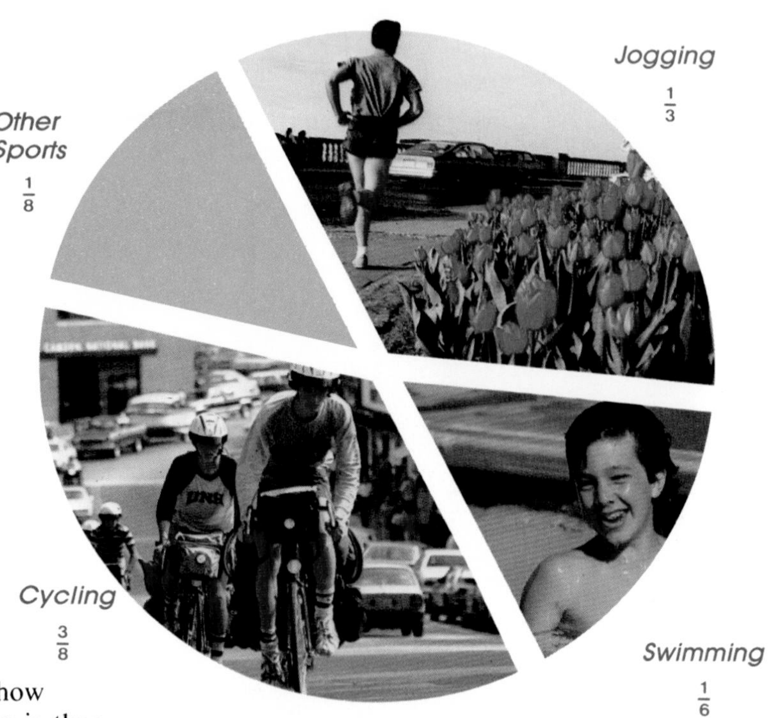

The circle graph shows the results of a teenage survey. Each teenager was asked to name his/her favorite after-school sport.

1. What fraction of those surveyed preferred swimming?
2. What fraction preferred cycling?
3. What fraction preferred jogging?
4. Would you add or subtract to find how much greater the fraction for cycling is than the fraction for jogging?

Here's how *to subtract fractions with different denominators.* $\frac{3}{8} - \frac{1}{3} = ?$

Find the least common denominator.

$$\frac{3}{8} - \frac{1}{3} \quad \boxed{24}$$

Change to equivalent fractions.

$$\frac{3}{8} = \frac{9}{24}, \quad -\frac{1}{3} = -\frac{8}{24}$$

Subtract.

$$\frac{3}{8} = \frac{9}{24}, \quad -\frac{1}{3} = -\frac{8}{24}, \quad \frac{1}{24}$$

5. Look at the *Here's how*. How much greater was the fraction of teenagers who preferred cycling than the fraction who preferred jogging?
6. Check these examples. Give each difference in simplest form.

a. $\frac{7}{3} - \frac{1}{3} = \frac{6}{3} = ?$

b. $\frac{5}{6} = \frac{5}{6}$; $-\frac{1}{3} = -\frac{2}{6}$; $\frac{3}{6} = ?$

c. $\frac{5}{3} = \frac{25}{15}$; $-\frac{3}{5} = -\frac{9}{15}$; $\frac{16}{15} = ?$

EXERCISES

Subtract. Give the difference in simplest form.

Here are scrambled answers for the next row of exercises: $\frac{3}{4}$ $\frac{3}{10}$ $\frac{1}{9}$ $\frac{1}{3}$ $\frac{5}{12}$ $\frac{13}{24}$ $\frac{1}{4}$

7. $\frac{2}{3} - \frac{5}{9}$ **8.** $\frac{3}{2} - \frac{3}{4}$ **9.** $\frac{9}{10} - \frac{3}{5}$ **10.** $\frac{5}{6} - \frac{1}{2}$ **11.** $\frac{7}{8} - \frac{1}{3}$ **12.** $\frac{7}{12} - \frac{1}{3}$ **13.** $\frac{3}{4} - \frac{1}{3}$

14. $\frac{5}{6} - \frac{2}{3}$ **15.** $\frac{3}{4} - \frac{3}{8}$ **16.** $\frac{2}{3} - \frac{5}{12}$ **17.** $\frac{3}{2} - \frac{7}{8}$ **18.** $\frac{5}{6} - \frac{0}{3}$ **19.** $\frac{3}{4} - \frac{2}{3}$ **20.** $\frac{5}{6} - \frac{1}{4}$

21. $\frac{3}{8} - \frac{1}{3}$ **22.** $\frac{5}{9} - \frac{1}{6}$ **23.** $\frac{7}{4} - \frac{3}{4}$ **24.** $\frac{9}{5} - \frac{3}{10}$ **25.** $\frac{7}{8} - \frac{5}{6}$ **26.** $\frac{1}{2} - \frac{1}{3}$ **27.** $\frac{7}{10} - \frac{1}{5}$

Solve. Use the circle graph on page 166.

28. How much greater was the fraction of teens who preferred jogging than the fraction of teens who preferred swimming?

29. How much greater was the fraction of teens who preferred cycling than the fraction of teens who preferred swimming?

30. What fraction of those surveyed preferred either jogging or swimming?

31. What fraction did not prefer the three most-preferred sports?

32. What fraction did not choose jogging?

33. What fraction did not choose either cycling or swimming?

Check the differences

34. Find and correct the two wrong answers.

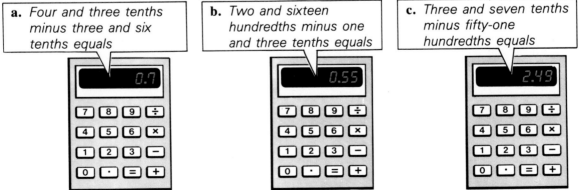

a. *Four and three tenths minus three and six tenths equals*

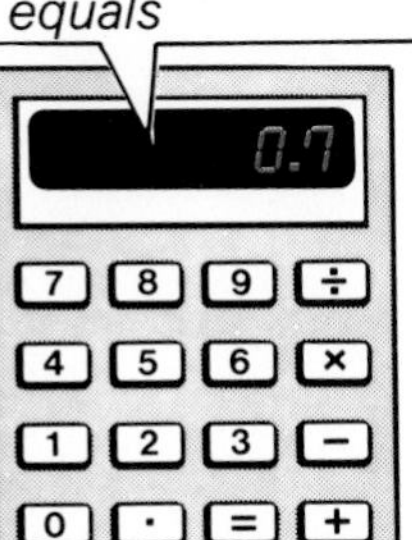

b. *Two and sixteen hundredths minus one and three tenths equals*

c. *Three and seven tenths minus fifty-one hundredths equals*

Subtracting mixed numbers without regrouping

I'm $3\frac{1}{4}$ inches shorter than Steve.

Arlo

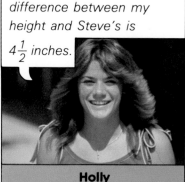

I'm the shortest. The difference between my height and Steve's is $4\frac{1}{2}$ inches.

Holly

I'm $68\frac{3}{4}$ inches tall.
Steve

1. Who is the shortest?
2. Who is the tallest?
3. To find how many inches tall Holly is, you subtract $4\frac{1}{2}$ from what number?

Here's how *to subtract mixed numbers.* $68\frac{3}{4} - 4\frac{1}{2} = ?$

Write equivalent fractions with a common denominator.

$$\begin{array}{rcr} 68\frac{3}{4} & = & 68\frac{3}{4} \\ -\ 4\frac{1}{2} & = & -4\frac{2}{4} \\ \hline \end{array}$$

Subtract the fractions.
Subtract the whole numbers.

$$\begin{array}{rcr} 68\frac{3}{4} & = & 68\frac{3}{4} \\ -\ 4\frac{1}{2} & = & -4\frac{2}{4} \\ \hline & & 64\frac{1}{4} \end{array}$$

4. Look at the *Here's how*. How tall is Holly?
5. Check these examples. Is Arlo $65\frac{1}{2}$ inches or 72 inches tall?

a. $$\begin{array}{r} 68\frac{3}{4} \\ +\ 3\frac{1}{4} \\ \hline 71\frac{4}{4} \end{array} = 72$$

b. $$\begin{array}{r} 68\frac{3}{4} \\ -\ 3\frac{1}{4} \\ \hline 65\frac{2}{4} \end{array} = 65\frac{1}{2}$$

EXERCISES

Subtract. Give each difference in simplest form.

Here are scrambled answers for the next row of exercises: $3\frac{3}{8}$ $4\frac{1}{8}$ $2\frac{1}{4}$ $1\frac{1}{4}$ $5\frac{1}{4}$ $2\frac{3}{8}$

6. $4\frac{3}{8} - 2\frac{1}{8}$ **7.** $8\frac{1}{2} - 5\frac{1}{8}$ **8.** $10\frac{3}{4} - 5\frac{1}{2}$ **9.** $6\frac{7}{8} - 2\frac{3}{4}$ **10.** $3\frac{1}{2} - 2\frac{1}{4}$ **11.** $4\frac{5}{8} - 2\frac{1}{4}$

12. $19\frac{4}{5} - 8\frac{3}{10}$ **13.** $17\frac{5}{12} - 14\frac{1}{3}$ **14.** $36\frac{1}{2} - 25\frac{3}{10}$ **15.** $17\frac{3}{8} - 12\frac{1}{8}$ **16.** $3\frac{4}{5} - \frac{3}{5}$ **17.** $2\frac{5}{9} - 1\frac{1}{3}$

18. $5\frac{1}{3} - 2\frac{1}{4}$ **19.** $3\frac{2}{3} - 1\frac{1}{2}$ **20.** $12\frac{3}{4} - 1\frac{1}{6}$ **21.** $8\frac{3}{4} - 2\frac{2}{5}$ **22.** $9\frac{1}{4} - 3\frac{1}{6}$ **23.** $10\frac{2}{9} - 3\frac{1}{10}$

24. $12\frac{3}{5} - 3\frac{1}{10}$ **25.** $16\frac{1}{2} - 8\frac{1}{4}$ **26.** $38\frac{1}{2} - 21\frac{3}{10}$ **27.** $15\frac{3}{4} - 6\frac{5}{8}$

28. $9\frac{7}{8} - 3\frac{1}{2}$ **29.** $15\frac{1}{4} - 3\frac{1}{6}$ **30.** $2\frac{7}{10} - 1\frac{3}{5}$ **31.** $8\frac{4}{5} - 2\frac{1}{4}$

32. $16\frac{1}{2} - 4\frac{1}{5}$ **33.** $3\frac{5}{12} - 1\frac{1}{4}$ **34.** $6\frac{4}{9} - 2\frac{1}{3}$ **35.** $7\frac{5}{8} - 1\frac{1}{6}$

How many pounds? **Logical reasoning**

Solve. Use the clues.

36. How much does Holly weigh?
Clues:
- Steve guessed 115 pounds and missed by $4\frac{1}{2}$ pounds.
- Arlo guessed 100 pounds and missed by $10\frac{1}{2}$ pounds.

37. How much does Arlo weigh?
Clues:
- Holly guessed 140 pounds and missed by $5\frac{3}{4}$ pounds.
- Steve guessed 148 pounds and missed by $2\frac{1}{4}$ pounds.

38. How much does Steve weigh?
Clues:
- Arlo guessed 160 pounds and missed by $16\frac{1}{2}$ pounds.
- Holly guessed 150 pounds and missed by $6\frac{1}{2}$ pounds.

39. Who do you think is the best guesser, Arlo, Holly, or Steve? Why?

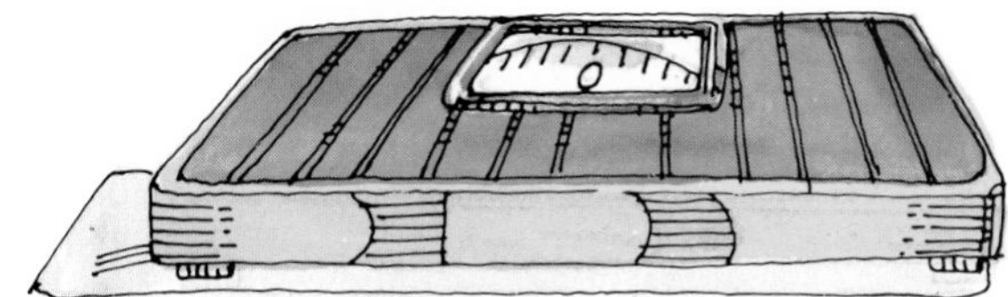

Subtracting mixed numbers with regrouping

At 300 feet
I can see
22 miles!

HEIGHT OF BALLOON (IN FEET)	DISTANCE SEEN FROM BALLOON (IN MILES)
10	$3\frac{7}{8}$
50	$8\frac{1}{2}$
100	$12\frac{3}{8}$
200	$17\frac{3}{8}$
300	22
1000	$38\frac{3}{4}$
3000	$67\frac{1}{8}$

1. Your hot-air balloon is 3000 feet above the ground. Your friend's balloon is at 100 feet. Look at the chart. What two numbers would you use to compute how many more miles you can see than your friend?

Here's how *to subtract mixed numbers.* $67\frac{1}{8} - 12\frac{3}{8} = ?$

Not enough eighths!

$$\begin{array}{r} 67\frac{1}{8} \\ -12\frac{3}{8} \\ \hline \end{array}$$

Regroup 1 for $\frac{8}{8}$.

$$\begin{array}{r} \overset{66}{\cancel{67}}\overset{9}{\cancel{\frac{1}{8}}} \\ -12\frac{3}{8} \\ \hline \end{array}$$

Subtract.

$$\begin{array}{r} \overset{66}{\cancel{67}}\overset{9}{\cancel{\frac{1}{8}}} \\ -12\frac{3}{8} \\ \hline 54\frac{6}{8} = 54\frac{3}{4} \end{array}$$

2. Look at the *Here's how.* How many miles farther can you see?

3. Study these examples. Is each difference in simplest form?

a. $$\begin{array}{rcr} 22 & = & 21\frac{2}{2} \\ -\ 8\frac{1}{2} & = & -\ 8\frac{1}{2} \\ \hline & & 13\frac{1}{2} \end{array}$$

Regrouped 1 for $\frac{2}{2}$.

b. $$\begin{array}{rcr} 8\frac{1}{2} & = & \overset{7}{\cancel{8}}\overset{12}{\cancel{\frac{4}{8}}} \\ -3\frac{7}{8} & = & -3\frac{7}{8} \\ \hline & & 4\frac{5}{8} \end{array}$$

Changed to a common denominator.
Regrouped 1 for $\frac{8}{8}$.

EXERCISES

Subtract. Write the difference in simplest form.

Here are scrambled answers for the next row of exercises: $3\frac{1}{4}$ $4\frac{3}{5}$ $7\frac{2}{9}$ $3\frac{3}{4}$ $2\frac{6}{7}$ $3\frac{4}{5}$

4. $6\frac{1}{8} - 2\frac{3}{8}$
5. $8\frac{7}{9} - 1\frac{5}{9}$
6. $9\frac{1}{8} - 5\frac{7}{8}$
7. $6\frac{5}{7} - 3\frac{6}{7}$
8. $8\frac{2}{5} - 3\frac{4}{5}$
9. $6 - 2\frac{1}{5}$
10. $4\frac{3}{7} - 1\frac{5}{7}$
11. $6\frac{5}{9} - 3\frac{8}{9}$
12. $7 - 3\frac{1}{2}$
13. $12\frac{1}{2} - 6\frac{1}{4}$
14. $20 - 8\frac{5}{8}$
15. $2\frac{2}{9} - 1\frac{1}{3}$
16. $4\frac{1}{8} - 2\frac{1}{2}$
17. $5\frac{3}{4} - 3\frac{1}{2}$
18. $9\frac{1}{10} - 3\frac{1}{5}$
19. $5\frac{3}{8} - 2\frac{1}{4}$
20. $14\frac{1}{8} - 6\frac{3}{4}$
21. $13\frac{1}{4} - 2\frac{1}{2}$
22. $8\frac{1}{3} - 2\frac{1}{2}$
23. $10\frac{1}{4} - 2\frac{2}{3}$
24. $6\frac{3}{8} - 4\frac{5}{6}$
25. $7\frac{7}{8} - 1\frac{3}{4}$
26. $15\frac{7}{8} - 12\frac{1}{4}$
27. $14\frac{1}{6} - 3\frac{2}{3}$
28. $6\frac{3}{4} - 1\frac{3}{5}$
29. $8\frac{1}{2} - 4\frac{2}{3}$
30. $7\frac{1}{5} - 2\frac{1}{10}$
31. $10\frac{3}{4} - 3\frac{7}{8}$
32. $10 - 6\frac{1}{2}$
33. $29\frac{2}{3} - 8\frac{1}{2}$
34. $24\frac{1}{2} - 1\frac{3}{4}$
35. $14\frac{2}{3} - 3\frac{1}{2}$
36. $10\frac{5}{8} - 4\frac{3}{4}$
37. $30 - 8\frac{3}{4}$

Oh, say can you see? Reading a map

Use the map scale and the chart on page 170 to solve these problems.

38. You are in a hot-air balloon 100 feet above Boone, Nebraska. What 4 cities can you see?
39. Now you are 300 feet above Petersburg. What 9 cities can you see?
40. When you are 3000 feet above O'Neill, can you see as far as Greeley?

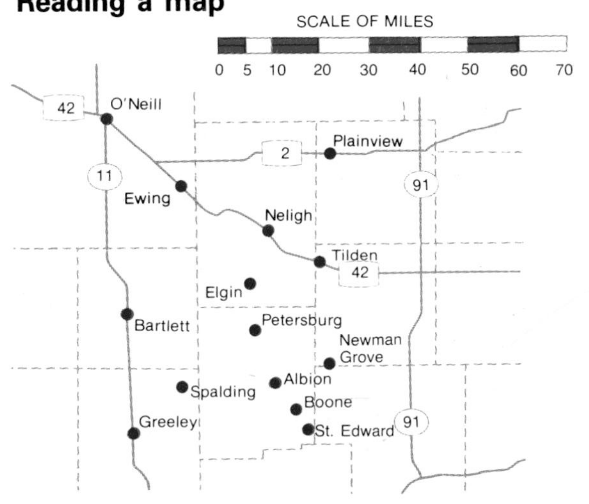

Cumulative Skill Practice

Find the mean. Round the answer to the nearest tenth. *(page 114)*

1. 19, 35, 28 **2.** 13, 42, 27 **3.** 28, 36, 1

4. 2.8, 4.7, 1.8 **5.** 1.8, 2.8, 1.9, 10.8 **6.** 28, 56, 32, 45

7. 13, 20, 17, 19, 15 **8.** 28, 14, 25, 13, 20 **9.** 3.7, 4.3, 4.4, 5.6

Write as a decimal. *(page 146)*

10. $\frac{1}{2}$ **11.** $\frac{7}{8}$ **12.** $\frac{3}{4}$ **13.** $\frac{2}{5}$ **14.** $\frac{5}{8}$ **15.** $3\frac{1}{2}$ **16.** $4\frac{3}{8}$

17. $\frac{3}{10}$ **18.** $\frac{4}{5}$ **19.** $1\frac{3}{5}$ **20.** $4\frac{1}{2}$ **21.** $6\frac{1}{8}$ **22.** $6\frac{2}{5}$ **23.** $3\frac{1}{10}$

24. $11\frac{1}{4}$ **25.** $16\frac{7}{10}$ **26.** $18\frac{1}{5}$ **27.** $21\frac{3}{20}$ **28.** $12\frac{7}{8}$ **29.** $42\frac{3}{4}$ **30.** $13\frac{1}{2}$

Change to a fraction or mixed number in simplest form. *(page 148)*

31. 0.6 **32.** 0.08 **33.** 0.25 **34.** 0.8 **35.** 0.5 **36.** 0.45 **37.** 0.75

38. 0.625 **39.** 1.75 **40.** 2.5 **41.** 6.125 **42.** 5.6 **43.** 9.45 **44.** 6.375

Add. Give the sum in simplest form. *(page 160)*

45. $8\frac{1}{3} + 4\frac{1}{6}$ **46.** $5\frac{1}{8} + 6\frac{3}{4}$ **47.** $6\frac{5}{8} + 3\frac{1}{4}$ **48.** $3\frac{1}{6} + 5\frac{5}{12}$ **49.** $2\frac{1}{6} + 7\frac{2}{3}$

50. $7\frac{2}{3} + 6\frac{1}{4}$ **51.** $8\frac{1}{5} + 3\frac{1}{2}$ **52.** $7\frac{2}{3} + 9\frac{1}{6}$ **53.** $12\frac{1}{8} + 4\frac{1}{2}$ **54.** $14\frac{3}{4} + 8\frac{1}{8}$

Subtract. Give the difference in simplest form. *(pages 168, 170)*

55. $6\frac{7}{8} - 3\frac{1}{8}$ **56.** $12\frac{5}{6} - 9\frac{1}{6}$ **57.** $23\frac{7}{8} - 17\frac{1}{4}$ **58.** $29\frac{2}{3} - 18\frac{1}{6}$ **59.** $24\frac{1}{3} - 7\frac{5}{6}$

60. $6\frac{1}{3} - 2\frac{3}{5}$ **61.** $11\frac{3}{8} - 8\frac{5}{6}$ **62.** $8\frac{1}{2} - 6\frac{7}{8}$ **63.** $14\frac{3}{5} - 9\frac{7}{10}$ **64.** $9\frac{5}{6} - 7\frac{2}{3}$

Problem solving

COMPUTERS IN AUTOMOBILES

You recently purchased a new car that has an advanced electronics system and a built-in computer. You are in your car driving up a steep hill and decide to use the Fuel Data Panel.

There are three buttons on the panel. You press the one on the left. The digital display shows the miles per gallon your car is producing at this instant.

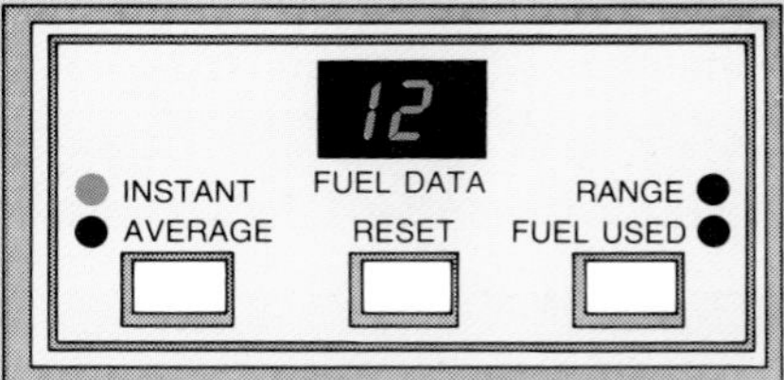

1. **a.** At this rate, how far will your car travel on 22 gallons of fuel?

   b. If the rate improves to 18 miles per gallon, how much further will your car travel at this new rate?

You want to know your car's average miles per gallon since the system was last reset. (To reset the system, you press the middle button.) You press the button on the left a second time.

2. **a.** At this rate, how many gallons have been used if the car was driven 247 miles? (Round the answer to the nearest tenth of a gallon.)

   b. At this rate, how many miles would the car have been driven if 17.5 gallons of fuel had been used?

You want to know how many miles you can travel on the fuel remaining in the tank. You press the button on the right.

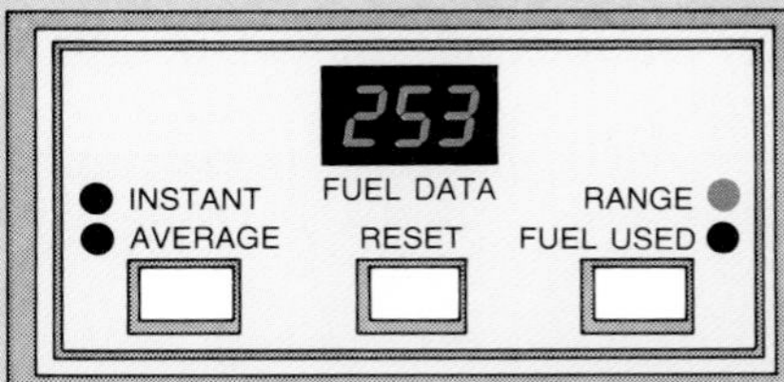

3. You plan to drive 185 miles to Lancaster and then drive on to Colebrook, another 91 miles. If the computer's estimate is accurate, can you make the trip to Colebrook without stopping for fuel?

You want to know how many gallons of fuel you have used since your last fill-up. You press the button on the right a second time.

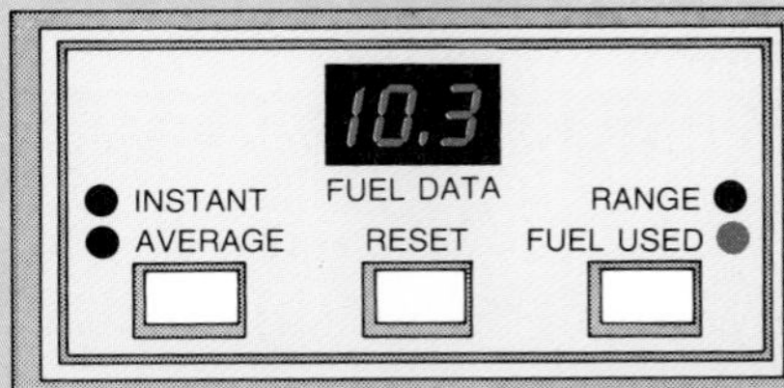

4. **a.** Your fuel tank holds 22 gallons of fuel. How many gallons are left in the tank?

   b. Gasoline costs $1.39 per gallon. Can you fill your tank for $15.00?

Chapter REVIEW

Here are scrambled answers for the review exercises:

8	add	equivalent	numerators	subtract
12	common	fractions	regroup	whole
20	denominator	numbers	simplest	

1. To complete this sum, you would [?] the numerators and use the common denominator. *(page 156)*

$$\frac{3}{5} + \frac{1}{5} = \frac{?}{?}$$

2. To complete this sum, you would first change to equivalent fractions with a [?] denominator. The least common denominator is [?]. *(page 158)*

$$\frac{3}{4} + \frac{2}{3} = \frac{?}{?} + \frac{?}{?}$$

3. To complete this addition exercise, you would add the [?] and then add the [?] numbers. The last step would be to write the sum in [?] form. *(page 160)*

$$\begin{array}{rcr} 2\frac{2}{3} & = & 2\frac{4}{6} \\ +1\frac{1}{2} & = & +1\frac{3}{6} \\ \hline \end{array}$$

4. To complete this difference, you would [?] the numerators and use the common [?]. *(page 164)*

$$\frac{5}{9} - \frac{4}{9} = \frac{?}{?}$$

5. To complete this difference, you would first change to [?] fractions with a common denominator. Then you would subtract the [?] and use the common denominator. *(page 166)*

$$\frac{5}{6} - \frac{2}{3} = \frac{?}{?} - \frac{?}{?}$$

6. To complete this subtraction exercise, you would first change to equivalent fractions using the least common denominator, [?]. Then you would subtract the fractions and whole [?]. *(page 168)*

$$\begin{array}{rcr} 4\frac{4}{5} & = & 4\frac{?}{?} \\ -2\frac{1}{4} & = & -2\frac{?}{?} \\ \hline \end{array}$$

7. The next step in this subtraction exercise would be to [?] one for [?] eighths. *(page 170)*

$$\begin{array}{rcr} 5\frac{1}{8} & = & 5\frac{1}{8} \\ -3\frac{1}{2} & = & -3\frac{4}{8} \\ \hline \end{array}$$

Chapter TEST

***Add.* Write the sum in simplest form.** *(pages 156, 158)*

1. $\frac{5}{9} + \frac{2}{9}$ **2.** $\frac{1}{8} + \frac{3}{8}$ **3.** $\frac{5}{6} + \frac{3}{6}$ **4.** $\frac{2}{3} + \frac{1}{3}$ **5.** $\frac{7}{9} + \frac{4}{9}$

6. $\frac{1}{6} + \frac{2}{3}$ **7.** $\frac{1}{2} + \frac{1}{3}$ **8.** $\frac{5}{8} + \frac{3}{4}$ **9.** $\frac{3}{4} + \frac{2}{3}$ **10.** $\frac{3}{4} + \frac{1}{2}$

***Add.* Write the sum in simplest form.** *(page 160)*

11. $3\frac{1}{3} + 2\frac{1}{3}$ **12.** $2\frac{1}{2} + 1\frac{1}{2}$ **13.** $5\frac{3}{5} + 3\frac{1}{5}$ **14.** $4\frac{3}{8} + 4\frac{1}{8}$ **15.** $2\frac{4}{9} + 4\frac{5}{9}$ **16.** $4\frac{3}{7} + 8\frac{5}{7}$

17. $5\frac{2}{5} + 2\frac{1}{2}$ **18.** $3\frac{1}{2} + 6\frac{1}{3}$ **19.** $4\frac{2}{3} + 5\frac{5}{6}$ **20.** $6\frac{3}{4} + 2\frac{5}{6}$ **21.** $5\frac{7}{8} + 5\frac{1}{2}$ **22.** $4\frac{1}{5} + 3\frac{1}{10}$

***Subtract.* Write the difference in simplest form.** *(pages 164, 166)*

23. $\frac{4}{5} - \frac{1}{5}$ **24.** $\frac{5}{6} - \frac{1}{6}$ **25.** $\frac{5}{8} - \frac{1}{8}$ **26.** $\frac{8}{9} - \frac{2}{9}$ **27.** $\frac{5}{7} - \frac{1}{7}$

28. $\frac{1}{2} - \frac{1}{4}$ **29.** $\frac{3}{4} - \frac{1}{3}$ **30.** $\frac{5}{9} - \frac{1}{6}$ **31.** $\frac{7}{8} - \frac{1}{3}$ **32.** $\frac{1}{2} - \frac{3}{8}$

***Subtract.* Write the difference in simplest form.** *(pages 168, 170)*

33. $5\frac{3}{5} - 2\frac{1}{5}$ **34.** $6\frac{3}{4} - 4\frac{1}{4}$ **35.** $7\frac{2}{3} - 1\frac{1}{6}$ **36.** $8\frac{4}{5} - 3\frac{1}{4}$ **37.** $6\frac{7}{8} - 2\frac{2}{3}$ **38.** $9\frac{4}{5} - 3\frac{1}{2}$

39. $9\frac{1}{4} - 6\frac{1}{2}$ **40.** $7\frac{1}{2} - 4\frac{3}{5}$ **41.** $8 - 5\frac{5}{6}$ **42.** $5 - 2\frac{7}{8}$ **43.** $6\frac{2}{3} - 3\frac{3}{4}$ **44.** $8\frac{1}{3} - 2\frac{4}{9}$

SEEDLESS
RYE BREAD

$2\frac{3}{4}$	cups rye flour	2	tablespoons honey
$3\frac{1}{2}$	cups white flour	1	tablespoon butter
1	tablespoon sugar	$1\frac{1}{2}$	cups milk
2	teaspoons salt	$\frac{1}{4}$	cup water
1	package yeast		

***Solve.* Write the answer in simplest form.**

45. How many cups of flour are needed?

46. You have $\frac{3}{4}$ cup of milk. How much more do you need?

Cumulative TEST Standardized Format

Choose the correct letter.

1. Give the sum.

   81.6 + 42.53 + 231.5

   A. 355.63
   B. 73.84
   C. 354.63
   D. none of these

2. Give the difference.

   64.03 − 2.946

   A. 34.57
   B. 3.457
   C. 61.084
   D. none of these

3. Give the product.

   20.6 × 1.28

   A. 26.268
   B. 26.368
   C. 263.68
   D. none of these

4. Give the quotient.

   516.3 ÷ 100

   A. 51,630
   B. 0.5163
   C. 5.163
   D. none of these

5. Give the quotient rounded to the nearest hundredth.

   21.57 ÷ 3.7

   A. 5.82
   B. 0.58
   C. 5.83
   D. none of these

6. The mean of 48, 52, 46, 46, and 53 is

   A. 49
   B. 46
   C. 48
   D. none of these

7. $2\frac{7}{8} = ?$

   A. 0.875
   B. 2.875
   C. 2.125
   D. none of these

8. 1.75 = ?

   A. $\frac{3}{4}$
   B. $1\frac{1}{4}$
   C. $1\frac{3}{4}$
   D. none of these

9. Add. $3\frac{3}{4} + 2\frac{2}{3}$

   A. $6\frac{5}{12}$ C. $5\frac{5}{7}$
   B. $5\frac{5}{12}$ D. none of these

10. Subtract. $5\frac{1}{3} - 3\frac{1}{2}$

    A. $2\frac{1}{6}$
    B. $2\frac{5}{6}$
    C. $1\frac{1}{6}$
    D. none of these

11. QUIZ SCORES

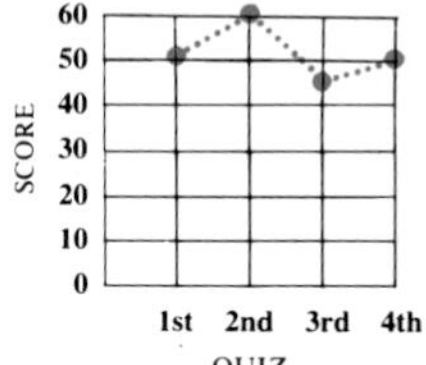

    The score on the third quiz was

    A. 60 B. 55
    C. 50 D. 45

12. You volunteer to work 12 hours on a class project. You work $2\frac{1}{2}$ hours on Friday and $6\frac{3}{4}$ hours on Saturday. How many hours do you have left to work?

    A. $7\frac{3}{4}$ B. $3\frac{3}{4}$
    C. $2\frac{3}{4}$ D. none of these

Chapter 8
Multiplying and Dividing Fractions and Mixed Numbers

Multiplying fractions

1. How many stamps are on the page?
2. How many stamps can be mounted on a full page?
3. What fraction of the page is covered with stamps?
4. To find what fraction of the page is covered with stamps, you could multiply $\frac{2}{3}$ by what fraction?

Here's how *to multiply fractions.* $\frac{2}{3} \times \frac{3}{4} = ?$

Multiply the numerators to get the numerator of the product and multiply the denominators to get the denominator of the product.

Multiply numerators.
Multiply denominators.

$$\frac{2}{3} \times \frac{3}{4} = \frac{6}{12}$$

Write the product
in simplest form.

$$\frac{2}{3} \times \frac{3}{4} = \frac{6}{12} = \frac{1}{2}$$

5. Look at the *Here's how*. What fraction of the page is covered with stamps?
6. Check these examples. Give each product in simplest form.

a. $\frac{2}{3} \times \frac{3}{8} = \frac{6}{24} = ?$

b. $2 \times \frac{3}{4} = \frac{2}{1} \times \frac{3}{4} = ?$ (with 2 shown as $\frac{2}{1}$)

EXERCISES

Multiply. Write the product in simplest form.

Here are scrambled answers for the next row of exercises: $\frac{5}{8}$ 1 $\frac{1}{5}$ $2\frac{1}{4}$ $\frac{1}{16}$ $\frac{2}{7}$

7. $\frac{1}{2} \times \frac{2}{5}$ **8.** $3 \times \frac{3}{4}$ **9.** $\frac{5}{6} \times \frac{3}{4}$ **10.** $\frac{2}{3} \times \frac{3}{2}$ **11.** $\frac{1}{4} \times \frac{1}{4}$ **12.** $\frac{2}{3} \times \frac{3}{7}$

13. $\frac{2}{3} \times 2$ **14.** $\frac{1}{2} \times \frac{2}{3}$ **15.** $\frac{1}{2} \times \frac{1}{3}$ **16.** $\frac{1}{4} \times \frac{5}{8}$ **17.** $3 \times \frac{1}{3}$ **18.** $\frac{1}{5} \times \frac{1}{5}$

19. $\frac{4}{3} \times \frac{2}{5}$ **20.** $\frac{3}{2} \times \frac{3}{4}$ **21.** $4 \times \frac{3}{4}$ **22.** $\frac{3}{8} \times \frac{2}{3}$ **23.** $\frac{0}{3} \times \frac{4}{5}$ **24.** $\frac{2}{7} \times \frac{7}{3}$

25. $\frac{2}{5} \times \frac{3}{2}$ **26.** $\frac{3}{4} \times \frac{2}{3}$ **27.** $4 \times \frac{2}{3}$ **28.** $\frac{5}{6} \times \frac{1}{3}$ **29.** $\frac{3}{4} \times \frac{3}{4}$ **30.** $10 \times \frac{4}{5}$

31. $\frac{3}{4} \times 3$ **32.** $\frac{3}{2} \times \frac{1}{4}$ **33.** $\frac{5}{2} \times \frac{2}{5}$ **34.** $\frac{2}{9} \times \frac{3}{4}$ **35.** $\frac{3}{2} \times \frac{0}{2}$ **36.** $\frac{3}{5} \times \frac{5}{8}$

37. $\frac{1}{3} \times \frac{3}{4}$ **38.** $\frac{5}{8} \times \frac{4}{5}$ **39.** $3 \times \frac{5}{6}$ **40.** $\frac{9}{2} \times \frac{4}{3}$ **41.** $\frac{3}{8} \times \frac{3}{8}$ **42.** $\frac{1}{2} \times \frac{1}{2}$

43. $\frac{5}{8} \times \frac{2}{5}$ **44.** $\frac{6}{5} \times \frac{15}{2}$ **45.** $\frac{7}{10} \times \frac{5}{4}$ **46.** $6 \times \frac{3}{10}$ **47.** $\frac{5}{6} \times \frac{6}{5}$ **48.** $\frac{3}{5} \times \frac{5}{3}$

49. $2 \times \frac{1}{2}$ **50.** $\frac{5}{12} \times \frac{3}{2}$ **51.** $\frac{4}{3} \times \frac{3}{4}$ **52.** $\frac{4}{3} \times \frac{7}{12}$ **53.** $\frac{15}{16} \times \frac{4}{5}$ **54.** $4 \times \frac{3}{4}$

55. $5 \times \frac{2}{5}$ **56.** $\frac{3}{5} \times \frac{1}{3}$ **57.** $\frac{1}{5} \times \frac{1}{4}$ **58.** $8 \times \frac{9}{8}$ **59.** $\frac{2}{7} \times \frac{1}{2}$ **60.** $\frac{12}{13} \times \frac{1}{2}$

61. $\frac{1}{6} \times \frac{2}{3}$ **62.** $\frac{1}{2} \times \frac{4}{5}$ **63.** $6 \times \frac{1}{2}$ **64.** $\frac{1}{3} \times \frac{2}{5}$ **65.** $6 \times \frac{1}{6}$ **66.** $9 \times \frac{4}{3}$

Solve.

67. Two thirds of the stamps in a collection are U.S. stamps. One fourth of the U.S. stamps are airmail stamps. What fraction of the stamps are U.S. airmail stamps?

68. One eighth of the stamps in an album were from Germany and one third of the stamps were from France. What fraction of the stamps were not from Germany or France?

Airmail error

69. The most valuable United States stamp was printed in 1918. Its value resulted from a printer's error (the airplane was upside down). In 1979, 4 of these 24¢ stamps sold for a total of $500,000. The sale price was how many times the face value? Round the answer to the nearest tenth.

A fraction of a whole number

SHOE SALE!
Regular price $36
$\frac{2}{3}$ of Regular Price
Women's Jogging Shoes
Regular price $40
$\frac{1}{2}$ of Regular Price
Men's Tennis Shoes
Regular price $44
$\frac{3}{4}$ of Regular Price
Men's Jogging Shoes

1. What is the regular price of the women's jogging shoes?

2. The sale price of the women's jogging shoes is what fraction of the regular price?

3. To find the sale price, you would find $\frac{2}{3}$ of what price?

Here's how *to find a fraction of a number.* $\frac{2}{3}$ *of \$36 = ?*

SHORTCUT METHOD!

When the denominator is a divisor of the whole number, you can divide the whole number by the denominator and then multiply the result by the numerator.

$36 \div 3 \times 2 = 24$

$\frac{2}{3}$ of \$36 = \$24

REGULAR METHOD

Change the whole number to a fraction and multiply.

$$\frac{2}{3} \text{ of } \$36 = \frac{2}{3} \times \frac{\$36}{1} = \frac{\$72}{3} = \$24$$

Note:

Dividing a number by 3 gives $\frac{1}{3}$ of the number.

Multiplying that result by 2 gives $\frac{2}{3}$ of the number.

4. Look at the *Here's how.* What is the sale price of the women's jogging shoes?

5. In which method was the computing easier?

6. You can use the shortcut when the $\underset{\text{numerator/denominator}}{\underline{\quad ? \quad}}$ of the fraction is a divisor of the whole number.

EXERCISES

Use the shortcut to complete each exercise.

Here are scrambled answers for the next row of exercises: 4 12 3 27

7. $\frac{1}{4}$ of 12 = ?	**8.** $\frac{2}{3}$ of 18 = ?	**9.** $\frac{3}{4}$ of 36 = ?	**10.** $\frac{2}{5}$ of 10 = ?
11. $\frac{3}{5}$ of 20 = ?	**12.** $\frac{3}{8}$ of 48 = ?	**13.** $\frac{1}{5}$ of 15 = ?	**14.** $\frac{5}{6}$ of 30 = ?
15. $\frac{3}{10}$ of 60 = ?	**16.** $\frac{1}{3}$ of 33 = ?	**17.** $\frac{5}{8}$ of 48 = ?	**18.** $\frac{3}{4}$ of 48 = ?
19. $\frac{2}{3}$ of \$30 = ?	**20.** $\frac{3}{5}$ of \$30 = ?	**21.** $\frac{1}{2}$ of \$32 = ?	**22.** $\frac{9}{10}$ of \$100 = ?
23. $\frac{1}{8}$ of \$48 = ?	**24.** $\frac{7}{10}$ of \$60 = ?	**25.** $\frac{4}{5}$ of \$45 = ?	**26.** $\frac{7}{8}$ of \$56 = ?

You decide which method to use. Give the answer in simplest form.

Here are scrambled answers for the next row of exercises: $10\frac{1}{2}$ 21 15 $15\frac{1}{3}$

27. $\frac{1}{2}$ of 21 = ?	**28.** $\frac{3}{4}$ of 28 = ?	**29.** $\frac{2}{3}$ of 23 = ?	**30.** $\frac{5}{6}$ of 18 = ?
31. $\frac{4}{5}$ of 25 = ?	**32.** $\frac{2}{3}$ of 16 = ?	**33.** $\frac{1}{6}$ of 24 = ?	**34.** $\frac{3}{8}$ of 31 = ?
35. $\frac{3}{4}$ of 15 = ?	**36.** $\frac{1}{3}$ of 28 = ?	**37.** $\frac{7}{10}$ of 20 = ?	**38.** $\frac{7}{8}$ of 27 = ?
39. $\frac{11}{12}$ of 12 = ?	**40.** $\frac{2}{5}$ of 12 = ?	**41.** $\frac{1}{5}$ of 12 = ?	**42.** $\frac{3}{4}$ of 12 = ?
43. $\frac{3}{8}$ of \$40 = ?	**44.** $\frac{4}{5}$ of \$35 = ?	**45.** $\frac{5}{6}$ of \$48 = ?	**46.** $\frac{2}{3}$ of \$60 = ?

Solve. Use the ad on page 180.

47. What is the sale price of the men's tennis shoes?

48. What is the sale price of the men's jogging shoes?

49. What is the difference in the sale price of the two men's styles?

50. How much would one save by buying the men's jogging shoes on sale?

Pick-a-pair Using logical reasoning

51. You have 4 pairs of brown socks and 5 pairs of blue socks. It is dark and the lights go out in your room! How many socks must you pick to be sure that you have a pair that matches?

Multiplying mixed numbers

SPICE BARS

Makes 4 dozen bars

$1\frac{1}{2}$ cups all-purpose flour
$1\frac{1}{4}$ cups sugar
$\frac{1}{2}$ cup milk
$\frac{1}{2}$ cup vegetable oil
2 eggs
$\frac{3}{4}$ teaspoon salt
1 teaspoon baking soda
$1\frac{1}{4}$ teaspoons cinnamon
1 teaspoon cloves
$\frac{1}{2}$ cup chopped nuts
$\frac{1}{2}$ cup raisins

Preheat oven to 350°F. Grease 9″ x 10″ jelly-roll pan. Combine all ingredients in large bowl and mix well. Turn batter into prepared pan, spreading evenly. Bake until golden, about 20 minutes. Cool in pan on rack 10 minutes. Cut into bars.

1. How many bars does this recipe make?
2. How much sugar is needed to make the recipe?
3. You want to make $2\frac{1}{2}$ times the recipe. What two mixed numbers should you multiply to find how many cups of sugar you will need?

Here's how *to multiply mixed numbers.* $2\frac{1}{2} \times 1\frac{1}{4} = ?$

Change each mixed number to a fraction and multiply.

Change to fractions.	Multiply.	Write the product in simplest form.
$2\frac{1}{2} \times 1\frac{1}{4} = \frac{5}{2} \times \frac{5}{4}$	$2\frac{1}{2} \times 1\frac{1}{4} = \frac{5}{2} \times \frac{5}{4}$ $= \frac{25}{8}$	$2\frac{1}{2} \times 1\frac{1}{4} = \frac{5}{2} \times \frac{5}{4}$ $= \frac{25}{8}$ $= 3\frac{1}{8}$

4. Look at the *Here's how*. How many cups of sugar will you need? Does the answer seem reasonable?
5. Check these examples. Give each product in simplest form.

a. $3 \times 2\frac{2}{3} = \frac{3}{1} \times \frac{8}{3}$
$= \frac{24}{3}$
$= ?$

b. $2\frac{3}{4} \times 4\frac{2}{5} = \frac{11}{4} \times \frac{22}{5}$
$= \frac{242}{20}$
$= ?$

EXERCISES

Multiply. Write the product in simplest form.

Here are scrambled answers for the next row of exercises: $5\frac{1}{2}$ $4\frac{1}{6}$ 7 2 $6\frac{3}{5}$

6. $2 \times 3\frac{1}{2}$ **7.** $1\frac{1}{2} \times 1\frac{1}{3}$ **8.** $2\frac{3}{4} \times 2$ **9.** $1\frac{2}{3} \times 2\frac{1}{2}$ **10.** $2\frac{1}{5} \times 3$

11. $2\frac{1}{4} \times 3\frac{1}{2}$ **12.** $2\frac{4}{5} \times 3$ **13.** $3\frac{1}{2} \times 1\frac{3}{4}$ **14.** $2\frac{1}{2} \times 3\frac{1}{2}$ **15.** $2\frac{1}{2} \times 2\frac{1}{2}$

16. $2\frac{1}{3} \times 4\frac{1}{2}$ **17.** $3\frac{1}{6} \times 2\frac{3}{4}$ **18.** $3\frac{3}{4} \times 6$ **19.** $5\frac{1}{2} \times 4\frac{3}{4}$ **20.** $4\frac{1}{3} \times 3\frac{1}{2}$

21. $2\frac{3}{8} \times 4$ **22.** $3\frac{2}{3} \times 4\frac{1}{3}$ **23.** $5\frac{3}{4} \times 2\frac{1}{2}$ **24.** $2\frac{2}{3} \times 3\frac{1}{6}$ **25.** $2\frac{1}{5} \times 1\frac{1}{2}$

26. $4\frac{1}{5} \times 5\frac{3}{8}$ **27.** $3 \times 5\frac{2}{3}$ **28.** $1\frac{5}{8} \times 4\frac{1}{2}$ **29.** $3\frac{3}{8} \times 6\frac{3}{4}$ **30.** $1\frac{1}{3} \times 6$

31. $4\frac{1}{2} \times 3$ **32.** $1\frac{1}{2} \times 2\frac{1}{3}$ **33.** $4 \times 2\frac{1}{2}$ **34.** $3\frac{1}{3} \times 4\frac{1}{3}$ **35.** $1\frac{2}{3} \times 6$

Solve. Use the recipe on page 182.

36. You make $1\frac{1}{2}$ times the recipe. How many bars do you make?

37. How much more baking soda than salt is used in the recipe?

38. How much flour is needed to double the recipe?

39. How many teaspoons of spices (cinnamon and cloves) are used in the recipe?

40. You want to make $3\frac{1}{2}$ times the recipe. How much sugar will you need?

41. You have $1\frac{3}{4}$ cups of raisins. Do you have enough to make $3\frac{1}{2}$ times the recipe?

Check the products

42. Find and correct the two wrong answers.

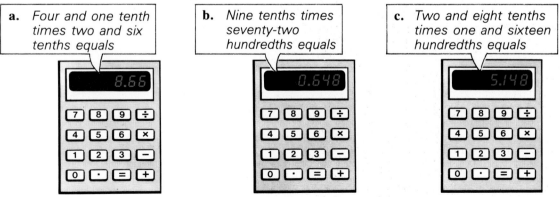

a. *Four and one tenth times two and six tenths equals*

8.66

b. *Nine tenths times seventy-two hundredths equals*

c. *Two and eight tenths times one and sixteen hundredths equals*

More on a fraction of a whole number

1. How many hours are there in 2 days?
2. How many hours are there in $\frac{1}{2}$ of a day?
3. If you know the number of hours in 2 days and the number of hours in $\frac{1}{2}$ of a day, how could you find the number of hours in $2\frac{1}{2}$ days?

1 day = 24 hours (h)
1 h = 60 minutes (min)
1 min = 60 seconds (s)

Here's how *to find the number of hours in $2\frac{1}{2}$ days.*

SHORTCUT METHOD!

First find the hours in 2 days and in $\frac{1}{2}$ of a day. Then add.

$2\frac{1}{2}$ days = 48 hours + 12 hours
= 60 hours

24 hours

REGULAR METHOD

Change the mixed number to a fraction and multiply.

$2\frac{1}{2}$ days $= 2\frac{1}{2} \times 24$ hours
$= \frac{5}{2} \times \frac{24}{1}$ hours
$= \frac{120}{2}$ hours
$= 60$ hours

24 hours

4. Look at the *Here's how*.
   a. How many hours are there in $2\frac{1}{2}$ days?
   b. Does the answer make sense? Is it between the number of hours in 2 days (48) and the number of hours in 3 days (72)?

EXERCISES

Complete. *Here are scrambled answers for the next row of exercises: 100 66 90*

5. $2\frac{3}{4}$ days = ? h
6. $1\frac{1}{2}$ h = ? min
7. $1\frac{2}{3}$ h = ? min
8. $1\frac{1}{3}$ min = ? s
9. $1\frac{3}{4}$ h = ? min
10. $1\frac{2}{3}$ days = ? h
11. $1\frac{5}{6}$ min = ? s
12. $2\frac{3}{8}$ days = ? h
13. $3\frac{2}{3}$ h = ? min

1 yard (yd) = 3 feet (ft)
1 ft = 12 inches (in.)
1 yd = 36 in.

14. $1\frac{1}{3}$ yd = ? ft **15.** $1\frac{1}{2}$ ft = ? in. **16.** $1\frac{1}{3}$ yd = ? in. **17.** $1\frac{3}{4}$ ft = ? in.

18. $2\frac{1}{3}$ yd = ? ft **19.** $1\frac{3}{4}$ yd = ? in. **20.** $2\frac{2}{3}$ yd = ? ft. **21.** $2\frac{1}{2}$ yd = ? in.

22. $2\frac{3}{4}$ ft = ? in. **23.** $3\frac{2}{3}$ yd = ? ft **24.** $3\frac{2}{3}$ ft = ? in. **25.** $3\frac{3}{4}$ yd = ? in.

1 gallon (gal) = 4 quarts (qt)
1 qt = 2 pints (pt)
1 pt = 2 cups (c)

26. $1\frac{1}{2}$ gal = ? qt **27.** $1\frac{1}{2}$ qt = ? pt

28. $2\frac{1}{2}$ pt = ? c **29.** $4\frac{1}{2}$ qt = ? pt

30. $2\frac{3}{4}$ gal = ? qt **31.** $4\frac{1}{2}$ pt = ? c

32. $3\frac{1}{2}$ gal = ? qt **33.** $3\frac{1}{2}$ pt = ? c

34. $2\frac{1}{2}$ qt = ? pt **35.** $2\frac{1}{4}$ gal = ? qt

36. $3\frac{1}{2}$ qt = ? pt **37.** $5\frac{1}{2}$ pt = ? c

What's the time?

38. A thunderstorm caused a power failure at 10:05 P.M. The next morning at 7:55 the electric clock showed 6:05.

a. How long was the electricity off?

b. At what time did the electricity come on again?

Cumulative Skill Practice

Give the sum. *(page 24)*

1. 3.4 + 2.36 **2.** 1.78 + 4.7 **3.** 6.14 + 15.9

4. 6.3 + 2.14 + 5.3 **5.** 20 + 0.5 + 2.9 **6.** 5.5 + 13 + 0.3

7. 40 + 3.7 + 0.25 **8.** 0.2 + 0.24 + 0.3 **9.** 12 + 2.5 + 0.75

10. 5.7 + 36 + 2.1 **11.** 6.34 + 18 + 96 **12.** 35 + 2.4 + 3.1

13. 9.03 + 4 + 1.2 **14.** 1.4 + 0.03 + 2 **15.** 14 + 6.2 + 4.05

Give the difference. *(page 46)*

16. 32.4 − 18.6 **17.** 20.6 − 15.8 **18.** 6.00 − 2.73 **19.** 4.02 − 3.8

20. 3.4 − 1.26 **21.** 16 − 12.5 **22.** 9.6 − 5.45 **23.** 6.4 − 3.91

24. 32.1 − 2.84 **25.** 9.7 − 2.74 **26.** 14 − 3.62 **27.** 15 − 2.8

28. 6.5 − 2.01 **29.** 16.8 − 3.24 **30.** 3.2 − 1.1 **31.** 2.8 − 2

32. 3.8 − 1.57 **33.** 2.91 − 1.7 **34.** 6 − 3.9 **35.** 6.9 − 3.15

Give the product. *(page 64)*

36. 2.3 × 0.4 **37.** 2.6 × 0.21 **38.** 0.44 × 0.6 **39.** 0.2 × 0.35

40. 14 × 1.2 **41.** 0.56 × 2.8 **42.** 3.21 × 1.1 **43.** 2.11 × 3.8

44. 9.24 × 3 **45.** 14.5 × 2.6 **46.** 125 × 1.4 **47.** 286 × 3.1

48. 6.1 × 4.2 **49.** 4.8 × 11 **50.** 37 × 0.2 **51.** 351 × 4.2

52. 7.35 × 0.01 **53.** 3.4 × 2.9 **54.** 6.01 × 3.7 **55.** 368 × 1.11

Give the quotient rounded to the nearest tenth. *(page 96)*

56. 4.64 ÷ 0.5 **57.** 8.43 ÷ 0.02 **58.** 56.5 ÷ 3 **59.** 8.65 ÷ 2

60. 42 ÷ 0.7 **61.** 3.8 ÷ 0.2 **62.** 6.38 ÷ 1.2 **63.** 3.78 ÷ 2.4

64. 0.8465 ÷ 7.1 **65.** 60.04 ÷ 5.2 **66.** 0.072 ÷ 0.36 **67.** 0.54 ÷ 0.21

68. 56 ÷ 0.24 **69.** 0.08 ÷ 2.5 **70.** 10.2 ÷ 2.8 **71.** 6.3 ÷ 0.5

Less than (<), equal to (=), or greater than (>)? *(page 132)*

72. $\frac{4}{5}$ ● $\frac{3}{5}$ **73.** $\frac{7}{5}$ ● $\frac{3}{5}$ **74.** $\frac{5}{9}$ ● $\frac{4}{9}$ **75.** $\frac{1}{7}$ ● $\frac{3}{7}$ **76.** $\frac{4}{3}$ ● $\frac{7}{3}$

77. $\frac{1}{8}$ ● $\frac{1}{6}$ **78.** $\frac{5}{8}$ ● $\frac{1}{2}$ **79.** $\frac{1}{4}$ ● $\frac{1}{5}$ **80.** $\frac{3}{4}$ ● $\frac{2}{3}$ **81.** $\frac{0}{5}$ ● $\frac{0}{4}$

82. $\frac{2}{5}$ ● $\frac{1}{2}$ **83.** $\frac{7}{3}$ ● $\frac{5}{2}$ **84.** $\frac{2}{3}$ ● $\frac{7}{10}$ **85.** $\frac{1}{9}$ ● $\frac{1}{8}$ **86.** $\frac{4}{5}$ ● $\frac{2}{3}$

Problem solving

You're the clerk

Use the information in the table to answer each customer's question.

	POUNDS				
APPLES	$\frac{1}{4}$	$\frac{1}{2}$	$\frac{3}{4}$	1	2
Granny Smith	\$.25	\$.50	\$.75	\$1.00	\$2.00
Delicious	\$.15	\$.30	\$.45	\$.60	\$1.20
McIntosh	\$.18	\$.36	\$.54	\$.72	\$1.44

1. *What is the cost of 2 pounds of McIntosh apples?*

2. *What is the cost of $1\frac{1}{2}$ pounds of Granny Smith apples?*

3. *How many pounds of Delicious apples can I buy for \$1.80?*

4. "What is the cost of $2\frac{1}{2}$ pounds of McIntosh apples?"

5. "How many pounds of Delicious apples can I buy for \$1.50?"

6. "What is the cost of $2\frac{3}{4}$ pounds of Granny Smith apples?"

7. "How many pounds of McIntosh apples can I buy for \$.90?"

Solve. Use the apple prices.

8. Mike gave the clerk \$5 for $2\frac{3}{4}$ pounds of Delicious apples. How much change did he get?

9. Karen spent \$3.60 for a 5-pound bag of apples. What kind of apples did she buy?

10. There are 4 pounds of apples in a bag. The total cost is \$2.40. What kind of apples are in the bag?

11. How much more do 10 pounds of McIntosh apples cost than 10 pounds of Delicious apples?

12. A customer bought $1\frac{1}{2}$ pounds of Granny Smith apples and some Delicious apples. She spent a total of \$3.30. How many pounds of Delicious apples did the customer buy?

13. How much does a 6-pound bag of apples cost if it is $\frac{1}{3}$ Granny Smith apples and $\frac{2}{3}$ Delicious apples?

Dividing fractions

1. a. How far is it around the track?
   b. How many times would you have to run around the track to run $\frac{1}{2}$ mile?
2. a. How many times would you have to run around the track to run 2 miles?
   b. Answer part **a** by dividing.

total miles		miles in each lap		laps
2	÷	$\mathbf{\frac{1}{4}}$	=	?

   c. Answer part **a** by multiplying.

total miles		laps for each mile		laps
2	×	**4**	=	?

   d. Look at parts **b** and **c**. Dividing by $\frac{1}{4}$ is the same as multiplying by what number?

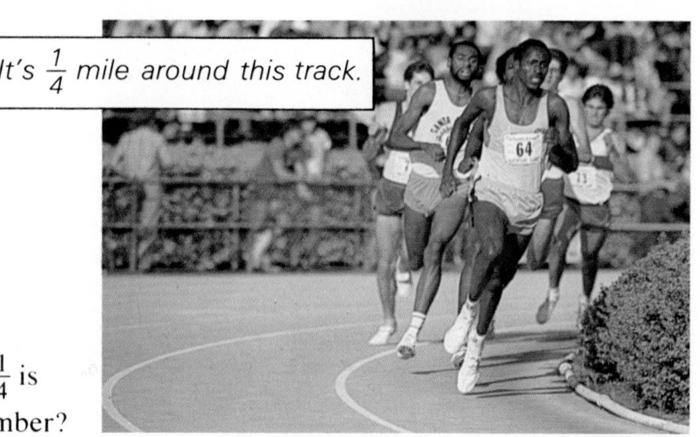

It's $\frac{1}{4}$ mile around this track.

TIME OUT! $\frac{3}{8} \times \frac{8}{3} = 1$

$\frac{8}{3}$ is the reciprocal of $\frac{3}{8}$.

$\frac{3}{8}$ is the reciprocal of $\frac{8}{3}$.

Two numbers are **reciprocals** if their product is 1.

For a fraction not equal to 0, you can find the reciprocal by inverting the fraction.

Here's how *to divide by a fraction.*

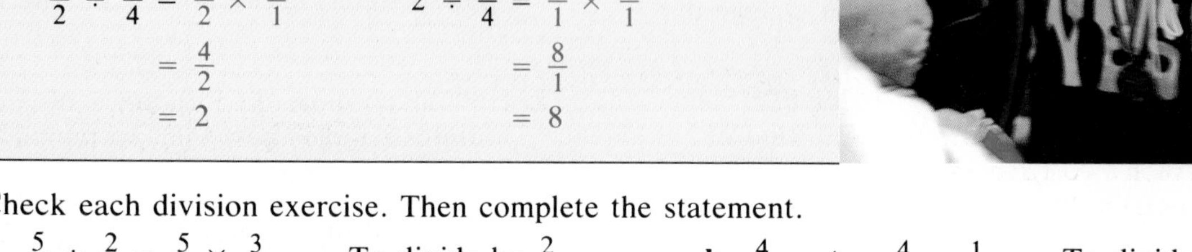

To divide by a fraction, multiply by its reciprocal.

$$\frac{1}{2} \div \frac{1}{4} = \frac{1}{2} \times \frac{4}{1} = \frac{4}{2} = 2$$

$$2 \div \frac{1}{4} = \frac{2}{1} \times \frac{4}{1} = \frac{8}{1} = 8$$

3. Check each division exercise. Then complete the statement.

   a. $\frac{5}{2} \div \frac{2}{3} = \frac{5}{2} \times \frac{3}{2} = \frac{15}{4} = 3\frac{3}{4}$

   To divide by $\frac{2}{3}$, multiply by ?

   b. $\frac{4}{5} \div 4 = \frac{4}{5} \times \frac{1}{4} = \frac{4}{20} = \frac{1}{5}$

   To divide by 4, multiply by ?

EXERCISES

Give the reciprocal of each number.

4. 5 **5.** $\frac{1}{3}$ **6.** $\frac{1}{8}$ **7.** $\frac{3}{8}$ **8.** $\frac{5}{7}$ **9.** $\frac{2}{5}$ **10.** 3

11. 6 **12.** $\frac{3}{5}$ **13.** $\frac{6}{5}$ **14.** $\frac{3}{2}$ **15.** $\frac{9}{10}$ **16.** 8 **17.** $\frac{14}{3}$

Divide. Write the quotient in simplest form.

Here are scrambled answers for the next row of exercises: $6 \quad 1 \quad \frac{1}{6} \quad 1\frac{1}{8} \quad \frac{9}{16} \quad \frac{2}{3}$

$\frac{2}{3} \times \frac{1}{4}$ $\frac{3}{2} \times \frac{4}{1}$ $\frac{3}{4} \times \frac{3}{2}$ $\frac{7}{5} \times \frac{5}{7}$ $\frac{3}{8} \times \frac{3}{2}$ $\frac{2}{9} \times \frac{3}{1}$

18. $\frac{2}{3} \div 4$ **19.** $\frac{3}{2} \div \frac{1}{4}$ **20.** $\frac{3}{4} \div \frac{2}{3}$ **21.** $\frac{7}{5} \div \frac{7}{5}$ **22.** $\frac{3}{8} \div \frac{2}{3}$ **23.** $\frac{2}{9} \div \frac{1}{3}$

24. $\frac{5}{9} \div \frac{1}{3}$ **25.** $\frac{5}{8} \div 2$ **26.** $\frac{4}{5} \div \frac{3}{3}$ **27.** $\frac{2}{3} \div \frac{5}{9}$ **28.** $5 \div \frac{2}{5}$ **29.** $\frac{2}{7} \div \frac{4}{5}$

30. $\frac{3}{5} \div \frac{2}{5}$ **31.** $\frac{3}{2} \div \frac{2}{3}$ **32.** $\frac{7}{9} \div \frac{4}{3}$ **33.** $\frac{2}{5} \div 5$ **34.** $\frac{7}{8} \div \frac{3}{4}$ **35.** $\frac{3}{7} \div \frac{7}{9}$

36. $\frac{4}{3} \div \frac{4}{3}$ **37.** $\frac{3}{8} \div \frac{3}{2}$ **38.** $\frac{3}{2} \div \frac{3}{8}$ **39.** $\frac{2}{5} \div \frac{1}{4}$ **40.** $\frac{9}{10} \div \frac{4}{5}$ **41.** $\frac{1}{5} \div 5$

42. $4 \div \frac{5}{8}$ **43.** $\frac{9}{4} \div \frac{7}{8}$ **44.** $6 \div \frac{3}{2}$ **45.** $\frac{7}{2} \div \frac{9}{4}$ **46.** $\frac{7}{8} \div \frac{5}{16}$ **47.** $8 \div \frac{1}{2}$

48. $\frac{0}{5} \div \frac{5}{6}$ **49.** $8 \div \frac{2}{5}$ **50.** $\frac{5}{9} \div \frac{4}{3}$ **51.** $\frac{5}{4} \div 3$ **52.** $\frac{5}{12} \div \frac{5}{12}$ **53.** $\frac{2}{3} \div \frac{2}{3}$

Solve.

54. How many $\frac{1}{4}$-mile laps must you run to run 4 miles? *Hint:* $4 \div \frac{1}{4} = ?$

55. You are on a $\frac{1}{2}$-mile relay team. Each runner runs $\frac{1}{8}$ mile. How many runners are on your team? *Hint:* $\frac{1}{2} \div \frac{1}{8} = ?$

You're the coach **Reading a chart**

Use the 100-yard-dash times.

56. Which two runners would make the fastest 2-person 200-yard relay team?

57. Which two runners would make the slowest 200-yard relay team?

58. Which of these teams should win a 200-yard relay, Jenny and Dan or Tom and Sandy?

100-yard Dash	
NAME	TIME
Jenny	15.7 seconds
Kim	13.9 seconds
Tom	16.1 seconds
Dan	14.3 seconds
Sandy	13.2 seconds

Dividing mixed numbers

H & W AUTO REPAIR	
JOB	TIME
Oil Change	$\frac{1}{3}$ hour
Wheel Alignment	$\frac{1}{2}$ hour
Minor Tune-up	$1\frac{1}{4}$ hours
Major Tune-up	$2\frac{1}{3}$ hours

1. How much time is needed for an oil change?
2. How many hours does a minor tune-up take?
3. To find how many minor tune-ups can be completed in $3\frac{3}{4}$ hours, the service manager would divide $3\frac{3}{4}$ by what number?

Here's how *to divide mixed numbers.*

Change to fractions.

$$3\frac{3}{4} \div 1\frac{1}{4} = \frac{15}{4} \div \frac{5}{4}$$

Divide. Write the quotient in simplest form.

$$3\frac{3}{4} \div 1\frac{1}{4} = \frac{15}{4} \div \frac{5}{4}$$
$$= \frac{15}{4} \times \frac{4}{5}$$
$$= \frac{60}{20}$$
$$= 3$$

4. Look at the *Here's how*. How many minor tune-ups can be completed in $3\frac{3}{4}$ hours?
5. Check these examples. Then answer the questions.

$$2\frac{1}{2} \div \frac{1}{2} = \frac{5}{2} \div \frac{1}{2}$$
$$= \frac{5}{2} \times \frac{2}{1}$$
$$= \frac{10}{2}$$
$$= 5$$

$$7 \div 2\frac{1}{3} = \frac{7}{1} \div \frac{7}{3}$$
$$= \frac{7}{1} \times \frac{3}{7}$$
$$= \frac{21}{7}$$
$$= 3$$

   a. How many cars can have wheel alignments in $2\frac{1}{2}$ hours?

   b. How many major tune-ups can be done in 7 hours?

EXERCISES

Divide. Write each quotient in simplest form.

Here are scrambled answers for the next row of exercises: $1\frac{1}{4}$ $4\frac{1}{8}$ $1\frac{4}{5}$ $2\frac{1}{7}$ $2\frac{1}{4}$

6. $2\frac{1}{4} \div 1\frac{1}{4}$	**7.** $5\frac{1}{2} \div 1\frac{1}{3}$	**8.** $5 \div 2\frac{1}{3}$	**9.** $4\frac{1}{2} \div 2$	**10.** $2\frac{1}{2} \div 2$
11. $6\frac{1}{2} \div 2\frac{2}{3}$	**12.** $6\frac{1}{2} \div 2\frac{1}{4}$	**13.** $8 \div 2\frac{1}{4}$	**14.** $6\frac{1}{4} \div 1\frac{1}{4}$	**15.** $1\frac{1}{6} \div 1\frac{1}{2}$
16. $5\frac{7}{8} \div 1\frac{3}{4}$	**17.** $7 \div 2\frac{1}{3}$	**18.** $4\frac{1}{3} \div 2\frac{1}{2}$	**19.** $2 \div 1\frac{1}{2}$	**20.** $4\frac{1}{2} \div 4$
21. $2\frac{3}{8} \div 1\frac{1}{3}$	**22.** $6\frac{3}{4} \div 3$	**23.** $1\frac{1}{5} \div 5$	**24.** $8\frac{1}{2} \div 1\frac{3}{4}$	**25.** $6 \div 1\frac{1}{2}$
26. $3\frac{3}{5} \div 1\frac{1}{5}$	**27.** $6\frac{2}{3} \div 2$	**28.** $9\frac{1}{4} \div 2\frac{1}{4}$	**29.** $8 \div 2\frac{1}{2}$	**30.** $2 \div \frac{2}{3}$
31. $6 \div 4\frac{1}{2}$	**32.** $9 \div 2\frac{1}{4}$	**33.** $2\frac{1}{3} \div 2\frac{1}{3}$	**34.** $2\frac{1}{2} \div 1\frac{1}{4}$	**35.** $3\frac{1}{2} \div 3\frac{1}{2}$
36. $1\frac{1}{2} \div 2$	**37.** $7\frac{1}{2} \div 1\frac{1}{2}$	**38.** $3\frac{2}{3} \div 1\frac{1}{3}$	**39.** $6 \div 1\frac{1}{3}$	**40.** $1\frac{1}{2} \div \frac{1}{2}$
41. $4\frac{4}{5} \div 4$	**42.** $3\frac{1}{3} \div 6$	**43.** $7\frac{1}{2} \div \frac{1}{2}$	**44.** $5\frac{1}{2} \div 10$	**45.** $10 \div \frac{1}{2}$

Solve. Use the auto-repair information on page 190.

46. How many oil changes can be done in $2\frac{2}{3}$ hours?

47. How many hours should it take for a major tune-up and an oil change?

48. How many hours should it take to do wheel alignments on 7 cars?

49. A mechanic starts a minor tune-up at 10:20. At what time should the job be done?

Check the quotients

50. Find and correct the two wrong answers.

a. *Five and six tenths divided by two tenths equals*

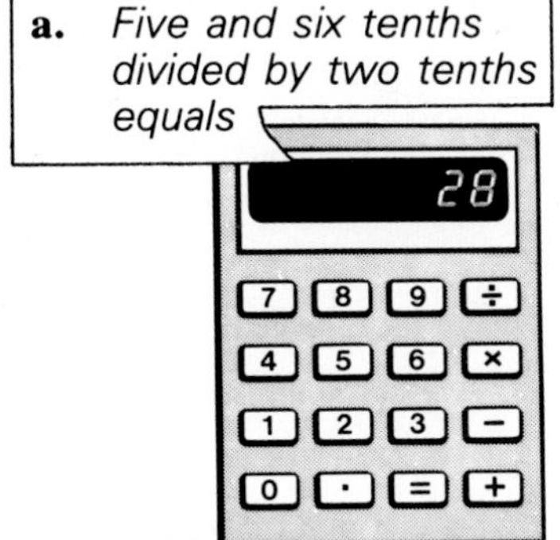

b. *Eight tenths divided by two and five tenths equals*

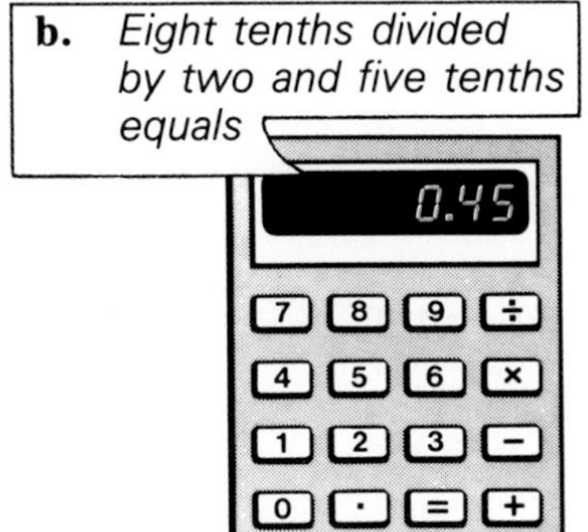

c. *Fourteen hundredths divided by seven tenths equals*

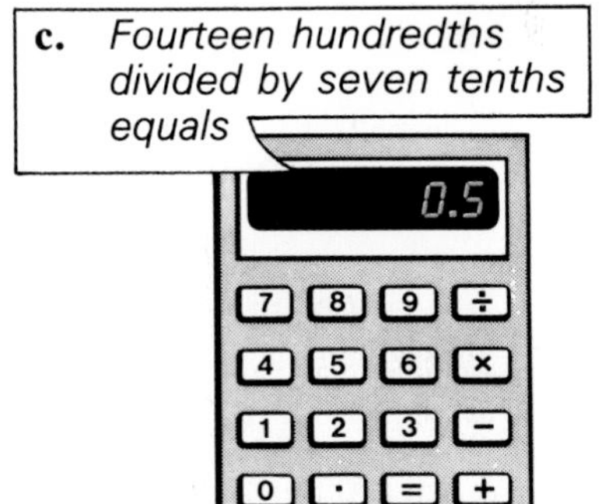

Cumulative Skill Practice

Change to a decimal rounded to the nearest hundredth. *(page 146)*

1. $\frac{1}{6}$ 2. $\frac{1}{3}$ 3. $\frac{13}{3}$ 4. $\frac{1}{9}$ 5. $\frac{5}{3}$ 6. $\frac{7}{3}$ 7. $\frac{10}{9}$

8. $\frac{1}{12}$ 9. $\frac{4}{9}$ 10. $\frac{2}{3}$ 11. $\frac{6}{11}$ 12. $\frac{5}{6}$ 13. $\frac{5}{7}$ 14. $\frac{3}{7}$

15. $\frac{11}{6}$ 16. $\frac{5}{9}$ 17. $\frac{16}{3}$ 18. $\frac{7}{9}$ 19. $\frac{5}{12}$ 20. $\frac{1}{7}$ 21. $\frac{11}{9}$

Give the sum in simplest form. *(page 158)*

22. $\frac{3}{5} + \frac{1}{5}$ 23. $\frac{1}{3} + \frac{1}{2}$ 24. $\frac{1}{6} + \frac{1}{3}$ 25. $\frac{3}{5} + \frac{7}{10}$ 26. $\frac{1}{8} + \frac{3}{4}$ 27. $\frac{2}{5} + \frac{1}{10}$

28. $\frac{1}{4} + \frac{1}{3}$ 29. $\frac{3}{10} + \frac{1}{5}$ 30. $\frac{4}{9} + \frac{2}{3}$ 31. $\frac{1}{8} + \frac{5}{16}$ 32. $\frac{1}{2} + \frac{1}{4}$ 33. $\frac{1}{9} + \frac{2}{3}$

34. $\frac{1}{2} + \frac{3}{4}$ 35. $\frac{1}{4} + \frac{5}{8}$ 36. $\frac{9}{16} + \frac{3}{8}$ 37. $\frac{1}{8} + \frac{1}{2}$ 38. $\frac{5}{12} + \frac{2}{3}$ 39. $\frac{3}{4} + \frac{1}{2}$

Give the difference in simplest form. *(pages 164, 166)*

40. $\frac{3}{4} - \frac{1}{4}$ 41. $\frac{7}{10} - \frac{1}{10}$ 42. $\frac{3}{2} - \frac{3}{4}$ 43. $\frac{2}{3} - \frac{4}{9}$ 44. $\frac{9}{10} - \frac{2}{5}$ 45. $\frac{4}{5} - \frac{1}{2}$

46. $\frac{7}{8} - \frac{1}{3}$ 47. $\frac{5}{12} - \frac{1}{3}$ 48. $\frac{3}{4} - \frac{2}{3}$ 49. $\frac{3}{2} - \frac{5}{8}$ 50. $\frac{5}{6} - \frac{0}{4}$ 51. $\frac{2}{3} - \frac{1}{9}$

52. $\frac{5}{6} - \frac{1}{4}$ 53. $\frac{3}{3} - \frac{1}{4}$ 54. $\frac{9}{5} - \frac{3}{10}$ 55. $\frac{7}{5} - \frac{2}{3}$ 56. $\frac{7}{8} - \frac{5}{6}$ 57. $\frac{5}{8} - \frac{1}{2}$

Give the product in simplest form. *(page 182)*

58. $2 \times 1\frac{1}{2}$ 59. $3 \times 2\frac{1}{3}$ 60. $4 \times 1\frac{2}{3}$ 61. $3\frac{1}{4} \times 5$ 62. $4 \times 2\frac{1}{2}$

63. $1\frac{1}{3} \times 1\frac{1}{2}$ 64. $1\frac{1}{2} \times 1\frac{2}{3}$ 65. $2\frac{1}{4} \times 3\frac{1}{2}$ 66. $3 \times 2\frac{2}{5}$ 67. $3\frac{1}{2} \times 1\frac{1}{4}$

68. $3\frac{1}{2} \times 1\frac{3}{4}$ 69. $2\frac{2}{3} \times 4\frac{1}{3}$ 70. $1\frac{3}{4} \times 1\frac{2}{3}$ 71. $2\frac{2}{3} \times 3\frac{4}{5}$ 72. $1\frac{1}{2} \times 2\frac{1}{3}$

Give the quotient in simplest form. *(page 190)*

73. $1\frac{1}{2} \div 2$ 74. $3\frac{3}{4} \div 3$ 75. $2 \div 1\frac{1}{3}$ 76. $4 \div 2\frac{3}{4}$ 77. $12\frac{1}{2} \div 6$

78. $5\frac{1}{2} \div 1\frac{1}{3}$ 79. $8 \div 2\frac{1}{2}$ 80. $6\frac{1}{4} \div 1\frac{1}{4}$ 81. $5\frac{7}{8} \div 1\frac{3}{4}$ 82. $6\frac{1}{2} \div 2$

Problem solving

COMPUTERS IN WATCHES

A tiny, battery-powered computer controls the electronic circuits used to display the time on a digital watch.

The diagram shows 24 electrodes. Each electrode controls a part of the display. When the electrode is charged, the part controlled by the computer turns black.

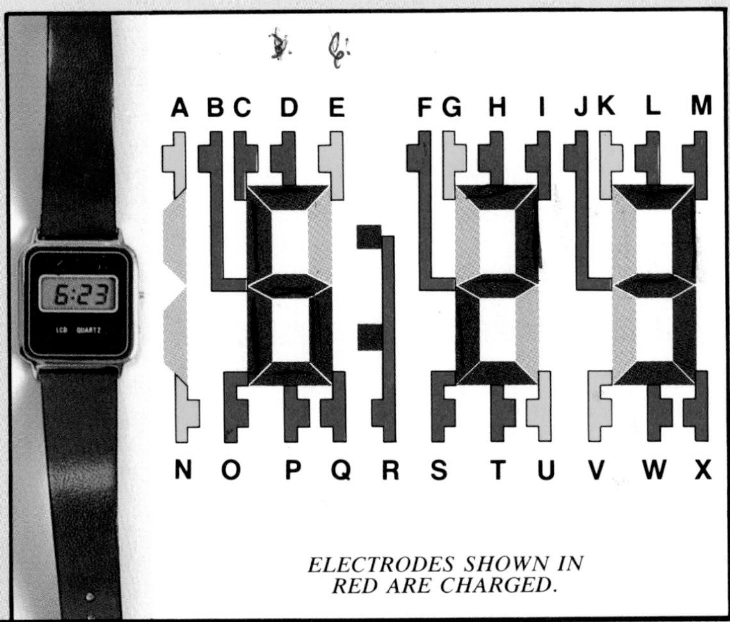

Solve. Use the diagram.

1. In the diagram, electrodes B, C, D, F, H, I, J, L, M, O, P, Q, R, S, T, W, and X are charged.
   a. What time is displayed?
   b. If electrode E was also charged, what time would be displayed?

2. After one minute passes, the computer will change the 3 to a 4. To make this change, the computer
   a. removes the charge from electrodes L and [?].
   b. charges electrode [?].

3. For each set of charged electrodes, give the time that would be displayed.
   a. E, F, G, I, J, K, L, M, Q, R, U, W, and X
   b. A, E, I, M, N, Q, R, U, and X
   c. A, B, D, E, F, H, I, K, L, M, N, O, P, R, T, U, V, W, and X

4. When 10:00 is displayed, all but 3 of the electrodes are charged.
   a. Can you find seven more times that use all but 3 of the electrodes?
   b. Can you find a time that uses all but 2 of the electrodes?

5. A computer can also make it possible for a watch to include a calendar, an alarm, and a calculator. What is the sale price of this watch?

Chapter REVIEW

Here are scrambled answers for the review exercises:

1	3	add	fraction	reciprocal
2	4	denominators	inverting	simplest
		divide	numerators	whole

1. To multiply these two fractions, you would multiply the [?] to get the numerator of the product and multiply the [?] to get the denominator of the product. *(page 178)*

$\frac{3}{4} \times \frac{1}{2} = ?$

2. To compute this fraction of a number, you could first divide 36 by [?] and then multiply the result by [?]. *(page 180)*

$\frac{3}{4}$ of $36 = ?$

3. To compute this fraction of a number, you would change the [?] number to a fraction and multiply. *(page 180)*

$\frac{2}{5}$ of $17 = ?$

4. To multiply these mixed numbers, change each mixed number to a [?] and multiply. *(page 182)*

$2\frac{1}{2} \times 1\frac{1}{4} = ?$

5. To change $2\frac{1}{2}$ feet to inches, you could first find how many inches in [?] feet and in $\frac{1}{2}$ of a foot and then [?]. *(page 184)*

$2\frac{1}{2}$ feet = ? inches

6. Two numbers are reciprocals if their product is [?]. For a fraction not equal to 0, you can find the reciprocal by [?] the fraction. *(page 188)*

7. To divide by a fraction, you would multiply by its [?]. To divide mixed numbers, change each mixed number to a fraction and [?]. *(pages 188, 190)*

8. The last step in this division exercise is to write the quotient in [?] form. *(page 190)*

$$2\frac{1}{2} \div 1\frac{3}{4} = \frac{5}{2} \div \frac{7}{4}$$
$$= \frac{5}{2} \times \frac{4}{7}$$
$$= \frac{20}{14}$$
$$= ?$$

Chapter TEST

Multiply. Write the product in simplest form. *(page 178)*

1. $2 \times \frac{1}{2}$ **2.** $\frac{1}{3} \times \frac{1}{3}$ **3.** $\frac{2}{5} \times \frac{1}{3}$ **4.** $\frac{3}{4} \times \frac{1}{2}$ **5.** $\frac{2}{3} \times \frac{3}{5}$ **6.** $\frac{2}{5} \times \frac{1}{2}$

7. $4 \times \frac{1}{2}$ **8.** $4 \times \frac{1}{8}$ **9.** $\frac{5}{2} \times \frac{4}{3}$ **10.** $\frac{4}{5} \times \frac{5}{4}$ **11.** $\frac{8}{3} \times \frac{5}{2}$ **12.** $4 \times \frac{5}{4}$

Complete. *(page 180)*

13. $\frac{1}{2}$ of 12 = ? **14.** $\frac{1}{3}$ of 24 = ? **15.** $\frac{2}{3}$ of 18 = ? **16.** $\frac{3}{4}$ of \$20 = ? **17.** $\frac{3}{4}$ of \$8 = ?

Multiply. Write the product in simplest form. *(page 182)*

18. $2 \times 1\frac{1}{2}$ **19.** $2\frac{1}{3} \times 3$ **20.** $3 \times 1\frac{1}{4}$ **21.** $2\frac{2}{3} \times 4$ **22.** $5 \times 1\frac{1}{2}$

23. $1\frac{2}{3} \times 2\frac{1}{2}$ **24.** $2\frac{3}{4} \times 2\frac{3}{4}$ **25.** $2\frac{5}{6} \times 1\frac{1}{4}$ **26.** $1\frac{3}{8} \times 3\frac{3}{5}$ **27.** $1\frac{1}{3} \times 1\frac{2}{3}$

Complete. *(page 184)*

28. $2\frac{1}{2}$ days = __?__ h **29.** $1\frac{3}{4}$ h = __?__ min **30.** $2\frac{1}{2}$ min = __?__ sec **31.** $1\frac{1}{3}$ yd = __?__ ft

Divide. Write each quotient in simplest form. *(page 188)*

32. $\frac{3}{4} \div 2$ **33.** $3 \div \frac{3}{8}$ **34.** $\frac{2}{3} \div \frac{1}{3}$ **35.** $\frac{1}{2} \div \frac{1}{3}$ **36.** $\frac{1}{3} \div \frac{1}{2}$ **37.** $4 \div \frac{1}{2}$

38. $\frac{5}{6} \div \frac{3}{4}$ **39.** $6 \div \frac{3}{5}$ **40.** $\frac{3}{5} \div 6$ **41.** $\frac{5}{8} \div \frac{3}{4}$ **42.** $\frac{3}{10} \div \frac{2}{5}$ **43.** $\frac{1}{2} \div \frac{3}{4}$

Divide. Write each quotient in simplest form. *(page 190)*

44. $2\frac{1}{2} \div 1\frac{1}{4}$ **45.** $3 \div 1\frac{1}{2}$ **46.** $2\frac{1}{2} \div 2$ **47.** $8 \div 2\frac{1}{3}$ **48.** $5 \div \frac{1}{2}$

49. $3\frac{1}{4} \div 6$ **50.** $4\frac{3}{4} \div 1\frac{1}{2}$ **51.** $9 \div 3\frac{3}{8}$ **52.** $5\frac{5}{6} \div 3\frac{1}{2}$ **53.** $2\frac{1}{3} \div 3$

Solve.

54. How many miles is it from Round Lake to Clear Falls if you hike by Lookout Point?

55. Which is the shorter route from Round Lake to Clear Falls?

56. How many miles long is the hiking trail?

57. You hiked the trail in $5\frac{1}{4}$ hours. How many miles per hour did you average?

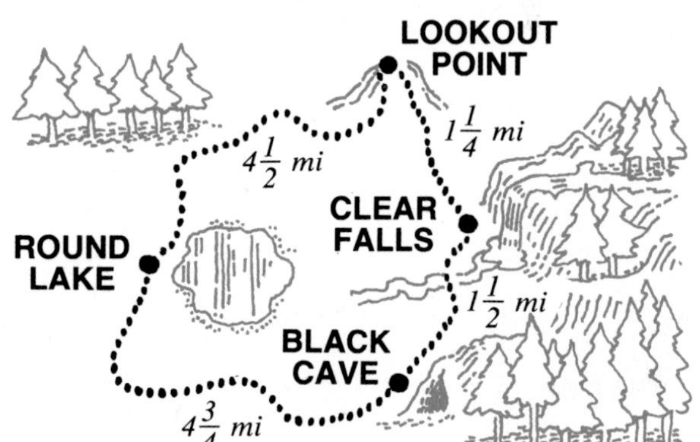

Cumulative TEST Standardized Format

Choose the correct letter.

1. Give the sum.

23.5 + 4.28 + 60.7

A. 12.70 **B.** 127.0
C. 88.48 **D.** none of these

2. Give the difference.

286.5 − 13.74

A. 273.24 **B.** 272.76
C. 149.1 **D.** none of these

3. Give the product.

3.57 × 2.70

A. 9.6390 **B.** 8.199
C. 963.90 **D.** none of these

4. Give the quotient rounded to the nearest tenth.

423.8 ÷ 1.62

A. 2.6 **B.** 0.3
C. 261.6 **D.** none of these

5. $\frac{7}{8} < ?$

A. $\frac{1}{2}$ **B.** $\frac{4}{5}$
C. $\frac{5}{6}$ **D.** none of these

6. Change to a decimal rounded to the nearest hundredth.

$\frac{5}{6} = ?$

A. 0.83 **B.** 0.84
C. 11.2 **D.** none of these

7. Give the sum in simplest form.

$\frac{2}{3} + \frac{3}{4}$

A. $\frac{5}{7}$ **B.** $\frac{1}{2}$
C. $1\frac{5}{12}$ **D.** none of these

8. Give the difference in simplest form.

$\frac{5}{6} - \frac{3}{8}$

A. 1 **B.** $\frac{11}{24}$
C. $\frac{1}{12}$ **D.** none of these

9. Give the product in simplest form.

$2\frac{1}{2} \times 1\frac{1}{4}$

A. 2 **B.** $6\frac{1}{4}$
C. $12\frac{1}{2}$ **D.** none of these

10. Give the quotient in simplest form.

$6 \div 3\frac{3}{4}$

A. $1\frac{3}{5}$
B. $\frac{3}{8}$
C. $22\frac{1}{2}$
D. none of these

11. STUDENT TRYOUTS

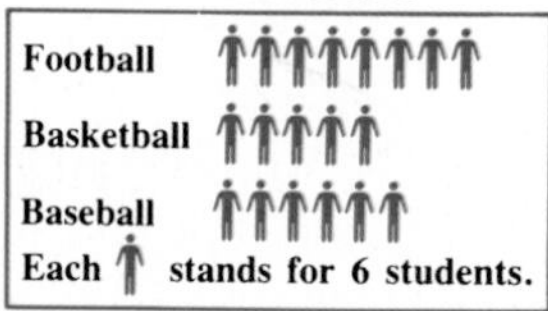

How many more students tried out for football than baseball?

A. 2 **B.** 12
C. 18 **D.** none of these

12. Sara jogged 3 miles one day and $4\frac{1}{2}$ miles on each of the next two days. How many miles did she average per day?

A. $3\frac{3}{7}$ **B.** $3\frac{3}{4}$
C. $4\frac{1}{14}$ **D.** none of these

Chapter 9
Measurement

Using a metric ruler

The **centimeter** (cm) is a unit of length in the metric system. The length of the 18K (18-carat) gold chain measured to the nearest centimeter is 6 centimeters.

1. What is the length of the 14K gold chain measured to the nearest centimeter?

Here's how *to measure to the nearest millimeter.*

Notice that one tenth of a centimeter is 1 millimeter (mm).

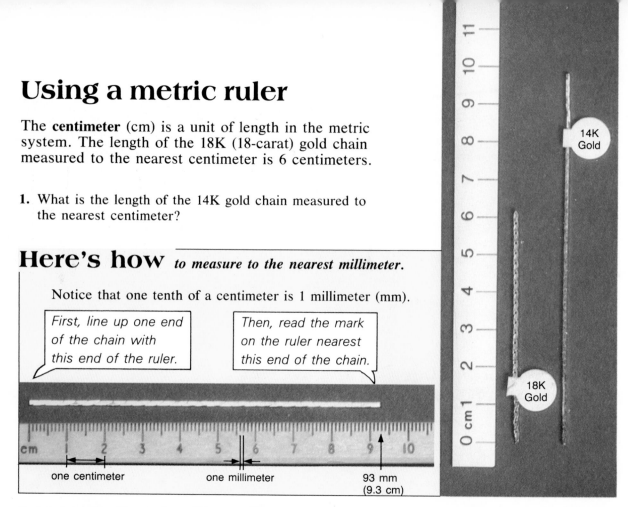

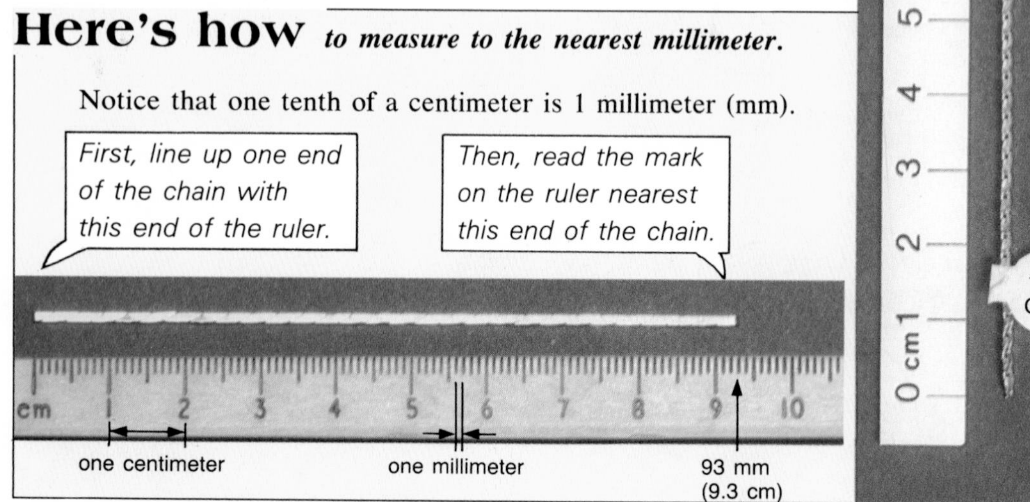

2. Look at the *Here's how*. What is the length of the chain measured to the nearest millimeter?
3. What is the length of the chain to the nearest tenth of a centimeter? to the nearest centimeter?
4. Look at the ruler. How many millimeters are in 1 centimeter?

EXERCISES

Use a metric ruler. Measure each chain to the nearest centimeter.

5.
6.
7.
8.

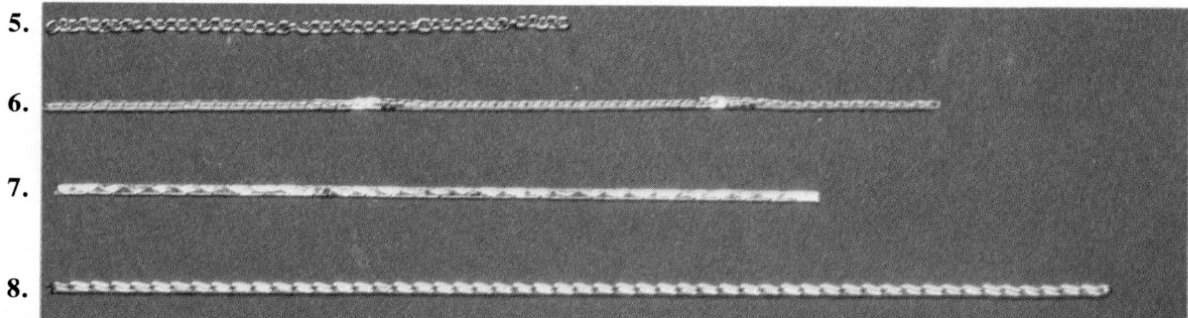

Measure each chain to the nearest millimeter.

9.

10.

11.

12.

13.

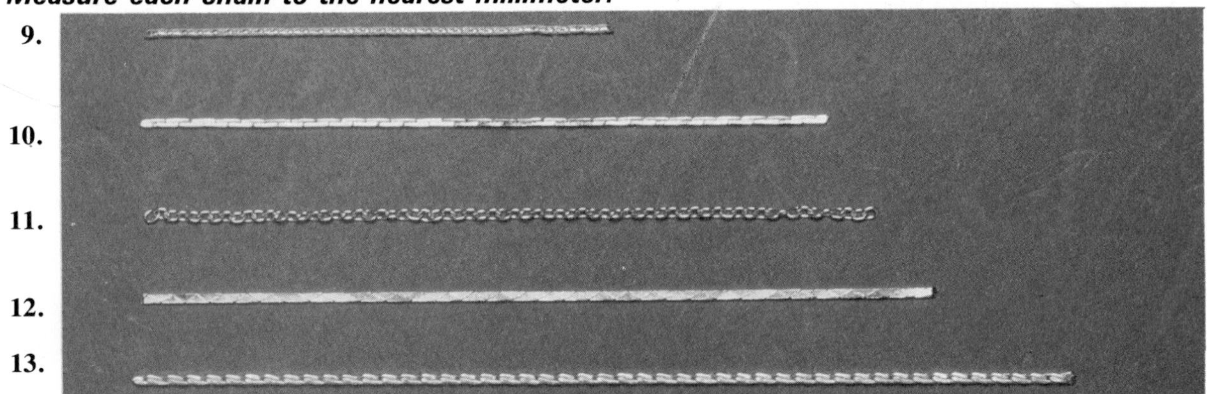

Draw "chains" of these lengths.

14. 3 cm **15.** 8 cm **16.** 12 cm **17.** 90 mm **18.** 78 mm

19. 58 mm **20.** 132 mm **21.** 8.6 cm **22.** 10.4 cm **23.** 12.5 cm

Solve. Use the chains pictured at the top of page 198.

24. The 14K gold chain costs $6 per centimeter. What is the cost of the 14K gold chain?

25. The 18K gold chain costs $48. What is the cost per centimeter?

26. Which costs more, the 14K gold chain or the 18K gold chain?

27. What would be the total cost for two 18K chains and one 14K chain?

Decoding

28. Use the code to get the answer to the riddle.

CODE: H O E T C W I D A J S L F N R

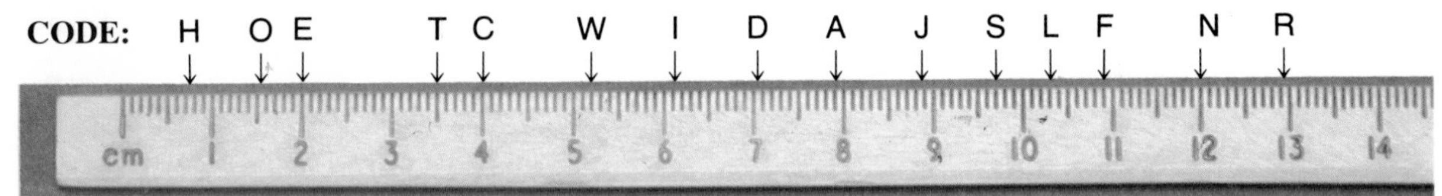

RIDDLE: What's the difference between a jeweler and a jailer?

ANSWER: 1.5 cm * 12 cm * 2 cm
9.7 cm * 20 mm * 10.3 cm * 103 mm * 97 mm
5.2 cm * 79 mm * 35 mm * 4 cm * 7 mm * 20 mm * 9.7 cm
52 mm * 0.7 cm * 6.1 cm * 103 mm * 2 cm
3.5 cm * 7 mm * 20 mm
15 mm * 3.5 cm * 7 mm * 2 cm * 129 mm
52 mm * 7.9 cm * 3.5 cm * 40 mm * 0.7 cm * 2 cm * 97 mm
4 cm * 20 mm * 10.3 cm * 103 mm * 9.7 cm.

Metric units of length

Could you hit a baseball 100 meters? *Hint: The longest home run ever hit went 188.4 meters. It was hit by Roy "Dizzy" Carlyle.*

The basic unit for measuring length in the metric system is the **meter** (m). A baseball bat is about 1 meter long.

These units are used to measure length in the metric system:

1 kilometer (km) = 1000 meters
1 hectometer (hm) = 100 meters
1 dekameter (dam) = 10 meters
1 meter (m) = 1 meter
1 decimeter (dm) = 0.1 meter
1 centimeter (cm) = 0.01 meter
1 millimeter (mm) = 0.001 meter

Note: The units listed in red are used most often.

Here's how

to estimate metric units of length.

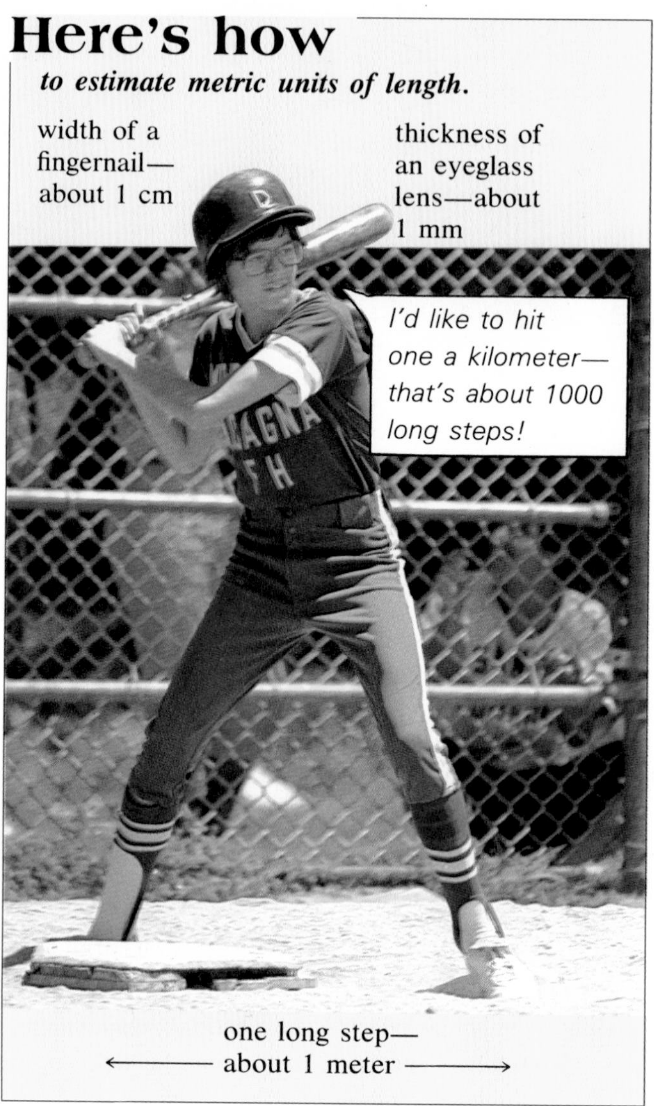
width of a fingernail— about 1 cm
thickness of an eyeglass lens—about 1 mm
I'd like to hit one a kilometer— that's about 1000 long steps!
one long step— about 1 meter

EXERCISES

Choose mm, cm, m, or km.

1. The distance from home plate to first base is 24.4 [?].
2. The height of a first baseman is 182 [?].
3. The thickness of a dime is 1 [?].
4. The length of a river is 450 [?].
5. The length of a tennis court is 20 [?].
6. The length of a paper clip is 3 [?].
7. The width of a door is 0.6 [?].
8. The length of a new pencil is 190 [?].

Which measurement is reasonable?

9. Length of a dollar bill:
a. 16 mm **b.** 16 cm **c.** 16 m

10. Length of an automobile:
a. 4.75 cm **b.** 4.75 mm **c.** 4.75 m

11. Length of a baseball bat:
a. 92 mm **b.** 92 cm **c.** 92 m

12. Height of a nine-story building:
a. 30 cm **b.** 30 m **c.** 30 km

13. Height of a soup can:
a. 10 mm **b.** 10 cm **c.** 10 m

14. Width of a thumb:
a. 20 mm **b.** 20 cm **c.** 20 m

15. Thickness of a nickel:
a. 2 mm **b.** 2 cm **c.** 2 m

16. Thickness of a dollar bill:
a. 0.1 mm **b.** 0.1 cm **c.** 0.1 m

AIR DISTANCES

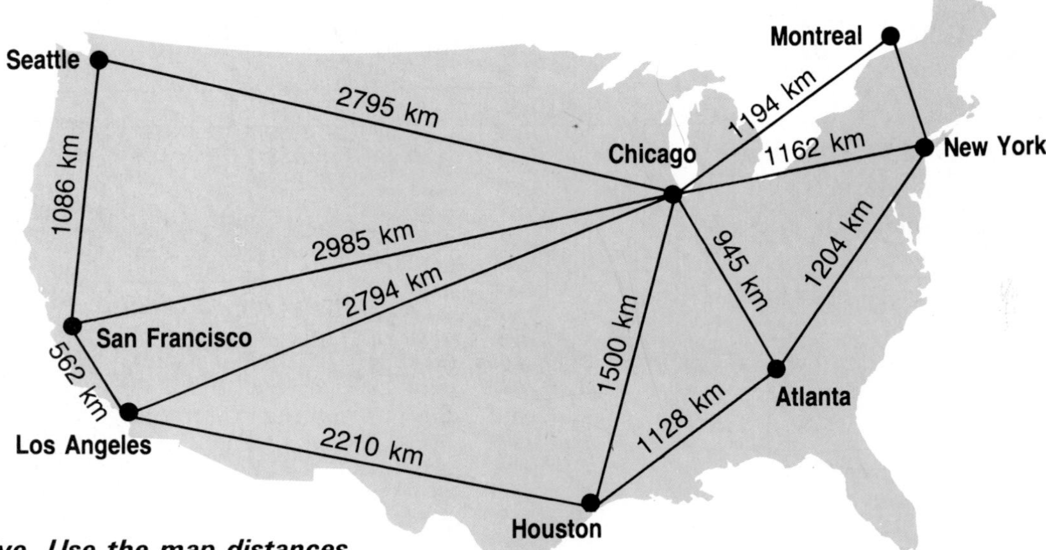

Solve. Use the map distances.

17. How far is it from
a. San Francisco to New York through Chicago?
b. New York to Houston through Atlanta?

18. How much farther is it from
a. Chicago to Los Angeles than from Chicago to Houston?
b. San Francisco to Chicago than from Los Angeles to Chicago?

Play ball!

Use the information on the map to answer the questions.

19. From New York the Mets baseball team flew to [?] to play a game. Then they flew to [?] to play another game. They traveled 2149 kilometers altogether. In which two cities did they play games?

20. The Dodgers flew from Los Angeles to [?] and then to [?] to play ball games. They traveled about 4300 kilometers altogether. In which two cities did they play games?

Changing units in the metric system

WHO CAUGHT THE BIGGER FISH?

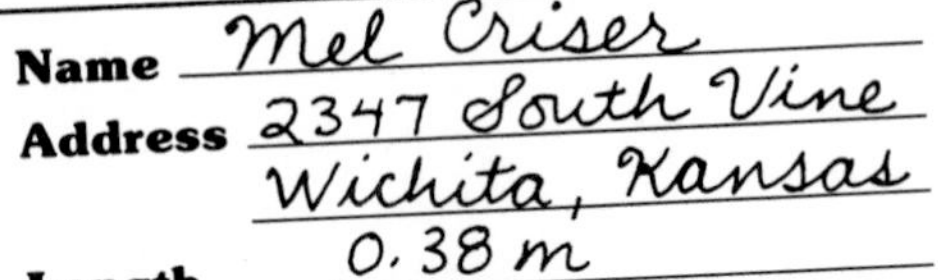

FISHING CONTEST

Prizes:
1st: $100.00 CASH
2nd: PICKWICK ULTRA LIGHT FISHING POLE
3rd: STAY-DRY HIP WADERS

Name Mel Criser
Address 2347 South Vine
Wichita, Kansas
Length 0.38 m

Name Nancy Perkins
Address 42 Falls Road
Salt Lake City, Utah
Length 475 mm

To change units in the metric system, multiply or divide by 10, 100, or 1000.

Here's how *to change from one unit of length to another.*

Mel's fish
0.38 m = ? cm

Since I'm changing to a smaller unit, I should get a larger number. So I should multiply.

Remember: 1 m = 100 cm

0.38 m = 38 cm
(× 100)

Nancy's fish
475 mm = ? cm

Now I'm changing to a larger unit, so I should get a smaller number. Therefore I should divide.

Remember: 10 mm = 1 cm

475 mm = 47.5 cm
(÷ 10)

1. Look at the *Here's how*. To change from meters to centimeters, multiply by [?].
2. To change from millimeters to centimeters, divide by [?].
3. Who caught the larger fish, Mel or Nancy?
4. Check these examples. Have the units been changed correctly?

a. 1395 m = ? km

Think: Changing smaller to larger units, so divide.

Remember: 1000 m = 1 km
1395 m = 1.395 km
(÷ 1000)

b. 8.53 km = ? m

Think: Changing larger to smaller units, so multiply.

Remember: 1 km = 1000 m
8.53 km = 8530 m
(× 1000)

EXERCISES

Copy and complete.

5. 7 cm = ? mm
6. 3 m = ? cm
7. 8 km = ? m
8. 45 cm = ? m
9. 63 mm = ? cm
10. 18 km = ? m
11. 4265 m = ? km
12. 7.3 km = ? m
13. 4.2 cm = ? mm
14. 95 m = ? cm
15. 4.8 m = ? cm
16. 420 cm = ? m
17. 68 mm = ? cm
18. 3.25 km = ? m
19. 1575 m = ? km
20. 15 m = ? cm
21. 14 mm = ? cm
22. 7.8 cm = ? mm
23. 250 km = ? m
24. 300 mm = ? m
25. 0.4 m = ? mm
26. 5 cm + 4 mm = ? mm
27. 20 cm + 4 mm = ? mm
28. 30 cm + 5 mm = ? cm
29. 10 cm + 12 mm = ? cm
30. 8 m + 75 cm = ? cm
31. 5 m + 125 cm = ? cm
32. 4 m + 50 cm = ? m
33. 7 m + 200 cm = ? m

Solve.

34. The largest salt water fish caught was a 1852-centimeter whale shark. How many meters was that?
35. The smallest fresh water fish caught was a dwarf pygmy goby. It was only 0.7 centimeter long. How many millimeters was that?
36. The greatest depth at which a fish was caught was 8299 meters in the Puerto Rico Trough. How many kilometers was that?
37. The fastest fish is the cosmopolitan sailfish. It can swim 110 kilometers per hour. How many meters per hour is that?

You be the judge **Logical reasoning**

38. Who caught the biggest fish? How big was it?

Clues:

- Susan's fish was 4 cm longer than Wilda's fish.
- Wilda's fish was 5 cm shorter than Rita's fish.
- Rita's fish was 1 cm longer than Monica's fish.
- Monica caught a 60-cm fish.

Liquid volume—metric system

WOULD YOU BELIEVE IT!

One drop of the world's most expensive perfume costs $1.50. One liter of the same perfume would cost about $15,000!

A unit for measuring liquid volume in the metric system is the **liter** (L). The **milliliter** (mL) is used to measure small liquid volumes.

1 L = 1000 mL

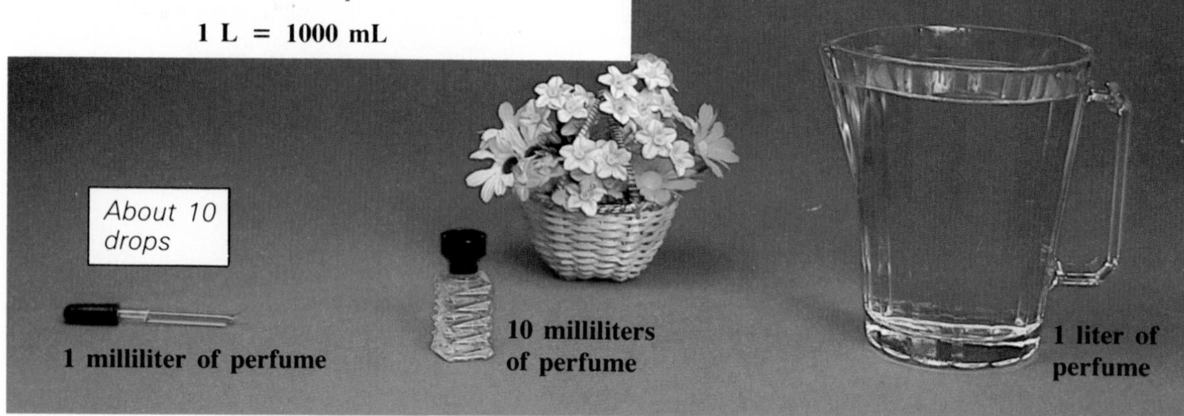

1. Which is more, 999 milliliters or 1 liter?
2. Choose mL or L.
   a. A 250-[?] bottle of shampoo costs $1.99.
   b. A 0.5-[?] bottle of liquid soap costs $1.89.

Here's how *to change from one unit of liquid volume to another.*

250 mL = ? L

Think: Changing from smaller units to larger units, so divide.

Remember: 1000 mL = 1 L

250 mL = 0.250 L
(÷ 1000)

0.5 L = ? mL

Think: Changing from larger units to smaller units, so multiply.

Remember: 1 L = 1000 mL

0.5 L = 500 mL
(× 1000)

3. Look at the *Here's how*. To change from milliliters to liters, divide by [?].
4. To change from liters to milliliters, multiply by [?].

EXERCISES

Which liquid volume seems reasonable?

5. A coffee cup:
   a. 300 mL **b.** 30 mL **c.** 3 mL
6. A soft drink can:
   a. 4 mL **b.** 40 mL **c.** 400 mL
7. A bathtub:
   a. 3 L **b.** 30 L **c.** 300 L
8. A tablespoon:
   a. 0.5 mL **b.** 5 mL **c.** 50 mL
9. A thermos bottle:
   a. 80 mL **b.** 800 mL **c.** 8000 mL
10. A fruit-juice pitcher:
    a. 0.1 L **b.** 1 L **c.** 10 L
11. An eyedropper:
    a. 1 mL **b.** 10 mL **c.** 100 mL
12. An automobile gas tank:
    a. 6 L **b.** 60 L **c.** 600 L

Copy and complete.

13. 6 L = ? mL
14. 15 L = ? mL
15. 2.7 L = ? mL
16. 4000 mL = ? L
17. 1725 mL = ? L
18. 500 mL = ? L
19. 5.75 L = ? mL
20. 0.756 L = ? mL
21. 0.35 L = ? mL
22. 12,000 mL = ? L
23. 870 mL = ? L
24. 25 mL = ? L
25. 6.05 L = ? mL
26. 175 mL = ? L
27. 100 mL = ? L
28. 986 mL = ? L
29. 790 L = ? mL
30. 2800 L = ? mL
31. 210 mL = ? L
32. 60 mL = ? L
33. 5640 L = ? mL
34. 2 L + 500 mL = ? mL
35. 5 L + 125 mL = ? mL
36. 4 L + 100 mL = ? L
37. 3 L + 625 mL = ? L
38. 46 L + 18 mL = ? mL
39. 16 L + 200 mL ? L
40. 75 L + 500 mL = ? mL
41. 35 L + 600 mL = ? L

Special smells

Use the information in the advertisement. Complete the sentences.

42. A 50-milliliter bottle of [?] costs $5.00.

43. A [?]-milliliter bottle of Sweet Rose costs $8.00.

44. A 40-milliliter bottle of Twilight costs [?] dollars.

45. A 20-milliliter bottle of Twilight and a [?]-milliliter bottle of New Spice cost a total of $10.00.

PERFUME $PECIAL$
Twilight .... $.05 per mL
Sweet Rose .... $.10 per mL
Always Yours .... $.20 per mL
New Spice .... $.30 per mL

Weight—metric system

AMAZING FACT!

Did you know that a honeybee can lift more than 300 times its own weight!

A unit for measuring weight (mass) in the metric system is the **gram** (g). The weight of a large paper clip is about 1 gram.

Here are some other units for measuring weight.

1 kilogram (kg) = 1000 g
1 milligram (mg) = 0.001 g

The weight of this textbook is about 1 kilogram.

Would you believe . . .
A honeybee can lift an object as heavy as an egg!
Wing— *about 1 mg*
Honeybee— *about 200 mg*

1. Which is heavier, 999 grams or 1 kilogram?
2. Which is heavier, 999 milligrams or 1 gram?

Here's how *to change from one metric unit of weight to another.*

0.06 kg = ? g

Changing from larger to smaller units, so multiply.

Remember: 1 kg = 1000 g

0.06 kg = 60 g
(× 1000)

200 mg = ? g

Think: Changing from smaller to larger units, so divide.

Remember: 1000 mg = 1 g

200 mg = 0.2 g
(÷ 1000)

3. Check these examples. Have the unit changes been done correctly?

a. 4.6 g = ? mg

Think: Changing from larger to smaller units, so multiply.

Remember: 1 g = 1000 mg

4.6 g = 4600 mg
(× 1000)

b. 358 g = ? kg

Think: Changing from smaller to larger units, so divide.

Remember: 1000 g = 1 kg

358 g = 0.358 kg
(÷ 1000)

EXERCISES

Which weight seems reasonable?

4. A bicycle:
a. 12 mg **b.** 12 g **c.** 12 kg

5. A dime:
a. 3 mg **b.** 3 g **c.** 3 kg

6. A straight pin:
a. 130 mg **b.** 130 g **c.** 130 kg

7. An automobile:
a. 2000 mg **b.** 2000 g **c.** 2000 kg

8. A can of tomatoes:
a. 464 mg **b.** 464 g **c.** 464 kg

9. An apple:
a. 330 mg **b.** 330 g **c.** 330 kg

Copy and complete.

10. 6000 mg = _?_ g
11. 4125 mg = _?_ g
12. 765 mg = _?_ g
13. 5000 g = _?_ kg
14. 7617 g = _?_ kg
15. 326 g = _?_ kg
16. 7 kg = _?_ g
17. 4.2 kg = _?_ g
18. 1.27 kg = _?_ g
19. 4 g = _?_ mg
20. 6.5 g = _?_ mg
21. 0.425 g = _?_ mg
22. 3.5 kg = _?_ g
23. 315 g = _?_ kg
24. 775 mg = _?_ g
25. 86.3 kg = _?_ g
26. 489 g = _?_ kg
27. 9163 g = _?_ kg
28. 1653 mg = _?_ g
29. 25.8 kg = _?_ g
30. 41.3 g = _?_ mg
31. 6 g + 325 mg = _?_ mg
32. 6 kg + 3500 g = _?_ g
33. 35 g + 1800 mg = _?_ mg
34. 85 kg + 6000 g = _?_ kg
35. 8 g + 435 mg = _?_ mg
36. 25 g + 1500 mg = _?_ mg
37. 4 g + 666 mg = _?_ g
38. 12 g + 2545 mg = _?_ g
39. 6 kg + 825 g = _?_ g
40. 5 kg + 2000 g = _?_ g
41. 9 kg + 125 g = _?_ kg
42. 3 kg + 3000 g = _?_ kg

Are you as strong as an ant?

43. a. An ant weighing 200 mg can lift (with its teeth) a weight of 10 g. How many times its weight can an ant lift?
b. Suppose that you could lift the same number of times your weight. How much weight would that be?
c. Are you as strong as an ant?

Cumulative Skill Practice

Multiply. *(page 64)*

1. 1.2×38	**2.** 5.9×3.2	**3.** 0.63×7.4	**4.** 0.82×23	**5.** 0.48×9.6	**6.** 6.09×3.4
7. 0.61×0.55	**8.** 0.46×72	**9.** 9.2×9.2	**10.** 5.12×35	**11.** 3.75×0.38	**12.** 2.15×0.2
13. 4.25×5.4	**14.** 8.91×0.58	**15.** 30.4×0.71	**16.** 55.5×1.93	**17.** 7.62×2.06	**18.** 3.88×1.01

Divide. Round the quotient to the nearest hundredth. *(page 96)*

19. $0.3\overline{)1.7}$	**20.** $0.6\overline{)4.77}$	**21.** $0.09\overline{)2.4}$	**22.** $0.06\overline{)5.8}$	**23.** $0.03\overline{)25}$
24. $0.6\overline{)0.5}$	**25.** $0.09\overline{)7.9}$	**26.** $0.13\overline{)0.7}$	**27.** $0.27\overline{)4.26}$	**28.** $0.35\overline{)29.5}$
29. $2.3\overline{)0.8}$	**30.** $5.4\overline{)3.4}$	**31.** $2.8\overline{)46.6}$	**32.** $0.77\overline{)80.5}$	**33.** $0.81\overline{)3.05}$

Change to a decimal. *(page 146)*

34. $\frac{1}{4}$	**35.** $\frac{4}{5}$	**36.** $\frac{7}{8}$	**37.** $\frac{3}{5}$	**38.** $\frac{1}{2}$	**39.** $\frac{1}{5}$	**40.** $\frac{3}{4}$
41. $\frac{1}{8}$	**42.** $\frac{3}{10}$	**43.** $\frac{3}{8}$	**44.** $\frac{5}{8}$	**45.** $\frac{9}{10}$	**46.** $\frac{2}{5}$	**47.** $\frac{7}{10}$
48. $1\frac{3}{8}$	**49.** $3\frac{4}{5}$	**50.** $2\frac{7}{8}$	**51.** $5\frac{7}{10}$	**52.** $4\frac{5}{16}$	**53.** $1\frac{1}{2}$	**54.** $2\frac{3}{5}$

Change to a mixed number in simplest form. *(page 148)*

55. 2.4	**56.** 3.5	**57.** 4.8	**58.** 9.6	**59.** 5.2	**60.** 6.9
61. 4.50	**62.** 6.60	**63.** 2.25	**64.** 7.75	**65.** 8.35	**66.** 3.14
67. 3.125	**68.** 6.625	**69.** 9.875	**70.** 8.200	**71.** 8.300	**72.** 2.190

Add. Give each sum in simplest form. *(page 160)*

73. $8\frac{1}{2} + 2\frac{1}{4}$	**74.** $3\frac{1}{2} + 4\frac{1}{3}$	**75.** $7\frac{3}{8} + 1\frac{1}{4}$	**76.** $9\frac{2}{5} + 1\frac{1}{5}$	**77.** $8 + 2\frac{2}{3}$	**78.** $6\frac{1}{2} + 3\frac{1}{3}$
79. $4\frac{2}{5} + 1\frac{3}{5}$	**80.** $6\frac{2}{3} + 2\frac{1}{3}$	**81.** $2\frac{3}{4} + 2\frac{3}{4}$	**82.** $6 + 4\frac{1}{2}$	**83.** $8\frac{7}{8} + 3\frac{3}{4}$	**84.** $4\frac{5}{9} + 6\frac{1}{3}$

Problem solving

YOU'RE THE MANAGER!

1. You sell a certain brand of plain jeans for \$19.98 and the designer jeans for \$27.65. How much more do you charge for the designer jeans?
2. You buy 72 pairs of jeans for \$12.45 each and sell them for \$18.69 each. How much profit do you make on 72 pairs?
3. One day 42 customers spent \$964.50 in your store. What was the average amount spent per customer? Round the answer to the nearest cent.
4. One day you sold 60 pairs of jeans. Twenty-four pairs were designer jeans. What fraction of the jeans were not designer jeans? Give the answer in simplest form.
5. A denim shirt regularly sells for \$18.60. You put it on sale for $\frac{2}{3}$ of the regular price. What is the sale price?
6. Your store has an area of 996 square feet. Your yearly rent is \$14 per square foot. How much is your yearly rent? your monthly rent?
7. You pay each employee \$5.75 an hour. Your store hours are from 9:00 A.M. to 6:00 P.M. If an employee takes 1 hour off for lunch, how much does it cost per day for each full-time employee?
8. One employee works from 9:00 A.M. to 12:45 P.M. How many hours does she work each day? Give the answer as a mixed number in simplest form.
9. a. One employee works from 1:30 P.M. to 6:00 P.M. How many hours is that? Give your answer as a decimal.
   b. At \$5.75 per hour, how much will you pay him each day? Round the answer to the nearest cent.

Length—customary units

GUESS AND CHECK

1. Guess which pencil is longer. (Later, you will check your guess by measuring each pencil with an inch ruler.)

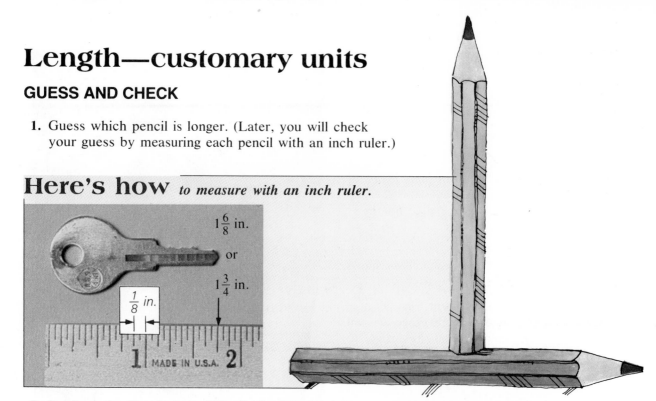

Here's how *to measure with an inch ruler.*

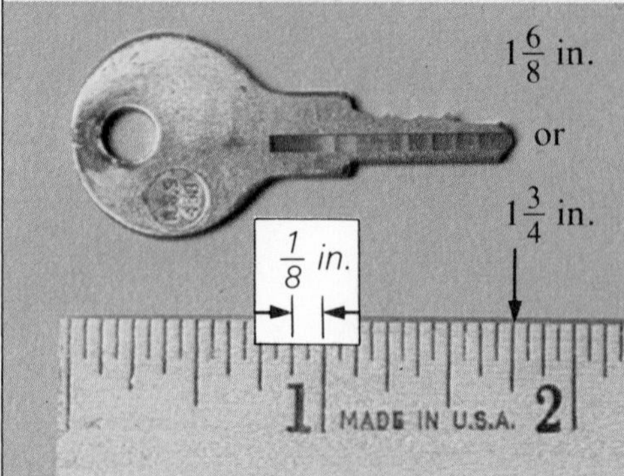

2. Look at the *Here's how*. What is the length of the key measured to the nearest $\frac{1}{8}$ inch? (Give the answer in simplest form.)

3. **a.** Measure the orange pencil to the nearest $\frac{1}{8}$ inch.

   b. Measure the green pencil to the nearest $\frac{1}{8}$ inch.

   c. Which pencil is longer?

4. Was your guess for question 1 correct?

EXERCISES

Measure each segment to the nearest $\frac{1}{8}$ inch. Give the answer in simplest form.

5. ____

6. ____________________

7. ____

8. ______________________________________

9. ____

10. _______________

Draw segments having these lengths.

11. $1\frac{1}{2}$ inches

12. $2\frac{1}{8}$ inches

13. $3\frac{3}{4}$ inches

14. $\frac{7}{8}$ inch

15. $4\frac{5}{8}$ inches

16. $6\frac{1}{4}$ inches

17. $\frac{1}{2}$ inch

18. $5\frac{3}{8}$ inches

19. $2\frac{1}{2}$ inches

20. $1\frac{1}{8}$ inches

21. $5\frac{5}{8}$ inches

22. $3\frac{7}{8}$ inches

23. Draw a segment that is 3 inches long.

- **a.** How many $\frac{1}{2}$ inches long is it?
- **b.** How many $\frac{1}{4}$ inches long is it?

24. Draw a segment that is $4\frac{3}{4}$ inches long.

- **a.** How many $\frac{1}{4}$ inches long is it?
- **b.** How many $\frac{1}{8}$ inches long is it?

Find the treasure **Following directions**

This treasure map was found in a bottle on a deserted island. Use the map to locate the buried treasure.

25. At the base of which tree would you dig to find the treasure?

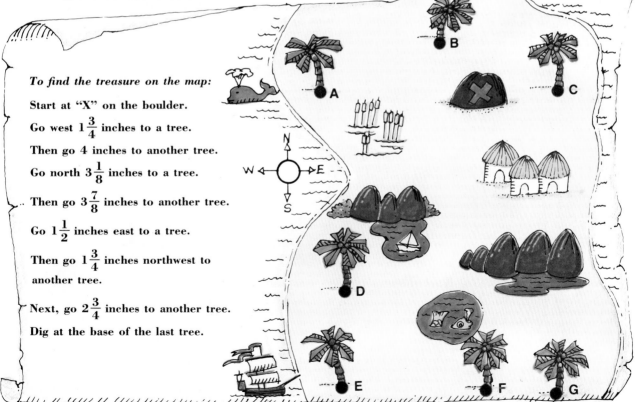

To find the treasure on the map:

Start at "X" on the boulder.

Go west $1\frac{3}{4}$ inches to a tree.

Then go 4 inches to another tree.

Go north $3\frac{1}{8}$ inches to a tree.

Then go $3\frac{7}{8}$ inches to another tree.

Go $1\frac{1}{2}$ inches east to a tree.

Then go $1\frac{3}{4}$ inches northwest to another tree.

Next, go $2\frac{3}{4}$ inches to another tree.

Dig at the base of the last tree.

Changing units of length—customary

RECORD BREAKER?

Is 185 inches of apple peel a new world record? The longest unbroken apple peel is 57 yards 1 foot by Kathy Wafler of Wolcott, New York.

This apple peel is 185 inches long. I bet that's a new world record!

Here are the facts you will need to know to change from one unit of length to another:

12 inches (in.) = 1 foot (ft)
3 ft = 1 yard (yd)
36 in. = 1 yd
5280 ft = 1 mile (mi)

Here's how *to change from one unit of length to another.*

185 in. = ? ft ? in.

Think: Changing to a larger unit, so divide.

Remember: 12 in. = 1 ft

$$\begin{array}{r} 15 \\ 12\overline{)185} \\ -12 \\ \hline 65 \\ -60 \\ \hline 5 \end{array}$$

185 in. = 15 ft 5 in.

57 yd 1 ft = ? ft

Think: Change to a smaller unit, so multiply.

Remember: 1 yd = 3 ft

$$\begin{array}{r} 57 \\ \times\ 3 \\ \hline 171 \\ +\ 1 \\ \hline 172 \end{array}$$

57 yd 1 ft = 172 ft

1. Look at the *Here's how.* Is 185 inches of apple peel a new world record?

2. Check these examples. Have the unit changes been done correctly?

a. 2 mi = ? ft

Think: Changing to a smaller unit, so multiply.

Remember: 1 mi = 5280 ft
2 mi = 10,560 ft
(× 5280)

b. 66 ft = ? yd

Think: Changing to a larger unit, so divide.

Remember: 3 ft = 1 yd
66 ft = 22 yd
(÷ 3)

EXERCISES

Copy and complete.

3. 6 ft = ? in.
4. 5 yd = ? ft
5. 1 mi = ? ft
6. 48 in. = ? ft
7. 12 ft = ? yd
8. 3 mi = ? ft
9. 36 in. = ? yd
10. 3 yd = ? in.
11. 5 ft = ? in.
12. 120 ft = ? yd
13. 13 yd = ? ft
14. 72 in. = ? yd
15. 26 in. = 2 ft ? in.
16. 7 ft = 2 yd ? ft
17. 40 in. = 1 yd ? in.
18. 50 in. = 4 ft ? in.
19. 11 ft = 3 yd ? ft
20. 49 in. = 1 yd ? in.
21. 80 in. = 6 ft ? in.
22. 17 ft = 5 yd ? ft
23. 68 in. = 1 yd ? in.
24. 2 ft 3 in. = ? in.
25. 3 yd 1 ft = ? ft
26. 2 yd 4 in. = ? in.
27. 3 ft 7 in. = ? in.
28. 7 yd 2 ft = ? ft
29. 3 yd 10 in. = ? in.
30. 4 ft 3 in. = ? in.
31. 8 yd 3 ft = ? ft
32. 7 yd 6 in. = ? in.

Solve.

33. The record for spitting watermelon seeds is 65 feet 4 inches. How many inches is that?
34. The record for an egg to be thrown and then caught without breaking is 116 yards 2 feet. How many feet is that?
35. The record for catching a thrown grape in the mouth is 319 feet 8 inches. Suppose you caught a grape that was thrown 89 yards 10 inches. Would you break the record?
36. The record for throwing a 2-pound rolling pin is 175 feet 5 inches. Suppose you threw a 2-pound rolling pin 58 yards 1 foot. Would you break the record?

How many apples? **Logical reasoning**

37. Study the clues to find how many apples are in the bag.

    Clues:
    - There are fewer than 30.
    - If you divided them among 4 people, you would have 3 left over.
    - If you divided them among 5 people, you would have 4 left over.

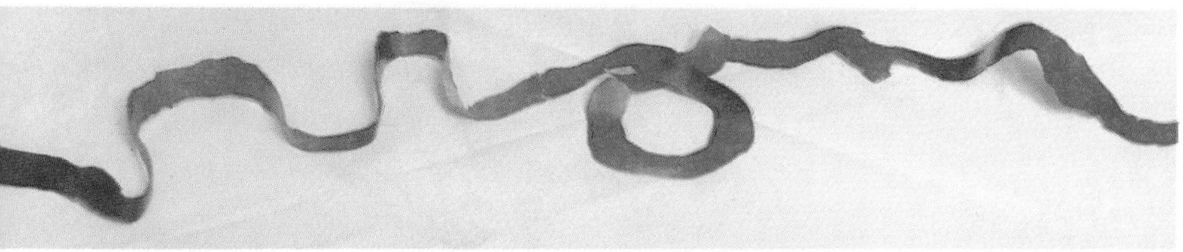

Liquid volume—customary units

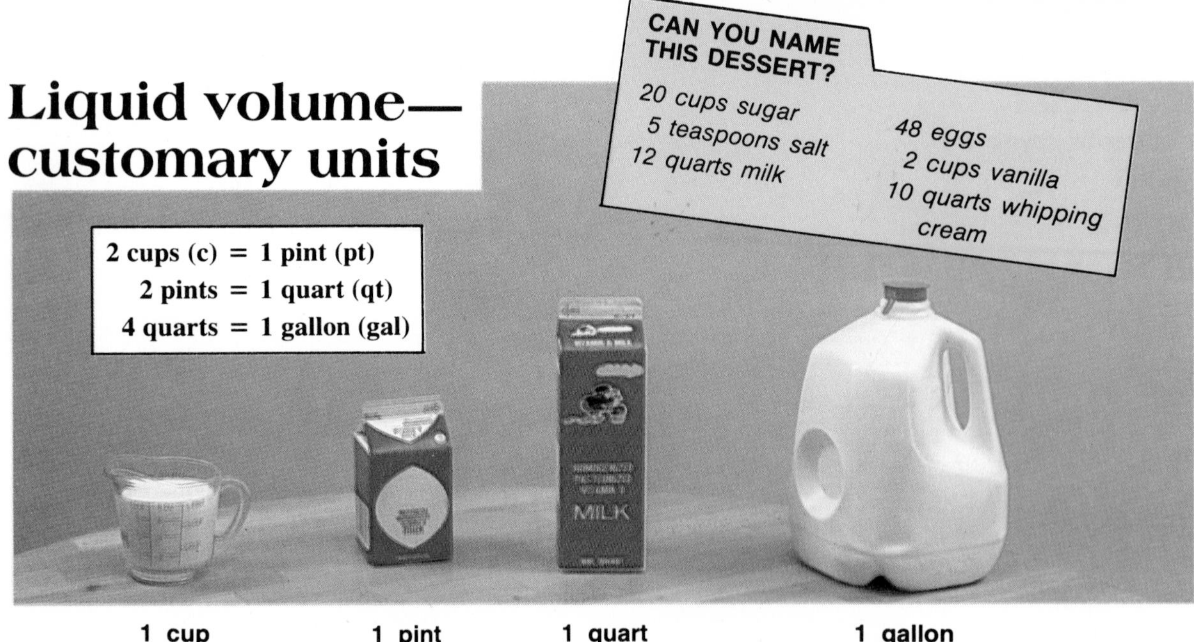

CAN YOU NAME THIS DESSERT?
20 cups sugar
5 teaspoons salt
12 quarts milk
48 eggs
2 cups vanilla
10 quarts whipping cream
2 cups (c) = 1 pint (pt)
2 pints = 1 quart (qt)
4 quarts = 1 gallon (gal)
MILK
1 cup
1 pint
1 quart
1 gallon

1. Read the recipe. How many quarts of milk are needed to make the dessert?
2. How many quarts are in 1 gallon?
3. To compute the number of gallons of milk, you would divide 12 by what number?

Here's how *to change from one unit of liquid volume to another.*

12 qt = ? gal	*10 qt = ? pt*
Think: Changing to a larger unit, so divide.	*Think:* Changing to a smaller unit, so multiply.
Remember: 4 qt = 1 gal 12 qt = 3 gal (÷ 4)	*Remember:* 1 qt = 2 pt 10 qt = 20 pt (× 2)

4. Check these examples. Have the units been changed correctly?

   a. 13 qt = ? gal ? qt

   Remember: 4 qt = 1 gal

   $$\begin{array}{r} 3 \\ 4\overline{)13} \\ -12 \\ \hline 1 \end{array}$$

   13 qt = 3 gal 1 qt

   b. 11 pt 1 c = ? c

   Remember: 1 pt = 2 c

   $$\begin{array}{r} 11 \\ \times 2 \\ \hline 22 \\ +1 \\ \hline 23 \end{array}$$

   11 pt 1 c = 23 c

EXERCISES

Copy and complete.

5. 18 pt = ? qt
6. 12 c = ? pt
7. 8 qt = ? gal
8. 6 qt = ? pt
9. 3 gal = ? qt
10. 6 pt = ? c
11. 1 qt = ? pt
12. 1 qt = ? c
13. 1 gal = ? c
14. 4 c = ? qt
15. 8 pt = ? gal
16. 16 c = ? gal
17. 3 pt 1 c = ? c
18. 5 qt 1 pt = ? pt
19. 3 gal 2 qt = ? qt
20. 3 gal 2 pt = ? qt
21. 8 qt 2 c = ? pt
22. 1 qt 1 pt = ? c
23. 15 pt = ? qt 1 pt
24. 19 qt = ? gal 3 qt
25. 34 pt = ? gal 1 qt
26. 17 pt = 8 qt ? pt
27. 15 qt = 3 gal ? qt
28. 25 pt = 3 gal ? pt

Solve. Use the recipe on page 214.

29. **a.** How many dozen eggs are needed?
b. If eggs cost $.89 a dozen, what will be the total cost of the eggs?

30. **a.** How many cups of whipping cream are needed?
b. If whipping cream costs $.98 a cup, what will be the total cost of the whipping cream?

31. **a.** How many $\frac{1}{4}$-cup bottles of vanilla are needed?
b. If a $\frac{1}{4}$-cup bottle of vanilla costs $1.98, what will be the total cost for the vanilla?

32. **a.** The recipe makes 40 quarts of vanilla ice cream. How many gallons is that?
b. If you bought the same amount of ice cream for $4.89 per gallon, what would be the total cost?

What's number one?

33. What is the most popular flavor of ice cream?

Clues:

- More people like vanilla than cherry.
- More people like chocolate than strawberry.
- Fewer people like chocolate than vanilla.

Weight—customary units

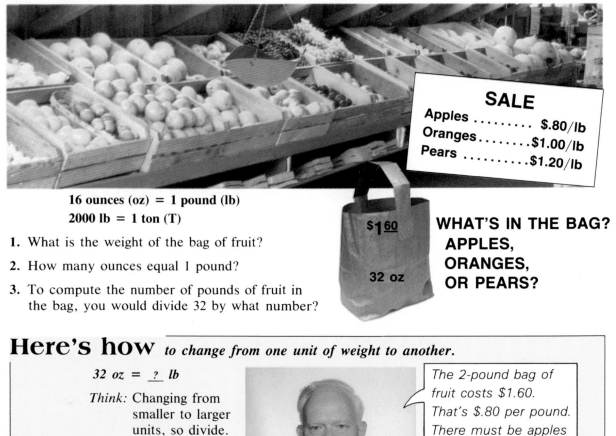

SALE
Apples .... $.80/lb
Oranges $1.00/lb
Pears $1.20/lb

$1.60

32 oz

WHAT'S IN THE BAG?
APPLES,
ORANGES,
OR PEARS?

16 ounces (oz) = 1 pound (lb)
2000 lb = 1 ton (T)

1. What is the weight of the bag of fruit?

2. How many ounces equal 1 pound?

3. To compute the number of pounds of fruit in the bag, you would divide 32 by what number?

Here's how *to change from one unit of weight to another.*

32 oz = __?__ *lb*

Think: Changing from smaller to larger units, so divide.

Remember: 16 oz = 1 lb
32 oz = 2 lb
↑÷ 16↑

The 2-pound bag of fruit costs $1.60. That's $.80 per pound. There must be apples in the bag!

4. Use the sale prices. How much would 32 ounces of pears cost?

5. How much would a ton of oranges cost?

6. Check these examples. Have the units been changed correctly?

a. 6000 lb = __?__ T

Think: Changing to a larger unit, so divide.
6000 lb = 3 T
↑÷ 2000↑

b. 2 lb 5 oz = __?__ oz

Think: Changing to a smaller unit, so multiply.
2 lb 5 oz = 37 oz
↑× 16 + 5↑

EXERCISES

Copy and complete.

7. 3 lb = ? oz
8. 48 oz = ? lb
9. 4 T = ? lb
10. 8000 lb = ? T
11. 10 lb = ? oz
12. 160 oz = ? lb
13. 80 oz = ? lb
14. 10,000 lb = ? T
15. 14 lb = ? oz
16. 1 lb 8 oz = ? oz
17. 2 lb 3 oz = ? oz
18. 4 lb 10 oz = ? oz
19. 20 oz = ? lb 4 oz
20. 52 oz = ? lb 4 oz
21. 30 oz = ? lb 14 oz
22. 7500 lb = ? T 1500 lb
23. 9050 lb = 4 T ? lb
24. 2060 lb = ? T 60 lb
25. 18 oz = 1 lb ? oz
26. 5000 lb = ? T 1000 lb
27. 100 oz = ? lb 4 oz
28. 22 lb = ? oz
29. 64 oz = ? lb
30. 56,000 lb = ? T
31. 6016 lb = 3T ? lb
32. 40 oz = 2 lb ? oz
33. 2500 lb = 1T ? lb

Solve.

34. An empty truck weighs 12,500 pounds. When full of apples, it weighs 8 tons. What is the weight of the apples in pounds?

35. A truck contained 3 tons of oranges. After some oranges were unloaded, 1 ton 450 pounds of oranges remained. How many pounds of oranges were unloaded?

36. A 2-pound bag of bananas costs 78¢. A 16-ounce bag of bananas costs 45¢. Which costs less per pound?

37. A 2-pound 8-ounce bag of peaches costs $4.00. A 1-pound 4-ounce bag of peaches costs $2.25. Which costs less per ounce?

Fruit salad! **Logical reasoning**

38. Study the clues to find how many apples, oranges, and pears are in the fruit salad.

    Clues:
    - There are 12 oranges.
    - If you add the number of pears and apples, you get 2 more than the number of oranges.
    - There are 4 more pears than apples.

Computing with customary units

DO YOU REMEMBER THESE MEASUREMENT FACTS?

LENGTH	LIQUID VOLUME	WEIGHT
1 ft = 12 in. 1 yd = 3 ft = 36 in. 1 mi = 5280 ft	1 pt = 2 c 1 qt = 2 pt 1 gal = 4 qt	1 lb = 16 oz 1 T = 2000 lb

Here's how

to compute with customary units of measurement.

EXAMPLE 1. *15 ft 4 in. + 12 ft 10 in. = ?*

Step 1. Add inches and regroup.

```
    1 ft
   15 ft  4 in.
 + 12 ft 10 in.
 --------------
          2 in.
```

14 in. = 1 ft 2 in.

Step 2. Add feet.

```
    1 ft
   15 ft  4 in.
 + 12 ft 10 in.
 --------------
   28 ft  2 in.
```

EXAMPLE 2. *14 lb 9 oz − 8 lb 12 oz = ?*

Step 1. Regroup.

16 oz + 9 oz

```
   13 lb 25 oz
   14 lb  9 oz   (crossed out)
 −  8 lb 12 oz
 -------------
```

Step 2. Subtract.

```
   13 lb 25 oz
   14 lb  9 oz   (crossed out)
 −  8 lb 12 oz
 -------------
    5 lb 13 oz
```

EXERCISES

Add. *Here are scrambled answers for the next row of exercises:* *6 ft 7 in.* *6 yd* *6 ft 3 in.* *7 yd 1 ft*

1. 3 ft 8 in. + 2 ft 7 in.

2. 2 yd 2 ft + 4 yd 2 ft

3. 4 ft 10 in. + 1 ft 9 in.

4. 1 yd 1 ft + 4 yd 2 ft

5. 3 gal 3 qt
+1 gal 2 qt

6. 4 qt 1 pt
+3 qt 1 pt

7. 2 gal 2 qt
+5 gal 1 qt

8. 2 pt 1 c
+4 pt 1 c

9. 6 lb 12 oz
+3 lb 8 oz

10. 2 T 1500 lb
+3 T 1400 lb

11. 8 lb 14 oz
+9 lb 10 oz

12. 6 T 1000 lb
+3 T 1800 lb

Here are scrambled answers for the next row of exercises: *3 yd 1 ft* *2 ft 6 in.* *2 ft 11 in.* *2 yd 2 ft*

13. 5 ft 9 in.
−2 ft 10 in.

14. 4 yd 1 ft
−1 yd 2 ft

15. 7 ft 2 in.
−4 ft 8 in.

16. 6 yd
−2 yd 2 ft

17. 5 lb 2 oz
−2 lb 12 oz

18. 6 T 500 lb
−3 T 1000 lb

19. 4 lb 10 oz
−1 lb 11 oz

20. 30 T 1800 lb
− 9 T 1900 lb

21. 4 gal 1 qt
−1 gal 2 qt

22. 4 qt
−2 qt 1 pt

23. 5 gal 2 qt
−2 gal 3 qt

24. 4 gal
−1 gal 1 qt

Solve.

25. You and a friend cut a watermelon into two pieces. Your piece weighed 14 pounds 9 ounces, and her piece weighed 12 pounds 10 ounces. How much more did your piece weigh?

26. You bought 3 pounds 7 ounces of green grapes and 2 pounds 9 ounces of red grapes. How many pounds of grapes did you buy altogether?

Antique math **Reading a table**

Use the table to complete each exercise.

27. 27 barleycorns = ? in.

28. 15 in. = ? palms

29. 2 spans + 1 hand = ? in.

30. 1 pace + 1 cubit = ? in.

31. 1 pace = ? cubits

32. 6 palms = ? spans

33. 2 cubits = ? spans

34. 3 hands = ? palms

35. 1 pace − 1 cubit = ? spans

36. 1 cubit − 1 span = ? palms

37. 1 hand + 1 palm = ? barleycorns

38. 1 hand − 1 palm = ? barleycorns

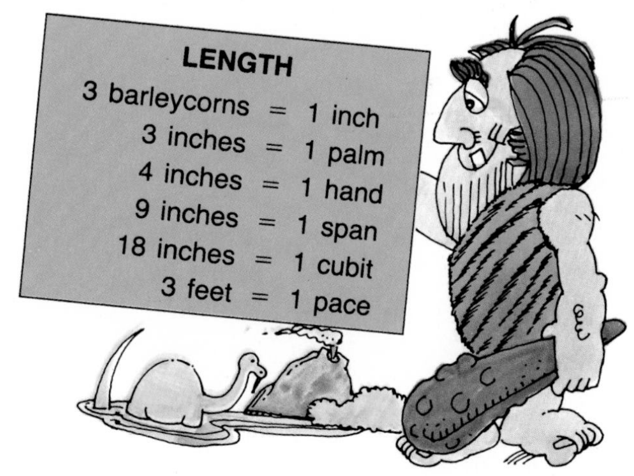

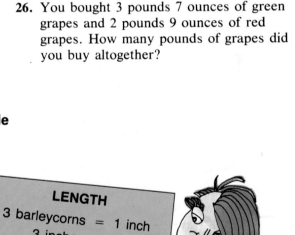

LENGTH		
3 barleycorns	=	1 inch
3 inches	=	1 palm
4 inches	=	1 hand
9 inches	=	1 span
18 inches	=	1 cubit
3 feet	=	1 pace

Cumulative Skill Practice

Subtract. Give the difference in simplest form. *(page 168, 170)*

1. $3\frac{3}{4} - 1\frac{1}{4}$
2. $5\frac{5}{6} - 2\frac{1}{6}$
3. $4 - 2\frac{1}{3}$
4. $6 - 4\frac{1}{2}$
5. $9 - 3\frac{3}{5}$
6. $8\frac{1}{2} - 2\frac{3}{4}$
7. $7\frac{1}{3} - 1\frac{1}{2}$
8. $3\frac{5}{8} - 2\frac{3}{4}$
9. $6\frac{1}{3} - 4\frac{3}{8}$
10. $16\frac{3}{4} - 10\frac{7}{8}$
11. $20\frac{3}{10} - 12\frac{5}{6}$
12. $14\frac{5}{8} - \frac{15}{16}$

Give the product in simplest form. *(page 178)*

13. $\frac{1}{3} \times \frac{1}{3}$
14. $\frac{3}{4} \times \frac{2}{3}$
15. $\frac{3}{2} \times \frac{3}{2}$
16. $\frac{5}{9} \times \frac{3}{2}$
17. $\frac{4}{5} \times \frac{7}{2}$
18. $\frac{7}{8} \times \frac{4}{3}$
19. $\frac{0}{2} \times \frac{3}{8}$
20. $\frac{3}{4} \times \frac{4}{3}$
21. $\frac{5}{6} \times \frac{10}{3}$
22. $\frac{5}{9} \times \frac{3}{3}$

Give the quotient in simplest form. *(page 188)*

23. $\frac{4}{9} \div \frac{1}{3}$
24. $6 \div \frac{2}{3}$
25. $\frac{5}{6} \div \frac{1}{2}$
26. $4 \div \frac{2}{3}$
27. $\frac{5}{8} \div \frac{1}{4}$
28. $\frac{9}{4} \div \frac{9}{4}$
29. $\frac{3}{2} \div \frac{3}{4}$
30. $\frac{2}{5} \div 4$
31. $\frac{3}{5} \div \frac{3}{8}$
32. $\frac{3}{10} \div \frac{2}{5}$
33. $\frac{5}{6} \div 3$
34. $\frac{9}{5} \div \frac{3}{8}$
35. $\frac{1}{8} \div \frac{1}{4}$
36. $\frac{2}{3} \div \frac{1}{6}$
37. $\frac{0}{4} \div \frac{1}{2}$

Complete. *(page 202)*

38. 9 cm = ? mm
39. 4 m = ? cm
40. 3 km = ? m
41. 3715 m = ? km
42. 5.9 km = ? m
43. 6.3 cm = ? mm
44. 58 mm = ? cm
45. 35 cm = ? m
46. 26 km = ? m
47. 1368 m = ? km
48. 5.75 km = ? m
49. 1.6 m = ? mm

Subtract. *(page 218)*

50. 6 ft 4 in. − 2 ft 8 in.
51. 6 yd 1 ft − 3 yd 2 ft
52. 8 ft − 5 ft 7 in.
53. 9 yd − 2 yd 1 ft
54. 8 lb 3 oz − 2 lb 10 oz
55. 4 T 200 lb − 2 T 500 lb
56. 10 lb 6 oz − 3 lb 12 oz
57. 6 T − 2 T 1000 lb
58. 3 gal 1 qt − 1 gal 2 qt
59. 8 qt − 2 qt 1 pt
60. 4 gal 2 qt − 2 gal 3 qt
61. 5 gal − 3 gal 1 qt

Problem solving

GARDENING WITH A COMPUTER

Richard Dorr used his home computer to help his family plan their garden. THE HOME GARDENER program helped them decide how much to plant, how much seed to buy, and how much fertilizer to buy. The steps used to plan one part of the garden are shown below.

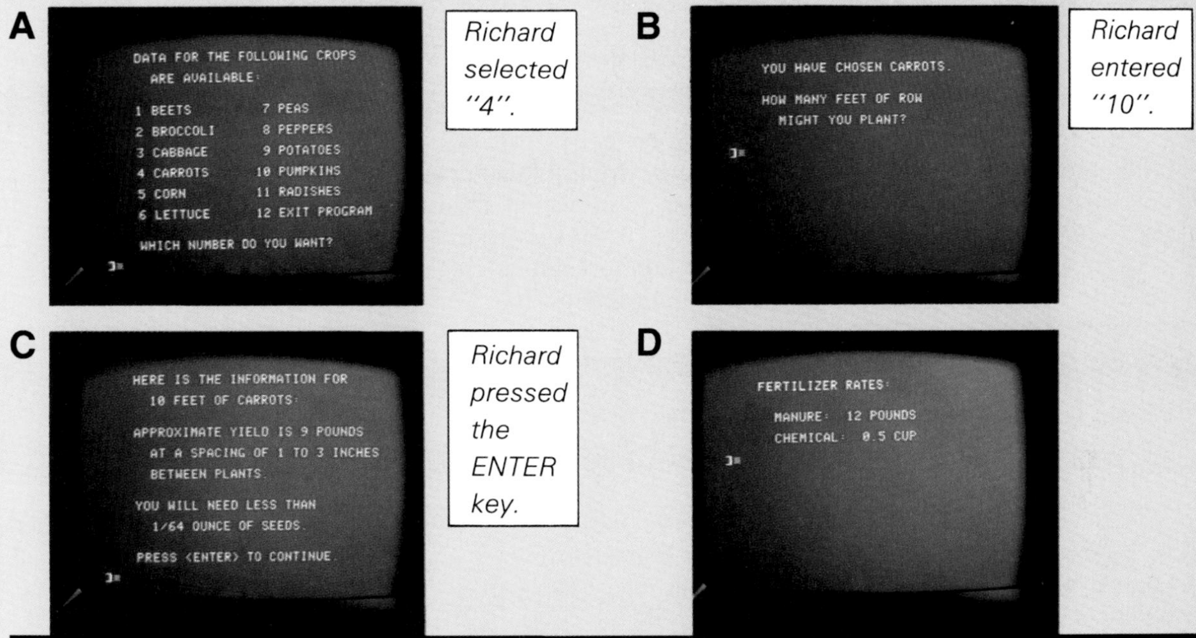

A
DATA FOR THE FOLLOWING CROPS ARE AVAILABLE:
1 BEETS
2 BROCCOLI
3 CABBAGE
4 CARROTS
5 CORN
6 LETTUCE
7 PEAS
8 PEPPERS
9 POTATOES
10 PUMPKINS
11 RADISHES
12 EXIT PROGRAM
WHICH NUMBER DO YOU WANT?
Richard selected "4".
B
YOU HAVE CHOSEN CARROTS.
HOW MANY FEET OF ROW MIGHT YOU PLANT?
Richard entered "10".
C
HERE IS THE INFORMATION FOR 10 FEET OF CARROTS:
APPROXIMATE YIELD IS 9 POUNDS AT A SPACING OF 1 TO 3 INCHES BETWEEN PLANTS.
YOU WILL NEED LESS THAN 1/64 OUNCE OF SEEDS.
PRESS <ENTER> TO CONTINUE.
Richard pressed the ENTER key.
D
FERTILIZER RATES:
MANURE: 12 POUNDS
CHEMICAL: 0.5 CUP

Use the data from the screens to solve these problems.

1. How many different crops does the program provide data for?

2. The progam assumes that the crops are planted in rows. How long a row of carrots was planned?

3. **a.** What is the suggested spacing for the seeds?

   b. If they used the widest spacing suggested, would they have more than 3 dozen plants in the row?

4. **a.** How many pounds of carrots should they expect to grow?

   b. A similar row of tomato plants would yield 3 times the weight yielded by the carrot plants. How many pounds of tomatoes could they grow in the row?

5. Richard's father found about 6 ounces of chemical fertilizer left in a bottle. Was this enough fertilizer for the row of carrots? (*Hint: There are 8 ounces in a cup.*)

6. Assume the weight of the seeds used to plant the row of carrots was $\frac{1}{64}$ ounce. How many pounds of carrots could they grow if they planted 1 ounce of seeds?

Chapter REVIEW

Here are scrambled answers for the review exercises:

1000	feet	kilogram	multiply
5280	gallon	meters	pound
centimeter	grams	milliliters	ton
divide	inch	millimeters	yard

1. One tenth of a [?] is 1 millimeter. The length of this segment is 23 [?]. *(page 198)*

centimeters 1 2 3 4

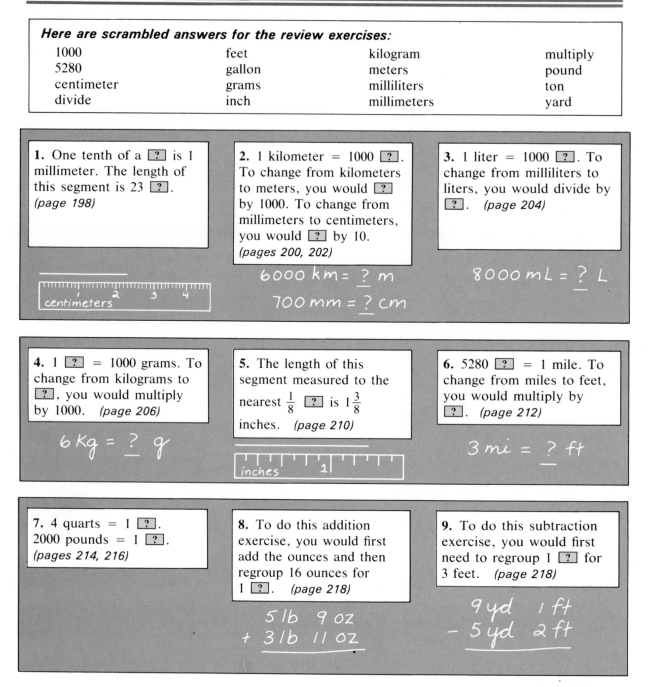

2. 1 kilometer = 1000 [?]. To change from kilometers to meters, you would [?] by 1000. To change from millimeters to centimeters, you would [?] by 10. *(pages 200, 202)*

6000 km = ? m

700 mm = ? cm

3. 1 liter = 1000 [?]. To change from milliliters to liters, you would divide by [?]. *(page 204)*

8000 mL = ? L

4. 1 [?] = 1000 grams. To change from kilograms to [?], you would multiply by 1000. *(page 206)*

6 Kg = ? g

5. The length of this segment measured to the nearest $\frac{1}{8}$ [?] is $1\frac{3}{8}$ inches. *(page 210)*

inches 1

6. 5280 [?] = 1 mile. To change from miles to feet, you would multiply by [?]. *(page 212)*

3 mi = ? ft

7. 4 quarts = 1 [?]. 2000 pounds = 1 [?]. *(pages 214, 216)*

8. To do this addition exercise, you would first add the ounces and then regroup 16 ounces for 1 [?]. *(page 218)*

5 lb 9 oz
+ 3 lb 11 oz

9. To do this subtraction exercise, you would first need to regroup 1 [?] for 3 feet. *(page 218)*

9 yd 1 ft
− 5 yd 2 ft

Chapter TEST

Measure each length to the nearest centimeter. *(page 198)*

1. ______________________ **2.** ______________________

3. ______________________ **4.** ______________________

5. ______________________

Which measurement is reasonable? *(page 200)*

6. Length of a key:
a. 52 mm **b.** 52 cm **c.** 52 m

7. Length of a baseball bat:
a. 91 mm **b.** 91 cm **c.** 91 m

8. Height of a door:
a. 2.1 cm **b.** 2.1 m **c.** 2.1 km

9. Length of a train:
a. 0.6 cm **b.** 0.6 m **c.** 0.6 km

Copy and complete. *(pages 202, 204, 206)*

10. 6 cm = _?_ mm **11.** 4 m = _?_ cm **12.** 9 km = _?_ m

13. 82 mm = _?_ cm **14.** 3.8 m = _?_ cm **15.** 7.4 cm = _?_ mm

16. 8 L = _?_ mL **17.** 1.5 L = _?_ mL **18.** 1250 mL = _?_ L

19. 0.475 L = _?_ mL **20.** 750 mL = _?_ L **21.** 65 mL = _?_ L

22. 5000 mg = _?_ g **23.** 3000 g = _?_ kg **24.** 2.1 kg = _?_ g

25. 8.4 g = _?_ mg **26.** 438 mg = _?_ g **27.** 395 g = _?_ kg

Measure each segment to the nearest $\frac{1}{8}$ inch. Give the answer in simplest form. *(page 210)*

28. ______________________ **29.** ______________________

30. ______________________

Copy and complete. *(pages 212, 214, 216)*

31. 7 ft = _?_ in. **32.** 1 mi = _?_ ft **33.** 33 ft = _?_ yd

34. 72 in. = _?_ yd **35.** 2 ft 4 in. = _?_ in. **36.** 4 yd 1 ft = _?_ ft

37. 16 pt = _?_ qt **38.** 14 c = _?_ pt **39.** 16 qt = _?_ gal

40. 8 c = _?_ qt **41.** 13 pt = 6 qt _?_ pt **42.** 9 qt = 2 gal _?_ qt

43. 4 lb = _?_ oz **44.** 64 oz = _?_ lb **45.** 3 T = _?_ lb

46. 24 oz = 1 lb _?_ oz **47.** 3500 lb = 1 T _?_ lb **48.** 36 oz = _?_ lb 4 oz

Add or subtract. *(page 218)*

49.
```
  5 ft 9 in.
+3 ft 8 in.
```

50.
```
  8 lb 14 oz
+5 lb  7 oz
```

51.
```
  7 yd 1 ft
-2 yd 2 ft
```

52.
```
  4 gal
-1 gal 3 qt
```

Cumulative TEST Standardized Format

Choose the correct letter.

1. Multiply.
$$\begin{array}{r} 5.637 \\ \times 2.04 \\ \hline \end{array}$$

A. 114.9948
B. 13.5288
C. 11.49948
D. none of these

2. Divide. Round the quotient to the nearest hundredth.
$$0.65\overline{)6.69}$$

A. 1.03
B. 1.29
C. 10.29
D. none of these

3. Change to a decimal.
$$2\frac{7}{8} = ?$$

A. 2.78
B. 3.375
C. 2.875
D. none of these

4. Change to a mixed number in simplest form.
3.200

A. $3\frac{1}{4}$
B. $3\frac{200}{1000}$
C. $3\frac{1}{5}$
D. none of these

5.

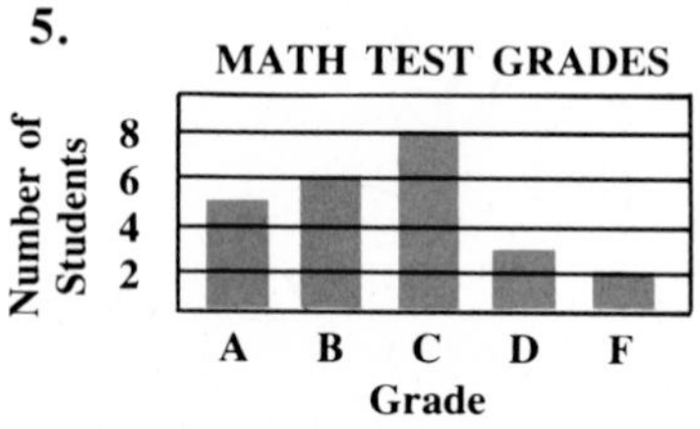

How many students made a grade of C or better?

A. 8 B. 11
C. 13 D. none of these

6. Add.
$$\begin{array}{r} 3\frac{2}{3} \\ +2\frac{3}{4} \\ \hline \end{array}$$

A. $5\frac{5}{12}$
B. $6\frac{5}{12}$
C. $5\frac{5}{7}$
D. none of these

7. Subtract.
$$\begin{array}{r} 4\frac{1}{5} \\ -2\frac{1}{2} \\ \hline \end{array}$$

A. $2\frac{3}{10}$ B. $2\frac{7}{10}$
C. $1\frac{7}{10}$ D. none of these

8. Give the product.
$$\frac{3}{8} \times \frac{4}{5} = ?$$

A. $\frac{3}{10}$ B. $\frac{7}{40}$
C. $\frac{12}{13}$ D. none of these

9. Give the quotient.
$$\frac{6}{5} \div \frac{3}{4} = ?$$

A. $1\frac{1}{9}$ B. $\frac{9}{10}$
C. $1\frac{3}{5}$ D. none of these

10. Complete.
236 cm = ? m

A. 23.6
B. 236
C. 23,600
D. none of these

11. Subtract.
$$\begin{array}{r} 8 \text{ ft } 2 \text{ in.} \\ -3 \text{ ft } 9 \text{ in.} \\ \hline \end{array}$$

A. 5 ft 7 in.
B. 4 ft 5 in.
C. 4 ft 3 in.
D. none of these

12. You had \$27. Then you worked 2.5 hours for \$3.80 per hour. How much money did you have then?

A. \$36.50 B. \$30.80
C. \$71.30 D. none of these

Chapter 10

Ratio and Proportion

Ratios

You can use a **ratio** to compare two numbers. The paint for the birdhouse was a custom mixture of yellow and blue. The ratio of yellow paint to blue paint was 2 to 3. Here are three ways to write the ratio:

2 to 3 $\quad \frac{2}{3} \quad$ **2 : 3**

Read each ratio as "2 to 3."

1. Look at the jars of paint shown above. What is the ratio of jars of yellow paint to jars of blue paint?
2. What is the ratio of jars of blue paint to jars of yellow paint?
3. Suppose that you wanted to mix the same color and use 4 jars of yellow paint. How many jars of blue paint should you use?

Here's how *to find equal ratios.*

You can find equal ratios by thinking about equivalent fractions.

		1 batch		2 batches		3 batches
jars of yellow paint jars of blue paint	→ →	$\frac{2}{3}$	=	$\frac{4}{6}$	=	$\frac{6}{9}$

4. Look at the *Here's how.*
   a. How many jars of yellow paint would you mix with 6 jars of blue paint?
   b. How many jars of blue paint would you mix with 6 jars of yellow paint?
   c. You would have to multiply both the numerator and the denominator of $\frac{2}{3}$ by [?] to get $\frac{4}{6}$.
   d. You would have to divide both numerator and denominator of $\frac{6}{9}$ by [?] to get $\frac{2}{3}$.
5. Suppose you decide to use 12 jars of yellow paint. How many jars of blue paint would you need to mix the custom green?

EXERCISES

Give each ratio as a fraction in lowest terms.

Here are scrambled answers for the next row of exercises: $\frac{4}{3}$ $\frac{1}{4}$ $\frac{5}{2}$ $\frac{1}{2}$ $\frac{4}{9}$

6. 4 to 8 **7.** 3 to 12 **8.** 15 to 6 **9.** 8 to 6 **10.** 16 to 36

11. $\frac{14}{21}$ **12.** $\frac{10}{4}$ **13.** $\frac{16}{6}$ **14.** $\frac{9}{45}$ **15.** $\frac{18}{27}$

16. 12 : 20 **17.** 14 : 8 **18.** 18 : 32 **19.** 12 : 18 **20.** 24 : 18

21. 32 : 18 **22.** 17 : 51 **23.** 70 : 50 **24.** 26 : 39 **25.** 22 : 33

Copy and complete. *Hint: Think about equivalent fractions.*

26. $\frac{3}{4} = \frac{?}{8}$ **27.** $\frac{1}{4} = \frac{?}{12}$ **28.** $\frac{8}{5} = \frac{40}{?}$ **29.** $\frac{4}{3} = \frac{12}{?}$

30. $\frac{8}{3} = \frac{?}{21}$ **31.** $\frac{?}{16} = \frac{5}{4}$ **32.** $\frac{?}{3} = \frac{10}{30}$ **33.** $\frac{1}{3} = \frac{?}{12}$

34. $\frac{12}{?} = \frac{24}{22}$ **35.** $\frac{?}{15} = \frac{2}{3}$ **36.** $\frac{15}{30} = \frac{3}{?}$ **37.** $\frac{7}{9} = \frac{?}{54}$

38. $\frac{6}{5} = \frac{36}{?}$ **39.** $\frac{5}{7} = \frac{?}{28}$ **40.** $\frac{4}{?} = \frac{16}{28}$ **41.** $\frac{?}{3} = \frac{50}{30}$

42. $\frac{1}{3} = \frac{?}{75}$ **43.** $\frac{3}{20} = \frac{9}{?}$ **44.** $\frac{10}{3} = \frac{100}{?}$ **45.** $\frac{16}{18} = \frac{?}{9}$

46. $\frac{2}{3} = \frac{?}{24}$ **47.** $\frac{3}{4} = \frac{27}{?}$ **48.** $\frac{5}{8} = \frac{?}{32}$ **49.** $\frac{3}{2} = \frac{30}{?}$

50. $\frac{7}{8} = \frac{21}{?}$ **51.** $\frac{?}{100} = \frac{9}{5}$ **52.** $\frac{4}{3} = \frac{40}{?}$ **53.** $\frac{?}{100} = \frac{4}{5}$

54. $\frac{?}{24} = \frac{3}{8}$ **55.** $\frac{6}{5} = \frac{?}{50}$ **56.** $\frac{?}{18} = \frac{5}{3}$ **57.** $\frac{5}{2} = \frac{100}{?}$

You mix it!

To get Sunset Orange, mix 1 part white, 3 parts yellow, and 2 parts red.

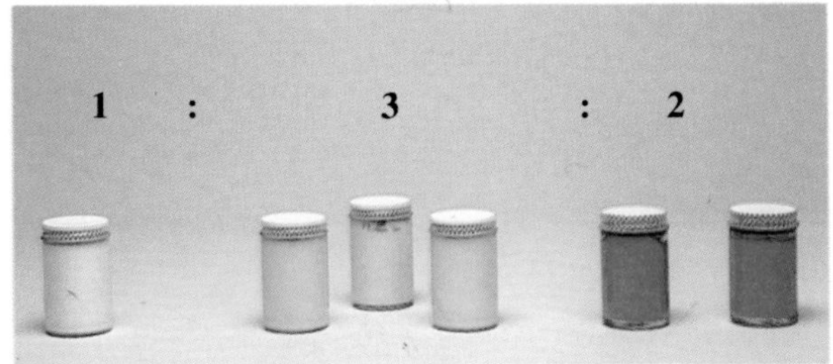

58. How many jars of white paint would you need if you used 4 jars of red?

59. How many jars of red would you need to mix with 9 jars of yellow?

60. Suppose you needed 12 jars of Sunset Orange. How many jars of each of the three colors would you need?

Proportions

FREE THROWS DURING GAMES

PLAYER	FREE THROWS MADE	FREE THROWS ATTEMPTED
Nancy B.	|||	𝍸
Linda D.	||||	𝍸 |||
Ingrid G.	||||	𝍸 |
Susan L.	|||	𝍸 |
Amanda M.	𝍸	𝍸 𝍸 |
Paige R.	𝍸 |	𝍸 ||||
Kathy R.	𝍸 |	𝍸 𝍸
Maria T.	𝍸	𝍸 𝍸 ||

1. Look at the table. How many free throws did Nancy make?
2. How many free throws did Nancy attempt?
3. What is Nancy's ratio of free throws made to free throws attempted?
4. What is Kathy's ratio of free throws made to free throws attempted?

TIME OUT! An equation stating that two ratios are equal is called a **proportion.** Every proportion has a related multiplication equation.

	Proportion		**Multiplication Equation**
Nancy's ratio	$\frac{3}{5} = \frac{6}{10}$	Kathy's ratio	$3 \times 10 = 5 \times 6$

The two products 3×10 and 5×6 are called **cross products.**

Here's how *to use the cross products to tell whether or not two ratios are equal.*

If the cross products are equal, then the ratios are equal.

Nancy's ratio $\frac{3}{5} \bullet \frac{6}{10}$ Kathy's ratio

Since $3 \times 10 = 5 \times 6$ we know that $\frac{3}{5} = \frac{6}{10}$.

If the cross products are not equal, then the ratios are not equal.

Nancy's ratio $\frac{3}{5} \bullet \frac{4}{6}$ Ingrid's ratio

Since $3 \times 6 \neq 5 \times 4$ we know that $\frac{3}{5} \neq \frac{4}{6}$.

5. Look at the *Here's how*. Is Nancy's ratio equal to Kathy's ratio?
6. Is Nancy's ratio equal to Ingrid's ratio?

EXERCISES

Tell whether the ratios are equal (=) or not equal (≠). *Hint: Compare the cross products.*

7. $\frac{1}{2}$ ● $\frac{3}{4}$
8. $\frac{4}{12}$ ● $\frac{1}{3}$
9. $\frac{5}{9}$ ● $\frac{2}{5}$
10. $\frac{3}{2}$ ● $\frac{9}{6}$
11. $\frac{4}{7}$ ● $\frac{3}{5}$
12. $\frac{5}{8}$ ● $\frac{3}{5}$
13. $\frac{3}{9}$ ● $\frac{4}{12}$
14. $\frac{5}{10}$ ● $\frac{2}{4}$
15. $\frac{5}{4}$ ● $\frac{3}{2}$
16. $\frac{7}{2}$ ● $\frac{12}{4}$
17. $\frac{14}{8}$ ● $\frac{21}{12}$
18. $\frac{13}{16}$ ● $\frac{9}{12}$
19. $\frac{12}{15}$ ● $\frac{8}{10}$
20. $\frac{6}{9}$ ● $\frac{4}{6}$
21. $\frac{15}{9}$ ● $\frac{14}{8}$
22. $\frac{2}{12}$ ● $\frac{3}{18}$
23. $\frac{8}{10}$ ● $\frac{16}{20}$
24. $\frac{9}{8}$ ● $\frac{6}{5}$
25. $\frac{13}{15}$ ● $\frac{11}{13}$
26. $\frac{14}{16}$ ● $\frac{35}{40}$
27. $\frac{3}{4}$ ● $\frac{0.5}{1}$
28. $\frac{2}{0.5}$ ● $\frac{8}{2}$
29. $\frac{5}{0.75}$ ● $\frac{4}{1}$
30. $\frac{5}{1}$ ● $\frac{2}{0.4}$
31. $\frac{0.6}{2}$ ● $\frac{3}{5}$
32. $\frac{6}{9}$ ● $\frac{0.4}{0.6}$
33. $\frac{0.6}{0.5}$ ● $\frac{4}{3}$
34. $\frac{0.3}{0.6}$ ● $\frac{0.4}{0.8}$
35. $\frac{4.5}{6.0}$ ● $\frac{7.5}{10.0}$
36. $\frac{1.5}{0.5}$ ● $\frac{6.0}{2.0}$
37. $\frac{3}{4}$ ● $\frac{1\frac{1}{2}}{2}$
38. $\frac{3}{2}$ ● $\frac{2}{1\frac{1}{4}}$
39. $\frac{1\frac{1}{3}}{4}$ ● $\frac{2}{6}$
40. $\frac{2}{1\frac{3}{8}}$ ● $\frac{5}{3}$
41. $\frac{2\frac{1}{2}}{5}$ ● $\frac{4}{9}$
42. $\frac{9}{3}$ ● $\frac{7\frac{1}{2}}{2\frac{1}{2}}$
43. $\frac{1\frac{1}{4}}{7\frac{1}{2}}$ ● $\frac{2}{12}$
44. $\frac{1\frac{1}{4}}{2}$ ● $\frac{2\frac{1}{8}}{3}$
45. $\frac{2\frac{2}{3}}{1\frac{1}{2}}$ ● $\frac{3}{2\frac{3}{4}}$
46. $\frac{3\frac{3}{5}}{2\frac{1}{4}}$ ● $\frac{1\frac{1}{5}}{1}$

Solve. Use the table on page 228.

47. What is Linda's ratio of free throws made to free throws attempted?
48. What is Susan's ratio of free throws made to free throws attempted?
49. Compare the ratios from exercises 47 and 48. Is Linda's ratio equal to Susan's ratio?
50. Which player's ratio (free throws made to free throws attempted) is equal to Ingrid's ratio?
51. What is Paige's ratio of free throws missed to free throws attempted?
52. What is Amanda's ratio of free throws made to free throws missed?

Who won?

53. With only two minutes left to play, the Jefferson Tigers were ahead of the Washington Badgers 48 to 47. During the last two minutes, the two teams made a total of 3 field goals (2-point goals) and no free throws. Both teams scored 50 or more points. Which team won, and what was the final score?

Solving proportions

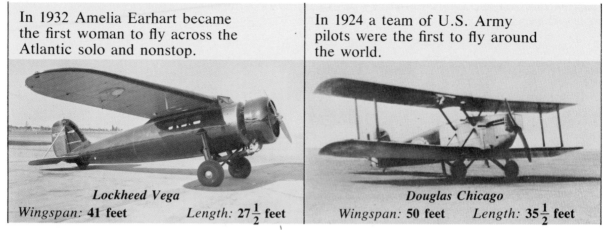

In 1932 Amelia Earhart became the first woman to fly across the Atlantic solo and nonstop.

Lockheed Vega

Wingspan: **41 feet** *Length:* **$27\frac{1}{2}$ feet**

In 1924 a team of U.S. Army pilots were the first to fly around the world.

Douglas Chicago

Wingspan: **50 feet** *Length:* **$35\frac{1}{2}$ feet**

1. What is the wingspan of the 1924 *Douglas Chicago?*

A model of the *Douglas Chicago* is to be $\frac{1}{20}$ the size of the real airplane. To find how many feet the wingspan of the model should be, you can set up and solve a proportion.

Here's how *to set up and solve a proportion.*

When setting up a proportion, make sure that the ratios are in the same order.

wingspan of model airplane → $\frac{n}{50} = \frac{1}{20}$ ← model airplane
wingspan of real airplane → ← real airplane

Write the multiplication equation. $20n = 50 \times 1$

20n is a short way to write 20 × n.

Solve the multiplication equation.

$20n = 50$

$n = \frac{50}{20}$ Since 20 times n equals 50, divide 50 by 20 to find n.

$n = 2\frac{1}{2}$

Check: $\frac{2\frac{1}{2}}{50} = \frac{1}{20}$ $2\frac{1}{2} \times 20 = 50 \times 1$

2. Look at the *Here's how*. If the model is $\frac{1}{20}$ the size of the real airplane, how long should the wingspan of the model be?

EXERCISES

Copy and complete. Give answers in simplest form.

Here are scrambled answers for the next row of exercises: $20 \quad 3\frac{1}{2} \quad 4\frac{4}{5} \quad 3$

3. $\frac{5}{2} = \frac{n}{8}$ | $2n = 40$, $n = ?$

4. $\frac{8}{6} = \frac{4}{n}$ | $8n = 24$, $n = ?$

5. $\frac{n}{8} = \frac{3}{5}$ | $5n = 24$, $n = ?$

6. $\frac{1}{2} = \frac{n}{7}$ | $2n = 7$, $n = ?$

7. $\frac{2}{n} = \frac{4}{1\frac{1}{2}}$ | $4n = 2 \times 1\frac{1}{2}$; $4n = 3$; $n = ?$

8. $\frac{2\frac{1}{2}}{4} = \frac{n}{8}$ | $4n = 2\frac{1}{2} \times 8$; $4n = 20$; $n = ?$

9. $\frac{3}{5} = \frac{n}{2\frac{1}{2}}$ | $5n = 3 \times 2\frac{1}{2}$; $5n = 7\frac{1}{2}$; $n = ?$

10. $\frac{n}{1\frac{3}{4}} = \frac{4}{5}$ | $5n = 1\frac{3}{4} \times 4$; $5n = 7$; $n = ?$

Solve each proportion. Give the answer in simplest form.

11. $\frac{1}{2} = \frac{6}{n}$ **12.** $\frac{1}{4} = \frac{12}{n}$ **13.** $\frac{n}{5} = \frac{2}{10}$ **14.** $\frac{5}{n} = \frac{10}{20}$ **15.** $\frac{1}{6} = \frac{7}{n}$

16. $\frac{3}{10} = \frac{n}{5}$ **17.** $\frac{7}{12} = \frac{4}{n}$ **18.** $\frac{8}{n} = \frac{10}{3}$ **19.** $\frac{n}{6} = \frac{5}{9}$ **20.** $\frac{11}{4} = \frac{n}{12}$

21. $\frac{1\frac{1}{2}}{3} = \frac{n}{2}$ **22.** $\frac{10}{7} = \frac{1\frac{1}{4}}{n}$ **23.** $\frac{4}{n} = \frac{8}{2\frac{3}{4}}$ **24.** $\frac{n}{2\frac{1}{2}} = \frac{4}{6}$ **25.** $\frac{5}{4} = \frac{1\frac{1}{4}}{n}$

Solve. Refer to the airplanes pictured on page 230.

26. Suppose that you want to make a model of the *Lockheed Vega* that is $\frac{1}{30}$ the size of the real airplane.

a. What should the wingspan of the model be?

b. How long should the model be?

Check it out!

27. Find and correct the two wrong answers.

a. $\frac{3.2}{5} = \frac{n}{7.5}$ n =

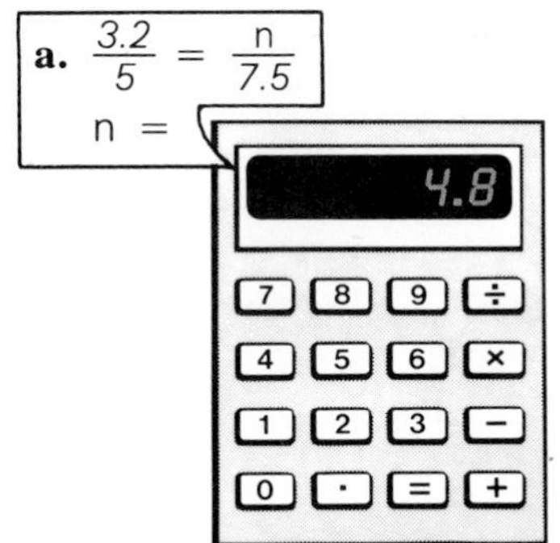

b. $\frac{6.5}{3} = \frac{9.1}{n}$ n =

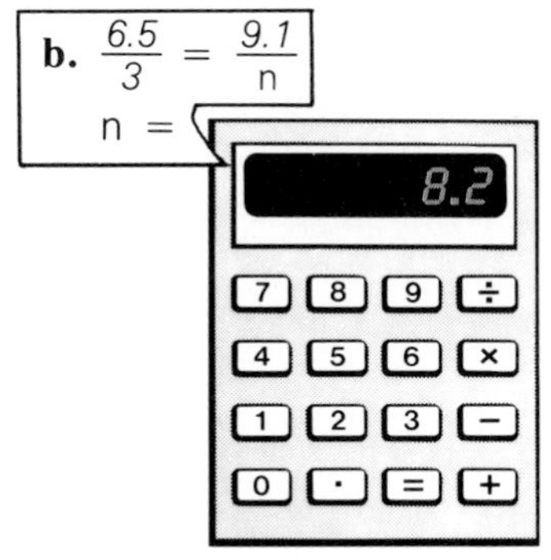

c. $\frac{n}{8.8} = \frac{7.5}{26.4}$ n =

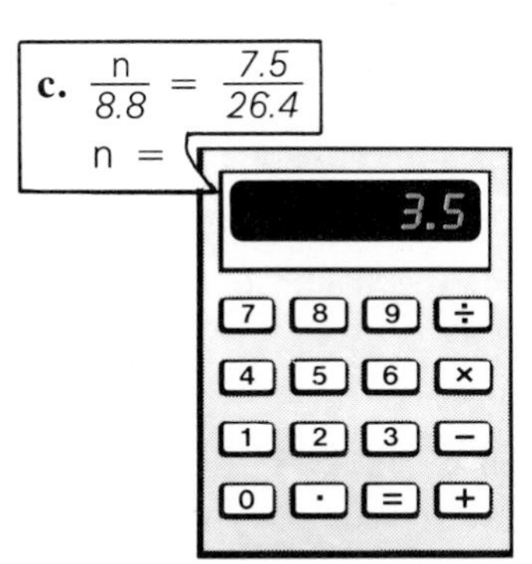

Rates

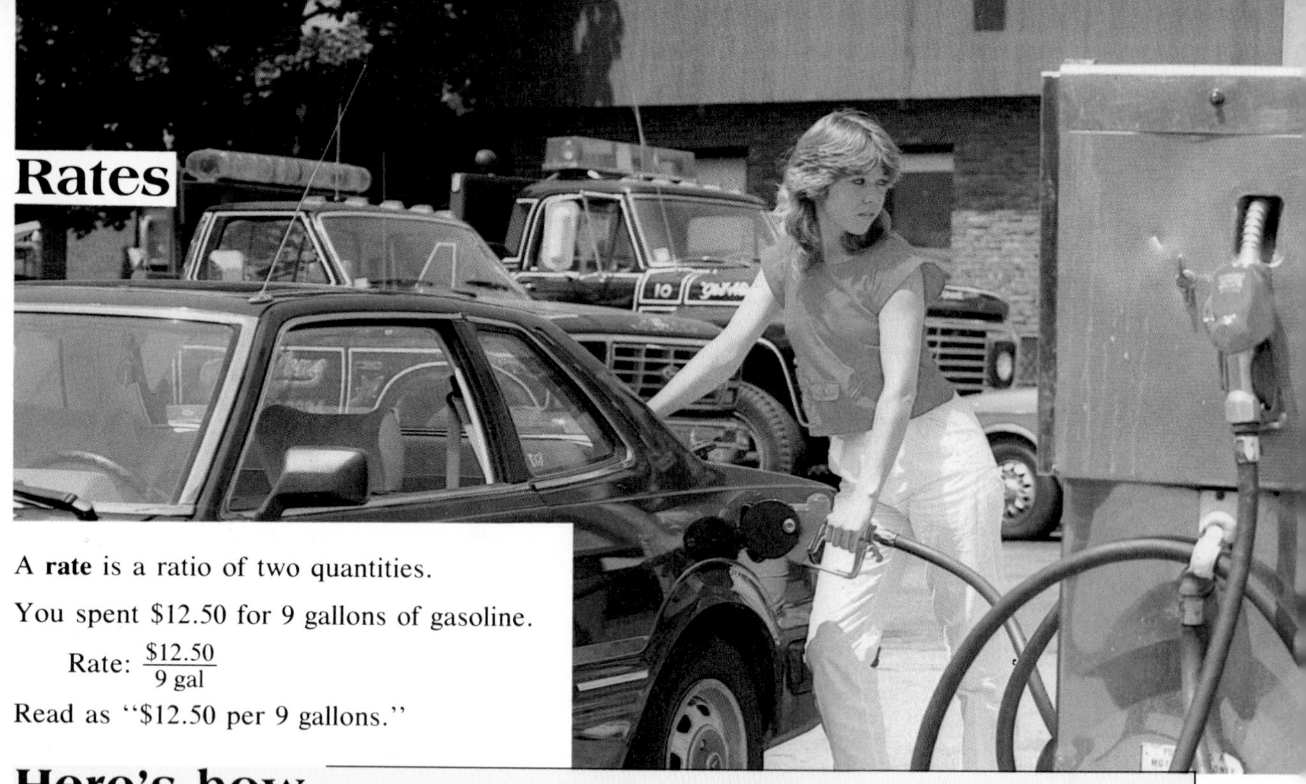

A **rate** is a ratio of two quantities.

You spent \$12.50 for 9 gallons of gasoline.

Rate: $\frac{\$12.50}{9 \text{ gal}}$

Read as "\$12.50 per 9 gallons."

Here's how *to use proportions to solve rate problems.*

PROBLEM 1. If you spent \$12.50 for 9 gallons of gasoline, how much would you spend for 14 gallons?

dollars → $\frac{12.50}{9} = \frac{n}{14}$ ← dollars
gallons → ← gallons

Remember: When setting up a proportion, you must be sure that the ratios are in the same order!

$$9n = 12.50 \times 14$$
$$9n = 175$$
$$n \approx 19.44$$

$$9\overline{)175.000} = 19.444$$

Read ≈ as "is approximately equal to."

So, at that rate, you would spend \$19.44 for 14 gallons of gasoline.

PROBLEM 2. You drive 196 miles in 4 hours. At that rate, how many hours will it take you to drive 320 miles?

miles → $\frac{196}{4} = \frac{320}{n}$ ← miles
hours → ← hours

$$196n = 4 \times 320$$
$$196n = 1280$$
$$n \approx 6.53$$

$$196\overline{)1280.0000} = 6.5306$$

So, at that rate, it would take you about 6.53 hours to drive 320 miles.

EXERCISES

Solve by using proportions. If an answer does not come out evenly, round it to the nearest hundredth.

1. You spend $18 for 12 gallons of gasoline. At that price,
   a. how many gallons could you buy for $15?

   Hint: $\frac{18}{12} = \frac{15}{n}$

   b. how many gallons could you buy for $6.50?
   c. how much would 9 gallons cost?
   d. how much would 10.4 gallons cost?

2. You drive 128 miles in 3 hours. At that speed,
   a. how many miles could you drive in 5 hours?

   Hint: $\frac{128}{3} = \frac{n}{5}$

   b. how many miles could you drive in 7 hours?
   c. how many hours would it take you to drive 200 miles?
   d. how many hours would it take you to drive 286 miles?

3. You drive 124 miles and use 4.8 gallons of gasoline. At that rate,
   a. how many miles could you drive on 8 gallons?
   b. how many miles could you drive on 15 gallons?
   c. how many gallons would you need for 200 miles?
   d. how many gallons would you need for 260 miles?

4. You spend $3.60 to drive 110 miles on a toll road. At that rate,
   a. how many miles could you drive for $1.60?
   b. how many miles could you drive for $2.00?
   c. how much would it cost to drive 150 miles?
   d. how much would it cost to drive 85 miles?

5. During the first 2 days of your trip you spend $43 for meals. At that rate,
   a. how much will your meals cost for 5 days?
   b. how many days of meals could you buy for $215?

6. You drive 4 hours and use 8.2 gallons of gasoline. At that rate,
   a. how many hours could you drive on 6 gallons?
   b. how many gallons would you need to drive 7 hours?

Check your instruments

7. You are 157 miles from Chicago. You want to be in Chicago by 11 o'clock. You look at your speedometer and clock.

   Will you be on time if you keep driving at the same rate?

Cumulative Skill Practice

Multiply. *(page 64)*

1. 1.4×52	**2.** 4.9×5.2	**3.** 0.58×6.8	**4.** 0.94×37	**5.** 0.39×9.7	**6.** 2.04×3.1
7. 0.78×0.44	**8.** 0.53×66	**9.** 8.4×8.4	**10.** 4.18×41	**11.** 2.67×0.71	**12.** 6.11×0.23
13. 4.56×3.6	**14.** 8.03×0.62	**15.** 50.8×0.73	**16.** 66.6×1.84	**17.** 8.49×2.05	**18.** 9.14×3.23

Divide. Round the quotient to the nearest tenth. *(page 96)*

19. $0.6\overline{)4.3}$	**20.** $0.3\overline{)3.91}$	**21.** $0.09\overline{)5.2}$	**22.** $0.03\overline{)8.7}$	**23.** $0.06\overline{)50}$
24. $1.3\overline{)5.3}$	**25.** $0.11\overline{)37}$	**26.** $2.7\overline{)3.7}$	**27.** $3.7\overline{)5.04}$	**28.** $0.65\overline{)9.1}$
29. $0.41\overline{)7.5}$	**30.** $9.7\overline{)5.09}$	**31.** $3.3\overline{)0.66}$	**32.** $0.55\overline{)79}$	**33.** $9.3\overline{)4.05}$

$<$, $=$, or $>$? *(page 132)*

34. $\frac{1}{2}$ ● $\frac{4}{8}$	**35.** $\frac{3}{8}$ ● $\frac{5}{8}$	**36.** $\frac{1}{2}$ ● $\frac{1}{4}$	**37.** $\frac{3}{9}$ ● $\frac{1}{3}$	**38.** $\frac{1}{3}$ ● $\frac{1}{2}$
39. $\frac{5}{8}$ ● $\frac{3}{4}$	**40.** $\frac{2}{3}$ ● $\frac{10}{15}$	**41.** $\frac{3}{4}$ ● $\frac{2}{3}$	**42.** $\frac{5}{6}$ ● $\frac{7}{8}$	**43.** $\frac{5}{6}$ ● $\frac{3}{4}$
44. $\frac{12}{16}$ ● $\frac{3}{4}$	**45.** $\frac{9}{16}$ ● $\frac{5}{8}$	**46.** $\frac{9}{10}$ ● $\frac{7}{8}$	**47.** $\frac{4}{5}$ ● $\frac{5}{4}$	**48.** $\frac{1}{2}$ ● $\frac{50}{100}$

Change to a decimal rounded to the nearest hundredth. *(page 146)*

49. $\frac{1}{3}$	**50.** $\frac{1}{9}$	**51.** $\frac{1}{6}$	**52.** $\frac{1}{8}$	**53.** $\frac{1}{16}$	**54.** $\frac{3}{4}$	**55.** $\frac{5}{8}$
56. $\frac{2}{3}$	**57.** $\frac{5}{6}$	**58.** $\frac{3}{8}$	**59.** $\frac{9}{16}$	**60.** $\frac{7}{12}$	**61.** $\frac{7}{8}$	**62.** $\frac{5}{16}$
63. $\frac{11}{9}$	**64.** $\frac{15}{6}$	**65.** $\frac{19}{8}$	**66.** $\frac{21}{12}$	**67.** $\frac{25}{16}$	**68.** $\frac{13}{4}$	**69.** $\frac{16}{3}$

Give the sum in simplest form. *(page 158)*

70. $\frac{3}{4} + \frac{1}{4}$	**71.** $\frac{1}{2} + \frac{1}{4}$	**72.** $\frac{5}{9} + \frac{1}{3}$	**73.** $4 + \frac{2}{5}$	**74.** $\frac{2}{3} + 3$
75. $\frac{7}{8} + \frac{3}{4}$	**76.** $\frac{1}{2} + \frac{3}{8}$	**77.** $\frac{3}{10} + \frac{1}{5}$	**78.** $\frac{5}{6} + \frac{2}{3}$	**79.** $\frac{2}{3} + \frac{1}{4}$

BE A DETECTIVE

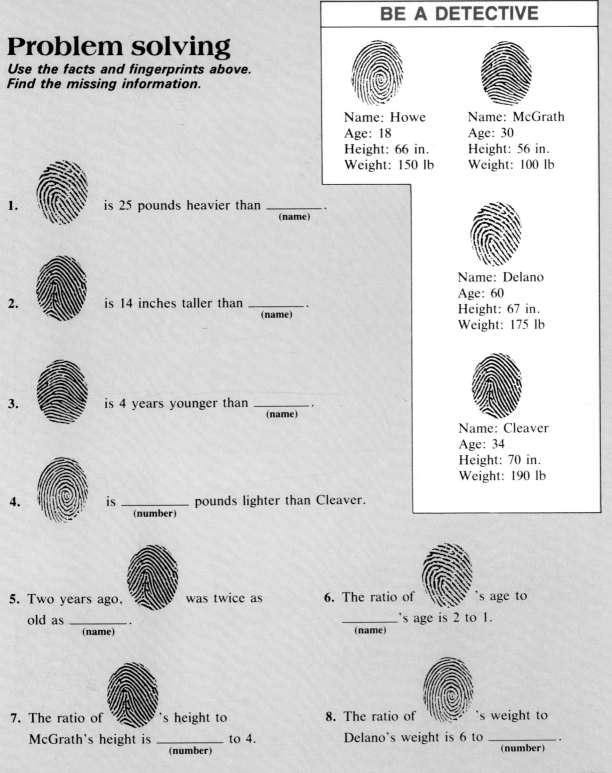

Name: Howe
Age: 18
Height: 66 in.
Weight: 150 lb

Name: McGrath
Age: 30
Height: 56 in.
Weight: 100 lb

Name: Delano
Age: 60
Height: 67 in.
Weight: 175 lb

Name: Cleaver
Age: 34
Height: 70 in.
Weight: 190 lb

Problem solving

Use the facts and fingerprints above. Find the missing information.

1.  is 25 pounds heavier than ________ **(name)**.

2.  is 14 inches taller than ________ **(name)**.

3.  is 4 years younger than ________ **(name)**.

4.  is ________ **(number)** pounds lighter than Cleaver.

5. Two years ago,  was twice as old as ________ **(name)**.

6. The ratio of 's age to ________ **(name)**'s age is 2 to 1.

7. The ratio of 's height to McGrath's height is ________ **(number)** to 4.

8. The ratio of 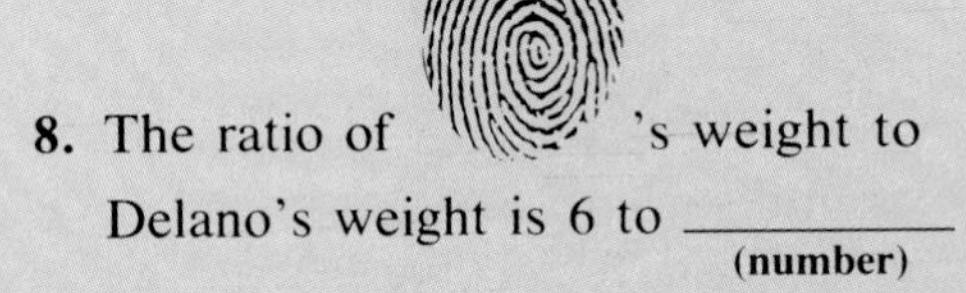's weight to Delano's weight is 6 to ________ **(number)**.

Scale drawings

A map is an example of a scale drawing.
On this map, 1 centimeter stands for 150 kilometers.

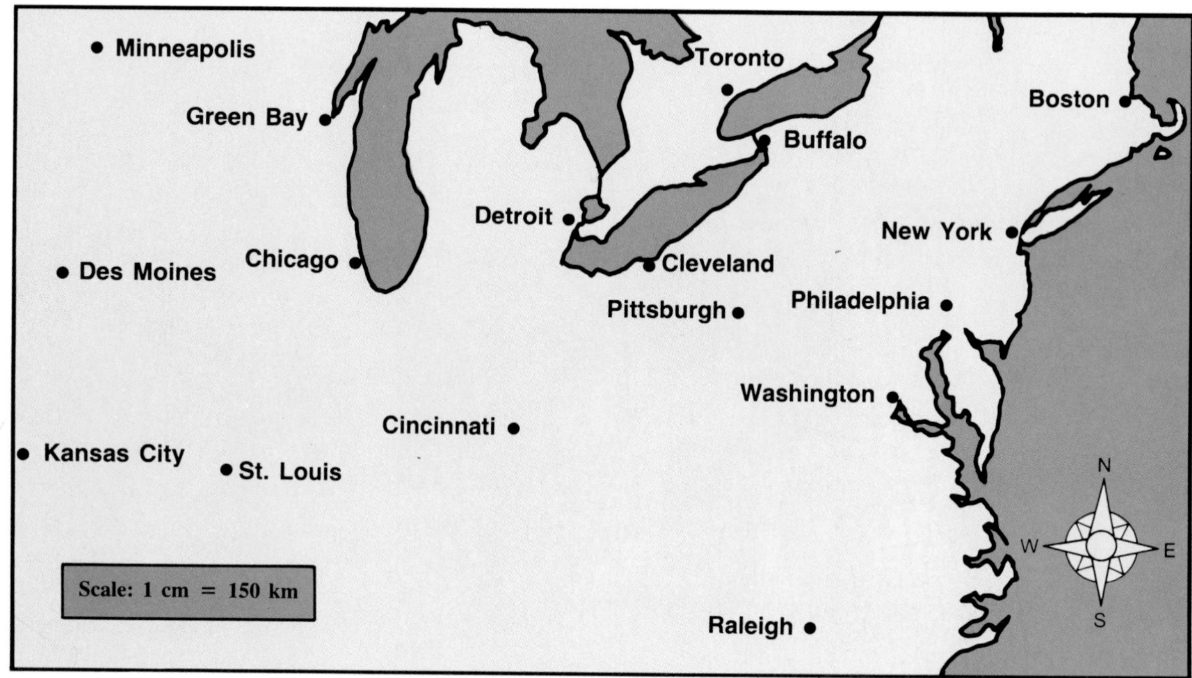

Here's how *to solve a scale-drawing problem.*

> *Since we know the scale, we can measure a distance on the map and solve a proportion to find the actual distance.*

PROBLEM. The distance from Minneapolis to Cincinnati on the map is 7.5 centimeters. What is the actual distance from Minneapolis to Cincinnati?

$$\begin{array}{lcl} \text{cm on map} \rightarrow & \dfrac{1}{150} = \dfrac{7.5}{n} & \leftarrow \text{cm on map} \\ \text{actual km} \rightarrow & & \leftarrow \text{actual km} \end{array}$$

$$n = 7.5 \times 150$$
$$n = 1125$$

The actual distance from Minneapolis to Cincinnati is about 1125 kilometers.

EXERCISES

Find the actual distance between the cities. The map distances from page 236 are given.

1. Chicago to Raleigh, 7.8 cm
2. Detroit to New York, 5.9 cm
3. Minneapolis to Toronto, 8.3 cm
4. Boston to Washington, 4.8 cm
5. Green Bay to Buffalo, 5.8 cm
6. Chicago to New York, 8.6 cm
7. St. Louis to Detroit, 5.6 cm
8. Detroit to Cleveland, 1.2 cm
9. Minneapolis to Raleigh, 12.3 cm
10. Kansas City to Toronto, 10.4 cm

Solve. Use a ruler and the map on page 236.

11. How far is it from Minneapolis to Detroit?
12. How far is it from Cleveland to Boston?
13. How far is it from Minneapolis to Detroit to Washington?
14. How far is it from Toronto to Washington to Raleigh?
15. How much farther is it from Chicago to Pittsburgh than from Cincinnati to Pittsburgh?
16. How much farther is it from Kansas City to Pittsburgh than from St. Louis to Pittsburgh?
17. Which city is about 1350 kilometers east of Des Moines?
18. Which city is about 700 kilometers northwest of Raleigh?

You be the pilot!

19. *My airspeed is 600 kilometers per hour. About how many hours is it from Des Moines to Philadelphia?*
20. *I'm flying from Philadelphia to St. Louis. My airspeed is 750 kilometers per hour. About how many hours should the flight take?*
21. *At 600 kilometers per hour, how many hours will it take to fly from St. Louis to Toronto?*

Similar figures

The sails on the box and on the model are the same shape. They are **similar figures.**

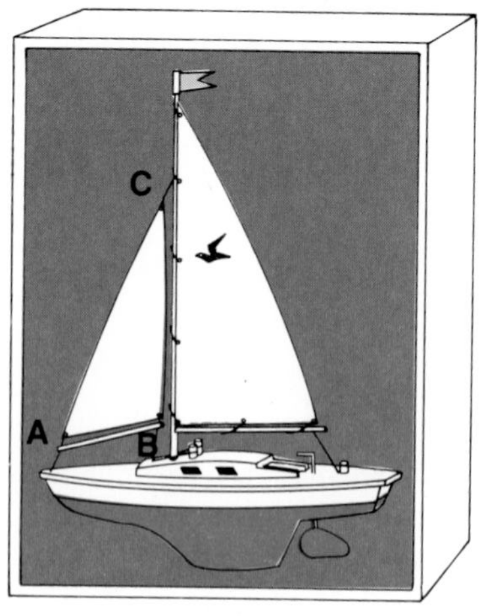

Look at the small sail on the box and on the model.

Side AB corresponds to side RS.
Side AC corresponds to side RT.
Side BC corresponds to side ST.

In similar figures, the ratios of the lengths of corresponding sides are equal.

Here's how *to use a proportion to solve a similar-figures problem.*

PROBLEM. These two flags are similar. What is the length of side n?

Step 1. Write a proportion.

small flag → $\frac{1.5}{2.5} = \frac{3}{n}$ ← small flag
large flag → ← large flag

Step 2. Solve the proportion.

$1.5n = 3 \times 2.5$
$1.5n = 7.5$
$n = 5$

$$\begin{array}{r} 5. \\ 1.5\overline{)7.5.} \\ -7\,5 \\ \hline 0 \end{array}$$

The length of side n is 5 centimeters.

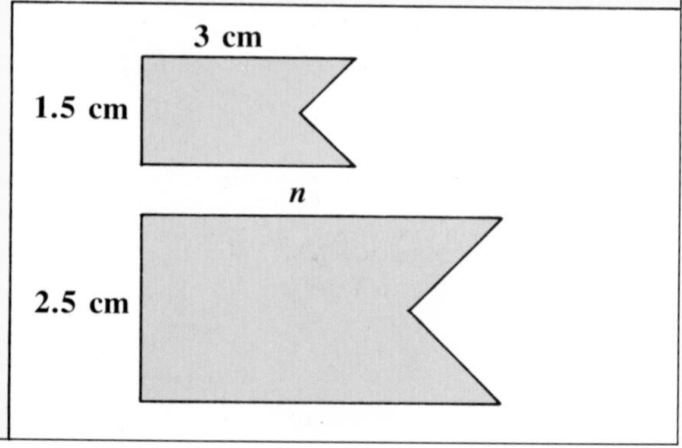

EXERCISES

The two figures are similar. Solve a proportion to find the length of side **n.**

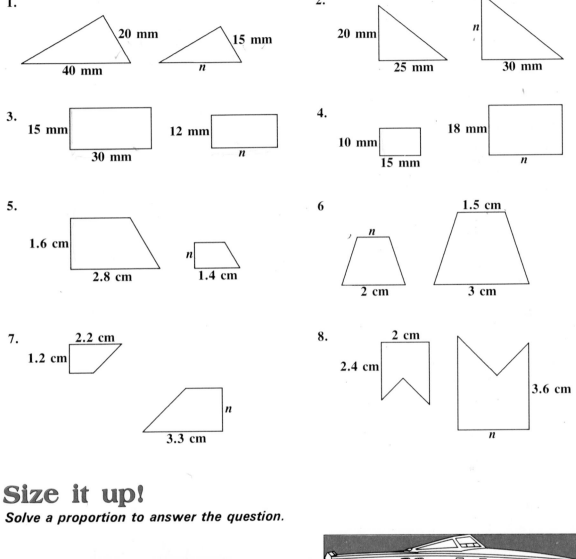

1.

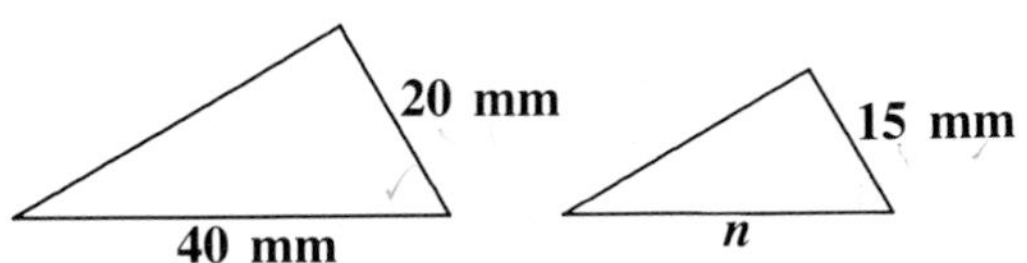

2.

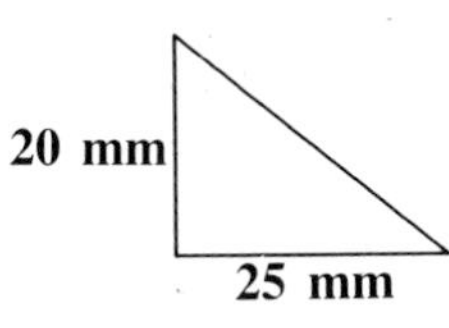

3.

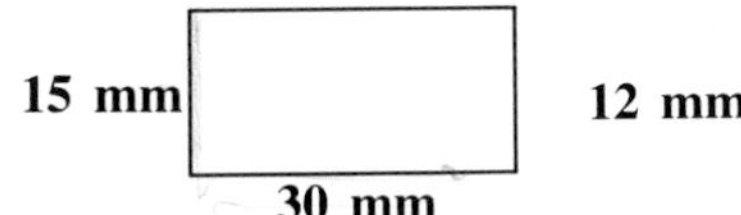

4.

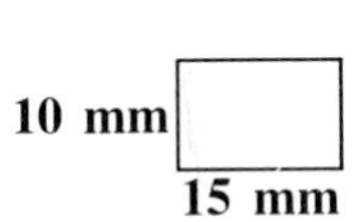

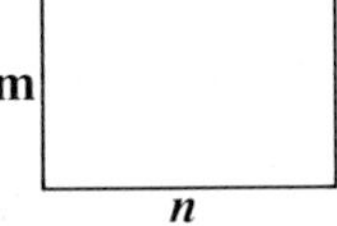

5.

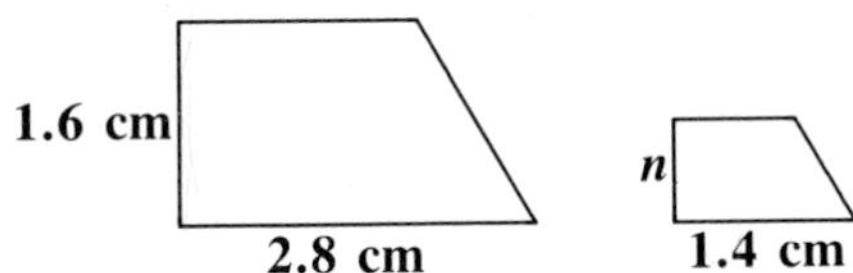

6

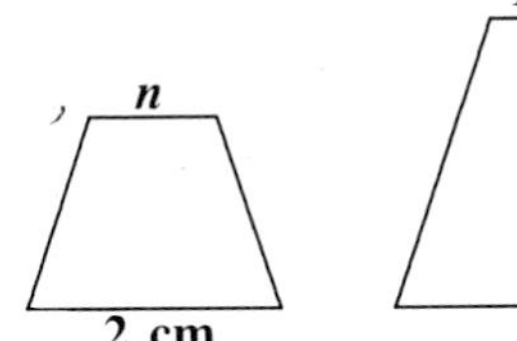

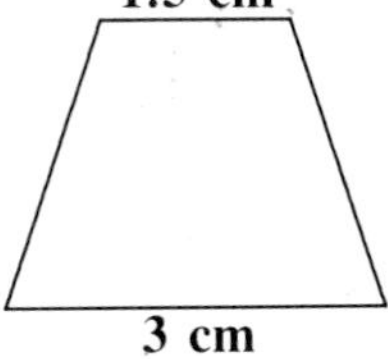

7.

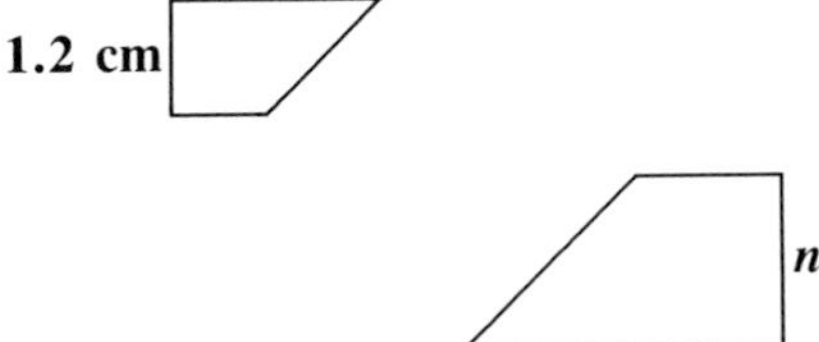

8.

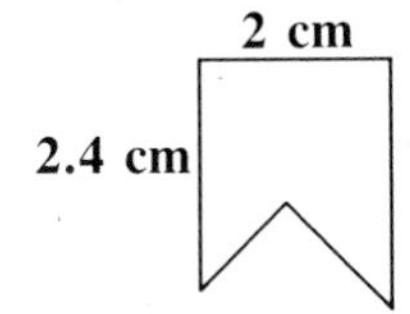

Size it up!

Solve a proportion to answer the question.

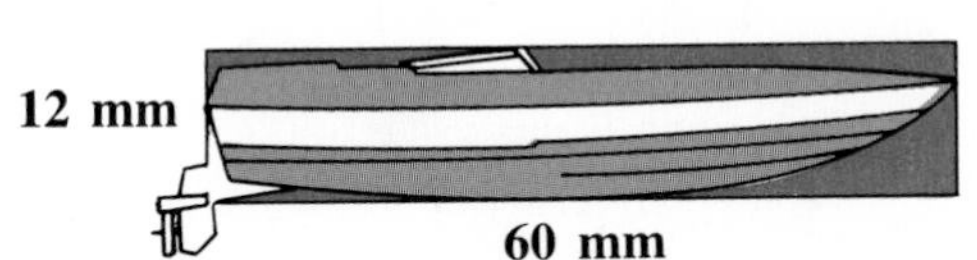

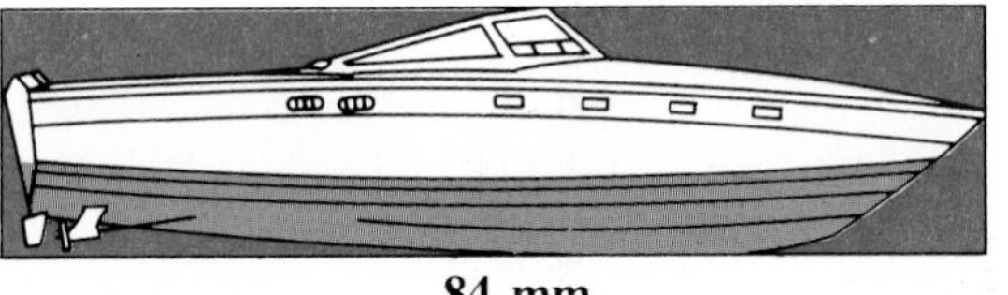

9. The *Starfire* is actually 1.64 meters high. What is its actual length?

10. The *Sport Special* is actually 2.9 meters high. What is its actual length?

Indirect measurement

MAKE A GUESS!

WHAT IS THE HEIGHT OF THE LOOP-THE-LOOP RIDE?

Here's how *similar triangles can be used to find lengths that are difficult to measure directly.*

The triangle made by the man and his shadow is similar to the triangle made by the loop-the-loop ride and its shadow. We can use this proportion to find the height of the ride.

height of loop-the-loop → $\frac{n}{2} = \frac{5}{0.5}$ ← shadow of loop-the-loop
height of man → ← shadow of man

$$0.5n = 2 \times 5$$

$$0.5n = 10$$

$$n = 20$$

The height of the loop-the-loop ride is 20 meters.

EXERCISES

Solve. Round the answer to the nearest hundredth of a meter.

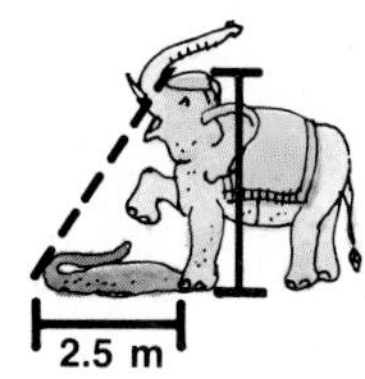

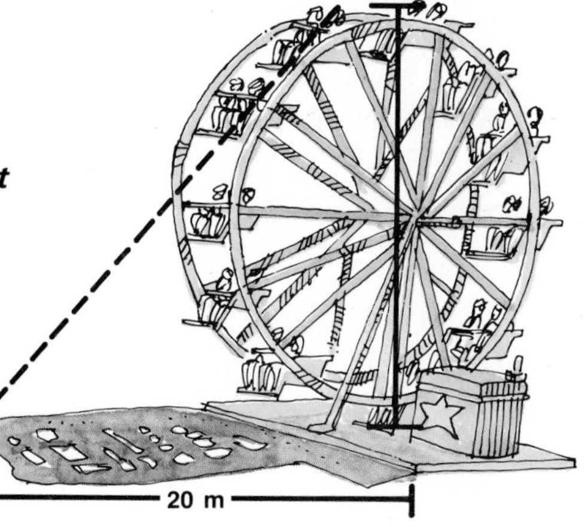

1. The elephant casts a 2.5-meter shadow. A man 2 meters tall casts a 1.5-meter shadow. How tall is the elephant?

2. The Ferris wheel casts a 20-meter shadow. How tall is the Ferris wheel? Round the answer to the nearest hundredth of a meter. *Hint: Use the facts about the man and his shadow.*

Make your own drawings. Then solve the problem.

3. A high-diving pole casts a 21-meter shadow. A man 2 meters tall casts a 1-meter shadow. How tall is the high-diving pole?

4. A woman 1.5 meters tall casts a 0.75-meter shadow. A diving tank casts a 1.2-meter shadow. How deep is the diving tank?

5. An animal trainer is 2 meters tall and casts a 2.2-meter shadow. A black bear casts a 3.3-meter shadow. How tall is the black bear?

6. A 2-meter sign casts a 3-meter shadow. A flagpole casts a 45-meter shadow. How tall is the flagpole?

7. A TV tower is 30 meters high and casts a 10-meter shadow. How tall is a nearby tree that casts a 6-meter shadow?

8. The fence around a water tower is 2.5 meters high and casts a 4-meter shadow. The water tower casts a 48-meter shadow. How tall is the water tower?

Animal tracks

9. Unscramble the letters to name each animal.

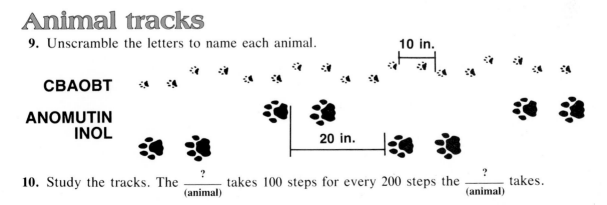

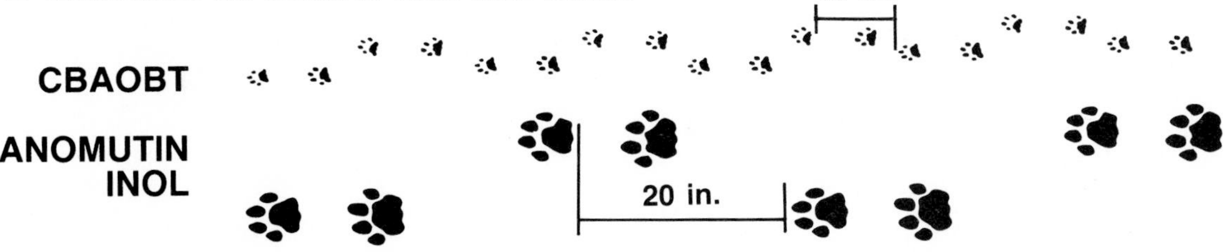

10. Study the tracks. The $\underset{\text{(animal)}}{\underline{\quad ? \quad}}$ takes 100 steps for every 200 steps the $\underset{\text{(animal)}}{\underline{\quad ? \quad}}$ takes.

Cumulative Skill Practice

Give the difference in simplest form. *(page 166)*

1. $\frac{3}{5} - \frac{1}{5}$ **2.** $\frac{3}{4} - \frac{1}{4}$ **3.** $\frac{1}{2} - \frac{1}{4}$ **4.** $\frac{1}{3} - \frac{1}{6}$ **5.** $\frac{3}{8} - \frac{1}{4}$

6. $\frac{7}{8} - \frac{3}{4}$ **7.** $\frac{1}{2} - \frac{3}{8}$ **8.** $\frac{3}{10} - \frac{1}{5}$ **9.** $\frac{5}{6} - \frac{2}{3}$ **10.** $\frac{2}{3} - \frac{1}{4}$

11. $1 - \frac{7}{10}$ **12.** $1 - \frac{2}{5}$ **13.** $\frac{5}{6} - \frac{3}{4}$ **14.** $\frac{9}{16} - \frac{3}{8}$ **15.** $\frac{7}{12} - \frac{1}{8}$

Complete. *(page 180)*

16. $\frac{1}{2}$ of 12 = ? **17.** $\frac{1}{3}$ of 15 = ? **18.** $\frac{2}{3}$ of 18 = ? **19.** $\frac{3}{4}$ of 24 = ?

20. $\frac{7}{8}$ of 16 = ? **21.** $\frac{3}{5}$ of 25 = ? **22.** $\frac{5}{8}$ of 32 = ? **23.** $\frac{3}{4}$ of 48 = ?

Give the quotient in simplest form. *(page 190)*

24. $1\frac{1}{2} \div 3$ **25.** $2\frac{1}{2} \div 2$ **26.** $2 \div 1\frac{1}{2}$ **27.** $4 \div 2\frac{1}{4}$

28. $2\frac{2}{3} \div 1\frac{1}{4}$ **29.** $5\frac{1}{2} \div 1\frac{3}{8}$ **30.** $6\frac{1}{4} \div 1\frac{1}{4}$ **31.** $3\frac{3}{4} \div 2\frac{1}{3}$

32. $6 \div 2\frac{2}{3}$ **33.** $3\frac{5}{8} \div 2\frac{1}{4}$ **34.** $4\frac{5}{6} \div 2\frac{5}{12}$ **35.** $5\frac{7}{8} \div 4$

Complete. *(page 204)*

36. 5 L = _?_ mL **37.** 12 L = _?_ mL **38.** 3.4 L = _?_ mL

39. 3000 mL = _?_ L **40.** 1635 mL = _?_ L **41.** 400 mL = _?_ L

42. 4.75 L = _?_ mL **43.** 0.530 L = _?_ mL **44.** 0.75 mL = _?_ L

Add. *(page 218)*

45. 4 ft 7 in. + 2 ft 10 in.

46. 3 yd 2 ft + 1 yd 2 ft

47. 5 ft 9 in. + 3 ft 8 in.

48. 4 gal 3 qt + 1 gal 2 qt

49. 5 qt 1 pt + 2 qt 1 pt

50. 2 gal 3 qt + 3 gal 3 qt

51. 4 pt 1 c + 4 pt 1 c

52. 8 lb 9 oz + 5 lb 9 oz

Solve. Give the answer in simplest form. *(page 230)*

53. $\frac{1}{4} = \frac{n}{12}$ **54.** $\frac{5}{6} = \frac{7}{n}$ **55.** $\frac{5}{n} = \frac{3}{15}$ **56.** $\frac{n}{12} = \frac{5}{8}$ **57.** $\frac{9}{n} = \frac{2}{3}$

58. $\frac{2}{7} = \frac{5}{n}$ **59.** $\frac{4}{8} = \frac{n}{9}$ **60.** $\frac{9}{6} = \frac{n}{4}$ **61.** $\frac{5}{2} = \frac{n}{3}$ **62.** $\frac{3}{5} = \frac{10}{n}$

Problem solving

USING COMPUTER SOFTWARE

Maria Cataldo uses a **software** package to draw geometric figures on her computer screen. The software also allows her to enlarge any part of the drawing.

Maria uses a number and a letter to locate each section in her drawing.

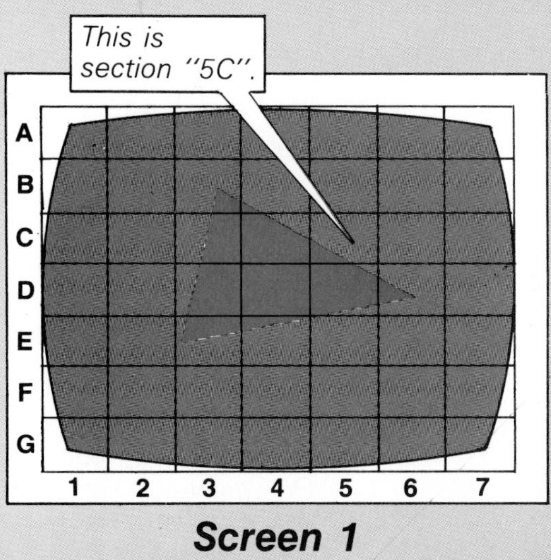

Screen 1

When Maria commands the computer to enlarge section 5C, the computer screen looks like this:

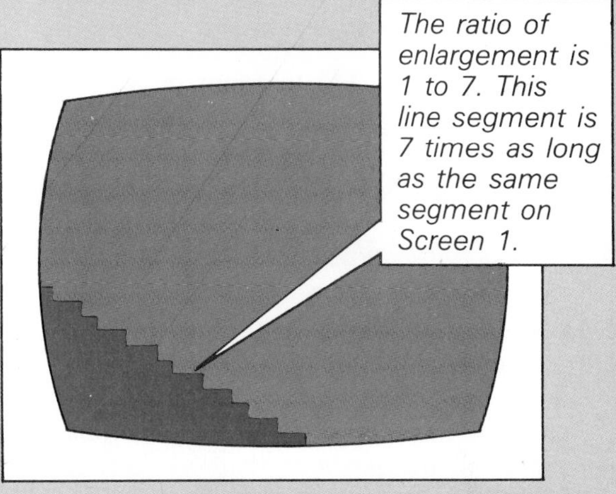

The ratio of enlargement is 1 to 7. This line segment is 7 times as long as the same segment on Screen 1.

Screen 2

Which section from Screen 1 has been enlarged?

1. 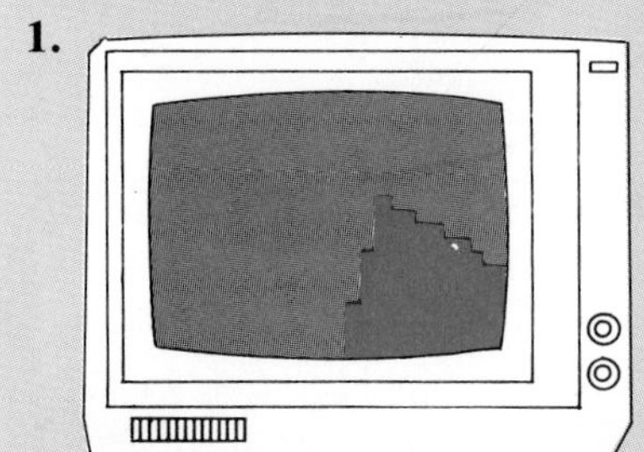

2. 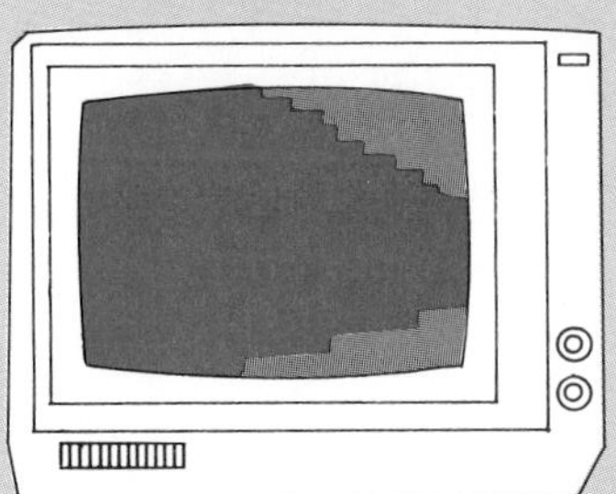

3. 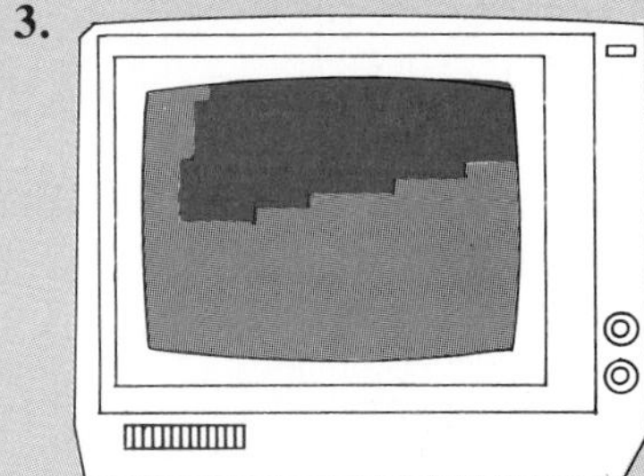

Complete.

4. If the ratio of enlargement is 1 to 7, a 2-inch line segment in an original picture would be [?] inches in an enlargement.

5. If the ratio of enlargement is 1 to 8, a 1.5-inch line segment in an original picture would be [?] inches in an enlargement.

6. An original picture has a line segment that is 2 inches long. The same line segment is 12 inches long in an enlargement. The ratio of enlargement is 1 to [?].

7. A line segment is enlarged from 1.75 inches in the original drawing to 15.75 inches in an enlargement. The ratio of enlargement is 1 to [?].

Chapter REVIEW

Here are scrambled answers for the review exercises:

approximately	divide	height	proportion	scale
corresponds	equal	multiplication	rate	similar
cross	fractions	order	ratio	

1. You can use a [?] to compare two numbers. You can find equal ratios by thinking about equivalent [?]. *(page 226)*

2. A [?] is an equation that says two ratios are equal. Every proportion has a related [?] equation. *(page 228)*

3. You can use the [?] products to find whether these two ratios are equal. Since 3 × 15 = 5 × 9, you know that the ratios are equal. *(page 228)*

$$\frac{3}{5} \bullet \frac{9}{15}$$

4. The last step in solving this proportion is to [?] 24 by 5. *(page 230)*

$$\frac{5}{6} = \frac{4}{n}$$

$$5n = 6 \times 4$$

$$5n = 24$$

5. When setting up a proportion, you must be sure that the ratios are in the same [?]. In this proportion, n is [?] equal to 3.11. *(pages 230, 232)*

$$\frac{9}{4} = \frac{7}{n}$$

$$9n = 28$$

$$n \approx 3.11$$

6. A [?] is a ratio of two quantities. A map is an example of a [?] drawing. *(pages 232, 236)*

7. Figures that are the same shape are called [?] figures. In these similar figures, side AB [?] to side RS. In similar figures, the ratios of the lengths of corresponding sides are [?]. *(page 238)*

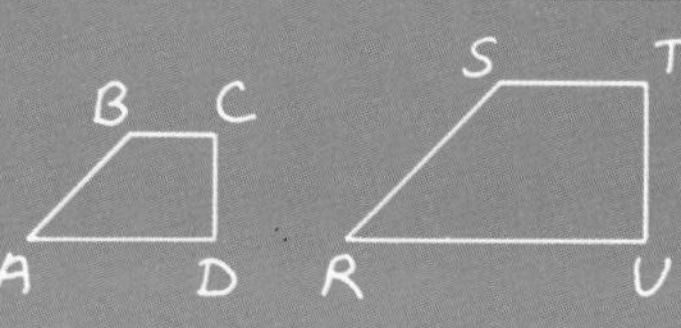

8. You can solve this proportion to find the [?] of the flagpole. *(page 240)*

$$\frac{n}{1.9} = \frac{7.2}{2.4}$$

1.9 m
n
2.4 m
7.2 m

Chapter TEST

Give each ratio as a fraction in lowest terms. *(page 226)*

1. 3 to 9 **2.** 8 to 12 **3.** 16 to 10 **4.** 18 to 24 **5.** 7 to 14

6. 12 : 16 **7.** 15 : 10 **8.** 21 : 14 **9.** 32 : 8 **10.** 56 : 16

Tell whether the ratios are equal (=) or not equal (≠). *(page 228)*

11. $\frac{3}{4}$ ● $\frac{9}{12}$ **12.** $\frac{5}{6}$ ● $\frac{7}{8}$ **13.** $\frac{5}{2}$ ● $\frac{7}{4}$ **14.** $\frac{4}{6}$ ● $\frac{6}{9}$ **15.** $\frac{4}{8}$ ● $\frac{2}{4}$

16. $\frac{4}{3}$ ● $\frac{5}{4}$ **17.** $\frac{8}{5}$ ● $\frac{9}{6}$ **18.** $\frac{6}{16}$ ● $\frac{9}{24}$ **19.** $\frac{4}{7}$ ● $\frac{7}{12}$ **20.** $\frac{5}{6}$ ● $\frac{2}{3}$

Solve each proportion. Give the answer in simplest form. *(page 230)*

21. $\frac{2}{3} = \frac{n}{9}$ **22.** $\frac{1}{4} = \frac{10}{n}$ **23.** $\frac{5}{8} = \frac{n}{4}$ **24.** $\frac{2}{3} = \frac{9}{n}$ **25.** $\frac{4}{5} = \frac{8}{n}$

26. $\frac{n}{20} = \frac{3}{4}$ **27.** $\frac{11}{n} = \frac{5}{4}$ **28.** $\frac{3}{n} = \frac{2}{3}$ **29.** $\frac{2}{n} = \frac{5}{8}$ **30.** $\frac{1}{5} = \frac{2}{n}$

31. $\frac{6}{10} = \frac{n}{8}$ **32.** $\frac{4}{7} = \frac{12}{n}$ **33.** $\frac{7}{n} = \frac{2}{3}$ **34.** $\frac{7}{10} = \frac{n}{8}$ **35.** $\frac{2}{7} = \frac{n}{5}$

Solve by using a proportion. *(page 232)*

36. You jog 4.5 miles in 36 minutes. At that rate, how long will it take to jog 6 miles?

37. You buy 3 record albums for $16.50. At that rate, how much will 5 records cost?

38. You earn $48 in 12 hours. At that rate, how much would you earn in 7 hours?

39. You type 129 words in 3 minutes. At that rate, how many words could you type in 10 minutes?

***The two figures are similar. Solve a proportion to find the length of side* n.** *(page 238)*

40.

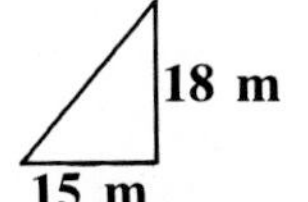

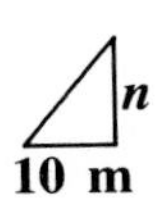

41.

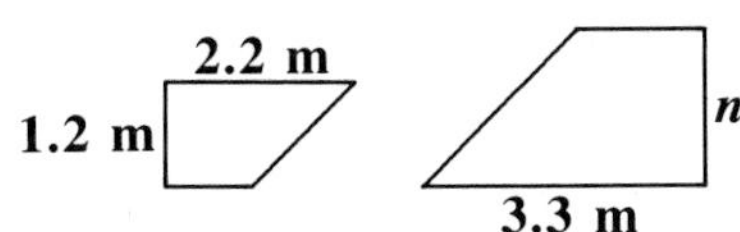

Make a drawing and solve the problem. *(page 240)*

42. A woman 1.8 m tall casts a 1.2-meter shadow. How tall is a nearby building that casts a 14.4-meter shadow?

43. A tower is 60 m high. It casts a 45-meter shadow. How tall is a nearby telephone pole that casts a 6-meter shadow?

Cumulative TEST Standardized Format

Choose the correct letter.

1. Multiply. $\begin{array}{r} 3.954 \\ \times\ 36.5 \\ \hline \end{array}$

A. 117.4790
B. 144.3210
C. 1174.790
D. none of these

2. Divide. Round the quotient to the nearest tenth.

$2.03\overline{)3.959}$

A. 1.95
B. 1.9
C. 2.0
D. none of these

3. $\frac{5}{8} < ?$

A. $\frac{1}{2}$
B. $\frac{4}{9}$
C. $\frac{3}{5}$
D. none of these

4. Change to a decimal rounded to the nearest hundredth.

$\frac{2}{3} = ?$

A. 0.67
B. 0.66
C. 0.667
D. none of these

5. Give the sum.

$\frac{5}{6} + \frac{3}{4}$

A. $\frac{4}{5}$
B. $\frac{1}{3}$
C. $1\frac{7}{12}$
D. none of these

6. Give the difference.

$\frac{7}{8} - \frac{1}{3}$

A. $\frac{7}{12}$
B. $1\frac{1}{5}$
C. $\frac{1}{4}$
D. none of these

7. Complete.

$\frac{3}{4}$ of 24 = ?

A. 32
B. 18
C. 16
D. none of these

8. Give the quotient.

$2\frac{1}{3} \div 1\frac{1}{2}$

A. $1\frac{5}{9}$
B. $\frac{2}{7}$
C. $3\frac{1}{2}$
D. none of these

9. Complete.

1.235 L = ? mL

A. 123.5
B. 0.001235
C. 1235
D. none of these

10. Add. $\begin{array}{r} 5 \text{ lb} \quad 9 \text{ oz} \\ +2 \text{ lb} \ 11 \text{ oz} \\ \hline \end{array}$

A. 9 lb
B. 8 lb 8 oz
C. 7 lb 4 oz
D. none of these

11. Solve. $\frac{9}{n} = \frac{2}{3}$

A. 9
B. $13\frac{1}{2}$
C. $1\frac{1}{2}$
D. none of these

12. You work 9 hours and earn $35. At that rate, how much would you earn in 13 hours? Round the answer to the nearest cent.

A. $50.56
B. $3.34
C. $24.23
D. none of these

Chapter 11
Percent

Changing a percent to a fraction

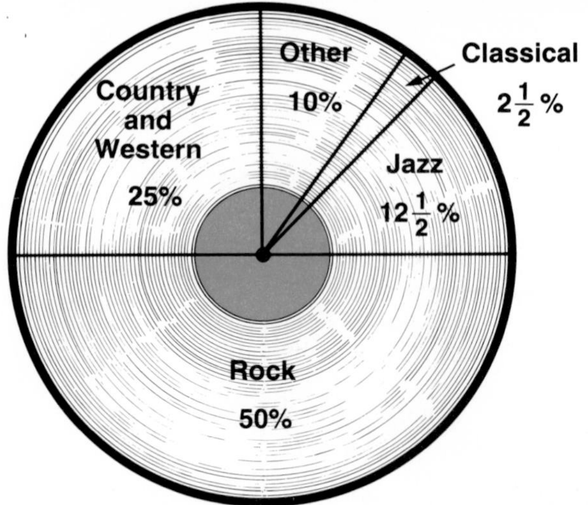

FAVORITE ALBUM SURVEY

In a survey of high school students, each person was asked to name his or her favorite album. Each album was placed in one of five categories. The graph shows the results of the survey.

Notice that 50% (50 percent) of those surveyed chose a rock album. This means that 50 out of 100, or $\frac{50}{100}$, chose a rock album.

1. What two categories of albums were most popular?

2. Were classical music albums more popular than country and western albums?

3. What percent of those surveyed chose a country and western album?

4. What percent of those surveyed chose a jazz album?

Here's how *to change a percent to a fraction.*

To change a percent to a fraction, first write the percent as a fraction with a denominator of 100. Then write the fraction in simplest form.

Country and Western

$$25\% = \frac{25}{100} = \frac{1}{4}$$

Jazz

$$12\frac{1}{2}\% = \frac{12\frac{1}{2}}{100}$$

Divide the numerator by the denominator.

$$= 12\frac{1}{2} \div 100$$
$$= \frac{25}{2} \div 100$$
$$= \frac{25}{2} \times \frac{1}{100}$$
$$= \frac{25}{200}$$
$$= \frac{1}{8}$$

5. Look at the *Here's how*. What fraction of those surveyed chose a country and western album?

6. What fraction of those surveyed chose a jazz album?

EXERCISES

Change to a fraction, whole number, or mixed number. Give the answer in simplest form.

Here are scrambled answers for the next row of exercises: $\frac{1}{4}$ $\frac{7}{10}$ $\frac{1}{2}$ $\frac{18}{25}$ 1 $1\frac{1}{4}$

7. 50%	**8.** 125%	**9.** 25%	**10.** 72%	**11.** 100%	**12.** 70%
13. 120%	**14.** 85%	**15.** 96%	**16.** 10%	**17.** 44%	**18.** 45%
19. 32%	**20.** 15%	**21.** 75%	**22.** 220%	**23.** 300%	**24.** 175%
25. 66%	**26.** 48%	**27.** 210%	**28.** 20%	**29.** 60%	**30.** 200%
31. 225%	**32.** 30%	**33.** 150%	**34.** 400%	**35.** 74%	**36.** 250%
37. 375%	**38.** 16%	**39.** 110%	**40.** 35%	**41.** 275%	**42.** 160%
43. 40%	**44.** 325%	**45.** 90%	**46.** 350%	**47.** 80%	**48.** 5%
49. $33\frac{1}{3}\%$	**50.** $106\frac{1}{4}\%$	**51.** $137\frac{1}{2}\%$	**52.** $18\frac{3}{4}\%$	**53.** $62\frac{1}{2}\%$	**54.** $8\frac{1}{3}\%$
55. $66\frac{2}{3}\%$	**56.** $16\frac{2}{3}\%$	**57.** $81\frac{1}{4}\%$	**58.** $133\frac{1}{3}\%$	**59.** $87\frac{1}{2}\%$	**60.** $162\frac{1}{2}\%$
61. $166\frac{2}{3}\%$	**62.** $212\frac{1}{2}\%$	**63.** $233\frac{1}{3}\%$	**64.** $206\frac{1}{4}\%$	**65.** $187\frac{1}{2}\%$	**66.** $116\frac{2}{3}\%$

Solve. Use the graph on page 248.

67. What fraction of those surveyed chose a classical album?

68. What fraction chose either a rock or a country and western album?

69. What fraction of those surveyed chose either a jazz or a rock album?

70. What fraction of those surveyed did not choose a jazz album?

Name that year

71. The first phonograph was made by Thomas Alva Edison. You can find the year by pressing the calculator keys as shown below.

[1] [4] [4] [÷] [4] [=] [×] [4] [8] [=] [+] [1] [6] [6] [=] [−] [1] [7] [=]

Changing a fraction to a percent

Look at the football helmets. Can you name the team for each helmet?

This question was part of a football survey conducted at Lancaster High School. The results are shown in the table.

NAME	NUMBER OF TEAMS NAMED CORRECTLY
Marty	12
Jill	16
David	18
Robert	14
Ann	20
Terry	17

1. How many teams did Marty name correctly?

2. How many teams are there in all?

3. What fraction of the teams did Marty name correctly?

4. What fraction of the teams did Jill name correctly?

ATTENTION, FOOTBALL FANS!

Here's how *to change a fraction to a percent.*

Changing Marty's fraction to a percent

Method 1. Change to an equivalent fraction with a denominator of 100. Then write as a percent.

$$\frac{1}{2} = \frac{50}{100}$$
$$= 50\%$$

Changing Jill's fraction to a percent

Method 2. Since there is no whole number that you can multiply by 3 to get the denominator of 100, solve a proportion.

$$\frac{2}{3} = \frac{n}{100}$$
$$3n = 200$$
$$n = 66\frac{2}{3}$$

$$\text{So } \frac{2}{3} = \frac{66\frac{2}{3}}{100}$$
$$= 66\frac{2}{3}\%$$

5. Which method would you use to change $\frac{3}{4}$ to a percent?

6. Which method would you use to change $\frac{1}{6}$ to a percent?

EXERCISES

Change to a percent. *Hint: First change to an equivalent fraction with a denominator of 100. Here are scrambled answers for the next row of exercises: 225% 40% 60% 90% 50% 125%*

7. $\frac{2}{5}$ 8. $\frac{9}{4}$ 9. $\frac{9}{10}$ 10. $\frac{3}{5}$ 11. $\frac{5}{4}$ 12. $\frac{1}{2}$

13. $\frac{1}{5}$ 14. $\frac{1}{4}$ 15. $\frac{4}{5}$ 16. 1 17. $\frac{1}{10}$ 18. $\frac{3}{10}$

19. $\frac{3}{2}$ 20. 2 21. $\frac{7}{5}$ 22. $\frac{3}{4}$ 23. $\frac{5}{2}$ 24. $\frac{7}{4}$

Change to a percent. *Hint: You may need to solve a proportion. Here are scrambled answers for the next row of exercises: 175% $16\frac{2}{3}$% $33\frac{1}{3}$% 120% $133\frac{1}{3}$% $83\frac{1}{3}$%*

25. $\frac{1}{3}$ 26. $\frac{1}{6}$ 27. $\frac{7}{4}$ 28. $\frac{6}{5}$ 29. $\frac{5}{6}$ 30. $\frac{4}{3}$

31. $\frac{9}{16}$ 32. $\frac{9}{25}$ 33. $\frac{5}{9}$ 34. $\frac{7}{2}$ 35. $\frac{2}{3}$ 36. $\frac{3}{8}$

37. $\frac{4}{9}$ 38. $\frac{9}{20}$ 39. $\frac{31}{50}$ 40. $\frac{5}{3}$ 41. $\frac{5}{12}$ 42. $\frac{1}{12}$

43. $\frac{7}{25}$ 44. $\frac{17}{10}$ 45. $\frac{7}{8}$ 46. 3 47. $\frac{5}{8}$ 48. $\frac{11}{25}$

Solve. Use the survey results on page 250.

49. What percent of the teams did David name correctly?

50. What percent of the teams did Robert name correctly?

51. What percent of the students surveyed knew more than 15 of the teams?

52. What percent of the students surveyed knew 15 or fewer of the teams? (*Hint: Use your answer from exercise 51.*)

How many fans?

The number on the first ticket sold for a ball game was 10394. The number on the last ticket was 19017.

53. How many tickets were sold? Be careful!

54. Three hundred of the tickets sold were not used. How many people were at the ball game?

Percents and decimals

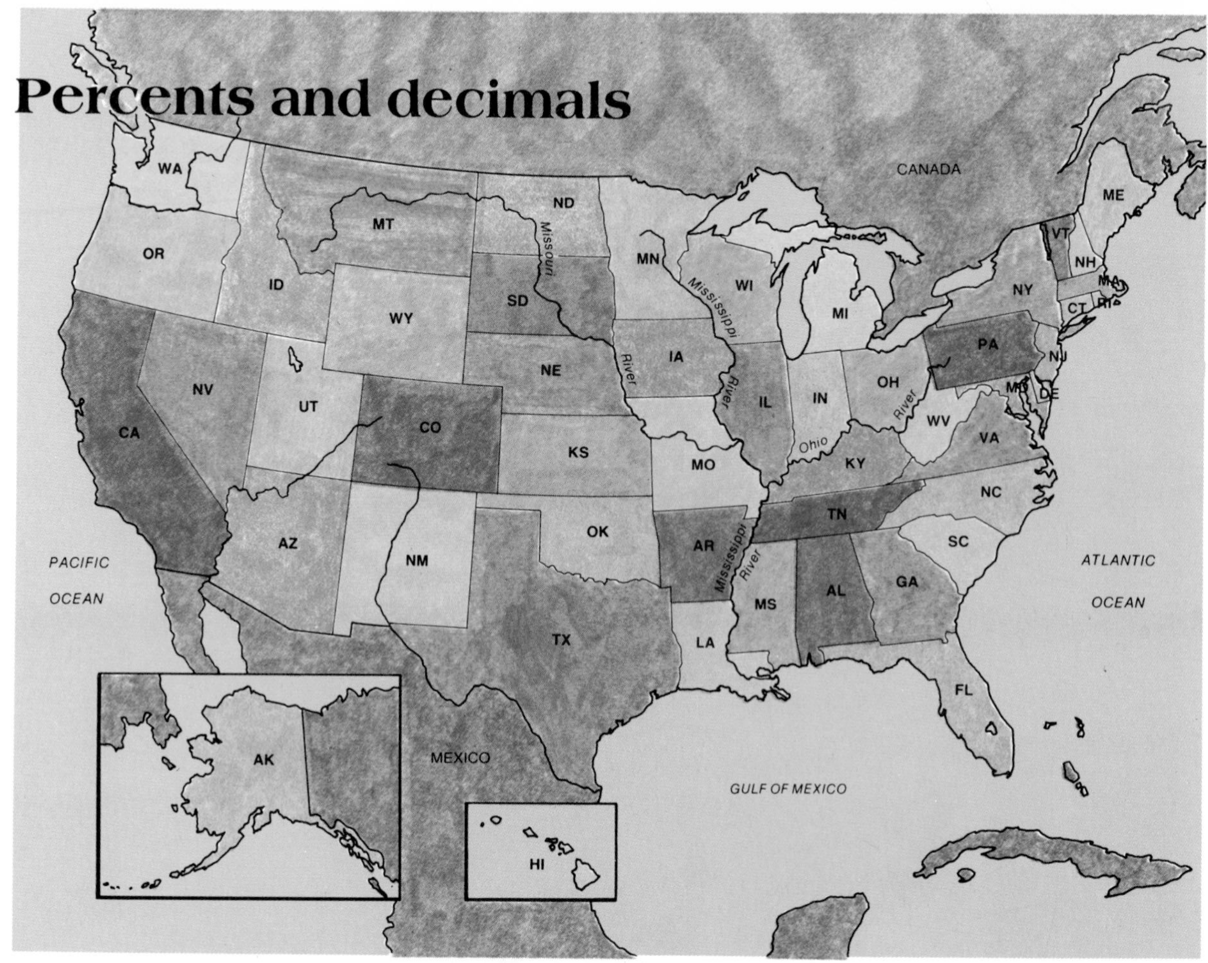

1. What percent of the states share part of their border with Texas?
2. What percent of the states have names beginning with the letter M?

Here's how *to change a percent to a decimal.*

$8\% = \frac{8}{100} = 0.08$

$16\% = \frac{16}{100} = 0.16$

$33\frac{1}{3}\% = \frac{33\frac{1}{3}}{100} = 0.33\frac{1}{3}$

Here is a **SHORTCUT.**

To change a percent to a decimal, move the decimal point two places to the left and remove the percent sign.

$8\% = 0.08$

$16\% = 0.16$

$33\frac{1}{3}\% = 0.33\frac{1}{3}$

$29.5\% = 0.295$

$115\% = 1.15$

Here's how *to change a decimal to a percent.*

$0.36 = \frac{36}{100} = 36\%$

$0.8 = \frac{8}{10} = \frac{80}{100} = 80\%$

$0.66\frac{2}{3} = \frac{66\frac{2}{3}}{100} = 66\frac{2}{3}\%$

Here is a **SHORTCUT.**

To change a decimal to a percent, move the decimal point two places to the right and write the percent sign.

$0.36 = 36\%$

$0.8 = 80\%$

$0.66\frac{2}{3} = 66\frac{2}{3}\%$

$0.02 = 2\%$

$1.375 = 137.5\%$

EXERCISES

Change each percent to a decimal. *Hint: Use the* SHORTCUT.

3. 5% **4.** 9% **5.** 6% **6.** 25% **7.** 72% **8.** 44%

9. 125% **10.** 150% **11.** 238% **12.** 282% **13.** 360% **14.** 400%

15. 6.25% **16.** 37.5% **17.** 9.6% **18.** 8.75% **19.** 62.5% **20.** 4.8%

21. $33\frac{1}{3}\%$ **22.** $16\frac{2}{3}\%$ **23.** $37\frac{1}{2}\%$ **24.** $166\frac{2}{3}\%$ **25.** $162\frac{1}{2}\%$ **26.** $187\frac{1}{2}\%$

Change each decimal to a percent. *Hint: Use the* SHORTCUT.

27. 0.06 **28.** 0.08 **29.** 0.02 **30.** 0.38 **31.** 0.65 **32.** 0.93

33. 0.5 **34.** 0.8 **35.** 0.7 **36.** 0.6 **37.** 0.2 **38.** 0.4

39. 1.50 **40.** 2.5 **41.** 1.375 **42.** 2.875 **43.** 0.002 **44.** 0.085

45. $0.12\frac{1}{2}$ **46.** $0.33\frac{1}{3}$ **47.** $0.66\frac{2}{3}$ **48.** $1.37\frac{1}{2}$ **49.** $2.16\frac{2}{3}$ **50.** $2.83\frac{1}{3}$

Solve. Use the map on page 252.

51. What percent of the states are east of the Mississippi River?

52. What percent of the states have names beginning with the letter N?

53. What fraction of the states share part of their border with Mexico?

54. What fraction of the states are completely surrounded by water?

Map madness!

55. Which 4 states share a common corner?

56. Name the two states each of which borders on eight other states.

Cumulative Skill Practice

Multiply. *(page 64)*

1. 64×1.3
2. 5.7×4.7
3. 0.65×9.4
4. 0.86×48
5. 0.36×7.2
6. 8.3×21
7. 0.85×0.55
8. 0.31×76
9. 9.3×9.3
10. 5.06×42
11. 3.74×0.52
12. 2.23×0.14
13. 3.42×2.7
14. 7.05×0.46
15. 20.5×0.83
16. 22.8×1.14
17. 9.46×3.06
18. 4.13×31.2

Divide. Round the quotient to the nearest tenth. *(page 96)*

19. $0.4\overline{)7.2}$
20. $0.3\overline{)2.81}$
21. $0.06\overline{)6.2}$
22. $0.03\overline{)6.5}$
23. $0.09\overline{)20}$
24. $2.3\overline{)5.7}$
25. $0.12\overline{)32}$
26. $3.6\overline{)5.2}$
27. $3.9\overline{)6.01}$
28. $0.56\overline{)8.9}$
29. $0.51\overline{)9.4}$
30. $7.3\overline{)5.07}$
31. $5.5\overline{)0.71}$
32. $0.33\overline{)97}$
33. $6.8\overline{)8.05}$

Give the mean. Round the answer to the nearest tenth. *(page 114)*

34. 46, 49, 51
35. 681, 694, 700
36. 89.6, 90.4, 100.7
37. 78, 65, 93, 88
38. 345, 361, 402, 390
39. 9.82, 7.55, 6.09, 10.32
40. 19, 36, 22, 27, 30
41. 309, 211, 213, 215, 217
42. 8.3, 9.4, 6.5, 8.0, 7.2

Give the sum in simplest form. *(page 158)*

43. $\frac{1}{2} + \frac{1}{4}$
44. $\frac{2}{3} + \frac{5}{6}$
45. $\frac{1}{4} + \frac{5}{8}$
46. $3 + \frac{2}{3}$
47. $\frac{4}{5} + \frac{3}{10}$
48. $\frac{1}{4} + \frac{5}{12}$
49. $\frac{3}{5} + 2$
50. $\frac{5}{9} + \frac{2}{3}$
51. $\frac{1}{3} + \frac{1}{2}$
52. $\frac{2}{3} + \frac{4}{5}$
53. $\frac{3}{4} + \frac{2}{3}$
54. $\frac{2}{5} + \frac{3}{5}$
55. $\frac{5}{8} + \frac{5}{16}$
56. $\frac{7}{12} + \frac{5}{8}$
57. $\frac{5}{9} + \frac{3}{4}$

Give the difference in simplest form. *(page 166)*

58. $\frac{3}{4} - \frac{1}{4}$
59. $\frac{7}{8} - \frac{3}{4}$
60. $1 - \frac{2}{3}$
61. $\frac{1}{2} - \frac{3}{8}$
62. $\frac{3}{10} - \frac{1}{5}$
63. $\frac{2}{3} - \frac{1}{4}$
64. $\frac{3}{4} - \frac{3}{8}$
65. $\frac{1}{2} - \frac{1}{3}$
66. $\frac{5}{6} - \frac{2}{3}$
67. $\frac{3}{4} - \frac{2}{3}$
68. $2 - \frac{5}{8}$
69. $\frac{9}{10} - \frac{3}{5}$
70. $\frac{5}{6} - \frac{1}{4}$
71. $\frac{9}{16} - \frac{1}{2}$
72. $\frac{9}{10} - \frac{2}{5}$

Problem solving

YOU'RE THE PARK RANGER

TRAIL RULES AND INFORMATION

All children under 12 years of age must be accompanied by an adult.

All litter is to be carried out by hikers.

All trails are closed at 6:00 P.M.

TRAIL NAME	DISTANCE (miles)	HIKING TIME (hours)
Deer	5.8	$2\frac{1}{2}$
Clear Falls	4.9	$3\frac{3}{4}$
Pine Ridge	5.6	$2\frac{1}{4}$

Use the trail information to answer each hiker's question.

1. *What is the total distance of the 2 shorter trails?*

2. *How long would it take us to hike both Deer Trail and Pine Ridge Trail?*

3. "How much longer would it take me to hike Clear Falls Trail than Pine Ridge Trail?"

4. "We've hiked 2.8 miles of Pine Ridge Trail. How far is it to the end of the trail?"

5. "I've hiked $\frac{1}{2}$ of Deer Trail. How far is it to the end of the trail?"

6. "It is now 8:00 A.M. Would we have time to hike both Deer Trail and Clear Falls Trail by 12:30 P.M.?"

Solve.

7. During the first 15 days of July there were 403 hikers. At that rate, how many hikers would there be for the entire month of July? Round your answer to the nearest whole number.

8. Small postcards cost \$.50 each, large postcards cost \$.85 each, and a photo book of all 3 trails costs \$5.97. A hiker buys 3 small postcards, 2 large postcards, and a photo book. How much change should he get from a \$10 bill?

Finding a percent of a number

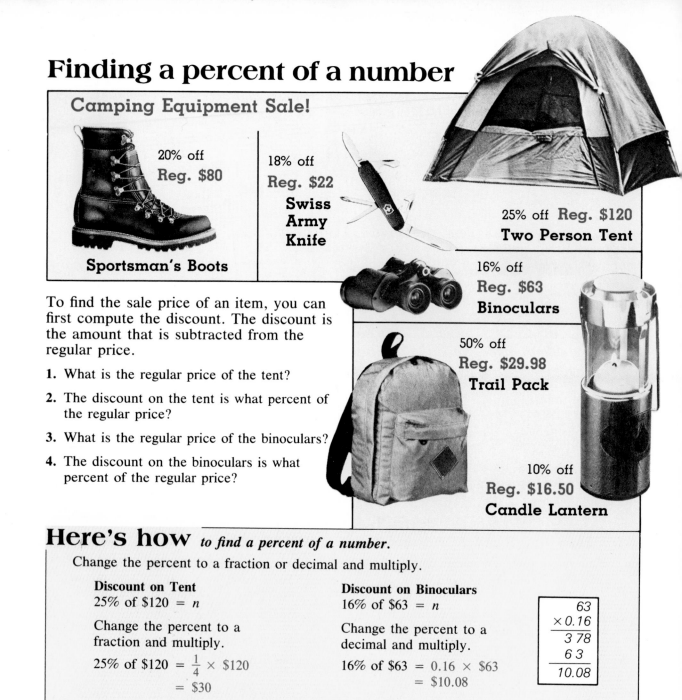

Camping Equipment Sale!

20% off
Reg. $80
Sportsman's Boots

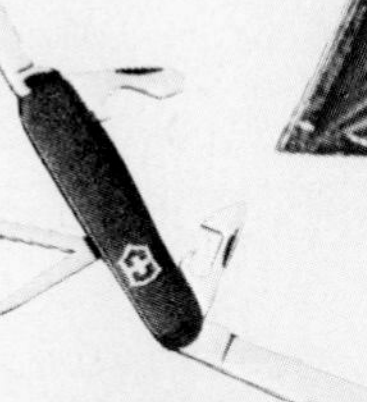

18% off
Reg. $22
Swiss Army Knife

25% off Reg. $120
Two Person Tent

16% off
Reg. $63
Binoculars

50% off
Reg. $29.98
Trail Pack

10% off
Reg. $16.50
Candle Lantern

To find the sale price of an item, you can first compute the discount. The discount is the amount that is subtracted from the regular price.

1. What is the regular price of the tent?
2. The discount on the tent is what percent of the regular price?
3. What is the regular price of the binoculars?
4. The discount on the binoculars is what percent of the regular price?

Here's how *to find a percent of a number.*

Change the percent to a fraction or decimal and multiply.

Discount on Tent
25% of $120 = n

Change the percent to a fraction and multiply.

$$25\% \text{ of } \$120 = \frac{1}{4} \times \$120 = \$30$$

Discount on Binoculars
16% of $63 = n

Change the percent to a decimal and multiply.

$$16\% \text{ of } \$63 = 0.16 \times \$63 = \$10.08$$

$$\begin{array}{r} 63 \\ \times 0.16 \\ \hline 3\,78 \\ 6\,3 \\ \hline 10.08 \end{array}$$

5. Look at the *Here's how*. What is the discount on the price of the tent?
6. What is the sale price of the tent?
7. What is the sale price of the binoculars?

EXERCISES

Solve by changing the percent to a fraction and multiplying.
Here are scrambled answers for the next row of exercises: 15 18 10

8. 50% of 36 $= n$ **9.** 25% of 40 $= n$ **10.** 60% of 25 $= n$

11. 75% of 24 $= n$ **12.** 30% of 60 $= n$ **13.** 10% of 80 $= n$

14. 20% of 30 $= n$ **15.** 40% of 40 $= n$ **16.** 25% of 44 $= n$

17. 75% of 32 $= n$ **18.** 100% of 24 $= n$ **19.** 150% of 18 $= n$

Solve by changing the percent to a decimal and multiplying.
Here are scrambled answers for the next row of exercises: 4.20 4.68 17.94

20. 12% of 35 $= n$ **21.** 9% of 52 $= n$ **22.** 23% of 78 $= n$

23. 32% of 156 $= n$ **24.** 54% of 264 $= n$ **25.** 78% of 165 $= n$

26. 5.6% of 61 $= n$ **27.** 8.75% of 46 $= n$ **28.** 12.5% of 132 $= n$

29. 0.75% of 50 $= n$ **30.** 0.35% of 21.5 $= n$ **31.** 14.8% of 36.7 $= n$

Solve. *Hint: First try to decide which method would be easier.*

32. 50% of 18 $= n$ **33.** 14% of 32 $= n$ **34.** 25% of 48 $= n$

35. 25% of 73 $= n$ **36.** 7.5% of 56 $= n$ **37.** 80% of 20 $= n$

38. 10% of 125 $= n$ **39.** 16.5% of 80 $= n$ **40.** 20% of 50 $= n$

Solve. Look at the items on page 256.

41. **a.** What is the discount on the price of the boots?
b. What is the sale price of the boots?

42. **a.** What is the discount on the price of the knife?
b. What is the sale price of the knife?

43. What is the sale price of the lantern?

44. What is the sale price of the small pack?

Be a super shopper

45. On which camping item can you save the largest amount of money?

46. Your rich uncle gave you a $100 bill. You bought two of the camping items on sale. You got $21.15 in change. What did you buy?

More on finding a percent of a number

The "menu" shows the results of a survey of 600 teenagers. They were asked to list some favorite foods and some least-favorite foods.

TEENAGER MENU

FAVORITE FOODS		LEAST-FAVORITE FOODS	
Pizza	47%	Spinach	20%
Steak	$33\frac{1}{3}$%	Liver	$16\frac{2}{3}$%
Hamburgers	25%	Beans	$8\frac{1}{3}$%
Chicken	$18\frac{1}{6}$%	Broccoli	8%
Potatoes	$12\frac{1}{2}$%	Peas	6%
Tacos	10%	Fish	5%

1. What percent of those surveyed listed pizza as a favorite food?
2. How many teenagers were surveyed?
3. What decimal would you multiply 600 by to compute the number of teenagers who listed pizza as a favorite food?
4. What fraction would you multiply 600 by to compute the number of teenagers who listed tacos as a favorite?
5. What percent of those surveyed listed liver as a least-favorite food?

Here's how *to find a percent of a number by solving a proportion.*

To find the number of those surveyed who listed liver as a least-favorite food, you would need to solve the equation $16\frac{2}{3}\%$ *of* $600 = n$.

When you cannot easily change the percent to a fraction or decimal, find n by solving a proportion.

$16\frac{2}{3}$ out of 100 . . . | . . . is how many out of 600?

$$\frac{16\frac{2}{3}}{100} = \frac{n}{600}$$

$$100n = 16\frac{2}{3} \times 600$$

$$= \frac{50}{3} \times 600$$

$$= 10{,}000$$

$$n = 100$$

6. Look at the *Here's how*. How many of those surveyed listed liver as a least-favorite food?

EXERCISES

Solve by solving a proportion. Round answers to the nearest hundredth.
Here are scrambled answers for the next row of exercises: 3.75 1.71 3.12

$6\frac{1}{3}$ out of 100 is equal to how many out of 27?	$8\frac{2}{3}$ out of 100 is equal to how many out of 36?	$12\frac{1}{2}$ out of 100 is equal to how many out of 30?

7. $6\frac{1}{3}\%$ of $27 = n$

8. $8\frac{2}{3}\%$ of $36 = n$

9. $12\frac{1}{2}\%$ of $30 = n$

10. $33\frac{1}{3}\%$ of $48 = n$

11. $66\frac{2}{3}\%$ of $69 = n$

12. $16\frac{2}{3}\%$ of $39 = n$

13. $6\frac{3}{4}\%$ of $45 = n$

14. $8\frac{7}{8}\%$ of $56 = n$

15. $5\frac{1}{3}\%$ of $18 = n$

Solve by multiplying by a fraction, by multiplying by a decimal, or by solving a proportion. *Hint: Look for the easiest method.*

16. 10% of $50 = n$

17. 23% of $125 = n$

18. $8\frac{1}{3}\%$ of $21 = n$

19. 22.5% of $86 = n$

20. 75% of $92 = n$

21. $66\frac{2}{3}\%$ of $33 = n$

22. 80% of $12 = n$

23. 8.5% of $120 = n$

24. 150% of $29 = n$

25. 20% of $144 = n$

26. 6.5% of $66 = n$

27. 1.9% of $164 = n$

28. $4\frac{2}{3}\%$ of $30 = n$

29. 50% of $124 = n$

30. 11% of $63 = n$

Solve. Use the survey on page 258.

31. How many of those surveyed listed hamburgers as a favorite food?

32. How many of those surveyed listed pizza as a favorite food?

33. How many listed spinach as a least favorite food?

34. How many more listed spinach than broccoli as a least-favorite food?

35. How many more listed hamburgers than chicken as a favorite food?

36. How many did not list tacos as a favorite food?

37. How many did not list the most popular favorite food?

38. Which food was chosen as a favorite food by 75 of the teenagers surveyed?

Your order, please

39. A vendor sells only hot dogs and hamburgers. You cannot order more than 3 sandwiches. How many different orders can you place? *Hint: Make a list.*

Finding the number when a percent is known

RULES OF THE ROAD

Here are the first few items on a driver's test.

Name *Ann Bender*

Number correct *52*

Percent correct *80%*

Part A. True or false?

t **1.** The RED LIGHT requires a stop at the marked stop line. If there is no marked stop line, stop before entering the crosswalk on the near side of the intersection.

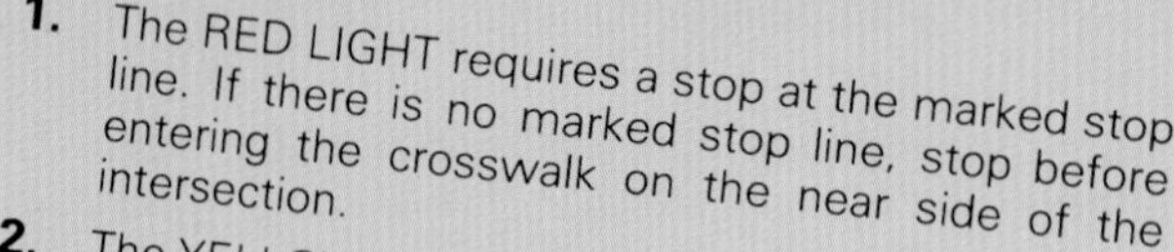

X *f* **2.** The YELLOW LIGHT warns that the signal is changing from green to red. When the red light appears, you are prohibited from entering the intersection.

t **3.** The GREEN LIGHT means you may proceed if it is safe to do so. You must first, however, yield the right-of-way to pedestrians and vehicles that are still within the intersection or an adjacent crosswalk.

t **4.** A YELLOW ARROW may appear after a green arrow. It means that the green arrow movement is ending.

t **5.** A GREEN ARROW, pointing right or left, means you may make a turn in the direction of the arrow, if you are in the proper lane for such a turn, after yielding the right-of-way to vehicles and pedestrians within the intersection.

f **6.** A GREEN ARROW pointing upward means you may turn left or right.

t **7.** A GREEN ARRO...

1. What percent of the total items did Ann get correct?
2. How many of the total items did she get correct?
3. Were there more or fewer than 52 items on the whole test?

Here's how *to find the number when a percent is known.*

To find the number of items on the test taken by Ann, you would need to solve the equation

$$80\% \text{ of } n = 52$$

You can find n by solving a proportion.

$$\boxed{\frac{\text{part}}{\text{whole}}} \quad \frac{80}{100} = \frac{52}{n} \quad \boxed{\frac{\text{part}}{\text{whole}}}$$

$$80n = 5200$$

$$n = 65$$

4. Look at the *Here's how*. How many items were on the test Ann took?

EXERCISES

Solve by solving a proportion.

Here are scrambled answers for the next row of exercises: 64 48 75

5. 25% of n = 12 **6.** 20% of n = 15 **7.** 75% of n = 48

8. 60% of n = 42 **9.** 40% of n = 56 **10.** 5% of n = 8

11. 50% of n = 17 **12.** 6% of n = 12 **13.** 80% of n = 20

14. 9% of n = 45 **15.** 10% of n = 18 **16.** 30% of n = 15

Solve. Round each answer to the nearest tenth.

17. 12.5% of n = 10.2 **18.** 6.4% of n = 1.3 **19.** 9.3% of n = 4.7

20. 5.8% of n = 6.4 **21.** 0.5% of n = 0.9 **22.** 0.8% of n = 1.3

23. 1.2% of n = 4.2 **24.** 4.8% of n = 1.2 **25.** 5.6% of n = 3.6

26. 125% of n = 2.3 **27.** 175% of n = 12.4 **28.** 150% of n = 10.5

Solve.

29. You took a test that had 72 questions. You got 18 questions wrong.
  a. What fraction of the questions did you get right?
  b. What percent of the questions did you get right?

30. You took a test that had 60 questions. You got 30 questions right.
  a. What fraction of the questions did you get right?
  b. What percent of the questions did you get right?

31. You took a test that had 120 questions. You got 80% of the questions right. How many questions did you get right? *Hint: 80% of 120* = n

32. You scored $66\frac{2}{3}\%$ on a 96-question test. How many questions did you get right?

33. You got 60 questions on a test right. You scored 75%. How many questions were on the test? *Hint: 75% of* n = *60.*

34. You scored 90% on a test. You got 135 of the questions right. How many questions were on the test?

What a jam!

35. The longest traffic jam ever reported was that of February 16, 1980. It stretched northward from Lyon, France, [?] miles toward Paris.

To find [?], write a *9* in the ones place, a *3* in the tenths place, a *0* in the tens place, and a *1* in the hundreds place.

More on percent

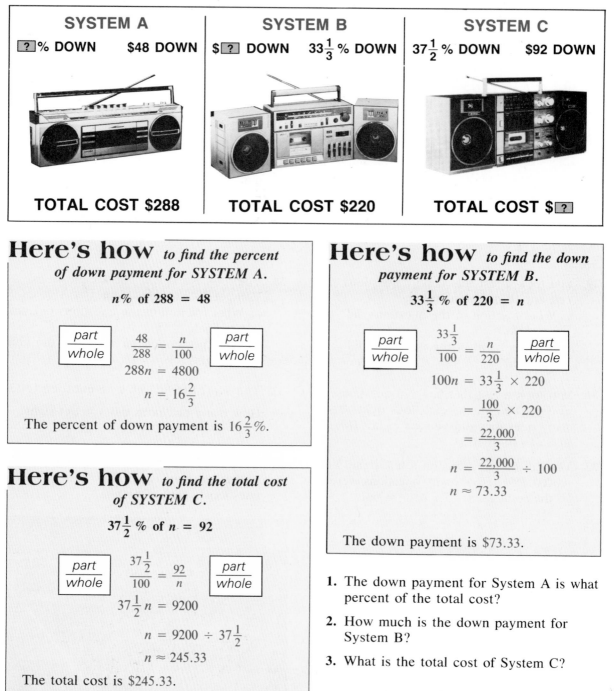

SYSTEM A		SYSTEM B		SYSTEM C	
?% DOWN	\$48 DOWN	\$? DOWN	$33\frac{1}{3}$% DOWN	$37\frac{1}{2}$% DOWN	\$92 DOWN
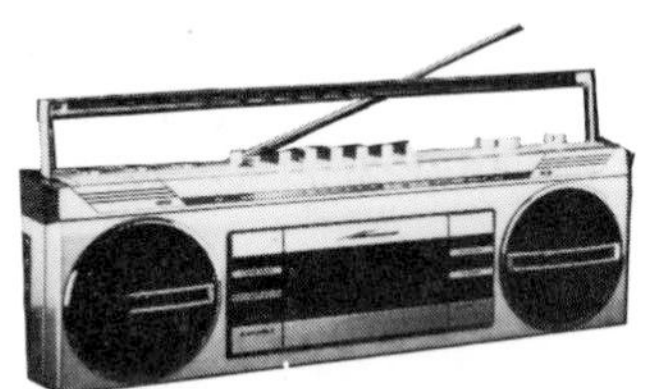					
TOTAL COST \$288		TOTAL COST \$220		TOTAL COST \$?	

Here's how *to find the percent of down payment for SYSTEM A.*

$$n\% \text{ of } 288 = 48$$

$$\frac{\text{part}}{\text{whole}} \quad \frac{48}{288} = \frac{n}{100} \quad \frac{\text{part}}{\text{whole}}$$

$$288n = 4800$$

$$n = 16\frac{2}{3}$$

The percent of down payment is $16\frac{2}{3}\%$.

Here's how *to find the total cost of SYSTEM C.*

$$37\frac{1}{2}\% \text{ of } n = 92$$

$$\frac{\text{part}}{\text{whole}} \quad \frac{37\frac{1}{2}}{100} = \frac{92}{n} \quad \frac{\text{part}}{\text{whole}}$$

$$37\frac{1}{2}n = 9200$$

$$n = 9200 \div 37\frac{1}{2}$$

$$n \approx 245.33$$

The total cost is \$245.33.

Here's how *to find the down payment for SYSTEM B.*

$$33\frac{1}{3}\% \text{ of } 220 = n$$

$$\frac{\text{part}}{\text{whole}} \quad \frac{33\frac{1}{3}}{100} = \frac{n}{220} \quad \frac{\text{part}}{\text{whole}}$$

$$100n = 33\frac{1}{3} \times 220$$

$$= \frac{100}{3} \times 220$$

$$= \frac{22{,}000}{3}$$

$$n = \frac{22{,}000}{3} \div 100$$

$$n \approx 73.33$$

The down payment is \$73.33.

1. The down payment for System A is what percent of the total cost?
2. How much is the down payment for System B?
3. What is the total cost of System C?

EXERCISES

Solve. *Here are scrambled answers for the next row of exercises: 75 125 5*

4. $n\%$ of $4 = 3$ **5.** $n\%$ of $4 = 5$ **6.** $n\%$ of $20 = 1$

7. $n\%$ of $8 = 4$ **8.** $n\%$ of $16 = 4$ **9.** $n\%$ of $1 = 5$

Solve. *Here are scrambled answers for the next row of exercises: 0.32 0.075 0.36*

10. $2\frac{2}{3}\%$ of $12 = n$ **11.** $1\frac{1}{4}\%$ of $6 = n$ **12.** $4\frac{1}{2}\%$ of $8 = n$

13. $16\frac{2}{3}\%$ of $72 = n$ **14.** $33\frac{1}{3}\%$ of $42 = n$ **15.** $8\frac{1}{3}\%$ of $96 = n$

Solve. *Here are scrambled answers for the next row of exercises: 34 45 48*

16. 20% of $n = 9$ **17.** 25% of $n = 12$ **18.** 50% of $n = 17$

19. 9% of $n = 36$ **20.** 1% of $n = 2.56$ **21.** 24% of $n = 12.48$

22. $12\frac{1}{2}\%$ of $n = 6$ **23.** $16\frac{2}{3}\%$ of $n = 24$ **24.** $33\frac{1}{3}\%$ of $n = 17$

Solve. *Here are scrambled answers for the next row of exercises: 120 $31\frac{1}{4}$ 6*

25. $12\frac{1}{2}\%$ of $n = 15$ **26.** $16\frac{2}{3}\%$ of $36 = n$ **27.** $n\%$ of $16 = 5$

28. $33\frac{1}{3}\%$ of $18 = n$ **29.** $n\%$ of $8 = 7$ **30.** 22% of $n = 11$

Solve.

31. A stereo system that costs $224 has a down payment of $56. What percent of the total cost is the down payment?

32. A tape deck sells for $279. The down payment is $33\frac{1}{3}\%$ of the selling price. How much is the down payment?

33. A set of speakers can be purchased for a down payment of $24. The down payment is $16\frac{2}{3}\%$ of the price. What is the price of the speakers?

34. A car radio sells for $275. The down payment is 25% of the selling price. How much is the down payment?

Name that year

35. You can find the year the radio was invented by pressing these calculator keys.

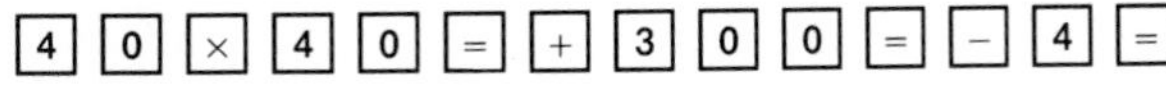

Cumulative Skill Practice

Give the product in simplest form. *(page 178)*

1. $\frac{2}{3} \times \frac{4}{4}$ 2. $\frac{1}{2} \times \frac{1}{4}$ 3. $\frac{1}{6} \times \frac{1}{8}$ 4. $\frac{3}{4} \times \frac{2}{3}$ 5. $\frac{2}{5} \times \frac{5}{6}$ 6. $\frac{3}{4} \times \frac{4}{7}$

7. $2 \times \frac{3}{5}$ 8. $\frac{3}{8} \times \frac{3}{8}$ 9. $\frac{0}{2} \times \frac{1}{6}$ 10. $\frac{3}{4} \times \frac{2}{5}$ 11. $4 \times \frac{2}{9}$ 12. $5 \times \frac{1}{2}$

13. $\frac{9}{10} \times \frac{2}{3}$ 14. $4 \times \frac{5}{6}$ 15. $\frac{2}{3} \times \frac{3}{10}$ 16. $\frac{7}{16} \times \frac{4}{5}$ 17. $3 \times \frac{11}{12}$ 18. $\frac{1}{2} \times \frac{1}{3}$

Give the quotient in simplest form. *(page 188)*

19. $2 \div \frac{1}{2}$ 20. $\frac{1}{2} \div \frac{2}{3}$ 21. $3 \div \frac{2}{3}$ 22. $\frac{3}{4} \div \frac{3}{8}$ 23. $\frac{2}{3} \div \frac{1}{2}$ 24. $4 \div \frac{1}{5}$

25. $\frac{3}{5} \div \frac{3}{8}$ 26. $\frac{3}{10} \div \frac{1}{5}$ 27. $\frac{5}{8} \div \frac{1}{4}$ 28. $\frac{5}{6} \div 2$ 29. $\frac{3}{10} \div \frac{3}{4}$ 30. $\frac{1}{6} \div 6$

31. $\frac{2}{3} \div \frac{3}{4}$ 32. $\frac{5}{16} \div \frac{3}{8}$ 33. $\frac{9}{10} \div \frac{3}{5}$ 34. $\frac{3}{4} \div \frac{2}{3}$ 35. $\frac{11}{12} \div \frac{5}{6}$ 36. $\frac{2}{3} \div \frac{2}{3}$

Complete. *(page 206)*

37. 4000 mg = __?__ g 38. 582 mg = __?__ g 39. 2000 g = __?__ kg

40. 238 g = __?__ kg 41. 5 kg = __?__ g 42. 2.64 kg = __?__ g

43. 2 g = __?__ mg 44. 8.3 g = __?__ mg 45. 0.375 g = __?__ mg

Subtract. *(page 218)*

46. 5 ft 6 in. − 2 ft 9 in.
47. 5 yd 1 ft − 1 yd 2 ft
48. 8 ft 4 in. − 6 ft 9 in.
49. 3 gal 2 qt − 1 gal 3 qt

50. 3 qt − 1 qt 1 pt
51. 4 gal 1 qt − 2 gal 3 qt
52. 5 pt − 3 pt 1 c
53. 9 lb 6 oz − 5 lb 10 oz

Solve. *(page 230)*

54. $\frac{2}{4} = \frac{n}{2}$ 55. $\frac{n}{6} = \frac{10}{12}$ 56. $\frac{5}{6} = \frac{11}{n}$ 57. $\frac{8}{3} = \frac{13}{n}$ 58. $\frac{n}{8} = \frac{7}{10}$

59. $\frac{3}{n} = \frac{4}{8}$ 60. $\frac{7}{4} = \frac{n}{8}$ 61. $\frac{n}{12} = \frac{15}{8}$ 62. $\frac{10}{9} = \frac{16}{n}$ 63. $\frac{8}{n} = \frac{5}{12}$

64. $\frac{n}{18} = \frac{6}{4}$ 65. $\frac{20}{n} = \frac{16}{9}$ 66. $\frac{13}{20} = \frac{n}{18}$ 67. $\frac{6}{8} = \frac{9}{n}$ 68. $\frac{6}{n} = \frac{3}{7}$

Change to a fraction in simplest form. *(page 248)*

69. 20% 70. 60% 71. 25% 72. 80% 73. 50%

74. 75% 75. 40% 76. 100% 77. 125% 78. 275%

79. $33\frac{1}{3}\%$ 80. $37\frac{1}{2}\%$ 81. $66\frac{2}{3}\%$ 82. $6\frac{1}{4}\%$ 83. $116\frac{2}{3}\%$

Problem solving

COMPUTERS AT HOME

Eric Jeffrey's home computer uses the telephone to communicate with a large **main frame** computer. This communication link allows him to use a wide variety of programs stored in the large computer.

Eric has just received a raise, and he uses a HOME MANAGEMENT program to answer some questions about his raise.

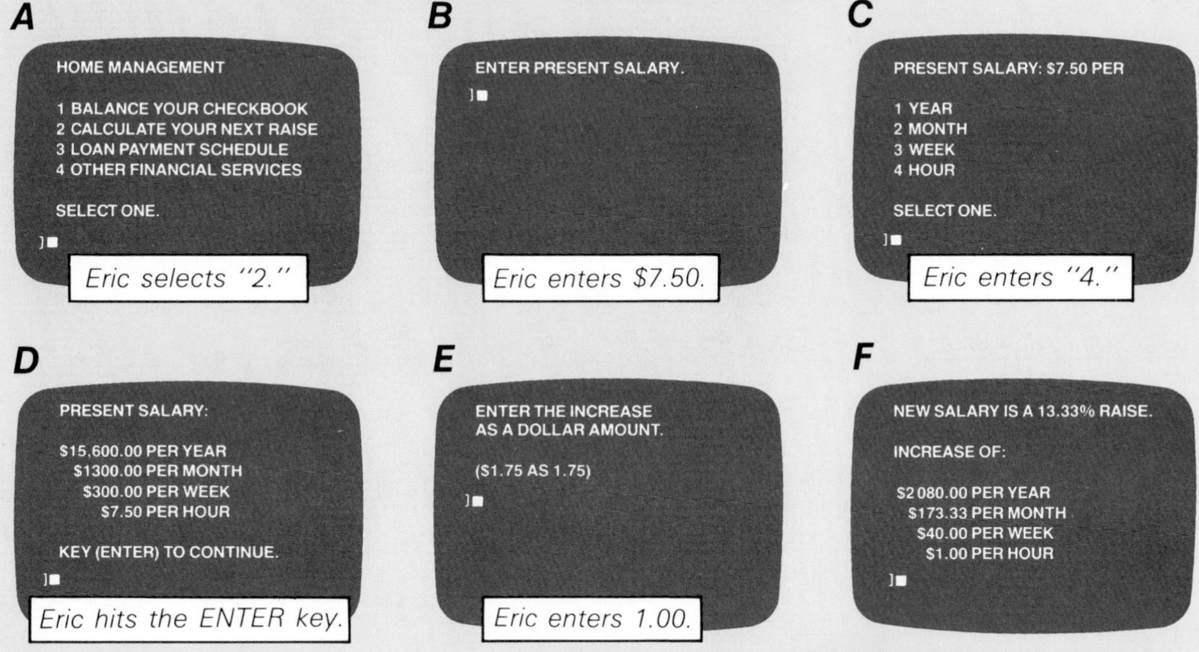

A
HOME MANAGEMENT
1 BALANCE YOUR CHECKBOOK
2 CALCULATE YOUR NEXT RAISE
3 LOAN PAYMENT SCHEDULE
4 OTHER FINANCIAL SERVICES
SELECT ONE.
Eric selects "2."
B
ENTER PRESENT SALARY.
Eric enters $7.50.
C
PRESENT SALARY: $7.50 PER
1 YEAR
2 MONTH
3 WEEK
4 HOUR
SELECT ONE.
Eric enters "4."
D
PRESENT SALARY:
$15,600.00 PER YEAR
$1300.00 PER MONTH
$300.00 PER WEEK
$7.50 PER HOUR
KEY (ENTER) TO CONTINUE.
Eric hits the ENTER key.
E
ENTER THE INCREASE
AS A DOLLAR AMOUNT.
($1.75 AS 1.75)
Eric enters 1.00.
F
NEW SALARY IS A 13.33% RAISE.
INCREASE OF:
$2080.00 PER YEAR
$173.33 PER MONTH
$40.00 PER WEEK
$1.00 PER HOUR

Use Screen D to answer these questions.

1. Is the weekly salary equal to 40 × $7.50?
2. How did the computer calculate Eric's salary per year?
3. How did the computer calculate Eric's salary per month?

Use Screen F to answer these questions.

4. What is the percent of increase of Eric's raise?
5. How much more money will Eric earn per week?

Use Screens D and F to answer these questions.

6. $1.00 is 13.33% of what amount?
7. What will Eric's new salary per year be?

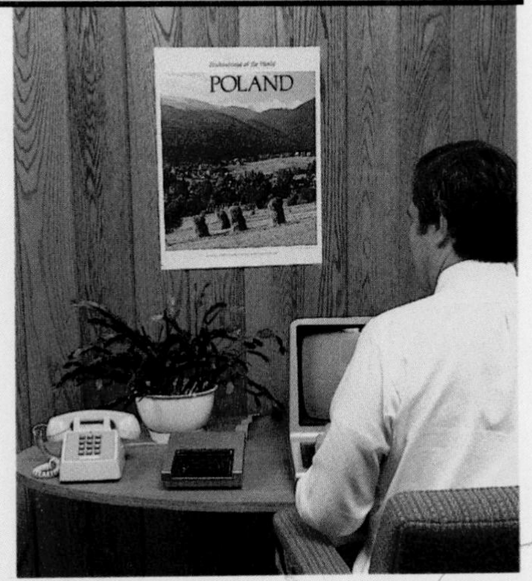

POLAND

Chapter REVIEW

Here are scrambled answers for the review exercises:

7	75	denominator	equivalent	multiply	proportion	simplest
12	100	divide	left	percent	right	

1. 25% means 25 out of [?]. To change a percent to a fraction, you can first write the percent as a fraction with a [?] of 100. Then you can write the fraction in [?] form. *(page 248)*

25%

2. To change this fraction to a percent, you could first write the [?] fraction with a denominator of 100. Then you would write that fraction as a [?]. *(page 250)*

$\frac{3}{4}$

3. To change $\frac{5}{6}$ to a percent, you could solve this [?]. *(page 250)*

$\frac{5}{6} = \frac{n}{100}$

4. To change a percent to a decimal, you can move the decimal point two places to the [?] and remove the percent sign.
To change a decimal to a percent, you can move the decimal point two places to the [?] and write a percent sign.
(pages 252, 253)

5. To find a percent of a number, you can change the percent to a fraction or decimal and [?].
25% of 48 is [?].
14% of 50 is [?].
(page 256)

6. You can find $8\frac{1}{3}$% of 60 by solving this proportion. The next step in solving the proportion would be to [?] both sides of the equation by 100. *(page 258)*

$8\frac{1}{3}\%$ of $60 = n$

$\frac{8\frac{1}{3}}{100} = \frac{n}{60}$

$100n = 8\frac{1}{3} \times 60$

$= 500$

7. You can solve a proportion to find the number when a percent of it is known. If you solve the proportion, you will find that n = [?]. *(page 260)*

24% of $n = 18$

$\frac{24}{100} = \frac{18}{n}$

Chapter TEST

Change to a fraction in simplest form. *(page 248)*

1. 20% **2.** 25% **3.** 80% **4.** 75% **5.** 50% **6.** 5%

7. 150% **8.** 225% **9.** $12\frac{1}{2}\%$ **10.** $62\frac{1}{2}\%$ **11.** $33\frac{1}{3}\%$ **12.** $66\frac{2}{3}\%$

Change to a percent. *(page 250)*

13. $\frac{1}{2}$ **14.** $\frac{2}{5}$ **15.** $\frac{3}{4}$ **16.** $\frac{1}{4}$ **17.** 2 **18.** 4

19. $\frac{7}{5}$ **20.** $\frac{9}{4}$ **21.** $\frac{1}{3}$ **22.** $\frac{1}{6}$ **23.** $\frac{5}{8}$ **24.** $\frac{7}{8}$

Change each percent to a decimal. *(page 252)*

25. 12% **26.** 9% **27.** 56% **28.** 125% **29.** 160% **30.** 250%

31. 15.3% **32.** 1.5% **33.** 6.85% **34.** $16\frac{2}{3}\%$ **35.** $37\frac{1}{2}\%$ **36.** $33\frac{1}{3}\%$

Change each decimal to a percent. *(page 253)*

37. 0.05 **38.** 0.09 **39.** 0.54 **40.** 0.8 **41.** 0.575 **42.** 0.625

43. 1.375 **44.** 2.326 **45.** 0.004 **46.** $0.12\frac{1}{2}$ **47.** $0.66\frac{2}{3}$ **48.** $1.33\frac{1}{3}$

Solve. *(pages 256, 258)*

49. 25% of $44 = n$ **50.** 75% of $52 = n$ **51.** 6.2% of $32 = n$

52. 0.75% of $12.4 = n$ **53.** $8\frac{1}{3}\%$ of $60 = n$ **54.** $16\frac{2}{3}\%$ of $72 = n$

Solve. *(page 260)*

55. 50% of $n = 19$ **56.** 40% of $n = 36$ **57.** 5% of $n = 15$

58. 150% of $n = 51$ **59.** 12.5% of $n = 3$ **60.** $33\frac{1}{3}\%$ of $n = 21$

Solve. *(page 262)*

61. How much is the down payment?

$? DOWN

25% DOWN

TOTAL COST $480

62. What is the total cost?

$112 DOWN

20% DOWN

TOTAL COST $?

Cumulative TEST Standardized Format

Choose the correct letter.

1. Multiply.

$$\begin{array}{r} 4.239 \\ \times\ 8.07 \\ \hline \end{array}$$

A. 342.0873
B. 36.8793
C. 34.20873
D. none of these

2. Divide. Round the quotient to the nearest tenth.

$$62.5\overline{)191.27}$$

A. 3.06
B. 3.1
C. 3.6
D. none of these

3. The mean of 81.5, 83.4, 86.9, 87.4, and 90.3 is

A. 85.9
B. 86.9
C. 87.9
D. none of these

4. Give the sum.

$\frac{5}{6} + \frac{5}{8}$

A. $\frac{5}{7}$
B. $\frac{5}{24}$
C. $1\frac{1}{4}$
D. none of these

5. Give the difference.

$\frac{7}{8} - \frac{2}{3}$

A. 1
B. $\frac{5}{24}$
C. $\frac{5}{11}$
D. none of these

6. Give the product.

$\frac{5}{6} \times \frac{3}{8}$

A. $\frac{5}{16}$
B. $2\frac{2}{9}$
C. $\frac{9}{20}$
D. none of these

7. Give the quotient.

$\frac{7}{8} \div \frac{3}{4}$

A. $\frac{21}{32}$
B. $\frac{6}{7}$
C. $1\frac{1}{6}$
D. none of these

8. Complete.

275 mg = ? g

A. 2.75
B. 275
C. 27.5
D. none of these

9. Subtract.

$$\begin{array}{r} 9 \text{ gal } 2 \text{ qt} \\ -3 \text{ gal } 3 \text{ qt} \\ \hline \end{array}$$

A. 6 gal 1 qt
B. 5 gal 3 qt
C. 5 gal 1 qt
D. none of these

10. Solve.

$\frac{7}{n} = \frac{5}{9}$

A. 3.89
B. 6.43
C. 12.6
D. none of these

11. Change to a fraction.

$16\frac{2}{3}\% = ?$

A. $\frac{1}{6}$
B. $\frac{1}{16}$
C. $\frac{1}{8}$
D. none of these

12. You took a 72-problem math test. You got 75% of the problems correct. How many was that?

A. 96
B. 36
C. 54
D. none of these

Chapter 12
Consumer Mathematics

Earning money

Read the want ads to find the jobs.

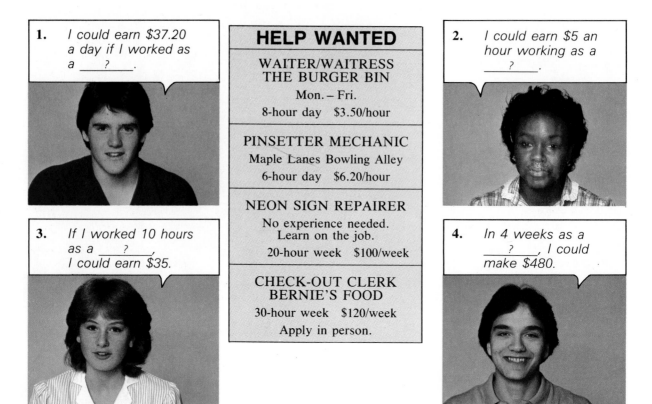

1. *I could earn $37.20 a day if I worked as a ___?___.*

3. *If I worked 10 hours as a ___?___, I could earn $35.*

HELP WANTED

WAITER/WAITRESS
THE BURGER BIN
Mon. – Fri.
8-hour day $3.50/hour

PINSETTER MECHANIC
Maple Lanes Bowling Alley
6-hour day $6.20/hour

NEON SIGN REPAIRER
No experience needed.
Learn on the job.
20-hour week $100/week

CHECK-OUT CLERK
BERNIE'S FOOD
30-hour week $120/week
Apply in person.

2. *I could earn $5 an hour working as a ___?___.*

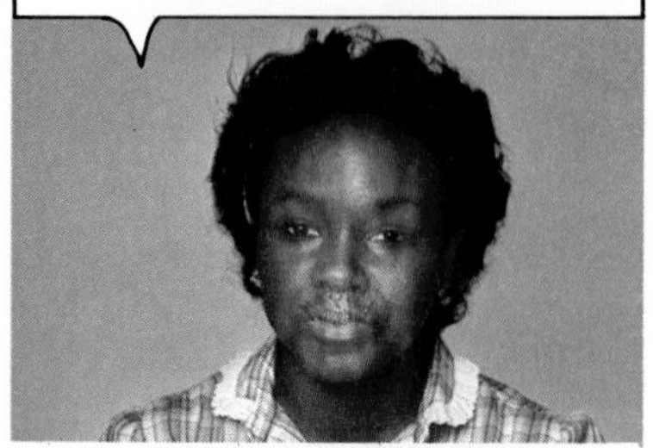

4. *In 4 weeks as a ___?___, I could make $480.*

EXERCISES

Solve.

5. The Ace Trucking Company pays its drivers 20¢ a mile.

a. How much would an Ace driver be paid for an 840-mile trip?

b. How many miles would a driver have to drive to make $150?

6. The Tip Top Café pays its cooks $5.40 an hour.

a. How much would a Tip Top cook be paid for a 7.5-hour day?

b. How much would a cook be paid for a 37.5-hour week?

7. The Happy Day Card Company pays its salespeople a commission of 20% on all sales.

a. How much would you earn for selling $300 worth of Happy Day cards? *Hint: What is 20% of $300?*

b. To earn $100 commission, would you have to sell more or less than $400 worth of Happy Day cards?

Cindy Davis is a cashier at Showtime Cinemas. Each week she receives with her paycheck a **statement of withholdings and deductions.** This statement lists the amount that her employer is required by law to deduct from her weekly paycheck.

SHOWTIME CINEMAS
College Mall
Cedar City

No 1914

March 8 19 85 53-7122 / 2113

PAY TO THE ORDER OF Cindy Davis $ 95.62

Ninety-five and 62/100 DOLLARS

Middle Savings Bank

Carol DeBold

EMPLOYEE	CHECK #	WEEK ENDING	HOURLY WAGE	HOURS	GROSS PAY	NET PAY
Davis, Cindy	1914	03/08/85	$3.80	32.5	$123.50	$95.62

TAX DEDUCTIONS				PERSONAL DEDUCTIONS	
FIT	FICA	STATE	LOCAL	MEDICAL	UNION DUES
$16.50	$8.54	$2.84	—	—	—

8. How much was Cindy paid per hour?
9. How many hours did she work?
10. To find Cindy's gross pay, $3.80 was multiplied by what number?
11. Social Security (FICA) withholding is for retirement income and disability income. How much was withheld for Social Security?
12. How much did her employer withhold for federal income tax (FIT)? State income tax?
13. How much was deducted altogether from Cindy's gross pay?
14. How much was Cindy's net, or "take home", pay?

You're the boss

15. Complete this statement by computing Cindy's gross and net pay.

EMPLOYEE	CHECK #	WEEK ENDING	HOURLY WAGE	HOURS	GROSS PAY	NET PAY
Davis, Cindy	1972	03/15/85	$3.80	29.5	?	?

TAX DEDUCTIONS				PERSONAL DEDUCTIONS	
FIT	FICA	STATE	LOCAL	MEDICAL	UNION DUES
$15.68	$7.42	$2.57	—	—	—

Buying on sale

BIG VALUES
LEATHER BOOTS
Reg. $66.60
NOW 15% OFF

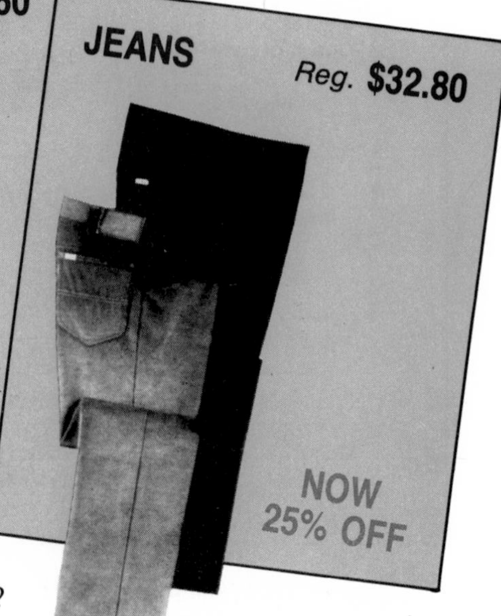

1. What is the regular price of the jeans?

2. Will the sale price of the jeans be more or less than $32.80?

Here's how *to find the sale price of a pair of jeans.*

METHOD 1.

```
 $32.80   ← Regular price
×  0.25
 16400
 6560
$8.2000   ← Discount is $8.20.

 $32.80 ← Regular price
−  8.20 ← Discount
 $24.60 ← Sale price
```

METHOD 2.

```
 $32.80   ← Regular price
×  0.75
  16400
 22960
$24.6000  ← Sale price is $24.60
```

If the discount is 25%, the sale price is 75% of the regular price.

3. Look at the *Here's how*. How much is the savings on a pair of jeans during the sale?

4. What is the sale price of a pair of jeans?

5. What is the sale price of a pair of leather boots?

6. What is the sale price of a flannel shirt?

EXERCISES

Find the sale price of each item.

7.

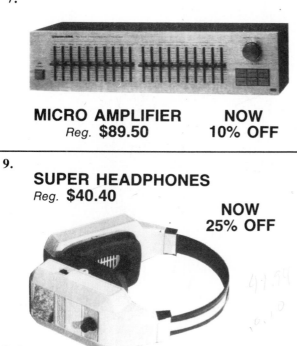

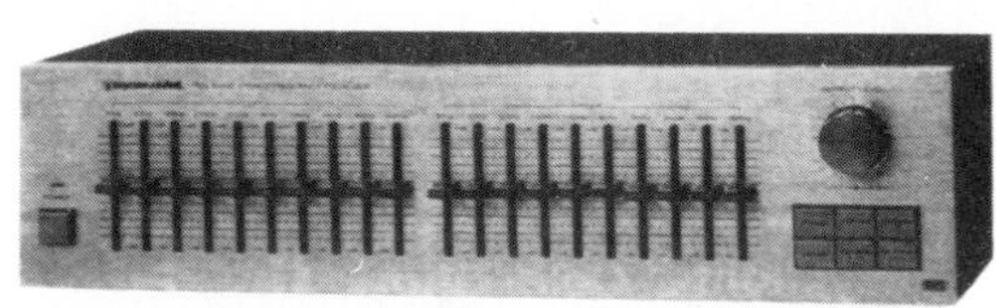

MICRO AMPLIFIER *Reg.* **$89.50**

NOW 10% OFF

8.

TURNTABLE *Reg.* **$69.90**

NOW 20% OFF

9.

SUPER HEADPHONES
Reg. **$40.40**

NOW 25% OFF

10.

HIGH-STYLE STEREO RADIO AND CASSETTE PLAYER

Reg. **$89.90**

NOW 30% OFF

Solve.

11. A calculator usually costs \$9.90. Now it is marked 10% off. What is the sale price?

12. A television set usually costs \$289. Now it is on sale at a 20% discount. What is the sale price?

13. A radio is on sale at a 25% discount. The regular price is \$39.88. How much would you save when buying the radio on sale?

14. How much would you save by purchasing a stereo set at 30% off the regular price? The regular price is \$186.

Check the ads

15. Two of these ads are incorrect. Find and correct the two wrong sale prices.

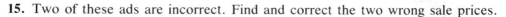

a. **SAVE $1.99**

Reg. **$7.29**
SALE $4.30

b. **$\frac{1}{3}$ OFF**
Reg. **$8.49**

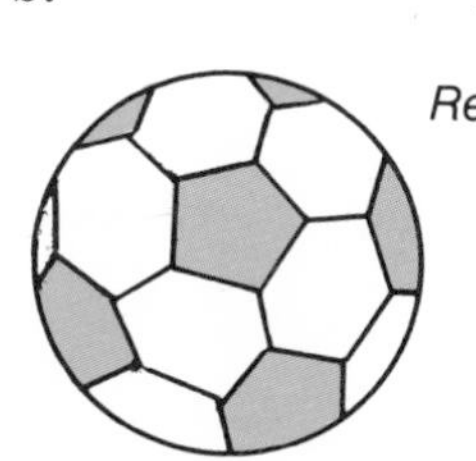

NOW $5.66

c. **15% OFF**

Reg. **$6.80**
SALE $5.69

Comparison buying

WHO'S RIGHT?

Which is the better buy, the 4.5-pound bag of apples or the 8-pound bag?

This 4.5-pound bag of apples is a better buy.
No! This 8-pound bag of apples costs less per pound.
$1.79
Orchard Fresh Fruit
$2.99

If the apples in each bag are the same quality and you could use either amount, you should compute the **unit price** (price per pound) to decide which is the better buy.

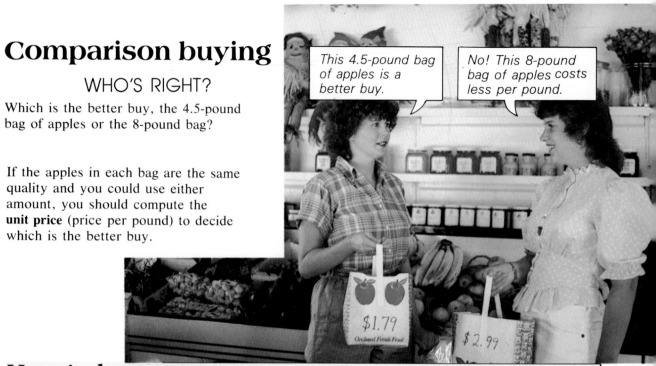

Here's how *to find the unit price.*

To compute the unit price of the apples, divide the price by the number of pounds. That will tell you the price per pound.

Small bag 4.5 pounds for \$1.79

```
     $ 0.397
4.5.) $1.7900
      -135
        440
       -405
        350
       -315
         35
```

Large bag 8 pounds for \$2.99

```
   $0.373
8 ) $2.990
    -24
      59
     -56
      30
     -24
       6
```

Round each unit price to the nearest cent.

Small bag
\$.40 per pound

Large bag
\$.37 per pound

1. Look at the *Here's how*. Which size bag of apples costs less per pound?
2. If both bags of apples are the same quality, which size bag is the better buy?
3. If you only need 4 pounds of apples, which size bag should you buy?

EXERCISES

Compute the unit price. Round each answer to the nearest cent.

Hint: The unit price is the cost per ounce.

4. Grapes
2 pounds for $1.89

5. Pickles
9 ounces for $.79

6. Crackers
10 ounces for 98¢

7. Ketchup
8 ounces for 69¢

8. Tomatoes
3 pounds for $2.69

9. Apples
4 pounds for $1.75

10. Peanuts
1.1 pounds for $1.99

11. Bread
14 ounces for $1.10

12. Sunflower seeds
6.5 ounces for 89¢

13. Spaghetti sauce
12 ounces for 99¢

Suppose that you could use either amount. Tell which is the better buy.
Hint: Compute and compare the unit prices.

14. Cheese
a. 3 pounds for $3.19
b. 2 pounds for $2.29

15. Bananas
a. 3 pounds for $.89
b. 5 pounds for $1.39

16. Carrots
a. 0.5 pound for $.29
b. 2 pounds for $.99

17. Beans
a. 8-ounce can for $.49
b. 12-ounce can for $.89

18. Cereal
a. 18-ounce box for $1.09
b. 12-ounce box for $.63

19. Olives
a. 6-ounce jar for $.99
b. 10-ounce jar for $1.79

20. Dinner napkins
a. 100 for $.85
b. 150 for $1.75

21. Milk
a. 1 quart for $.99
b. $\frac{1}{2}$ gallon for $1.79

What's in the bag?

Use the ad to find what fruit is in each bag.

22.

23.

PRODUCE SALE

PEARS	$ .88/lb
PEACHES	$ .75/lb
CHERRIES	$1.80/lb
GRAPES	$1.20/lb

Bargain buying

Shoppers who use coupons pay less than the regular price. They get the price reduced by the value of the coupon. For example, with the coupon, the pocket camera will cost $25.45.

POCKET CAMERA
Reg. **$29.95**

$29.95	*regular price*
− 4.50	*value of coupon*
$25.45	

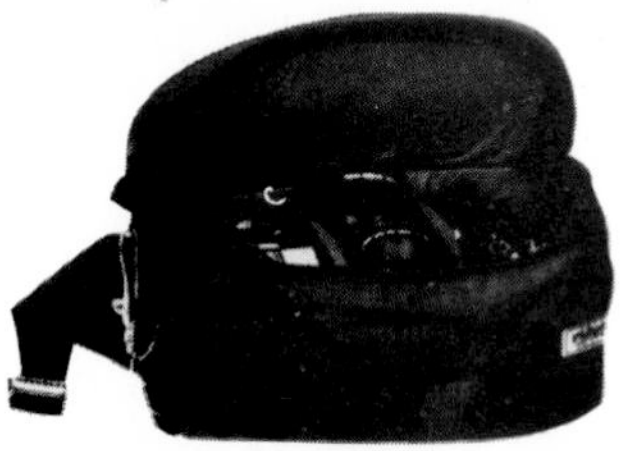

CAMERA BAG
Reg. **$48.29**

MOVIE PROJECTOR
$\frac{1}{4}$ OFF *Reg.* **$240.00**

MOVIE CAMERA
10% OFF
Reg. **$199.00**

$4.50 STORE COUPON **$4.50**
$4.50 OFF
POCKET CAMERA
LIMIT 1 PER CUSTOMER

STORE COUPON
30¢ OFF
ON 1 ROLL
OF 24-EXPOSURE
COLOR FILM
Reg. $2.49
100
$2.19

STORE COUPON

COLOR PRINT PROCESSING

	Reg.	*WITH COUPON*
12-EXPOSURE	$2.25	$1.99
20-EXPOSURE	$4.35	$3.79
36-EXPOSURE	$6.45	$5.89

BRING THIS COUPON WITH ORDER NO LIMIT

EXERCISES

Solve.

1. What is the regular price of a
   a. pocket camera?
   b. roll of 24-exposure color film?

2. With a coupon, how much can you save when you buy a
   a. pocket camera?
   b. camera bag?

3. How much more will it cost to process a roll of 36-exposure color film without a coupon?

4. With a coupon, how much would you pay for a camera bag?

5. You bought a movie camera. What was the sale price?

6. You are interested in buying a movie projector. How much can you save by buying it during the sale?

7. Mrs. Kelly bought a roll of 24-exposure color film and a camera bag. How much did she save by using coupons?

8. A customer paid for 2 rolls of 24-exposure color film with a $10 bill and got $5.62 in change. Did the customer use coupons?

9. Janet has a $15 gift certificate. How much more money does she need to buy a pocket camera using a coupon?

10. Mr. Harms was charged $13.05 to have 3 rolls of 20-exposure color film processed. Did he have a coupon?

11. Using only one coupon, what would be the total cost for two pocket cameras?

12. Which is the better buy, getting 10% off the regular price of a roll of 24-exposure color film or using the coupon?

You decide!

Use the coupons and the prices on page 276 to answer these questions.

13. *I bought a roll of 24-exposure color film and a pocket camera. I spent $27.94. Which coupon did I clip out and use?*

14. *I bought a camera bag, a pocket camera, and a roll of 24-exposure film. I spent a total of $78.44. Which coupons did I clip out and use?*

Cumulative Skill Practice

Add. Write the sum in simplest form. *(page 160)*

1. $3\frac{2}{3} + 1\frac{1}{2}$
2. $2\frac{1}{3} + 2\frac{3}{4}$
3. $1\frac{5}{6} + 2\frac{2}{3}$
4. $1\frac{3}{4} + 1\frac{1}{2}$
5. $4\frac{1}{2} + 2\frac{1}{4}$
6. $3\frac{1}{3} + 2\frac{1}{2}$
7. $12\frac{2}{3} + 6\frac{1}{2}$
8. $10\frac{1}{3} + 8\frac{4}{5}$
9. $16\frac{5}{9} + 7$
10. $15\frac{7}{8} + 12\frac{3}{4}$
11. $23\frac{2}{3} + 17\frac{3}{5}$
12. $20\frac{1}{3} + 6\frac{1}{5}$

Subtract. Write the difference in simplest form. *(page 170)*

13. $6\frac{3}{4} - 1\frac{1}{2}$
14. $5\frac{2}{3} - 3$
15. $4\frac{1}{2} - 1\frac{3}{4}$
16. $5\frac{1}{8} - 2\frac{1}{2}$
17. $6\frac{3}{5} - 2\frac{1}{2}$
18. $7\frac{2}{7} - 3\frac{1}{2}$
19. $8 - 2\frac{1}{3}$
20. $14 - 2\frac{5}{6}$
21. $11\frac{3}{8} - 9\frac{1}{2}$
22. $15\frac{1}{9} - 10\frac{5}{6}$
23. $24\frac{2}{3} - 16\frac{3}{4}$
24. $25\frac{1}{2} - 13\frac{5}{8}$

Give the product in simplest form. *(page 182)*

25. $3\frac{1}{2} \times 2\frac{1}{4}$
26. $1\frac{1}{3} \times 1\frac{1}{2}$
27. $4\frac{1}{2} \times 2\frac{1}{3}$
28. $2\frac{1}{2} \times 1\frac{1}{4}$
29. $1\frac{1}{4} \times 2\frac{1}{3}$
30. $1\frac{2}{3} \times 2\frac{1}{2}$
31. $1\frac{1}{3} \times 1\frac{1}{3}$
32. $2\frac{3}{4} \times 3\frac{2}{3}$
33. $2\frac{3}{8} \times 3$
34. $2\frac{2}{3} \times 1\frac{3}{4}$
35. $2\frac{1}{4} \times 2\frac{1}{4}$
36. $4 \times 3\frac{2}{3}$
37. $1\frac{3}{4} \times 1\frac{3}{4}$
38. $4\frac{2}{5} \times 3\frac{3}{4}$
39. $1\frac{5}{8} \times 9$

Give the quotient in simplest form. *(page 190)*

40. $3\frac{3}{4} \div 1\frac{1}{4}$
41. $5 \div 2\frac{1}{2}$
42. $5\frac{5}{6} \div 2\frac{1}{3}$
43. $5\frac{1}{2} \div 2\frac{1}{4}$
44. $6\frac{2}{3} \div 1\frac{1}{6}$
45. $6\frac{1}{4} \div 1\frac{1}{4}$
46. $5\frac{5}{8} \div 1\frac{1}{2}$
47. $5\frac{1}{4} \div 2\frac{1}{2}$
48. $10\frac{1}{2} \div 1\frac{3}{4}$
49. $8 \div 1\frac{2}{3}$
50. $6\frac{1}{2} \div 2\frac{1}{4}$
51. $7 \div 2\frac{1}{3}$
52. $8\frac{1}{3} \div 1\frac{1}{4}$
53. $12\frac{3}{4} \div 2\frac{1}{2}$
54. $3\frac{2}{3} \div 4$

Complete. *(page 202)*

55. 9 cm = ? mm
56. 6 km = ? m
57. 62 mm = ? cm
58. 3450 m = ? km
59. 8.4 km = ? m
60. 5.6 cm = ? m

Problem solving

*A **budget** is a plan for using one's money. Here's my weekly budget.*

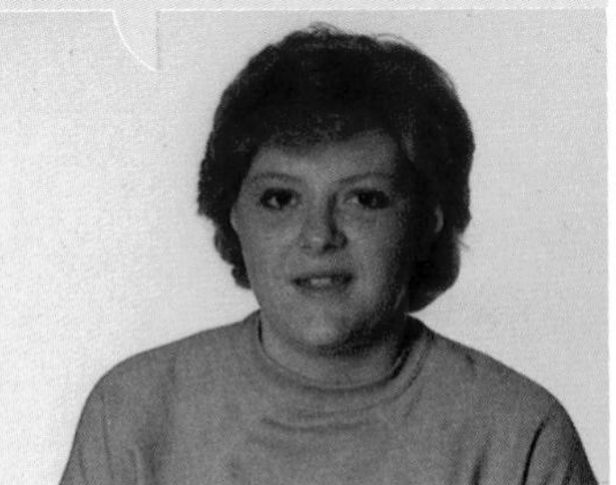

Kelly
EARNINGS: $30/week
BUDGET

Savings:	$6.00
Clothing:	4.50
Movies:	3.50
Records:	3.00
Lunches:	9.00
Other:	4.00

I use a budget to keep track of my spending so that I won't run out of money between paychecks.

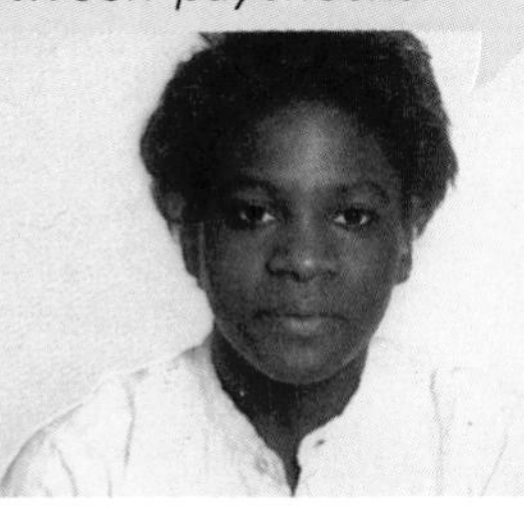

Rhonda
EARNINGS: $40/week
BUDGET

Savings:	$ 4.00
Clothing:	10.00
Movies:	7.00
Records:	3.00
Lunches:	10.00
Other:	6.00

I keep a budget to make sure I put some money into savings each week.

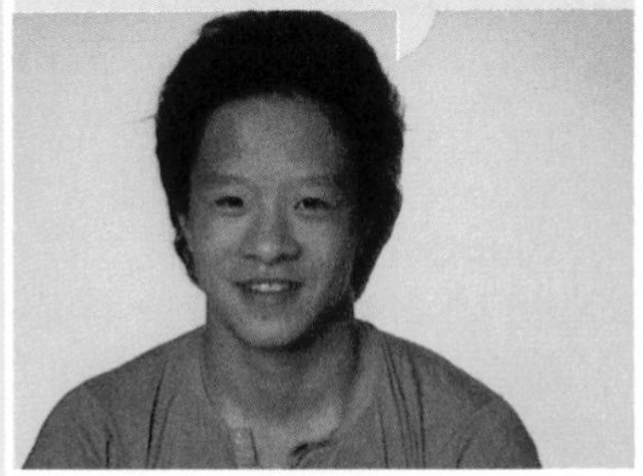

Walter
EARNINGS: $24/week
BUDGET

Savings:	$3.00
Clothing:	6.50
Movies:	4.00
Records:	2.00
Lunches:	6.50
Other:	2.00

Use the budgets to answer the questions.

1. Who budgets a total of $6 for movies and records?

2. Who budgets $2.50 more for clothing than for movies?

3. Which person budgets $\frac{1}{4}$ of total earnings for clothing?

4. Who budgets $\frac{1}{8}$ of total earnings for savings?

5. What fraction of Rhonda's total earnings does she save? Give the answer in lowest terms.

6. What fraction of his earnings does Walter save? Give the answer in lowest terms.

7. Who spends 10% of total earnings for records?

8. Who spends 50% of total earnings for clothing and lunches?

Solve.

9. Holly Moore earns $50 a week. She plans her budget using percents. Find the amount she plans to spend for each category.

10. How much more money does Holly plan to spend for clothing than for recreation?

HOLLY'S BUDGET		
CATEGORY	PERCENT	AMOUNT
Clothing	30%	$15.00
Savings	10%	?
Recreation	25%	?
Personal	15%	?
Other	20%	?

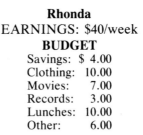

Checking accounts

CHECK IT OUT!

1. Whose check paid for the stereo?
   Clues:
   - The check was written for more than $300.
   - The check was dated in early March.
2. Whose check paid for a TV set?
   Clues:
   - The check number is less than 500.
   - The check was written for less than $400.

175
March 28 19 85
PAY TO THE ORDER OF Ace Electronics $ 426.93
Four hundred twenty-six and 93/100 DOLLARS
FIRST NATIONAL BANK
Lexington, MA
Julie Adams

326
PAY TO THE ORDER OF Ace Electronics March 15 19 85
Two hundred eighty-three and 17/100 $ 283.17 DOLLARS
UNITED BANK OF LEXINGTON
Lexington, MA
Frank Horowitz

1215
March 6 19 85
PAY TO THE ORDER OF Ace Electronics $ 379.86
Three hundred seventy-nine and 86/100 DOLLARS
PEOPLE'S BANK
LEXINGTON, MA
Tony Perez

EXERCISES

Use the checks to answer the questions.

3. Find check No. 175. Who signed the check? What was the amount of the check?
4. Who signed the check that tells the United Bank of Lexington to pay Ace Electronics $283.17 from his account?
5. What is the amount of check No. 1215? Why do you think the amount is written in both numerals and words?
6. Julie Adams keeps her money in the First National Bank. Her checking-account number is 127 415. Whose checking-account number is 741 105? What is Tony Perez's checking-account number?

Julie's checkbook has a section called a **check register** in which she keeps a record of her checking account.

NUMBER	DATE	DESCRIPTION OF TRANSACTION	AMOUNT OF CHECK	√	AMOUNT OF DEPOSIT	BALANCE	
						$173	96
173	3/14/85	Top Supervalue	$ 72.14		$	101	82
	3/16/85				500.00	601	82
174	3/21/85	cash	50.00			551	82
175	3/28/85	ace Electronics	426.93			124	89
176	4/2/85	Reed Bookstore	13.21				

7. On what date was a $500 deposit made?
8. For how much was the check that was written to Top Supervalue?
9. To whom was a check for $426.93 written?
10. Check No. 174 was written for what amount?
11. What was the balance in Julie's account after check 174 was written?
12. What two numbers would you use to find the balance in her account on April 2? Would you add or subtract to find the balance?
13. What was the balance in her account after check No. 176 was written?
14. On April 4, Julie wrote check No. 177 for $17.65. What was her balance after that?

Can you figure it?

Find each new balance.

15.

	AMOUNT OF CHECK	√	AMOUNT OF DEPOSIT	BALANCE	
				745	32
a.	53.10			?	
b.	17.28			?	
c.			105.00	?	
d.	283.17			?	
e.			45.75	?	
f.	58.38			?	

16.

	AMOUNT OF CHECK	√	AMOUNT OF DEPOSIT	BALANCE	
				434	80
a.	63.12			?	
b.	18.39			?	
c.	127.93			?	
d.			250.00	?	
e.	379.86			?	
f.	11.07			?	

Savings accounts

CAN YOU PASS THIS SAVINGS ACCOUNT QUIZ?

Word list

added	interest	subtracted
deposit	passbook	withdrawal

Use the word list to complete each statement.

1. To open a savings account, you must make a [?]. Each time you make a deposit, it is [?] to the balance of your account.
2. A [?] is an amount of money you take out of your savings account. When you make a withdrawal, it is [?] from your balance.
3. You may receive a [?] when you open a savings account. Bank tellers use it to record all deposits, withdrawals, [?] earned, and the new balance.

EXERCISES

Use James Stickney's passbook to answer the questions.

1. How much money did James deposit on January 19?
2. How much money did he withdraw on March 12?
3. What was the balance in his account on March 12?
4. On what date did James get $2.22 interest?
5. What was the balance on June 1?
6. How much interest did James receive for January 19 through June 1?

DEPOSITOR: JAMES STICKNEY
ACCOUNT NO. 26-01432

DATE	WITHDRAWAL	DEPOSIT	INTEREST	BALANCE
01-19		250.00		250.00
02-01			.65	250.65
02-18		115.50		366.15
03-01			1.79	367.94
03-12	65.50			302.44
04-01			2.22	304.66
05-01			2.01	306.67
05-17		180.75		487.42
06-01			2.52	?

The interest on savings accounts is often compounded daily. This means that the interest is added to the account each day. That way, you earn interest on your interest.

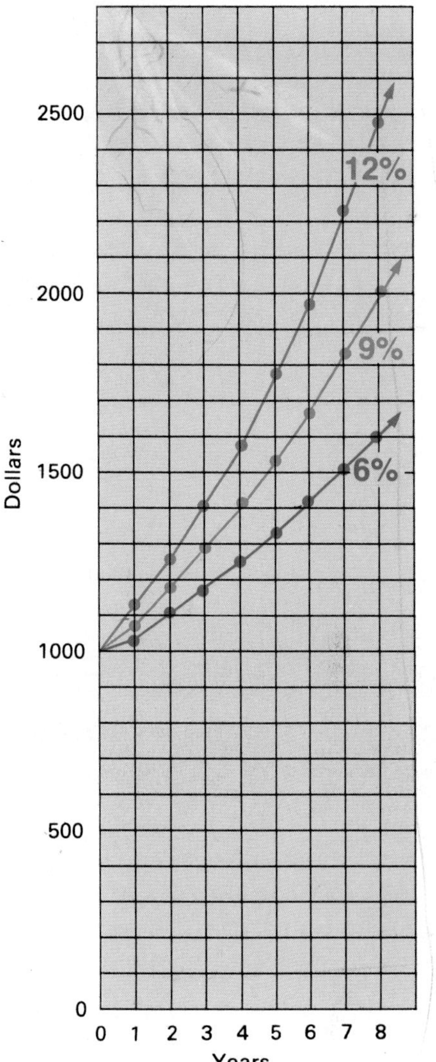

Use the graph to answer the questions.

7. At 6% interest, about how much would a $1000 deposit be worth at the end of 3 years? 5 years? 7 years?

8. At 9% interest, about how much would a $1000 deposit be worth at the end of 3 years? 5 years? 7 years?

9. At 12% interest, about how much would a $1000 deposit be worth at the end of 3 years? 5 years? 7 years?

10. About how many years does it take to double a $1000 deposit at 9% interest?

11. About how many years does it take to double a $1000 deposit at 12% interest?

12. Suppose you deposited $1000 at 9% interest and a friend deposited $1000 at 6% interest.

a. About how much more money would you have than your friend at the end of 4 years?

b. About how much more money would you have than your friend at the end of 8 years?

Want to be a millionaire?

Here's how to make $1,000,000.

13. Put [?] dollars in a savings account that pays [?]% interest compounded yearly. Then wait [?] years and your account will be worth $1,000,981.

To find [?], write a 5 in the ones place, a 6 in the hundreds place, and a 9 in the tens place.

To find [?], write a 1 in the tens place and a 6 in the ones place.

To find [?], write a 9 in the ones place and a 4 in the tens place.

Borrowing money

The amount of **interest** (rent for using the money) depends on the **principal** (the amount borrowed), the **rate** (percent of interest charged), and the **time** for which the money is borrowed.

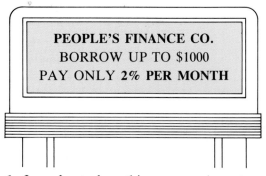

PEOPLE'S FINANCE CO.
BORROW UP TO $1000
PAY ONLY **2% PER MONTH**

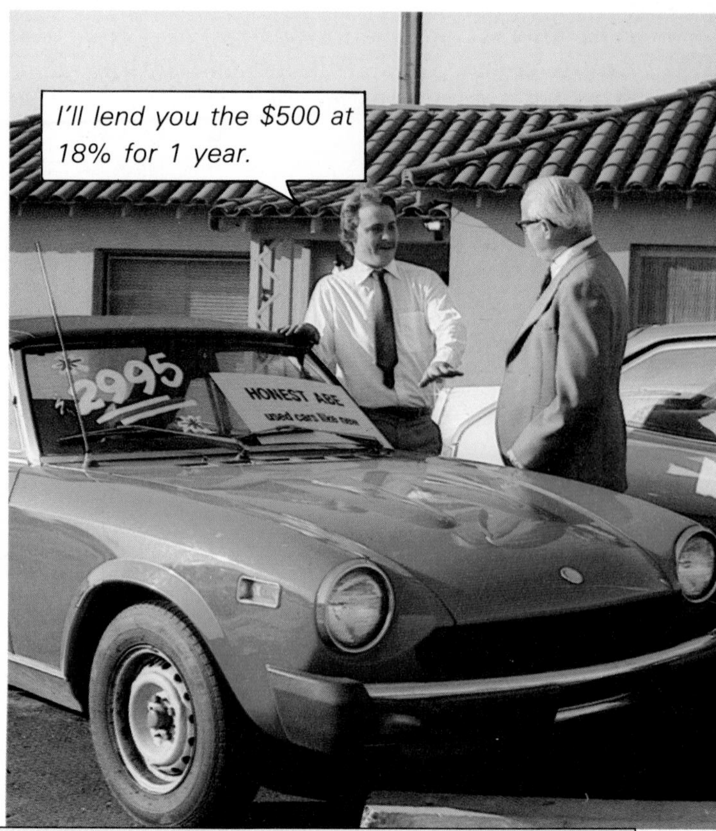

1. In order to buy this car, you have to borrow $500 for 6 months. Which loan would you choose, People's Finance Company's or Honest Abe's?

Here's how *to use a formula to find the interest* **(I)** *for a $500 loan for 6 months.*

People's Finance Co.
Principal (p) = $500
Rate (r) = 2% per month
Time (t) = 6 months

FORMULA $I = p \times r \times t$
$I = \$500 \times 0.02 \times 6$
$= \$60$

Honest Abe
Principal = $500
Rate = 18% per year
Time = 6 months ($\frac{1}{2}$ year)

$I = p \times r \times t$
$I = \$500 \times 0.18 \times 0.5$
$= \$45$

The time units must be the same. Since the rate is a yearly rate, use 0.5 of a year for t.

2. Look at the *Here's how.* How much interest is People's Finance Company charging? How much interest is Honest Abe charging?
3. Who is offering the better deal, People's Finance Company, or Honest Abe?

EXERCISES

Compute the interest.

Here are scrambled answers for the next row of exercises: $4.50 $240 $30

4. Principal = $1000
   Rate = 12% per year
   Time = 2 years

5. Principal = $600
   Rate = 10% per year
   Time = 6 months

6. Principal = $100
   Rate = 1.5% per month
   Time = 3 months

7. Principal = $300
   Rate = 16% per year
   Time = 1 year

8. Principal = $450
   Rate = 1% per month
   Time = 8 months

9. Principal = $700
   Rate = 14% per year
   Time = 9 months

10. Principal = $200
    Rate = 15% per year
    Time = 1.5 years

11. Principal = $4000
    Rate = 12% per year
    Time = 4 years

12. Principal = $300
    Rate = 18.5% per year
    Time = 18 months

Solve.

13. Brian borrowed $1500 for 1 year to buy a car. The yearly rate was 14%.
    a. How much interest will he owe at the end of the year?
    b. What is the total amount he will have to repay at the end of a year?

14. You need $300 to buy a motorcycle.
    a. A bank will lend you the money at 15% for 1 year. How much interest is that?
    b. A finance company will loan you the money at 1.5% per month for 12 months. How much interest is that?
    c. Which loan is the better deal, the bank's or the finance company's?

You're the loan officer

15. You work at a bank. Part of your job is to review loan applications. Complete the loan application. Then decide whether or not you would approve the loan.

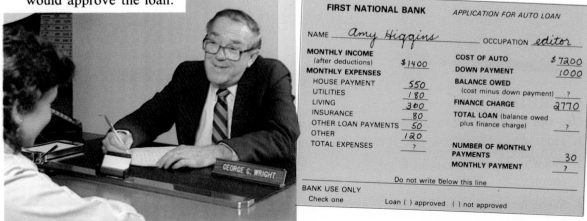

FIRST NATIONAL BANK *APPLICATION FOR AUTO LOAN*

NAME Amy Higgins OCCUPATION editor

MONTHLY INCOME (after deductions)	$1400
MONTHLY EXPENSES	
HOUSE PAYMENT	550
UTILITIES	180
LIVING	300
INSURANCE	80
OTHER LOAN PAYMENTS	50
OTHER	120
TOTAL EXPENSES	?

COST OF AUTO	$7200
DOWN PAYMENT	1000
BALANCE OWED (cost minus down payment)	?
FINANCE CHARGE	2770
TOTAL LOAN (balance owed plus finance charge)	?
NUMBER OF MONTHLY PAYMENTS	30
MONTHLY PAYMENT	?

Do not write below this line

BANK USE ONLY

Check one Loan ( ) approved ( ) not approved

Paying bills

BILLS, BILLS, BILLS!

At the end of each month, bills are sent to customers. Here are some monthly bills that George Mumby received.

BANK CARD STATEMENT

ACCOUNT NUMBER	CREDIT LIMIT	AVAILABLE CREDIT	STATEMENT DATE	PAYMENT DUE DATE	MINIMUM PAYMENT DUE
431 025 1506	$1000	$400	03/24	04/19	$30.00

DATE OF TRANSACTION	REFERENCE NUMBER	CHARGES SINCE LAST STATEMENT	AMOUNT
02/20	753152	QUIK-SERV CLEANERS	$ 7.15
02/22	817615	RALPH'S APPLIANCES	215.74
02/25	044162	YEN FOO RESTAURANT	16.25
02/28	516234	CORNER GIFT SHOP	12.50
03/04	711276	A-1 RENTALS	22.16
03/10	144261	C & C MUFFLER SHOP	47.72

PREVIOUS BALANCE	PAYMENTS	UNPAID BALANCE	FINANCE CHARGE	PURCHASES ADDED	NEW BALANCE
$322.79	$50.00	$272.79	$4.09	$321.52	$598.40

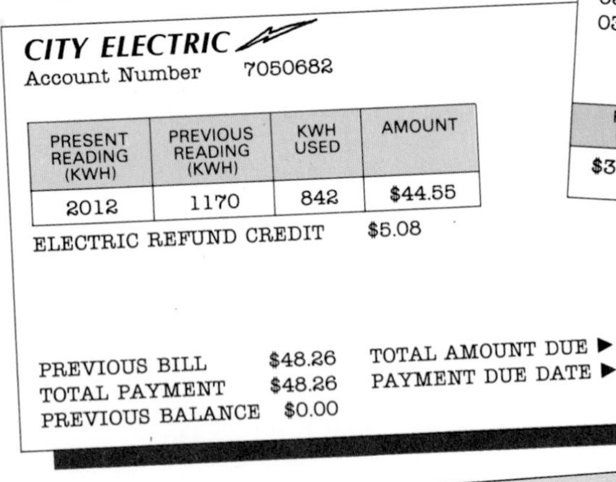

CITY ELECTRIC

Account Number 7050682

PRESENT READING (KWH)	PREVIOUS READING (KWH)	KWH USED	AMOUNT
2012	1170	842	$44.55

ELECTRIC REFUND CREDIT $5.08

PREVIOUS BILL $48.26
TOTAL PAYMENT $48.26
PREVIOUS BALANCE $0.00

TOTAL AMOUNT DUE ▶ $39.47
PAYMENT DUE DATE ▶ 04/15

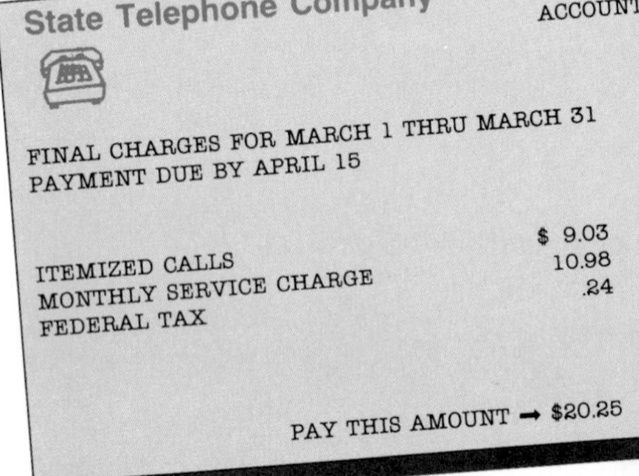

State Telephone Company PAGE 1

ACCOUNT NO. 216-9045

FINAL CHARGES FOR MARCH 1 THRU MARCH 31
PAYMENT DUE BY APRIL 15

ITEMIZED CALLS	$ 9.03
MONTHLY SERVICE CHARGE	10.98
FEDERAL TAX	.24

PAY THIS AMOUNT → $20.25

State Telephone Company PAGE 2

DETAILS OF ITEMIZED CALLS

DATE	TIME	PLACE CALLED	AREA	TEL NO	MIN	AMOUNT
03/09	8:21 AM	COLUMBUS, OH	614	666-8059	2	$2.16
03/15	3:15 PM	BOSTON, MA	617	999-4301	8	3.21
03/22	1:49 PM	MELBOURNE, FL	305	888-0122	11	2.25
03/24	5:05 PM	ST. LOUIS, MO	314	333-3001	6	1.41

TOTAL CHARGE FOR ITEMIZED CALLS $9.03

EXERCISES

Use the electric bill to answer these questions.

1. How many kilowatt hours (KWH) of electricity were used during the month?

2. What is the total amount George owes the electric company? On what date is the payment due?

3. What was the previous month's electricity bill? How much more was it than this month's bill?

Use the Bank Card statement to answer these questions.

4. How much did George charge at the Corner Gift Shop?
5. What was the amount of the charge at the C & C Muffler Shop?
6. What was the total amount of new charges?
7. What two numbers would you use to check the amount of the unpaid balance? Would you add or subtract?
8. Bank Card charges 1.5% per month interest (finance charge) on the unpaid balance. How much was last month's finance charge?
9. What three numbers would you add to check the amount of the new balance?
10. George's new balance is $598.40. If he makes the minimum payment, how much will he still owe?
11. At 1.5% per month, how much will the finance charge be on an unpaid balance of $570?

Use the telephone bill to answer these questions.

12. When must the telephone bill be paid? How much does George owe?
13. How much federal tax is included in the bill?
14. What is the monthly charge for service?
15. On March 15, George made a long-distance call to Boston, Massachusetts. How many minutes long was the call? What was the charge for the call?
16. How much did it cost per minute for George to call Columbus, Ohio?
17. If George makes a long-distance call between 11:00 P.M. and 8:00 A.M., he gets a 60% discount. How much would he have saved if he had made the call to Melbourne, Florida, between 11:00 P.M. and 8:00 A.M.?

Answer the phone

Use the phone rates to answer the questions.

18. Julie called a friend at 10 A.M. on Wednesday. They talked for 5 minutes. How much was she charged for the call?
19. Julie was charged $1.28 for a call she made on Friday at 9:30 P.M. How long was the call?

	LONG DISTANCE IN-STATE PHONE RATES Monday through Friday	
	8 A.M.—5 P.M.	5 P.M.—8 A.M.
First minute	**$.44**	**$.28**
Each additional minute	**$.25**	**$.20**

Chapter REVIEW

Here are scrambled answers for the review exercises:

18	40	72	200	interest	net	Robert Thayer	subtracted
38	60	75	added	less	pounds	Security	time

1. An employer is required by law to deduct from a paycheck money for federal income tax and social [?]. "Take home" pay is called an employee's [?] pay. *(page 271)*

2. If an item is on sale for 25% off the regular price, you can compute the sale price by taking [?]% of the regular price. The sale price of this TV is $[?]. *(page 272)*

3. To find the price per pound of these oranges, you divide the price by the number of [?]. The unit price of the oranges rounded to the nearest cent is [?]¢. *(page 274)*

5 pounds
$1.89

4. The check number is [?]. The check was written for [?] dollars. [?] signed the check. *(page 280)*
The balance in the checking account before the check was written was $100. The balance after the check was written was [?] dollars. *(page 280)*

200
March 3 19 85
PAY TO THE ORDER OF Mike's Market $ 40.00
Forty and 00/100 DOLLARS
Savings Bank
Robert Thayer
⑆211137122⑆ 123402543⑈ 200

5. Each time you make a deposit in a savings account, the amount is [?] to the balance of your account. Each time you make a withdrawal from a savings account, the amount is [?] from the balance of your account. *(page 282)*

6. The amount of interest charged for a loan depends on the principal, the interest rate, and the [?] for which the money is borrowed. You can use this formula to compute the [?] on a loan. *(page 284)*

$I = p \times r \times t$

7. The interest for this loan would be $[?]. *(page 284)*

Principal = $300
Rate = 12% per year
Time = 6 months

Chapter TEST

Solve. *(page 270, 271)*

SALES CLERK
No experience necessary.
Mon—Fri
8-hr day $4.25/hr
Apply in person
CAMPER'S SUPPLY

1. a. How much does the job pay each week?

b. Suppose that Camper's Supply withheld $23.75 for federal income tax and $11.50 for Social Security. What would the net pay be?

c. How much less would the net pay be than the gross pay?

Compute the sale price. *(page 272)*

2. 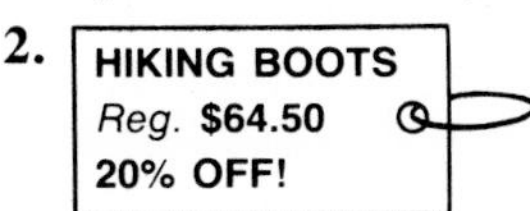

3. 

4. BACK PACK
Reg. $56
30% OFF!

Solve. *(pages 274, 276)*

3. What is the unit price of the smaller bag of trail mix?

4. Which is the better buy, the small bag or the large bag?

5. Camper's Supply Store gave out a 50¢ coupon that could be used on the purchase of a large bag of trail mix. If a customer used a coupon, how much would 3 small bags and 1 large bag of trail mix cost?

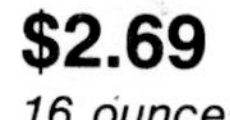

$2.69
16 ounces

$1.89
12 ounces

Solve. *(page 280)*

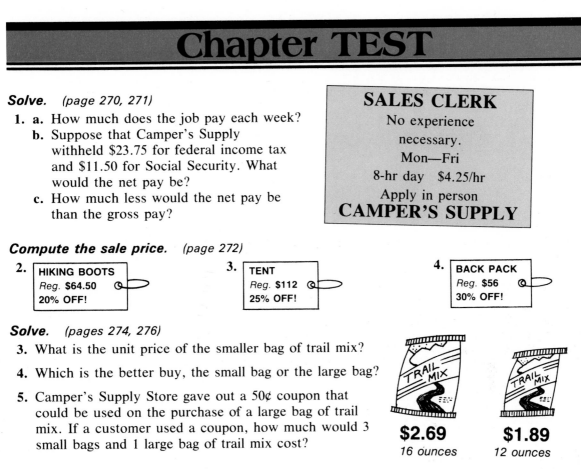

2003
March 4 19 85
PAY TO THE ORDER OF Camper's Supply $ 48.93
Forty-eight and 93/100 DOLLARS
Savings Bank
David Jones

6. Who signed the check?

7. What is the number of the check?

8. What is the amount of the check?

9. To whom was the check written?

10. David James had a balance of $167.34 in his checking account before he wrote the check. What was his balance after he wrote the check?

Solve. *(pages 282, 284)*

11. On March 24 you had a balance of $124 in your savings account. On March 25 you withdrew $35, and on March 31 the bank paid you $.82 interest. What was your balance then?

12. How much interest will you pay if you borrow $240 for 6 months if you are charged 1% per month?

Cumulative TEST Standardized Format

Choose the correct letter.

1. Add. $2\frac{5}{8} + 1\frac{1}{2}$

A. $3\frac{1}{8}$
B. $3\frac{3}{5}$
C. $4\frac{1}{8}$
D. none of these

2. Subtract. $3\frac{1}{4} - 1\frac{1}{3}$

A. $2\frac{11}{12}$
B. $1\frac{11}{12}$
C. $2\frac{1}{12}$
D. none of these

3. Give the product.
$2\frac{1}{2} \times 1\frac{1}{4}$

A. $3\frac{1}{8}$
B. 2
C. $\frac{8}{25}$
D. none of these

4. Give the quotient.
$4\frac{2}{3} \div 1\frac{3}{4}$

A. $8\frac{1}{6}$
B. $\frac{3}{8}$
C. $2\frac{2}{3}$
D. none of these

5. 425 mm = __?__ m

A. 4.25
B. 42.5
C. 4250
D. none of these

6. Add. 4 lb 9 oz + 5 lb 8 oz

A. 10 lb 7 oz
B. 10 lb 5 oz
C. 10 lb 3 oz
D. none of these

7. Change to a fraction.
$33\frac{1}{3}\% = ?$

A. $\frac{1}{3}$
B. $\frac{2}{3}$
C. 3
D. none of these

8. Change to a percent.
$\frac{5}{6} = ?$

A. $16\frac{2}{3}\%$
B. $66\frac{2}{3}\%$
C. $83\frac{1}{3}\%$
D. none of these

9. Solve.
12% of 42 = n

A. 350
B. 5.04
C. 50.4
D. none of these

10. Solve.
5% of n = 12

A. 60
B. 240
C. 0.6
D. none of these

11. You jog 3 miles in 24 minutes. At that rate, how far can you jog in 36 minutes?

A. 6 miles
B. 4.5 miles
C. 1.5 miles
D. none of these

12. Compute the interest.
Principal = $650
Rate = 15% per year
Time = 6 months

A. $97.50
B. $195
C. $585
D. none of these

Chapter 13

Geometry—Perimeter and Area

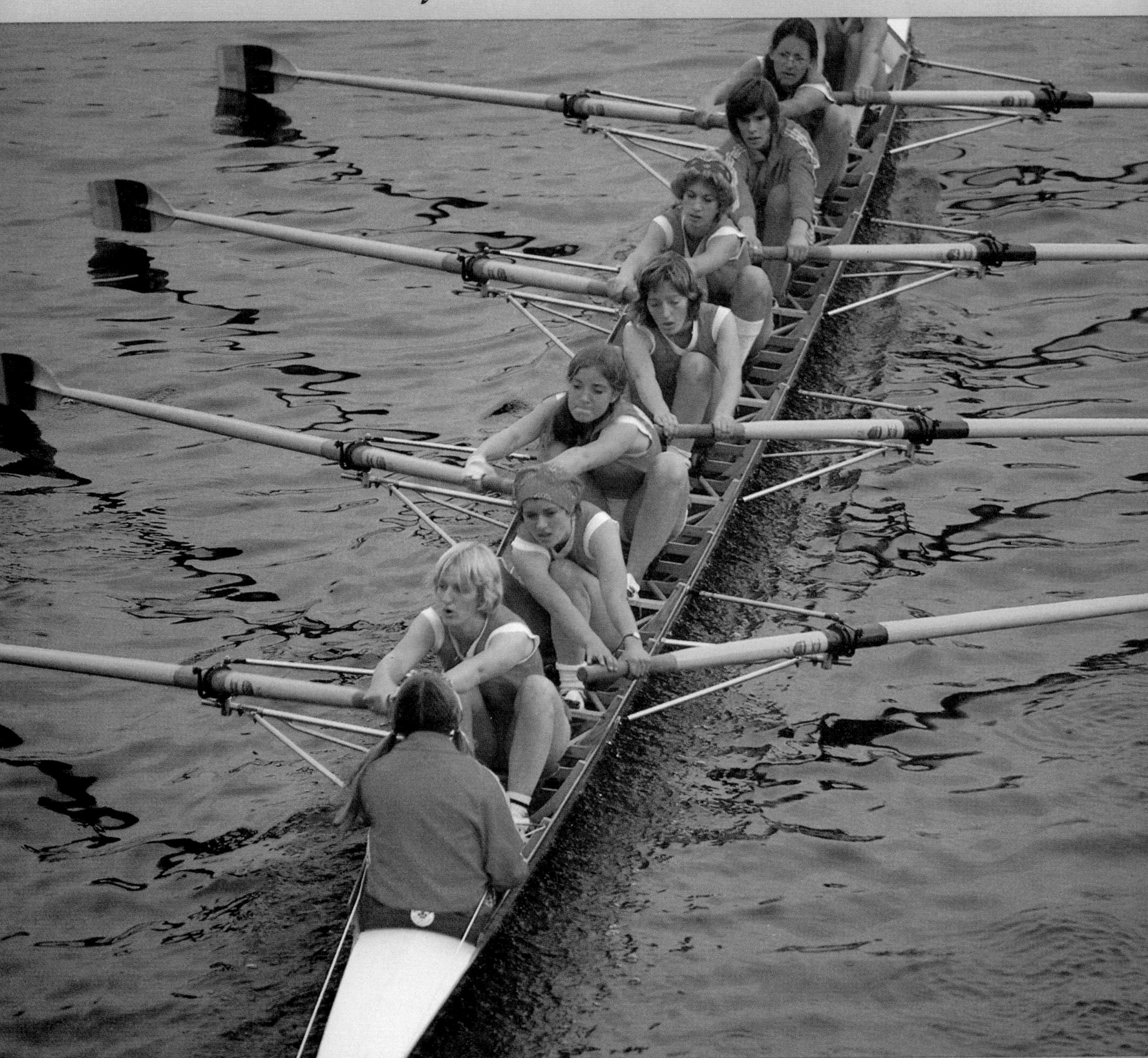

Measuring and classifying angles

Here's how *to use a* **protractor** *to measure an angle.*

Follow the steps to measure the angle.

Step 1. *Place the center of the protractor at the point where the sides of the angle meet.*

Step 2. *Place the 0 mark on one side of the angle.*

Step 3. *Read the measure of the angle where the other side crosses the protractor.*

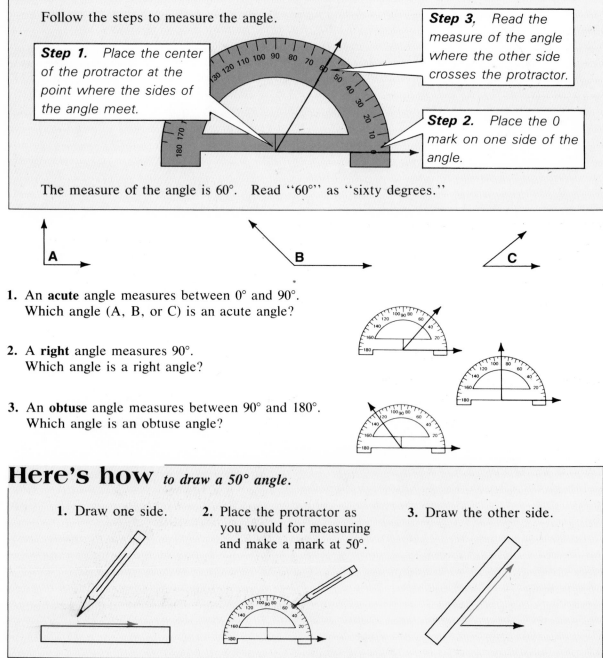

The measure of the angle is 60°. Read "60°" as "sixty degrees."

A B C

1. An **acute** angle measures between 0° and 90°. Which angle (A, B, or C) is an acute angle?

2. A **right** angle measures 90°. Which angle is a right angle?

3. An **obtuse** angle measures between 90° and 180°. Which angle is an obtuse angle?

Here's how *to draw a 50° angle.*

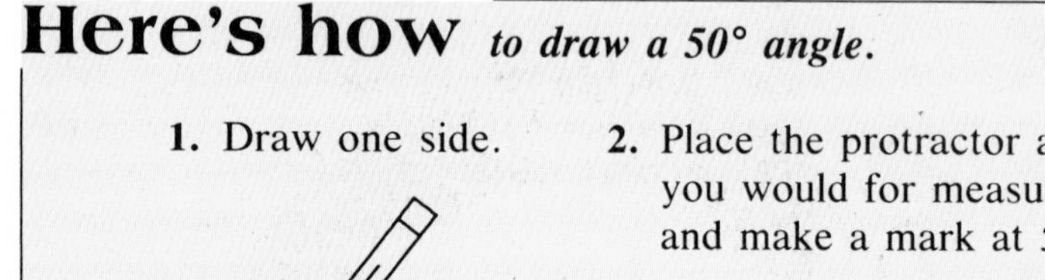

1. Draw one side.
2. Place the protractor as you would for measuring and make a mark at 50°.
3. Draw the other side.

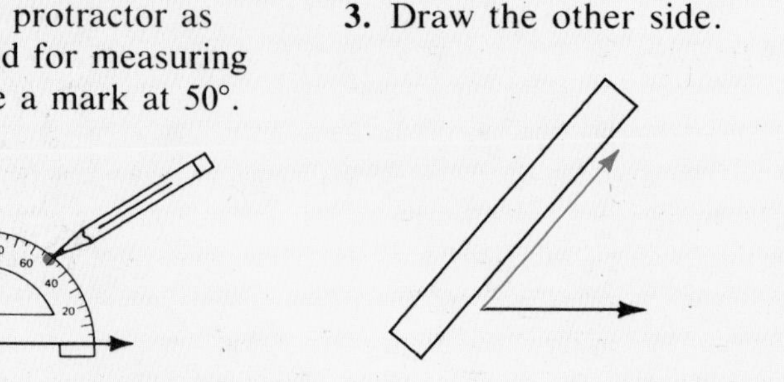

EXERCISES

Measure each angle.

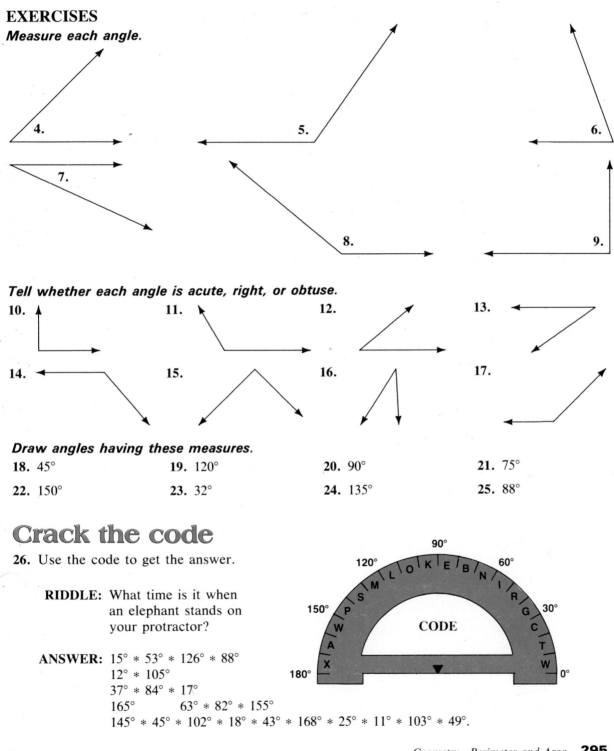

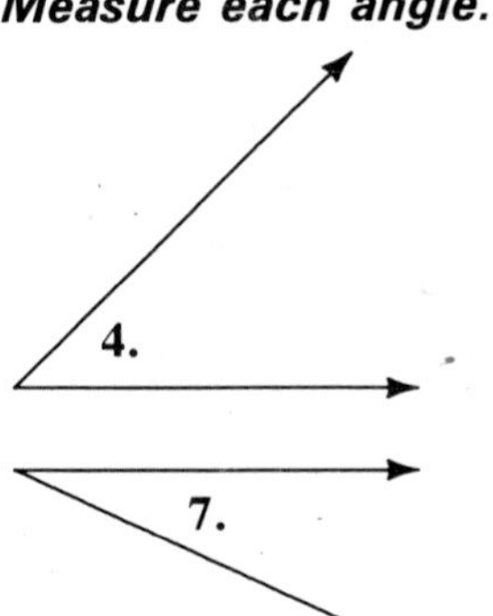

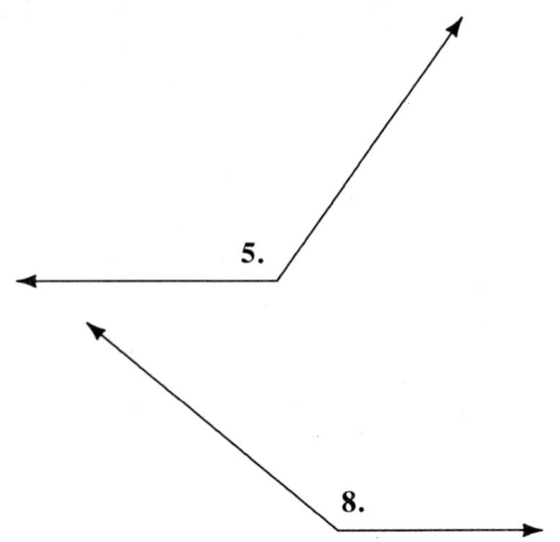

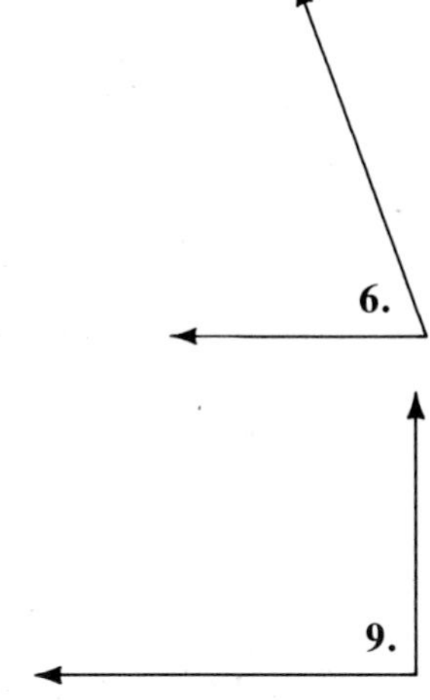

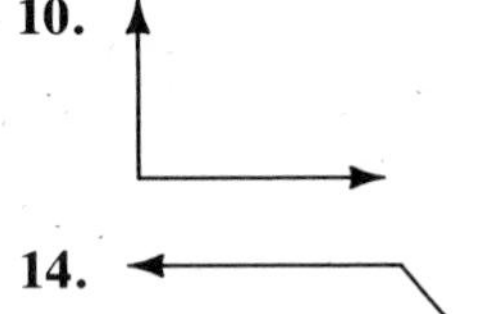

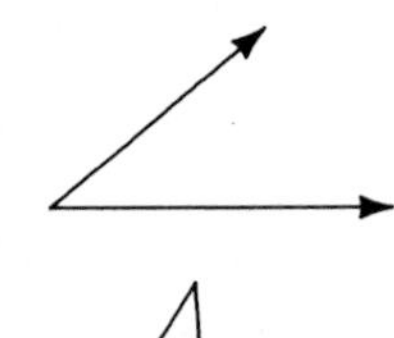

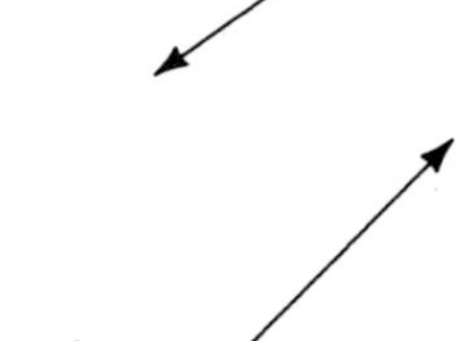

Tell whether each angle is acute, right, or obtuse.

10. **11.** **12.** **13.**

14. **15.** **16.** **17.**

Draw angles having these measures.

18. 45° **19.** 120° **20.** 90° **21.** 75°

22. 150° **23.** 32° **24.** 135° **25.** 88°

Crack the code

26. Use the code to get the answer.

RIDDLE: What time is it when an elephant stands on your protractor?

ANSWER: 15° * 53° * 126° * 88°
12° * 105°
37° * 84° * 17°
165° 63° * 82° * 155°
145° * 45° * 102° * 18° * 43° * 168° * 25° * 11° * 103° * 49°.

90° 120° 60° 150° 30° 180° 0°
X A W P S M L O K E B N I R G C T W
CODE

Perpendicular and parallel lines

MAP MATH

Two straight streets that intersect to form right angles are **perpendicular.**

Two straight streets that do not intersect (even if extended) are **parallel.**

On the map,
L Street is perpendicular to V Street.
L Street is parallel to M Street.

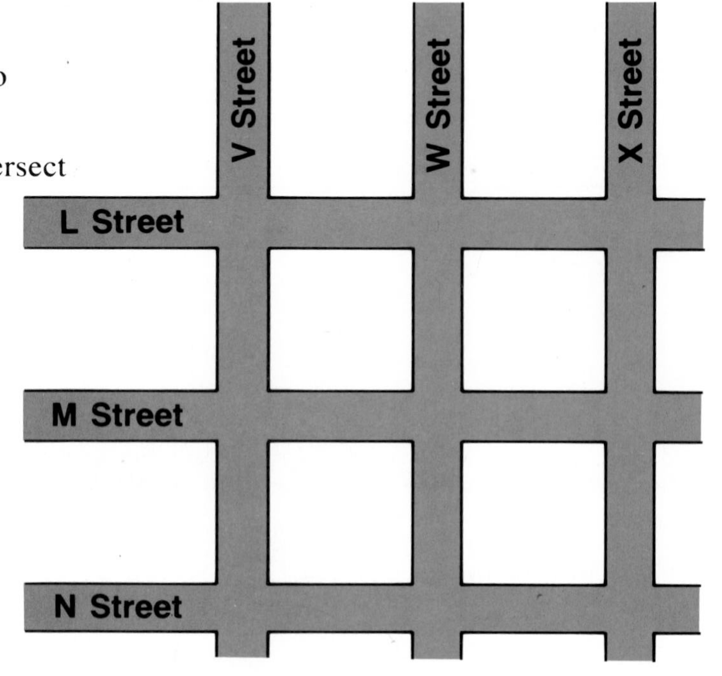

Parallel or perpendicular?

1. V Street is [?] to W Street.
2. W Street is [?] to M Street.
3. N Street is [?] to X Street.
4. L Street is [?] to N Street.
5. W Street is [?] to X Street.
6. L Street is [?] to W Street.

EXERCISES

True or false?

7. Line s is parallel to line r.
8. Line r is perpendicular to line s.
9. Line u is parallel to line t.
10. Line u is perpendicular to line r.
11. Line v is perpendicular to line s.
12. Line u is perpendicular to line s.
13. Line s is parallel to line t.
14. There are more than 10 right angles in the drawing.
15. There are 4 acute angles in the drawing.
16. There are more than 4 obtuse angles in the drawing.

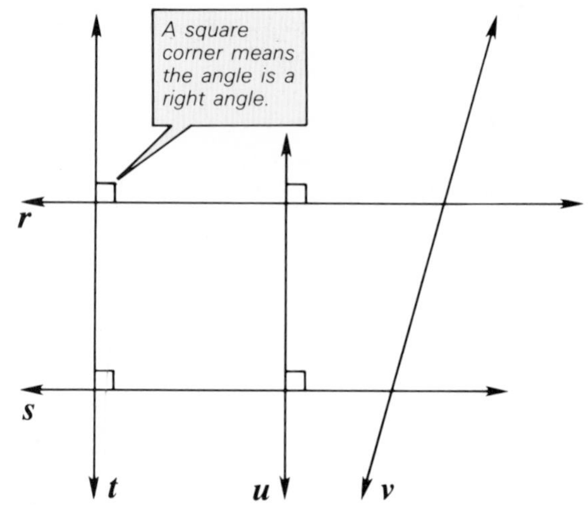

True or false?

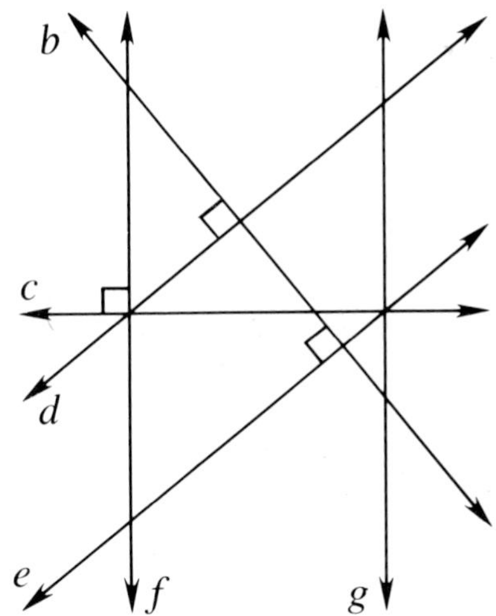

17. Lines b and d intersect.
18. Lines b and d are perpendicular.
19. Lines f and g intersect.
20. Lines c and f are parallel.
21. Lines c and g are perpendicular.
22. Lines d and e are parallel.
23. Lines e and g are perpendicular.
24. Lines c and d are perpendicular.
25. There are 16 right angles in the drawing.

Make a drawing. Then answer the questions.

26. Draw 2 perpendicular lines. How many right angles can you find?
27. Draw 2 intersecting lines that are not perpendicular. How many acute angles can you find?
28. Draw 2 parallel lines. Now draw a line that intersects the 2 parallel lines but is not perpendicular to the parallel lines.
    a. How many right angles can you find?
    b. How many acute angles can you find?
    c. How many obtuse angles can you find?

Street wise **Logical reasoning**

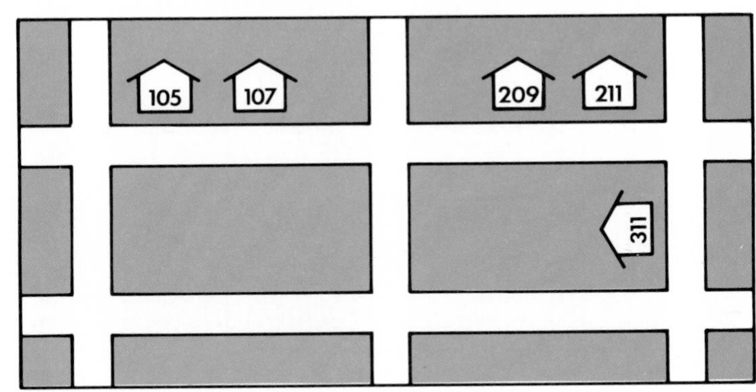

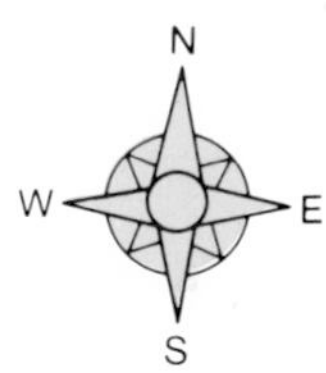

Clues:

- Paul lives east of Cindy.
- Darla lives west of Cindy.
- Paul lives between Cindy and Tim.
- Jan's street is perpendicular to Cindy's street.

Use the clues to answer the questions.

29. Who lives in house number 105?
30. Who lives in house number 209?
31. What is Cindy's house number?
32. What is Jan's house number?

Polygons

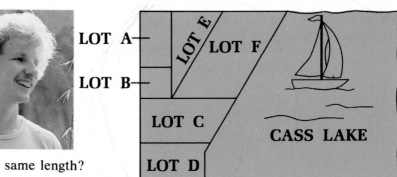

1. *Which lake lot is mine? My lot has 2 pairs of parallel sides. It has no right angles.*

LOT A
LOT B
LOT C
LOT D
LOT E
LOT F
CASS LAKE

2. Which lot has 4 sides all the same length?
3. Which lot has exactly 1 pair of parallel sides?

Here's how polygons *(closed shapes with straight sides) are named.*

NAME OF POLYGON	DESCRIPTION	EXAMPLES
Triangle	3 sides	
Square	4 sides the same length 4 right angles	
Rectangle	4 sides 4 right angles	A square is also a rectangle.
Parallelogram	4 sides 2 pairs of parallel sides	A rectangle is also a parallelogram.
Trapezoid	4 sides Exactly 1 pair of parallel sides	
Pentagon	5 sides	
Hexagon	6 sides	

4. Use the map and the *Here's how* chart to answer these questions.
   - **a.** Which lot is a square?
   - **b.** Which 2 lots are rectangles?
   - **c.** Which 3 lots are parallelograms?
   - **d.** Which lot is a triangle?
   - **e.** Which lot is a trapezoid?
   - **f.** Which lot is a pentagon?

EXERCISES

Name these polygons. Some shapes have more than one name.

5. 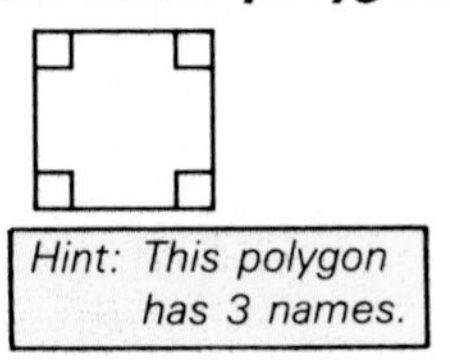

6. 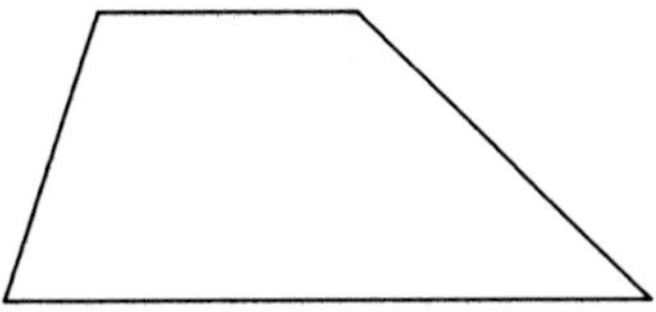

7. 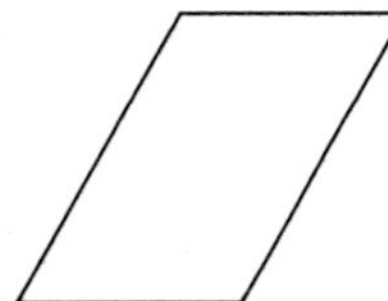

8. 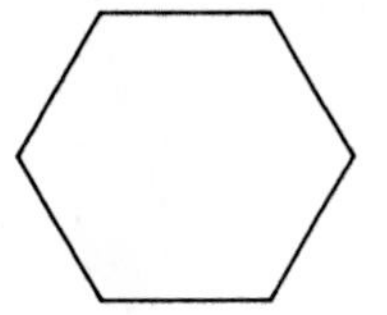

9. 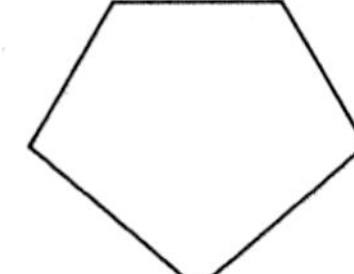

10. 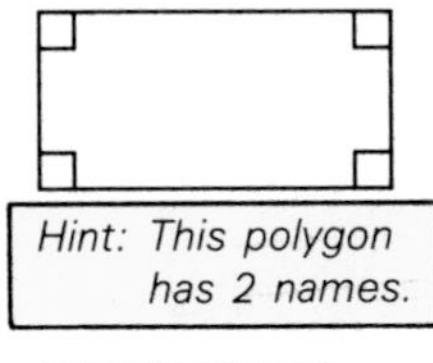

11. 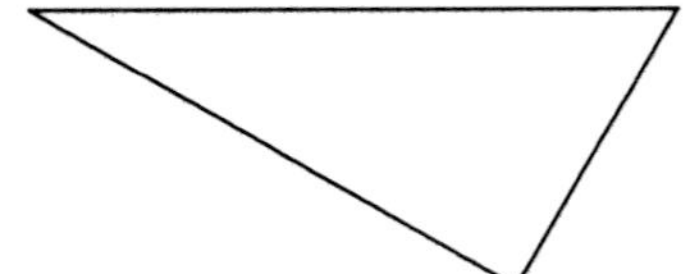

12. 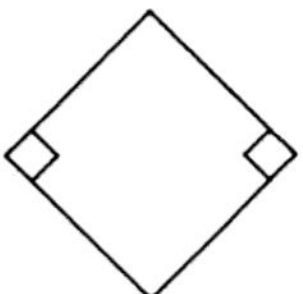

13. 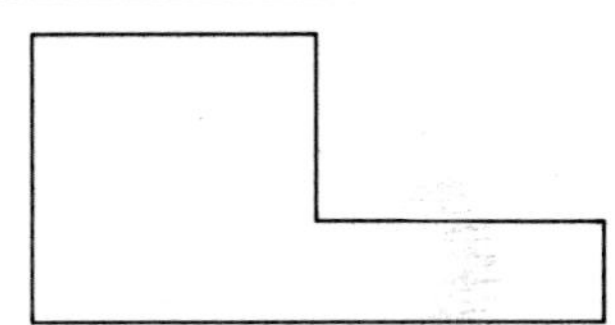

Use the clues. Draw and name each polygon.

14. Clues:
- This polygon has 4 sides.
- It has no right angles.
- It has 2 pairs of parallel sides.

15. Clues:
- This polygon has 2 right angles.
- It has 4 sides.
- It has 1 acute angle.
- It has 1 obtuse angle.

A lot of land

What is the price of each lake lot?

Hint: Find how many triangular lots were used to make each larger lot.

16. 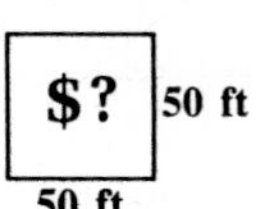

17. 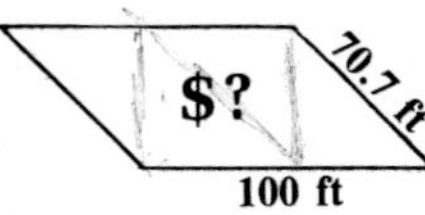

18. 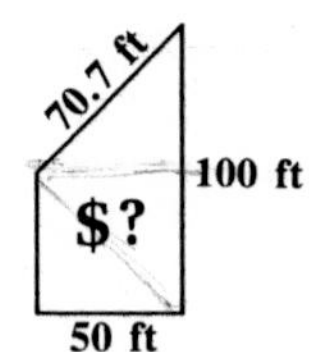

19. 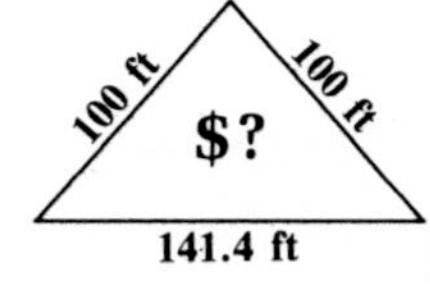

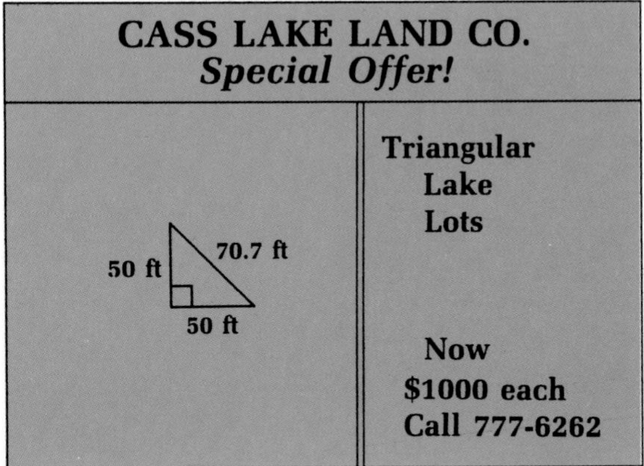

CASS LAKE LAND CO.
Special Offer!
50 ft
70.7 ft
50 ft
Triangular
Lake
Lots
Now
$1000 each
Call 777-6262

Perimeter

FRAMED?

One of these posters needs 96 centimeters of framing. Which one is it?

24 cm
24 cm

40 cm
32 cm

The **perimeter** of the figure is the distance around the figure.

Here's how ***to use formulas to find the perimeters of squares and rectangles.***

Square

24 cm
24 cm

The perimeter (P) of a square is 4 times the length of one side (s).

FORMULA $P = 4 \times s$

$P = 4 \times 24$ cm

$= 96$ cm

The perimeter is 96 cm.

Rectangle

40 cm
32 cm

The perimeter (P) of a rectangle is 2 times the sum of the length (l) and the width (w).

FORMULA $P = 2 \times (l + w)$

$P = 2 \times (40 \text{ cm} + 32 \text{ cm})$

$= 2 \times 72$ cm

$= 144$ cm

The perimeter is 144 cm.

1. Look at the *Here's how*. What is the formula for the perimeter of a square? What does the letter s stand for?
2. What is the formula for the perimeter of a rectangle? What does each letter stand for?

EXERCISES

Find each perimeter.

3. 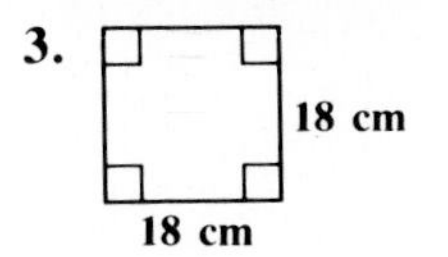

4. 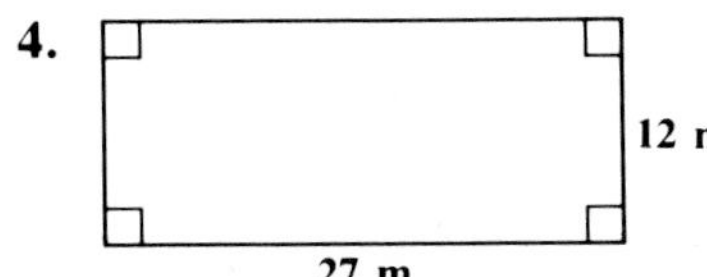

5. 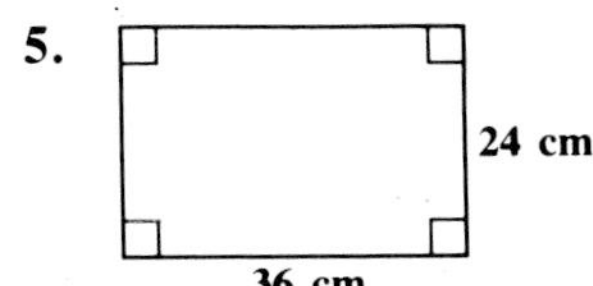

6. 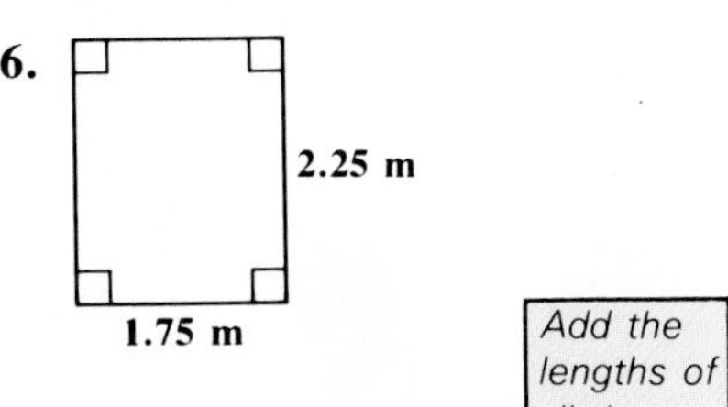

7. 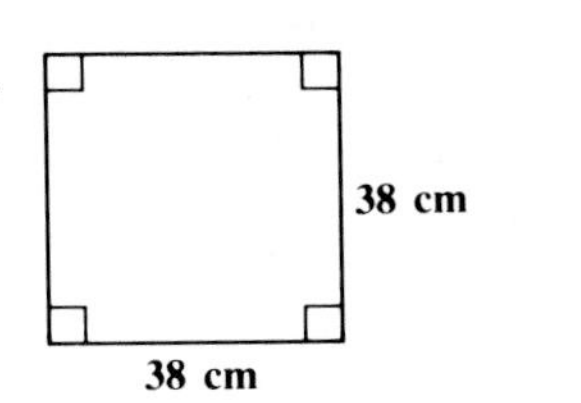

8. 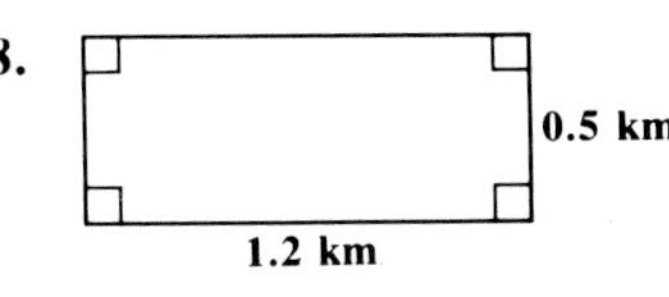

9. 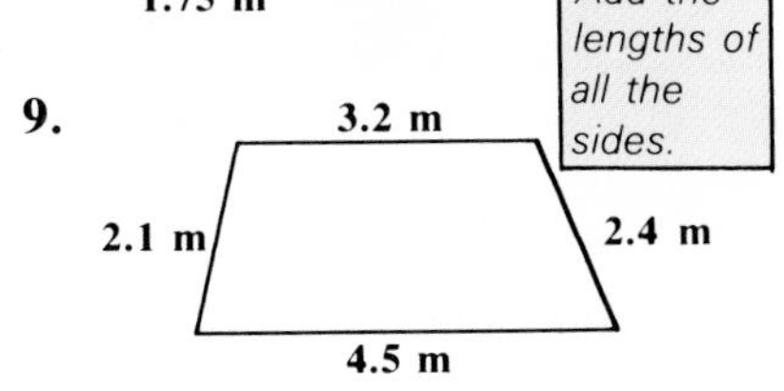

10. 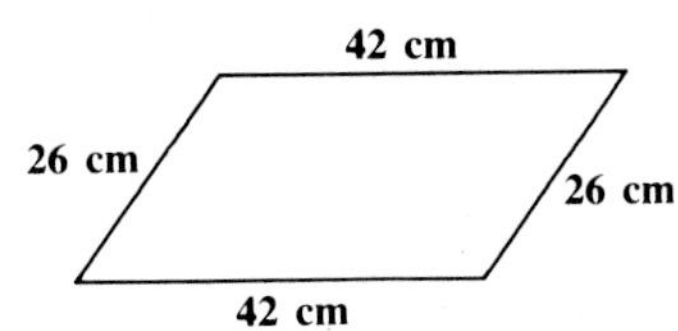

11. 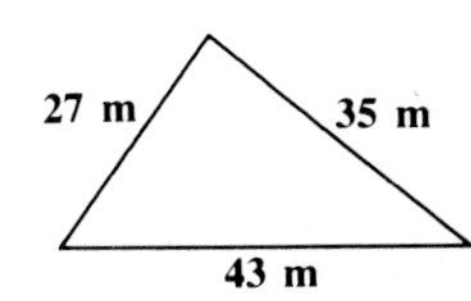

12. 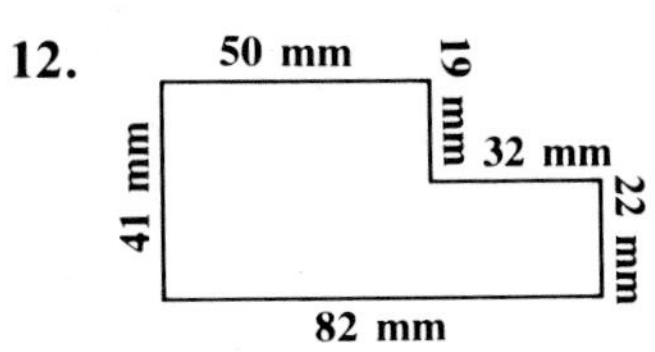

13. 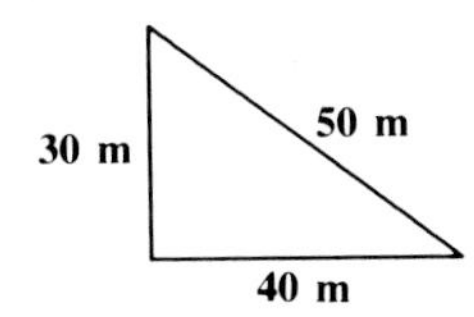

14. 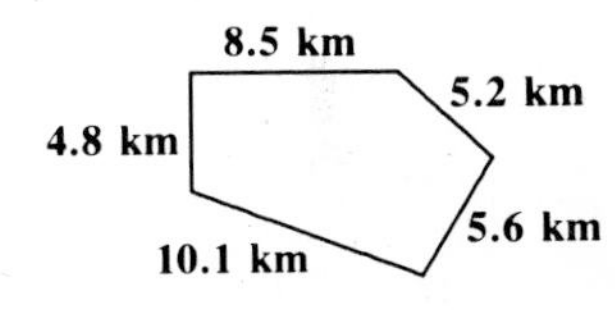

Solve.

15. How many centimeters of wood framing are needed to frame a painting that is 65 centimeters long and 40 centimeters wide?

16. A square photograph, 25 centimeters on each side, is to be framed. How many centimeters of framing are needed?

17. How much fencing is needed to enclose a rectangular yard that is 15 meters by 24 meters?

18. A square pen is built. The pen is 15.5 meters on each side. How many meters of fencing are needed?

Triangle tangle

19. Find the triangle that has the same perimeter as triangle *AEI*.

20. Find 5 triangles that have the same perimeter as triangle *ABL*.

21. Find the 2 parallelograms that have the same perimeter as parallelogram *LCFI*.

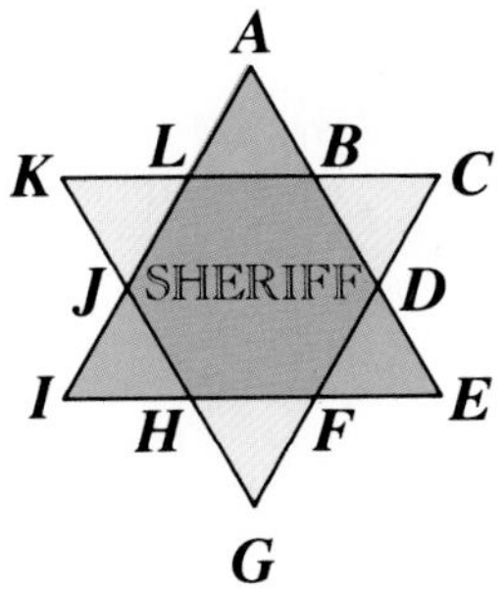

Circumference

The radius of the front wheel is 32 inches, and the radius of the back wheel is 10 inches.

1. Which wheel has a diameter of 64 inches, the front or the back?
2. Make a guess! When the front wheel goes around once, will the bicycle travel more or less than 150 inches?

Here's how *to use a formula to find the distance around a circle.*

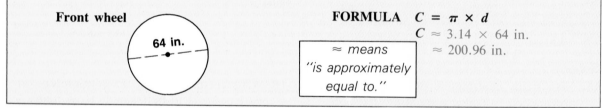

The distance around a circle is called the **circumference**. The circumference of a circle is a little more than 3 times the length of its diameter.

To find the circumference (C), multiply π (read as "pi") by the diameter (d). We'll use 3.14 as a decimal approximation for π.

Front wheel

64 in.

FORMULA $C = \pi \times d$

$C \approx 3.14 \times 64$ in.

≈ 200.96 in.

≈ means "is approximately equal to."

3. Look at the *Here's how*. About how far does the bicycle travel when the front wheel goes around once?
4. To compute the circumference of the back wheel, you would multiply 3.14 times what number?

EXERCISES

Find the circumference. Use 3.14 for π. *Here are scrambled answers for the next row of exercises:* *18.84 in. 31.4 in. 25.12 in. 12.56 in.*

5. 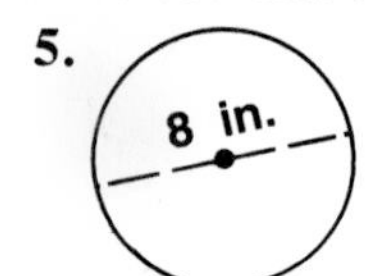

6. 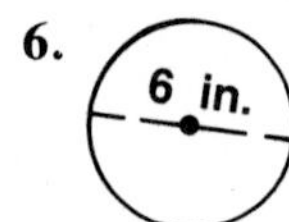

7. 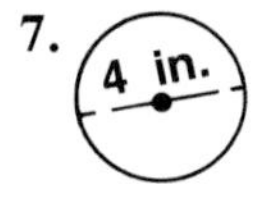

8. 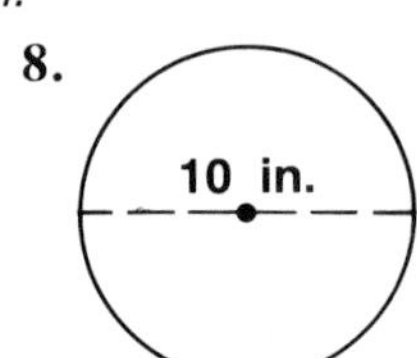

9.

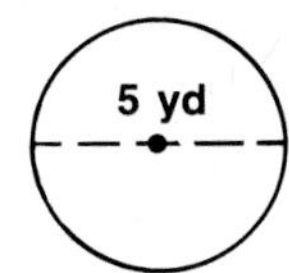

10.

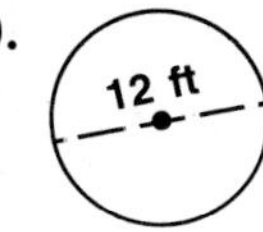

11.

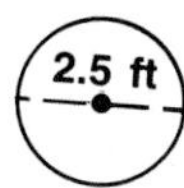

12.

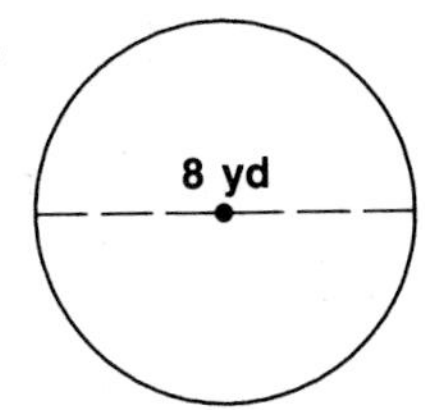

13.

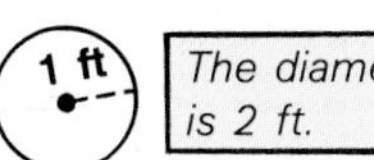

14.

15.

16.

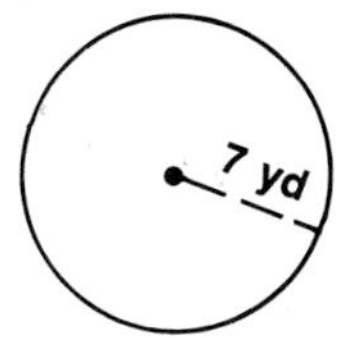

17. Find and correct the three wrong answers.

a. *Question:* What is the diameter of a wheel that has a radius of $1\frac{1}{2}$ feet?
Answer: The diameter is 3 feet.

b. *Question:* What is the radius of a circle that has a diameter of $6\frac{1}{2}$ feet?
Answer: The radius is 13 feet.

c. *Question:* Which has the larger circumference, a circle with a diameter of 3 feet or a circle with a radius of 2 feet?
Answer: The circle with a diameter of 3 feet.

d. *Question:* What is the circumference of a wheel that has a radius of 26 inches?
Answer: Approximately 81.64 inches.

e. *Question:* What do you get when you divide the circumference of a circle by π (3.14)?
Answer: You get the diameter of the circle.

Seeing is not believing

Are the red sides straight or curved? *Hint: Check with an edge of a paper.*

18.

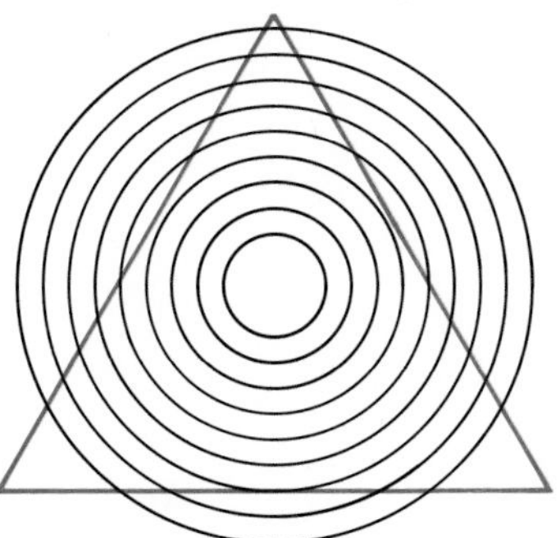

19.

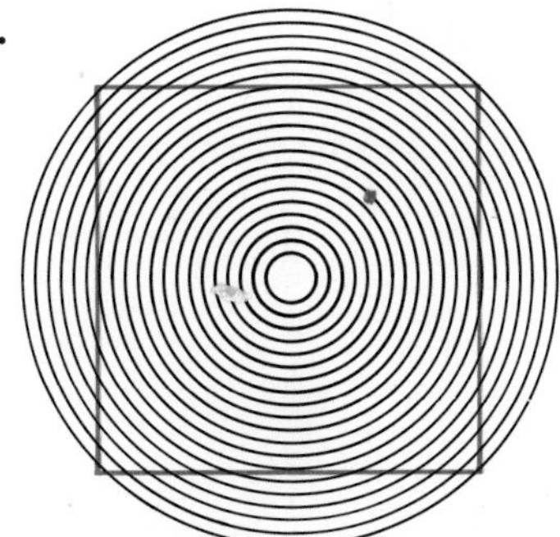

Cumulative Skill Practice

Change to a decimal. *(page 146)*

1. $2\frac{1}{5}$ **2.** $1\frac{1}{5}$ **3.** $1\frac{4}{5}$ **4.** $4\frac{1}{8}$ **5.** $3\frac{3}{10}$ **6.** $6\frac{1}{8}$ **7.** $3\frac{1}{2}$

8. $6\frac{3}{8}$ **9.** $8\frac{1}{2}$ **10.** $4\frac{5}{8}$ **11.** $5\frac{1}{4}$ **12.** $6\frac{3}{4}$ **13.** $4\frac{3}{10}$ **14.** $3\frac{1}{25}$

15. $8\frac{9}{10}$ **16.** $7\frac{2}{5}$ **17.** $3\frac{7}{8}$ **18.** $3\frac{2}{5}$ **19.** $16\frac{3}{5}$ **20.** $2\frac{1}{100}$ **21.** $4\frac{3}{25}$

Give the sum in simplest form. *(page 158)*

22. $\frac{3}{8} + \frac{1}{4}$ **23.** $\frac{3}{4} + \frac{1}{6}$ **24.** $\frac{1}{3} + \frac{1}{2}$ **25.** $\frac{3}{4} + \frac{2}{3}$ **26.** $\frac{5}{8} + 4$

27. $\frac{2}{3} + \frac{5}{9}$ **28.** $\frac{1}{2} + \frac{4}{5}$ **29.** $\frac{2}{3} + \frac{1}{6}$ **30.** $\frac{3}{5} + \frac{3}{4}$ **31.** $3 + \frac{3}{10}$

32. $\frac{1}{6} + \frac{3}{8}$ **33.** $\frac{7}{10} + \frac{1}{2}$ **34.** $\frac{1}{4} + \frac{3}{10}$ **35.** $\frac{5}{8} + \frac{3}{4}$ **36.** $\frac{7}{10} + \frac{3}{5}$

Give the difference in simplest form. *(page 166)*

37. $\frac{5}{6} - \frac{1}{3}$ **38.** $\frac{5}{12} - \frac{1}{6}$ **39.** $\frac{5}{9} - \frac{1}{3}$ **40.** $\frac{7}{8} - \frac{3}{4}$ **41.** $\frac{7}{10} - \frac{2}{5}$

42. $\frac{8}{9} - \frac{5}{6}$ **43.** $\frac{5}{3} - \frac{3}{4}$ **44.** $\frac{2}{3} - \frac{3}{8}$ **45.** $\frac{9}{10} - \frac{3}{4}$ **46.** $3 - \frac{1}{2}$

47. $\frac{9}{4} - \frac{5}{3}$ **48.** $\frac{4}{3} - \frac{3}{4}$ **49.** $1 - \frac{7}{8}$ **50.** $\frac{7}{6} - \frac{7}{8}$ **51.** $\frac{3}{2} - \frac{4}{3}$

Give the product in simplest form. *(page 178)*

52. $\frac{5}{8} \times \frac{2}{2}$ **53.** $\frac{1}{3} \times \frac{1}{3}$ **54.** $\frac{3}{8} \times \frac{4}{5}$ **55.** $\frac{3}{4} \times \frac{1}{2}$ **56.** $\frac{1}{4} \times 0$

57. $\frac{1}{2} \times \frac{1}{3}$ **58.** $\frac{2}{5} \times \frac{5}{8}$ **59.** $\frac{2}{3} \times \frac{2}{3}$ **60.** $\frac{3}{8} \times \frac{1}{3}$ **61.** $\frac{3}{10} \times \frac{5}{6}$

62. $\frac{3}{4} \times \frac{5}{9}$ **63.** $\frac{4}{5} \times \frac{5}{3}$ **64.** $\frac{7}{4} \times \frac{2}{7}$ **65.** $\frac{3}{2} \times 3$ **66.** $5 \times \frac{1}{3}$

Give the quotient in simplest form. *(page 188)*

67. $\frac{3}{4} \div \frac{1}{2}$ **68.** $\frac{5}{9} \div \frac{5}{3}$ **69.** $\frac{2}{5} \div \frac{3}{5}$ **70.** $\frac{2}{3} \div \frac{1}{4}$ **71.** $\frac{5}{6} \div \frac{5}{6}$

72. $\frac{3}{8} \div 2$ **73.** $\frac{5}{8} \div \frac{3}{4}$ **74.** $\frac{5}{6} \div 3$ **75.** $\frac{4}{3} \div \frac{3}{4}$ **76.** $0 \div \frac{2}{3}$

77. $\frac{3}{4} \div \frac{6}{5}$ **78.** $\frac{7}{8} \div 4$ **79.** $3 \div \frac{3}{10}$ **80.** $\frac{7}{8} \div \frac{4}{5}$ **81.** $3 \div \frac{2}{3}$

Problem solving

YOU'RE THE CLERK!

Use a drawing to help answer each customer's question.

MEL'S HARDWARE WEEKEND SPECIALS	
Wire Fence	$1 per foot
Steel Posts	$4.50 each
Gates	$25.50 each

1. *Is 200 feet of fence enough to build a pen that is 60 feet long by 30 feet wide?*

2. *How many feet of fence will I need to fence in my 120-foot by 75-foot yard?*

Use the weekend special prices. Find the total cost for each fencing project.

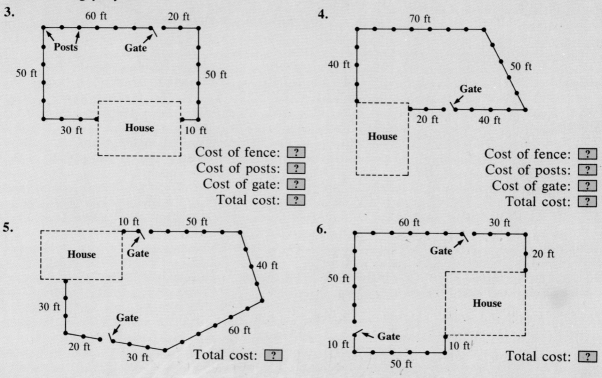

3.

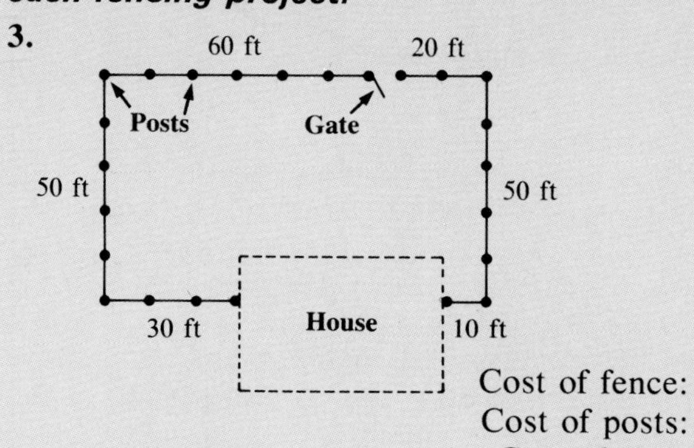

Cost of fence: ?
Cost of posts: ?
Cost of gate: ?
Total cost: ?

4.

70 ft
40 ft
50 ft
Gate
20 ft
40 ft
House

Cost of fence: ?
Cost of posts: ?
Cost of gate: ?
Total cost: ?

5.

10 ft
50 ft
House
Gate
40 ft
30 ft
Gate
60 ft
20 ft
30 ft

Total cost: ?

6.

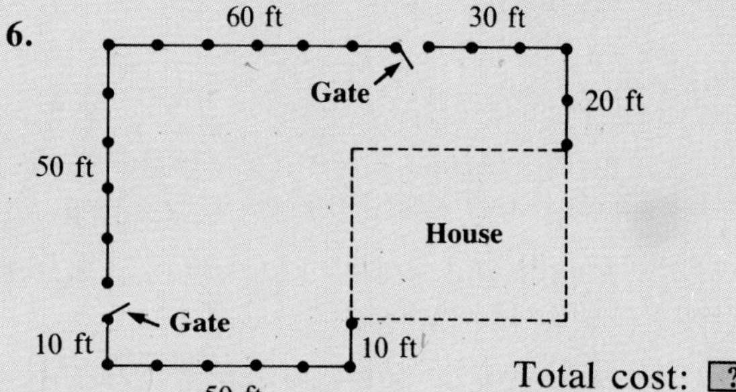

Total cost: ?

Area—squares and rectangles

The **area** of a region is the number of square units that it takes to cover the region.

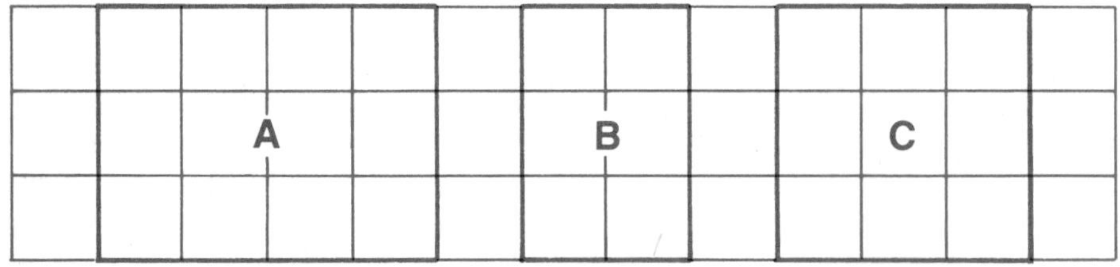

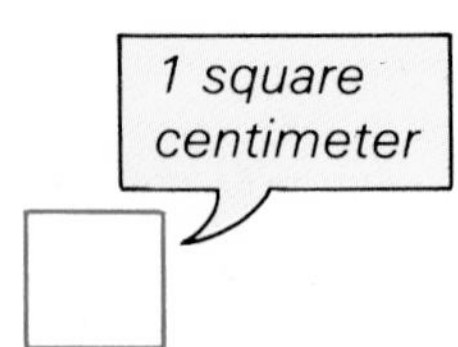

1. Count the squares. Which rectangle has an area of 12 square centimeters?
2. Which rectangle has an area of 6 square centimeters?
3. What is the area of square C?

Here's how *to use formulas to find the area of rectangles and squares.*

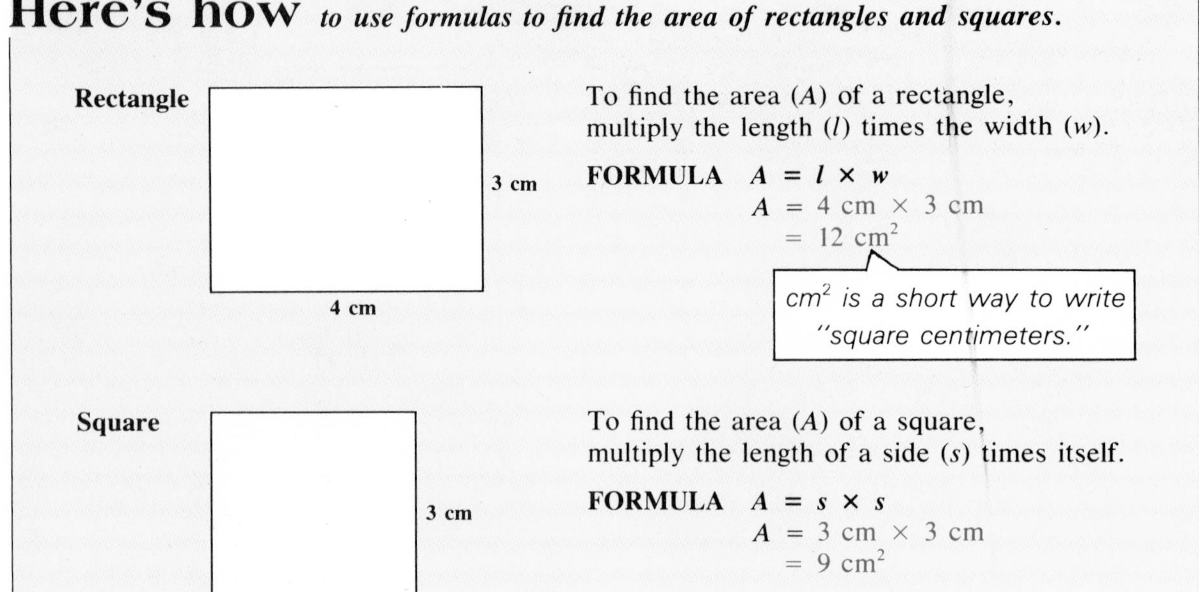

To find the area (A) of a rectangle, multiply the length (l) times the width (w).

FORMULA $A = l \times w$

$A = 4 \text{ cm} \times 3 \text{ cm}$

$= 12 \text{ cm}^2$

cm^2 is a short way to write "square centimeters."

To find the area (A) of a square, multiply the length of a side (s) times itself.

FORMULA $A = s \times s$

$A = 3 \text{ cm} \times 3 \text{ cm}$

$= 9 \text{ cm}^2$

4. Look at the *Here's how*. What is the formula for the area of a rectangle? What does each letter stand for?
5. If the length and width of a rectangle are 10 centimeters and 5 centimeters, the area is 50 [?] centimeters.
6. If the side of a square is 6 centimeters, its area is 36 square [?].

EXERCISES

Find the area.

7. 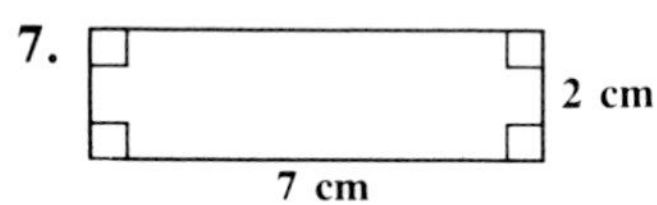

8. 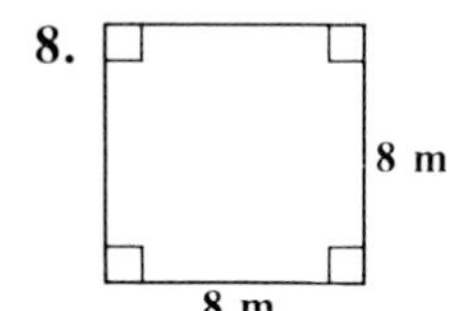

9. 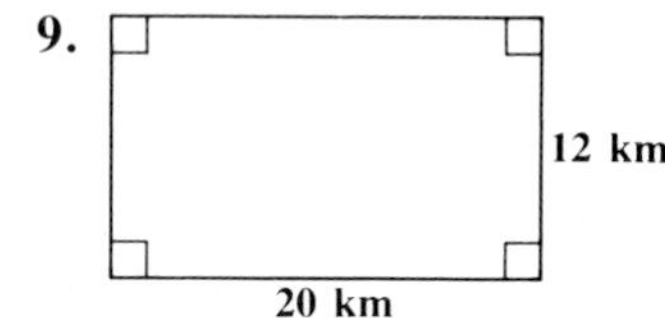

10. 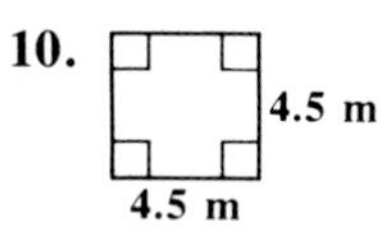

11. 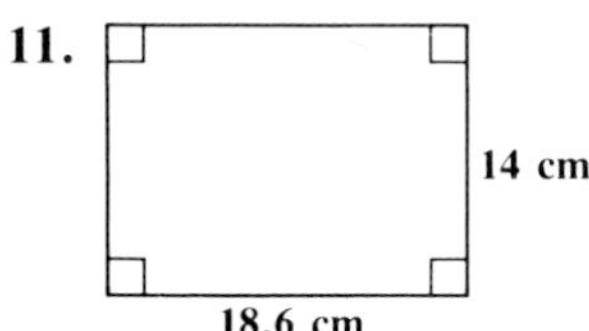

12. 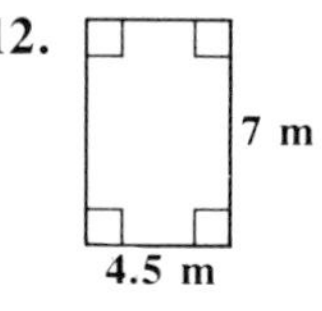

13. 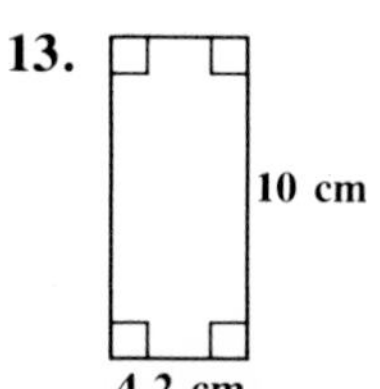

14. 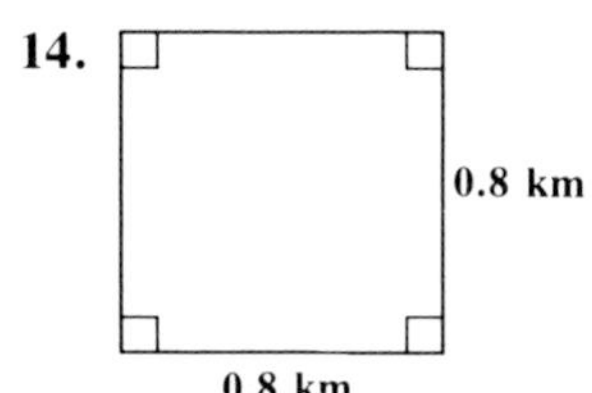

15. 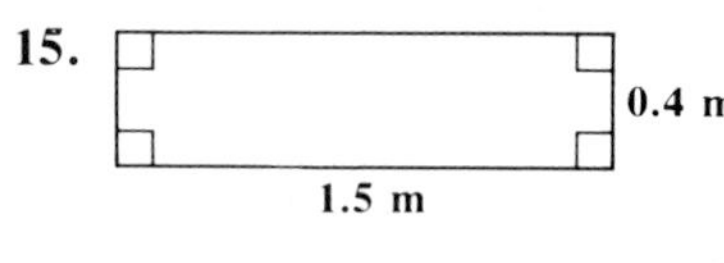

16. One of the squares above has a perimeter of 18 meters. Which one is it?

17. One of the rectangles above has a perimeter of 23 meters. Which one is it?

You decide!

First tell whether the problem is about perimeter or area. Then solve the problem.

18. *How much fencing do I need to enclose a field that is 20 yards long and 15 yards wide?*

19. *How many 1-foot-square tiles are needed to tile my 15-foot by 12-foot kitchen floor?*

20. How much sod is needed to cover a 20-yard by 40-yard lawn?

21. How much molding is needed to go around a 25-foot by 15-foot ceiling?

22. How much paint is needed to cover a floor that is 25 feet by 14 feet? A quart of paint covers about 50 square feet.

23. How much does it cost to frame a square painting that is $2\frac{1}{2}$ feet on each side? Framing costs \$.89 a foot.

Area—parallelograms

In each of these parallelograms, the **base** (b) is 4 centimeters and the **height** (h) is 3 centimeters.

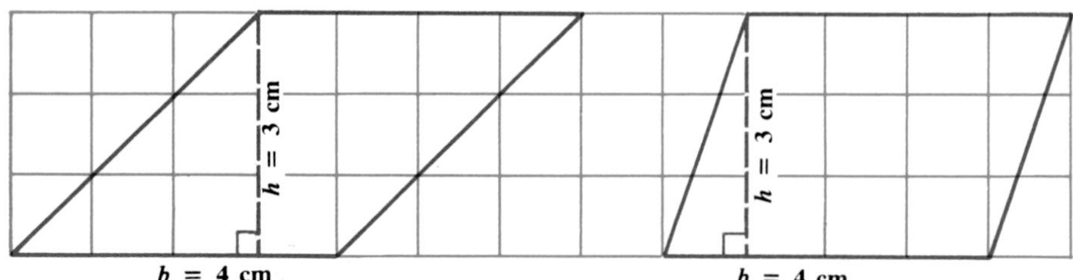

Count the squares. Each parallelogram has an area of 12 square centimeters.

Here's how *to use a formula to find the area of a parallelogram.*

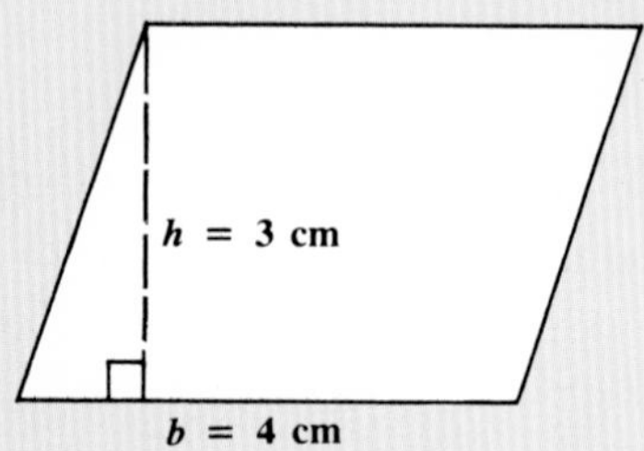

Notice that the height (h) is perpendicular to the base (b).

To find the area (A) of a parallelogram, multiply the base (b) times the height (h).

FORMULA $A = b \times h$

$A = 4 \text{ cm} \times 3 \text{ cm}$

$= 12 \text{ cm}^2$

The area of the parallelogram is 12 square centimeters.

1. Look at the *Here's how*. What is the formula for the area of a parallelogram? What does each letter stand for?
2. If the base and height of a parallelogram are 5 meters and 9 meters, the area is 45 square [?].

EXERCISES

Find the area.

3. 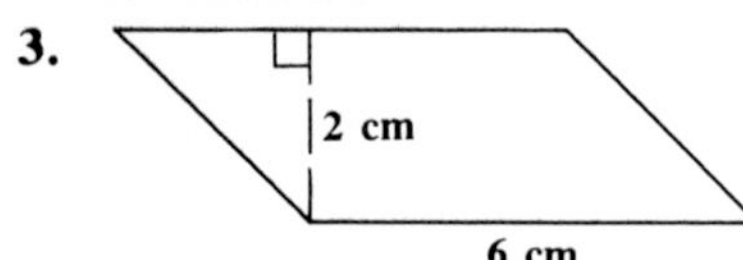

4. 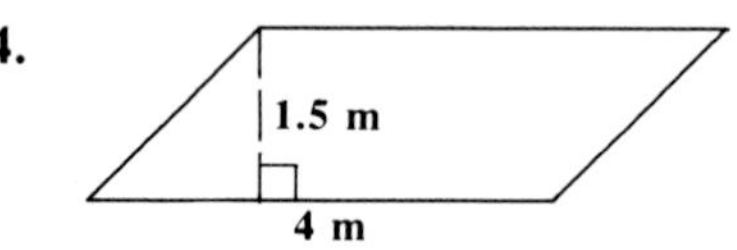

5. 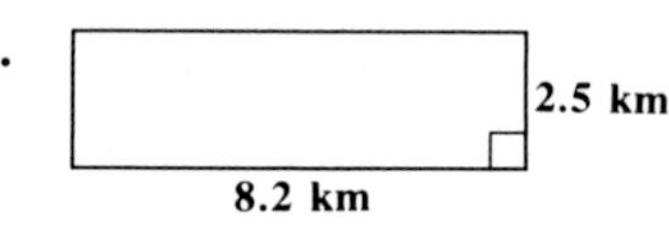

6. 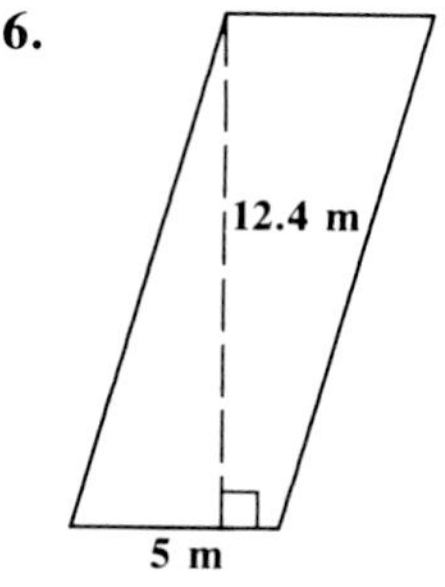

7. 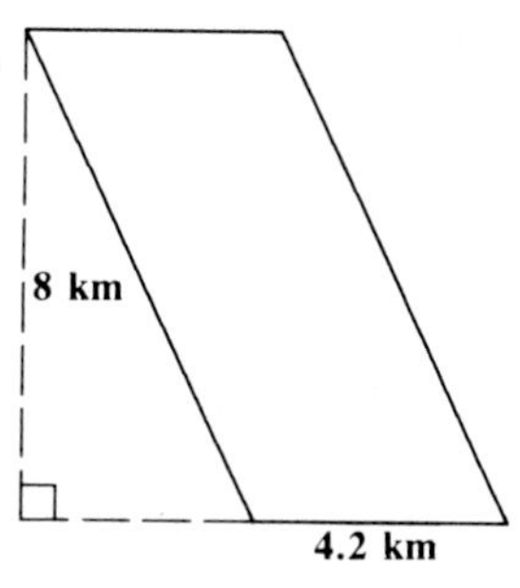

8. 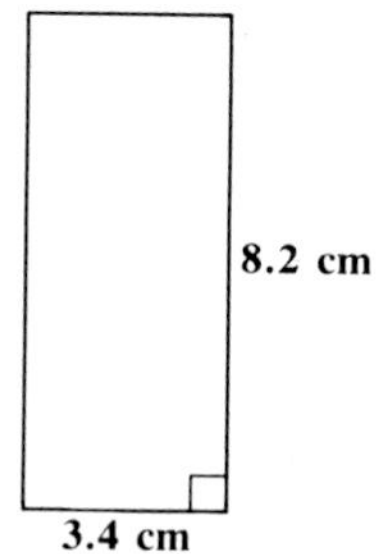

9. 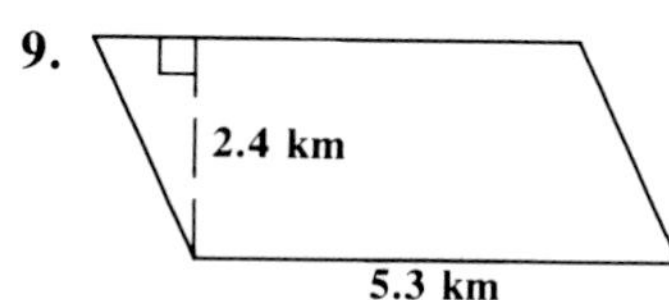

10. 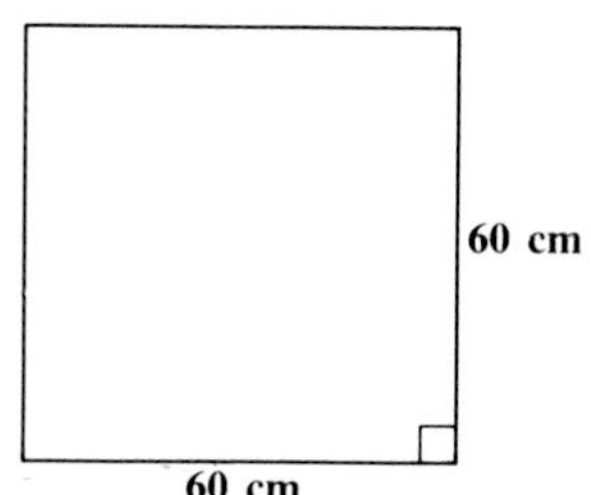

11. 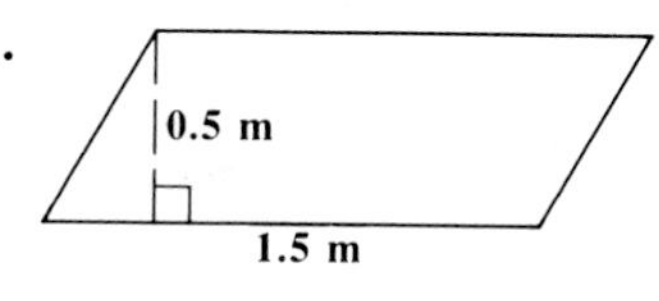

Use the formula $A = b \times h$. Find the area of each parallelogram.

12. $b = 15$ cm, $h = 3$ cm

13. $b = 20$ cm, $h = 6.5$ cm

14. $b = 10$ m, $h = 4.4$ m

15. $b = 2.1$ km, $h = 5$ km

16. $b = 100$ m, $h = 65$ m

17. $b = 8.4$ km, $h = 2.2$ km

18. $b = 6.1$ m, $h = 12$ m

19. $b = 500$ m, $h = 35$ m

20. $b = 85$ cm, $h = 25$ cm

21. $b = 16$ cm, $h = 40$ cm

22. $b = 15$ km, $h = 13$ km

23. $b = 68.3$ m, $h = 5.4$ m

Pick up on these

Toothpicks were used to make this array of 9 small squares.

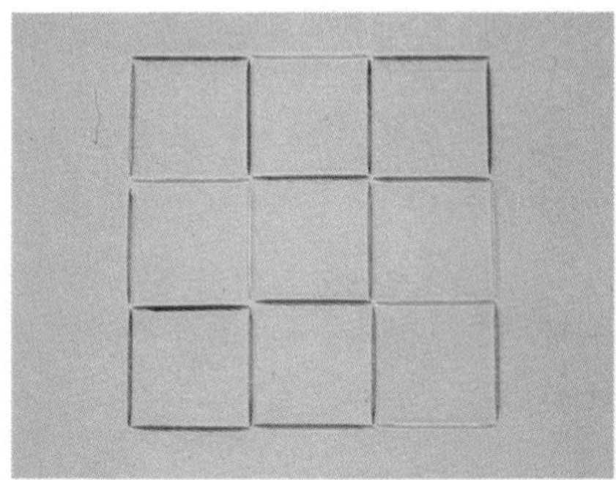

24. Draw a picture. Show how to remove 2 toothpicks to get 7 small squares.

25. Draw another picture. Show how to remove 4 toothpicks to get 5 small squares.

26. Show how to remove 4 toothpicks to get 6 small squares.

27. Show how to remove 8 toothpicks to get 5 small squares.

Area—triangles

CAN YOU CUT IT?

Think about cutting a parallelogram in half.

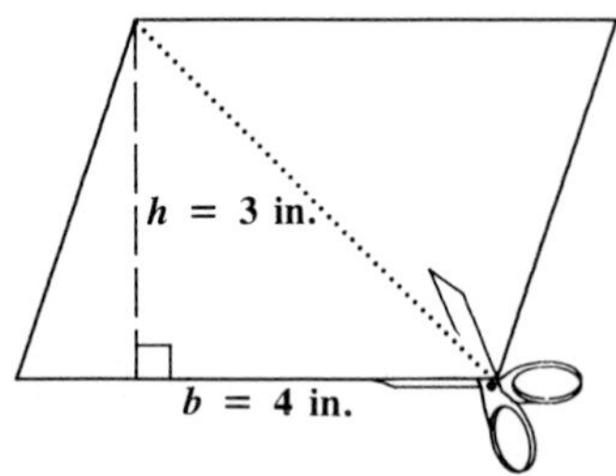

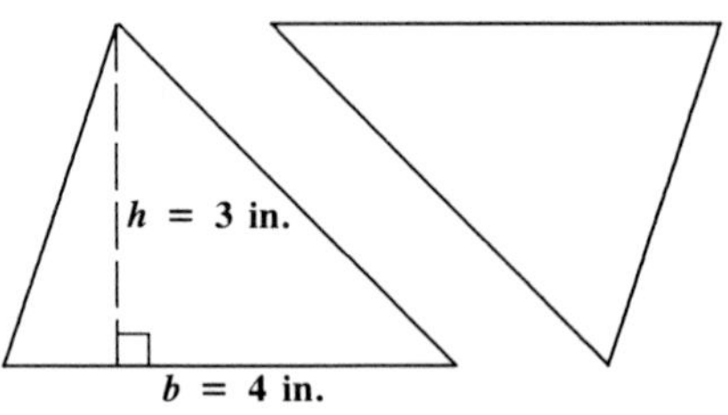

Two triangles are formed. The area of each triangle is half the area of the parallelogram.

1. The area of the parallelogram is 12 square [?].
2. The area of each triangle is [?] square inches.

Here's how ***to use a formula to find the area of a triangle.***

EXAMPLE 1.

h = 3 in.

b = 4 in.

To find the area (A) of a triangle, multiply $\frac{1}{2}$ times the base (b) times the height (h).

FORMULA $A = \frac{1}{2} \times b \times h$

$$A = \frac{1}{2} \times 4 \text{ in.} \times 3 \text{ in.}$$
$$= \frac{1}{2} \times 12 \text{ in.}^2$$
$$= 6 \text{ in.}^2$$

EXAMPLE 2.

$h = 2\frac{1}{2}$ ft

b = 12 ft

FORMULA $A = \frac{1}{2} \times b \times h$

$$A = \frac{1}{2} \times 12 \text{ ft} \times 2\frac{1}{2} \text{ ft}$$
$$= \frac{1}{2} \times 30 \text{ ft}^2$$
$$= 15 \text{ ft}^2$$

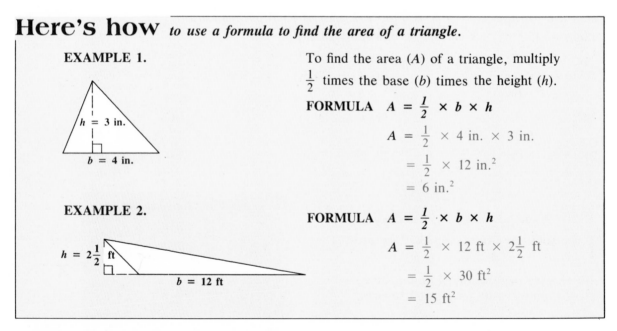

3. Look at the *Here's how*. What is the formula for the area of a triangle? What does each letter stand for?
4. If the base and height of a triangle are 5 yards and 6 yards, the area is [?] square yards.

EXERCISES

Find the area. Use the formula $A = \frac{1}{2} \times b \times h$.

Here are scrambled answers for the next three exercises: $45\ ft^2$ $12\ ft^2$ $35\ ft^2$

5. 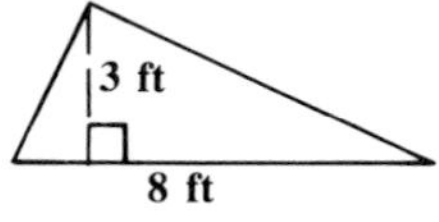

6. 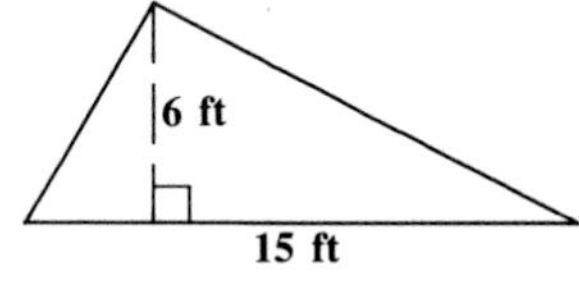

7. 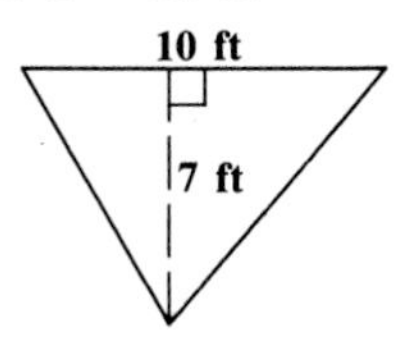

8. 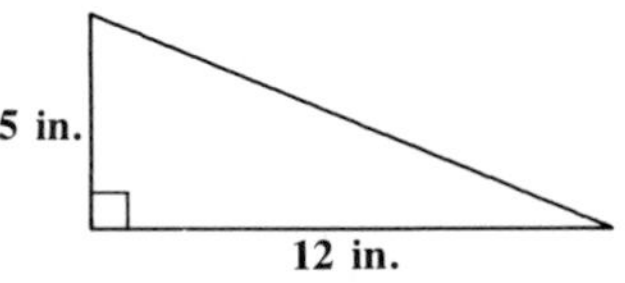

9. 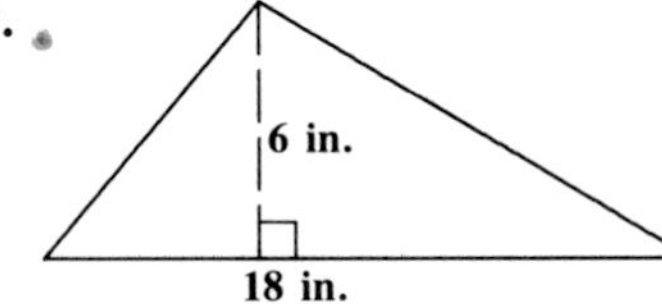

10. 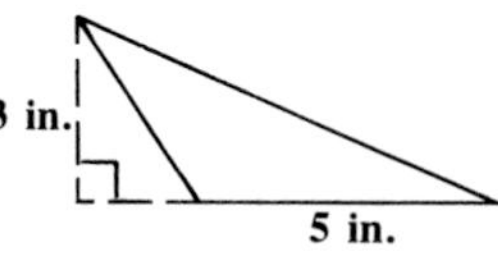

11. 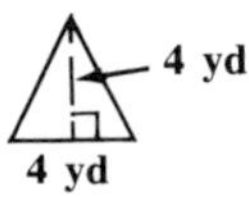

12. 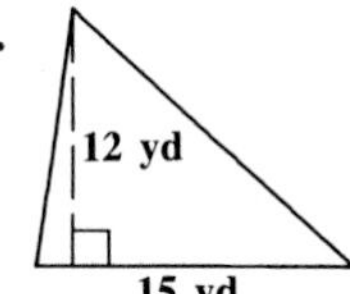

13. 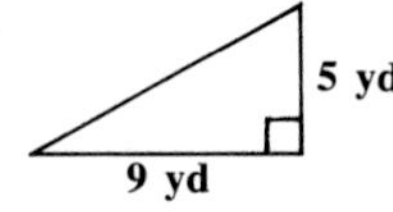

Use $A = \frac{1}{2} \times b \times h$. Find the area of each triangle.

14. $b = 9$ ft
$h = 4$ ft

15. $b = 21$ ft
$h = 10$ ft

16. $b = 40$ yd
$h = 7$ yd

17. $b = 4$ in.
$h = 5$ in.

18. $b = 20$ ft
$h = \frac{1}{2}$ ft

19. $b = 10$ yd
$h = 2\frac{1}{2}$ yd

Crack the code

20. Use the code to get the answer.

RIDDLE: What is the easiest way to double your money?

ANSWER: $6\ cm^2$* $2\ cm^2$* $4\ cm^2$* $5\ cm^2$
$12\ cm^2$* $8 cm^2$

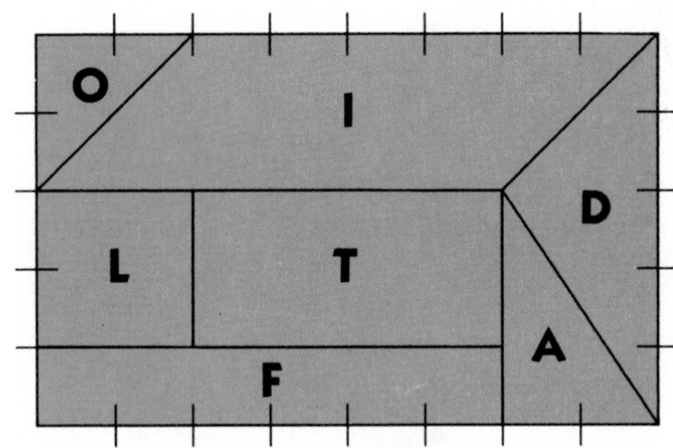

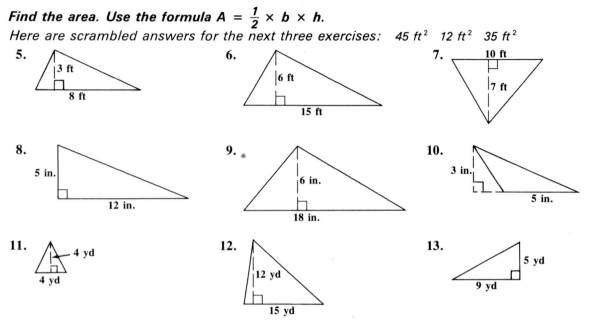

Area—circles

CIRCLE QUIZ

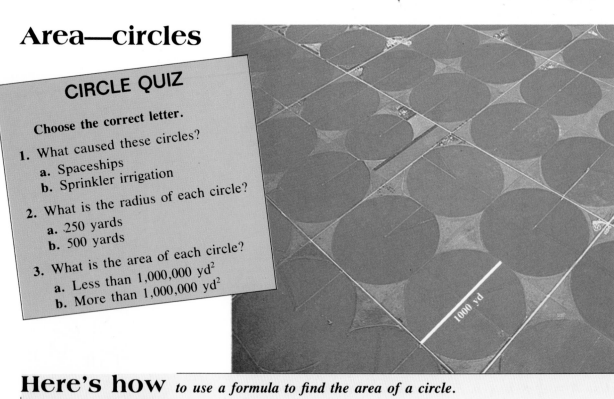

Choose the correct letter.

1. What caused these circles?
   a. Spaceships
   b. Sprinkler irrigation
2. What is the radius of each circle?
   a. 250 yards
   b. 500 yards
3. What is the area of each circle?
   a. Less than 1,000,000 yd^2
   b. More than 1,000,000 yd^2

Here's how *to use a formula to find the area of a circle.*

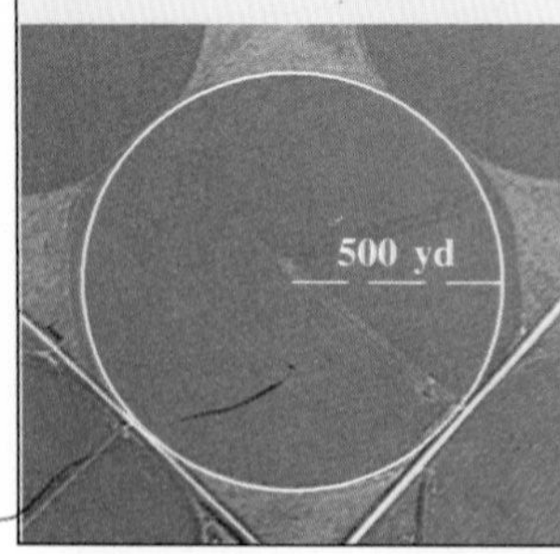

To find the area (A) of a circle, multiply π (about 3.14) times the radius (r) times the radius.

FORMULA $A = \pi \times r \times r$

$$\begin{aligned} A &\approx 3.14 \times 500 \text{ yd} \times 500 \text{ yd} \\ &\approx 3.14 \times 250{,}000 \text{ yd}^2 \\ &\approx 785{,}000 \text{ yd}^2 \end{aligned}$$

4. Look at the *Here's how*. The area of the circle is approximately 785,000 square [?].

EXERCISES

Find the area. Use 3.14 for π.

Here are scrambled answers for the next row of exercises: *200.96 ft^2 314 ft^2 50.24 ft^2*

5. 4 ft

6. 

7. 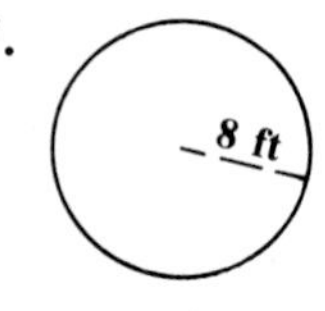

8. 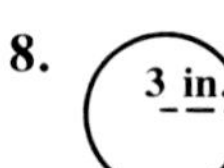

9. 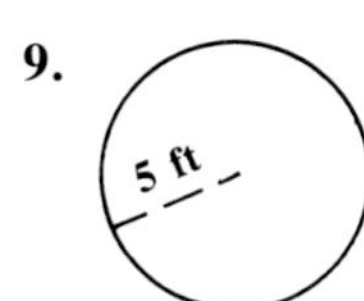

10. 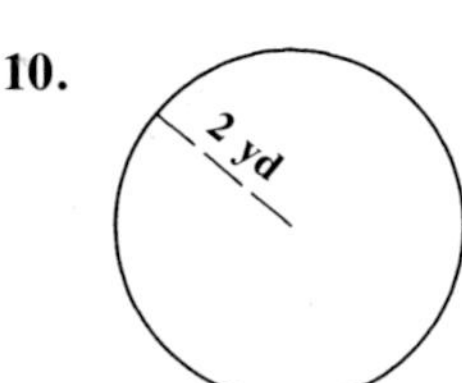

11. 

Be careful! How long is the radius?

12. 2 yd

13. 5 ft

Use the area clues. Find the area of each red region.
Note that you can add and subtract areas.

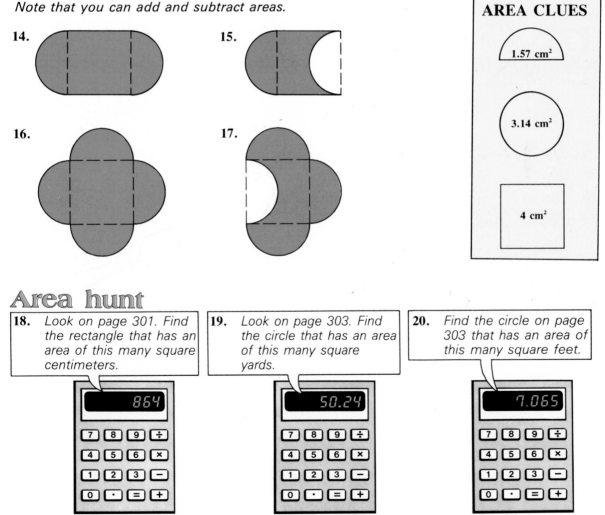

14. 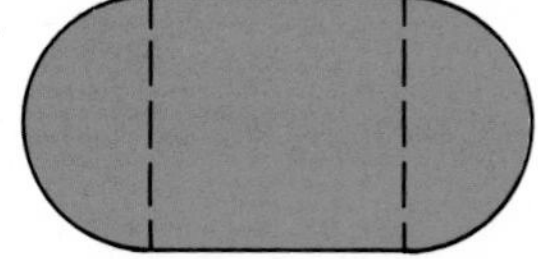

15. 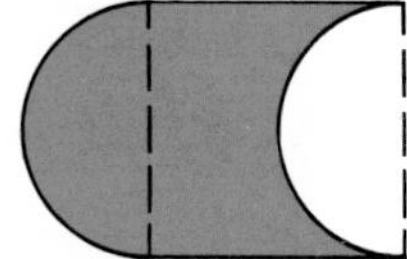

16. 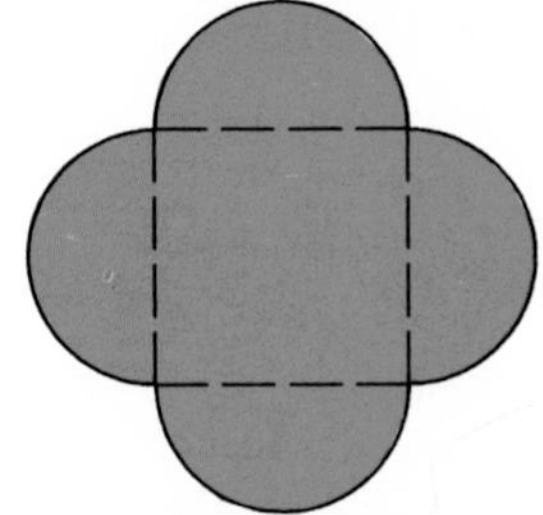

17. 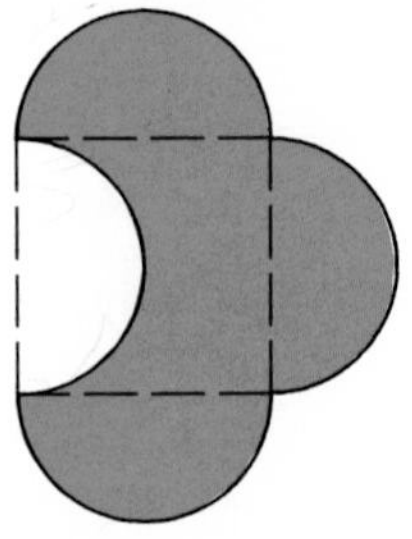

AREA CLUES

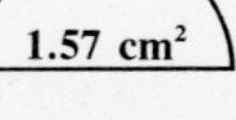

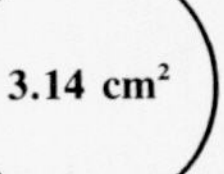

4 cm²

Area hunt

18. *Look on page 301. Find the rectangle that has an area of this many square centimeters.*

19. *Look on page 303. Find the circle that has an area of this many square yards.*

20. *Find the circle on page 303 that has an area of this many square feet.*

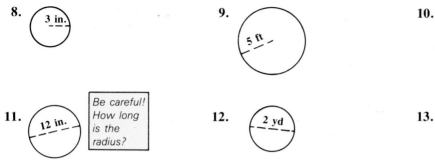

Cumulative Skill Practice

Complete. *(page 202)*

1. 36 cm = ? m
2. 63 mm = ? cm
3. 24 km = ? m
4. 3825 m = ? km
5. 8.2 km = ? m
6. 9.6 cm = ? mm
7. 52 cm = ? mm
8. 16 m = ? cm
9. 2.4 m = ? cm
10. 225 km = ? m
11. 400 mm = ? m
12. 0.6 m = ? mm

Solve. *(page 230)*

13. $\frac{8}{9} = \frac{5}{n}$
14. $\frac{9}{8} = \frac{n}{6}$
15. $\frac{4}{n} = \frac{5}{9}$
16. $\frac{7}{n} = \frac{5}{9}$
17. $\frac{6}{8} = \frac{n}{4}$
18. $\frac{n}{6} = \frac{8}{3}$
19. $\frac{n}{5} = \frac{3}{5}$
20. $\frac{n}{4} = \frac{5}{10}$
21. $\frac{8}{4} = \frac{7}{n}$
22. $\frac{n}{6} = \frac{3}{9}$
23. $\frac{12}{n} = \frac{5}{8}$
24. $\frac{15}{6} = \frac{10}{n}$
25. $\frac{12}{16} = \frac{n}{4}$
26. $\frac{n}{8} = \frac{10}{2}$
27. $\frac{1}{2} = \frac{5}{n}$
28. $\frac{9}{6} = \frac{12}{n}$
29. $\frac{15}{2} = \frac{n}{6}$
30. $\frac{8}{5} = \frac{n}{9}$
31. $\frac{12}{n} = \frac{8}{20}$
32. $\frac{13}{n} = \frac{5}{10}$

Change to a fraction in simplest form. *(page 248)*

33. 20%
34. 50%
35. 25%
36. 75%
37. 30%
38. 8%
39. 16%
40. 85%
41. 48%
42. 60%
43. 72%
44. 4%
45. 120%
46. 125%
47. 250%
48. 175%
49. 290%
50. 135%
51. $33\frac{1}{3}\%$
52. $66\frac{2}{3}\%$
53. $12\frac{1}{2}\%$
54. $83\frac{1}{3}\%$
55. $62\frac{1}{2}\%$
56. $37\frac{1}{2}\%$

Change to a percent. *(page 253)*

57. 0.05
58. 0.01
59. 0.42
60. 0.75
61. 0.4
62. 0.1
63. 0.7
64. 0.8
65. 0.003
66. 0.009
67. 0.3
68. 0.013
69. 2.5
70. 0.25
71. 3.4
72. 1.6
73. 2.375
74. 0.02
75. $0.16\frac{2}{3}$
76. $0.33\frac{1}{3}$
77. $0.12\frac{1}{2}$
78. $0.62\frac{1}{2}$
79. $1.87\frac{1}{2}$
80. $1.36\frac{1}{2}$

Solve. *(page 260)*

81. 10% of n = 12
82. 30% of n = 15
83. 50% of n = 16
84. 20% of n = 18
85. 60% of n = 30
86. 6% of n = 9
87. 5% of n = 10
88. 75% of n = 45
89. 80% of n = 25
90. 120% of n = 75
91. 150% of n = 72
92. 200% of n = 46

Problem solving

COMPUTERS AND SPORTS

Coaches at the Olympic Training Center in Colorado Springs use computer-produced stick figures to help athletes analyze and improve their performance. The stick figure superimposed on the photo at the right can be used by basketball coaches. It shows the preferred angles for the wrist and elbow during a typical shot.

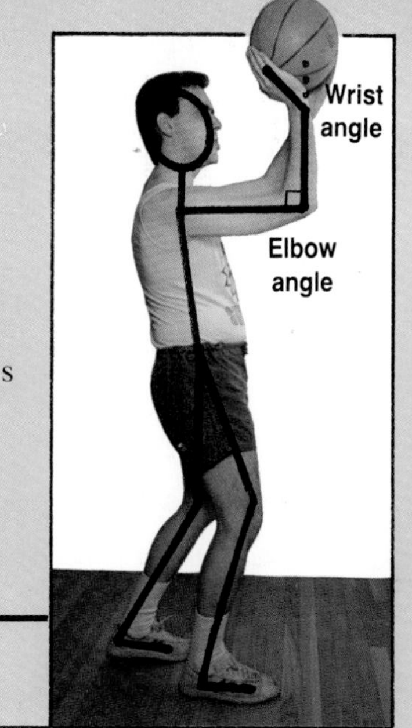

1. What is the elbow angle?
2. Is the wrist angle about 45°?

Study these computer-produced stick figures. Then match each of the coach's comments with the right player.

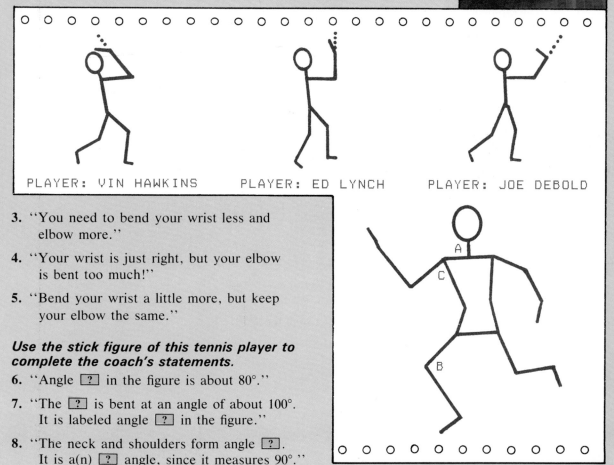

3. "You need to bend your wrist less and elbow more."
4. "Your wrist is just right, but your elbow is bent too much!"
5. "Bend your wrist a little more, but keep your elbow the same."

Use the stick figure of this tennis player to complete the coach's statements.

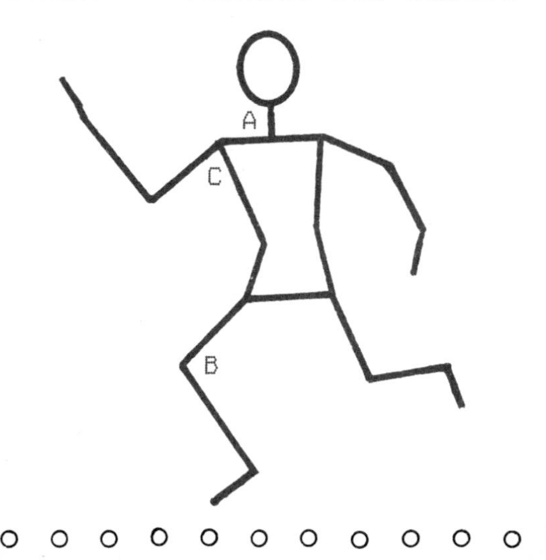

6. "Angle [?] in the figure is about 80°."
7. "The [?] is bent at an angle of about 100°. It is labeled angle [?] in the figure."
8. "The neck and shoulders form angle [?]. It is a(n) [?] angle, since it measures 90°."

Chapter REVIEW

Here are scrambled answers for the review exercises:

18	72	π	height	obtuse	perimeter	width
36	314	acute	hexagon	parallel	perpendicular	
50	628	base	multiply	parallelogram	trapezoid	

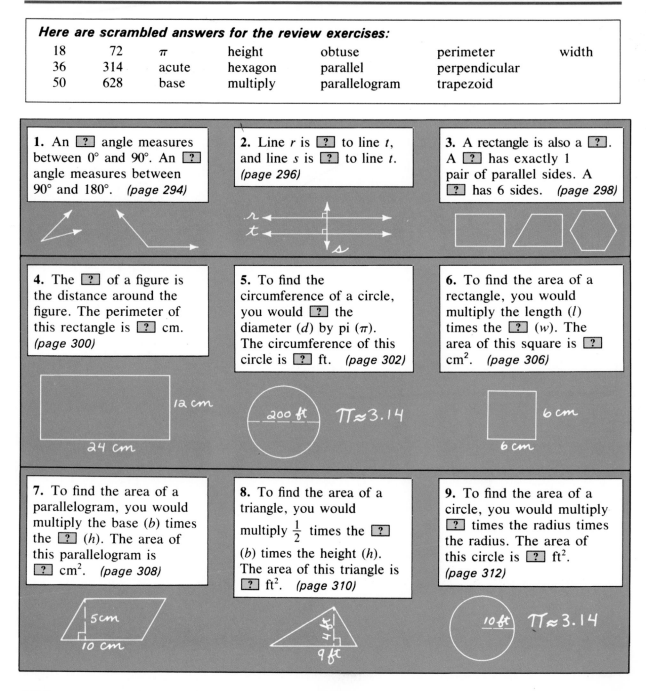

1. An [?] angle measures between 0° and 90°. An [?] angle measures between 90° and 180°. *(page 294)*

2. Line r is [?] to line t, and line s is [?] to line t. *(page 296)*

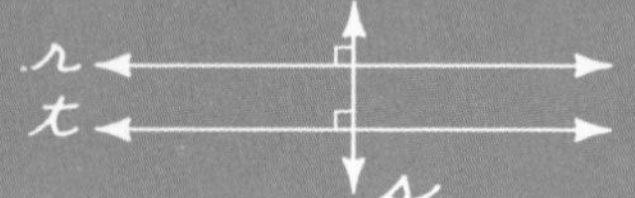

3. A rectangle is also a [?]. A [?] has exactly 1 pair of parallel sides. A [?] has 6 sides. *(page 298)*

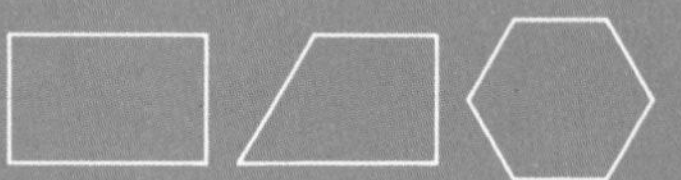

4. The [?] of a figure is the distance around the figure. The perimeter of this rectangle is [?] cm. *(page 300)*

5. To find the circumference of a circle, you would [?] the diameter (d) by pi (π). The circumference of this circle is [?] ft. *(page 302)*

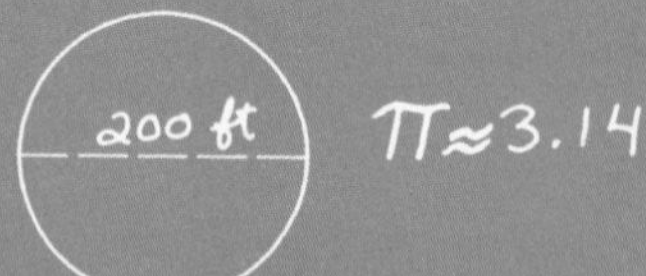

6. To find the area of a rectangle, you would multiply the length (l) times the [?] (w). The area of this square is [?] cm^2. *(page 306)*

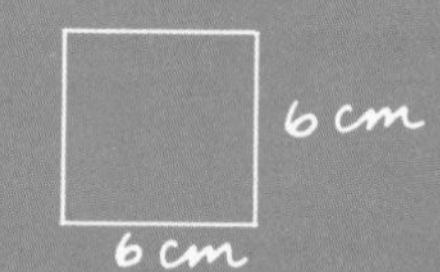

7. To find the area of a parallelogram, you would multiply the base (b) times the [?] (h). The area of this parallelogram is [?] cm^2. *(page 308)*

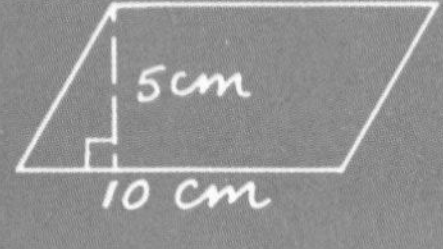

8. To find the area of a triangle, you would multiply $\frac{1}{2}$ times the [?] (b) times the height (h). The area of this triangle is [?] ft^2. *(page 310)*

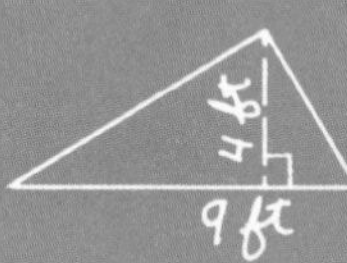

9. To find the area of a circle, you would multiply [?] times the radius times the radius. The area of this circle is [?] ft^2. *(page 312)*

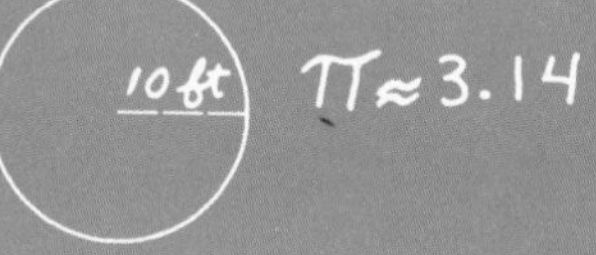

Chapter TEST

Complete. *(pages 294, 296, 298)*

1. A [?] is used to measure angles.
2. A right angle measures [?].
3. An acute angle measures between 0° and [?].
4. An obtuse angle measures between [?] and 180°.
5. Two lines that intersect to form right angles are [?].
6. Two lines on a flat surface that do not intersect are [?].
7. A triangle has [?] sides.
8. A rectangle has 4 sides and 4 [?] angles.
9. A parallelogram has 2 pairs of [?] sides.
10. A trapezoid has exactly 1 pair of [?] sides.
11. A pentagon has [?] sides.
12. A hexagon has [?] sides.

Find the perimeter. *(page 300)*

13.
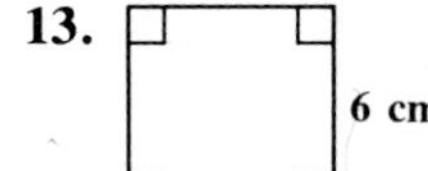
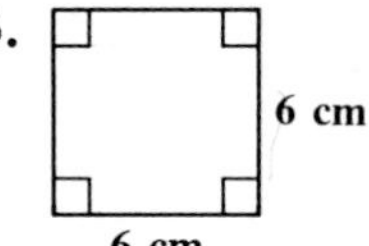

14.
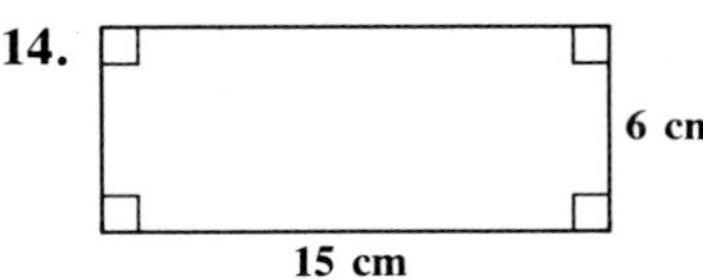

15.
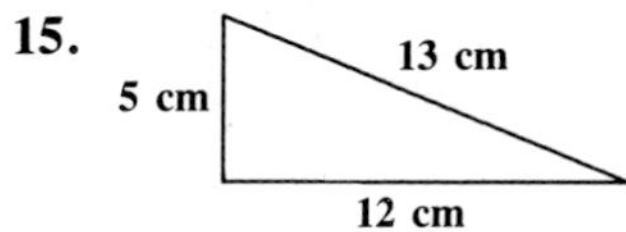

Find the circumference. Use 3.14 as an approximation for π. *(page 302)*

16.
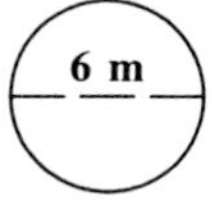

17.
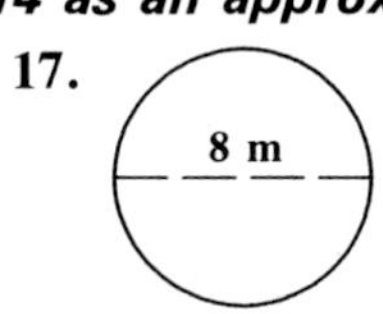

18.

Find the area. *(pages 306, 308, 310)*

19.
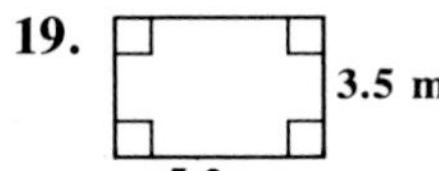

20.
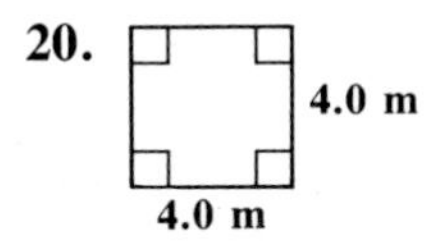

21.
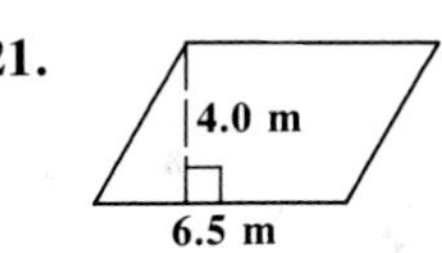

22.
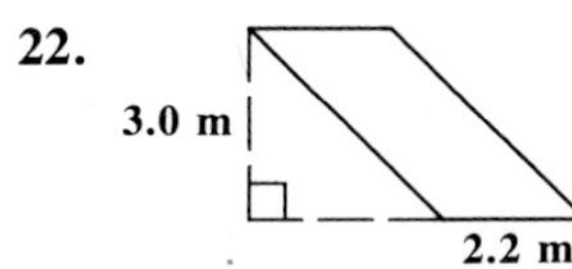

23.
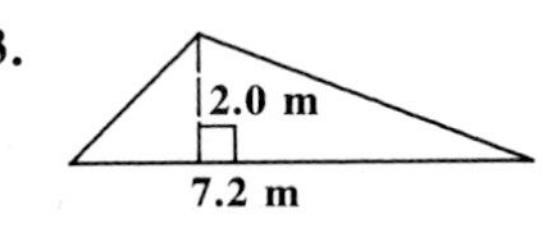

24.
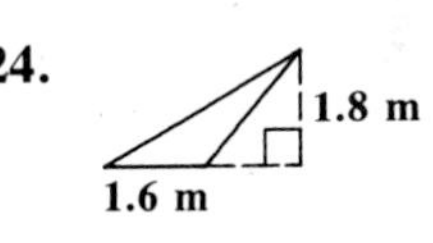

Find the area. Use 3.14 as an approximation for π. *(page 312)*

25.
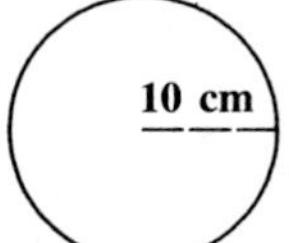

26.
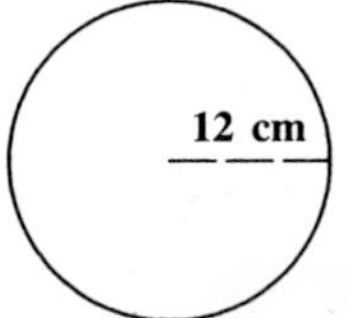

27.
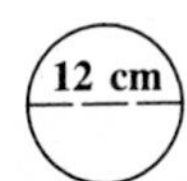

Cumulative TEST Standardized Format

Choose the correct letter.

1. Change to a decimal.

$5\frac{3}{4} = ?$

A. 0.75
B. 5.25
C. 5.75
D. none of these

2. Give the sum.

$\frac{5}{12} + \frac{7}{8}$

A. $1\frac{7}{24}$
B. $\frac{3}{5}$
C. $1\frac{1}{4}$
D. none of these

3. Give the difference.

$\frac{5}{6} - \frac{3}{4}$

A. 1
B. $\frac{1}{12}$
C. $\frac{1}{3}$
D. none of these

4. Give the product.

$\frac{5}{9} \times \frac{2}{3}$

A. $\frac{5}{6}$
B. $\frac{7}{27}$
C. $\frac{10}{27}$
D. none of these

5. Give the quotient.

$\frac{7}{8} \div \frac{1}{3}$

A. $\frac{7}{24}$
B. $2\frac{5}{16}$
C. $\frac{8}{21}$
D. none of these

6. 3475 m = __?__ km

A. 34.75
B. 3.475
C. 0.3475
D. none of these

7. Solve. $\frac{9}{n} = \frac{14}{5}$

A. 12
B. 11.25
C. 7.2
D. none of these

8. Change to a fraction.

$37\frac{1}{2}\% = ?$

A. $\frac{3}{8}$
B. $\frac{5}{8}$
C. $\frac{2}{5}$
D. none of these

9. Change to a percent.

0.06 = ?

A. 0.06%
B. 0.6%
C. 6%
D. none of these

10. Solve.

24% of n = 30

A. 125
B. 7.2
C. 22.8
D. none of these

11. A radio that regularly sells for $124 is on sale for 40% off. What is the sale price?

A. $49.60 B. $74.40
C. $173.60 D. none of these

12. Find the area.

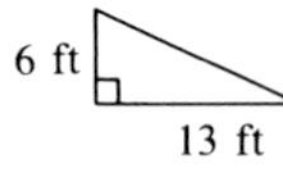

A. 78 ft^2 B. 9.5 ft^2
C. 39 ft^2 D. none of these

Chapter 14

Surface Area and Volume

Space figures

LOOK THEM OVER

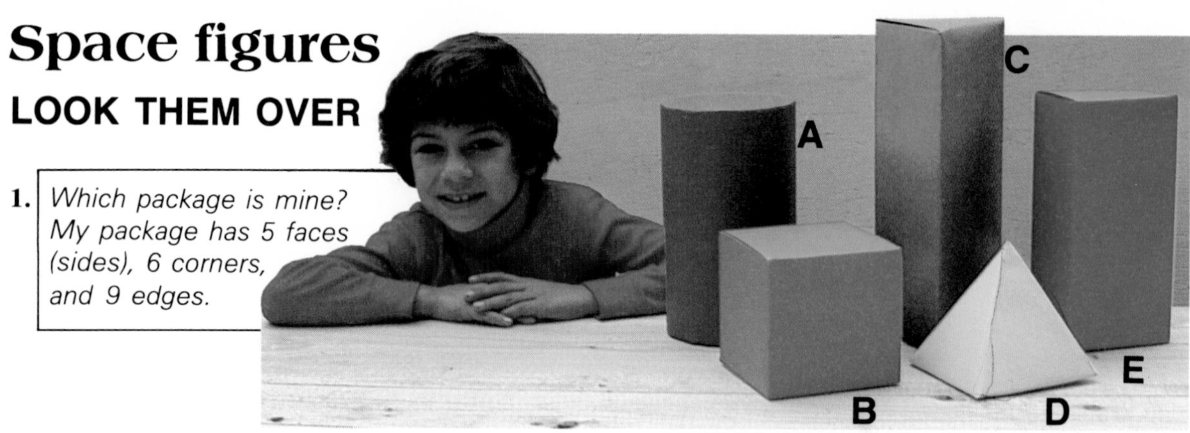

1. *Which package is mine? My package has 5 faces (sides), 6 corners, and 9 edges.*

2. Which package has 6 square faces?

3. Which package has 5 faces and 5 corners?

Here's how *space figures are named.*

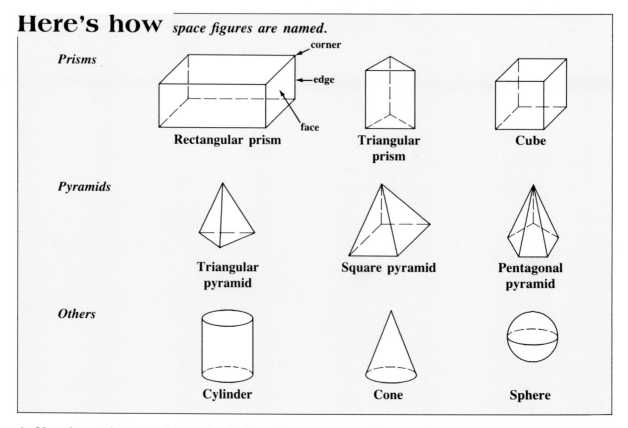

Prisms

corner
edge
face

Rectangular prism | **Triangular prism** | **Cube**

Pyramids

Triangular pyramid | **Square pyramid** | **Pentagonal pyramid**

Others

Cylinder | **Cone** | **Sphere**

4. Use the packages and the *Here's how* chart to answer the questions.
   - **a.** Which package is a cube?
   - **b.** Which package is a cylinder?
   - **c.** Which package is a rectangular prism?
   - **d.** Which package is a square pyramid?
   - **e.** Which package is a triangular prism?
   - **f.** Which 3 packages are prisms?

EXERCISES

Use the clues and the drawings on page 320. Name each space figure.

5. Clues:
- This space figure is a prism.
- All its faces are squares.

6. Clues:
- This space figure is a pyramid.
- It has 4 corners.

7. Clues:
- This space figure has 5 faces.
- One of its faces is square.
- It has 8 edges.

8. Clues:
- This space figure has 6 faces.
- None of its faces are square.
- It has 8 corners.

9. Clues:
- This space figure has 6 faces.
- One of its sides is a pentagon.

10. Clues:
- This space figure has 5 faces.
- It has 9 edges.

11. Clues:
- This space figure has 8 corners.
- All its edges are the same length.

12. Clues:
- This space figure has no corners.
- Two of its faces are circles.

13. Clues:
- This space figure has no corners.
- If you cut this figure using one straight cut, the shape that is formed is always a circle.

14. Clues:
- Cut this space figure one way and the shape that is formed is a circle.
- Cut it another way and the shape that is formed is a triangle.

What's on top?

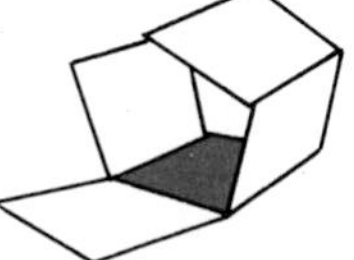

Each of these patterns can be folded to form a cube. If the red face is the bottom of the cube, which face is the top?

15.

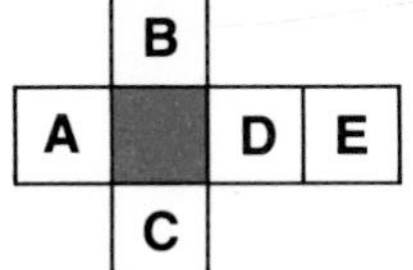

16.

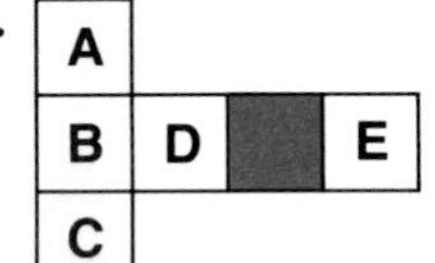

17.

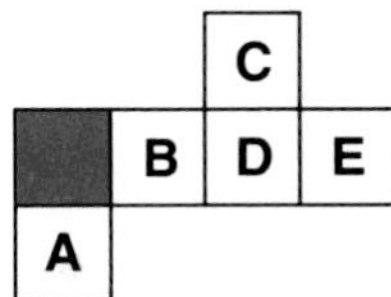

18.

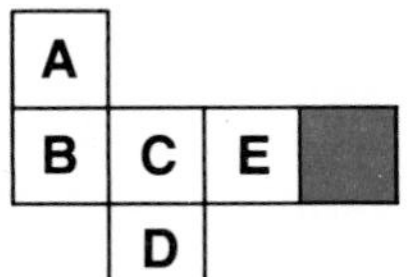

19.

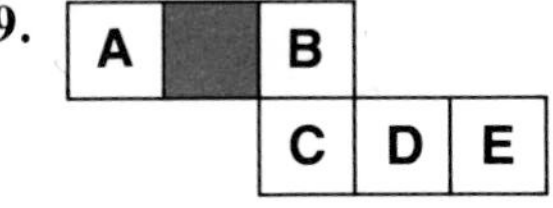

20.

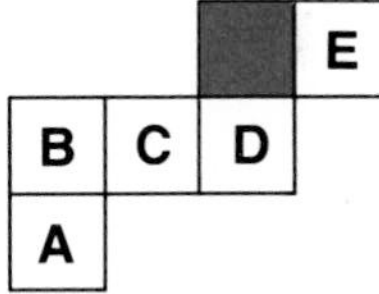

21.

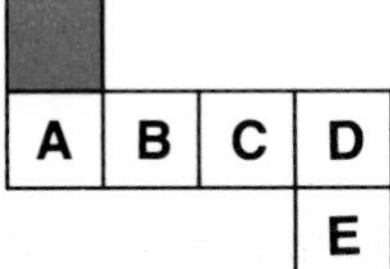

22.

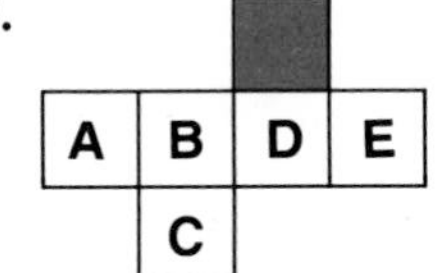

23.

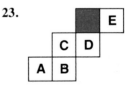

E
C D
A B

More on space figures

PIECES & PRICES

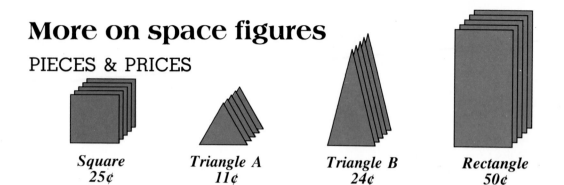

Square
25¢

Triangle A
11¢

Triangle B
24¢

Rectangle
50¢

Here is a model that was made from some pieces that are shown above.

1. How many pieces were used to make the model?
2. **a.** Which piece was used for the top and bottom?
   b. What is the total cost of the top and bottom?
3. **a.** Which piece was used for the other faces?
   b. What is their total cost?
4. What is the total cost of the model?

EXERCISES

Find the total cost of each model.

5. 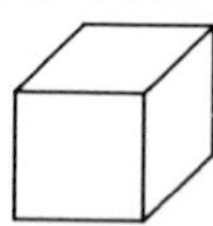

6. 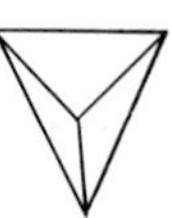

7. 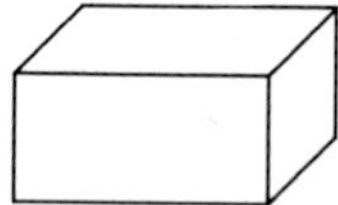

8. 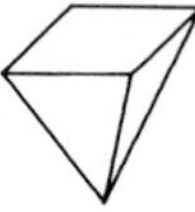

9. 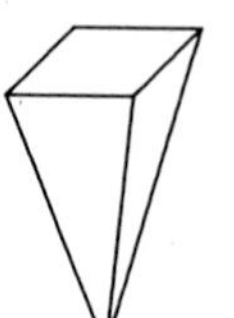

10. 

11. 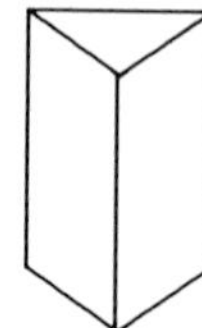

12. 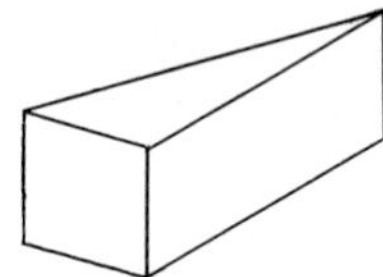

13. 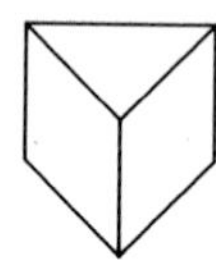

14. 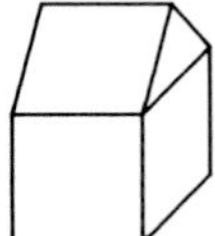

15. 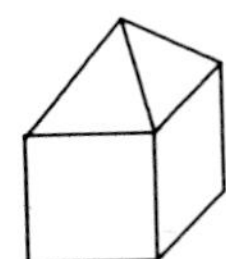

16. 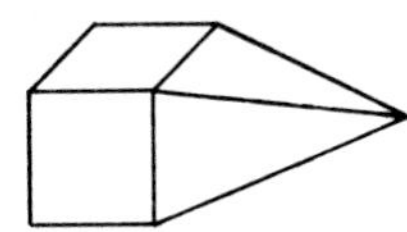

17. 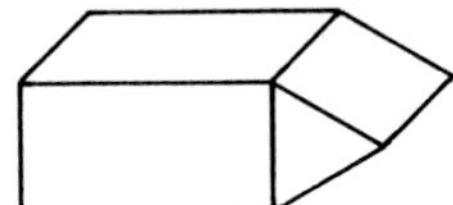

18. 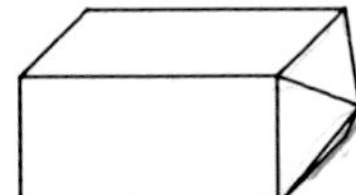

19. 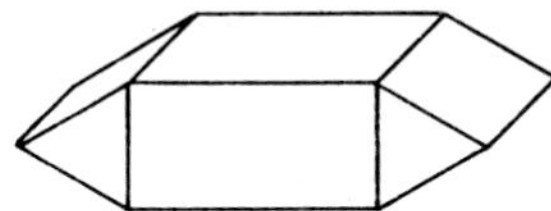

20. 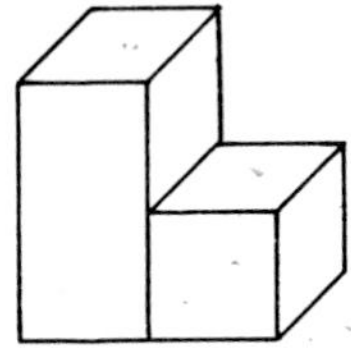

21. 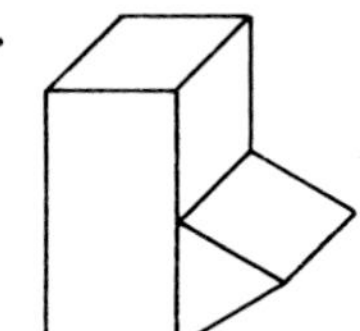

22. 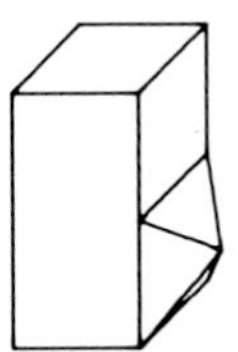

Solve.

23. Which 5 pieces would you use to make the least expensive prism?

24. Which pieces would you use to make the least expensive pyramid?

25. Which pieces would you use to make the most expensive pyramid?

26. What is the price of the least expensive model that you can build that has 6 faces? *Hint: The answer is not $1.50.*

Name that product

Can you identify, just from the shape, what product is in each can?

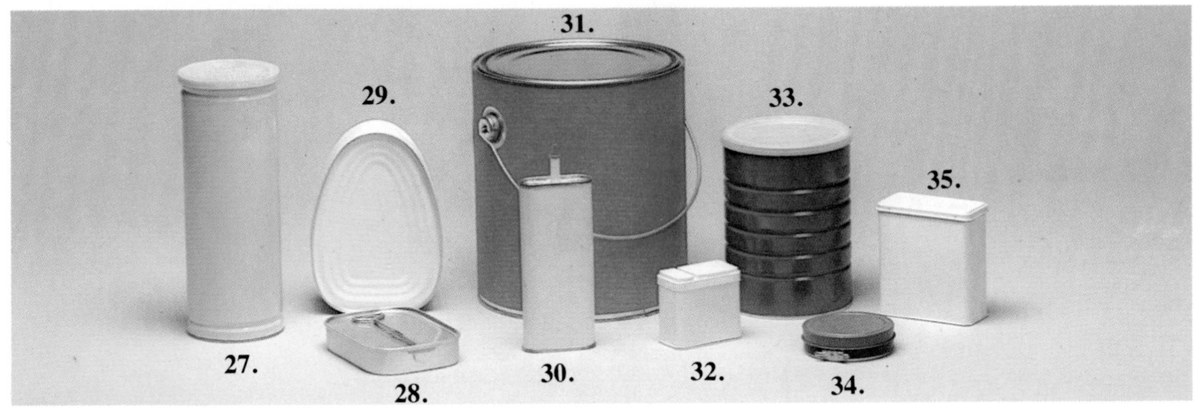

Surface area—rectangular prisms and cubes

CAN YOU PICTURE IT?

1. Greg used 52 pictures to cover the 6 faces of his photo box. Which photo box is Greg's?

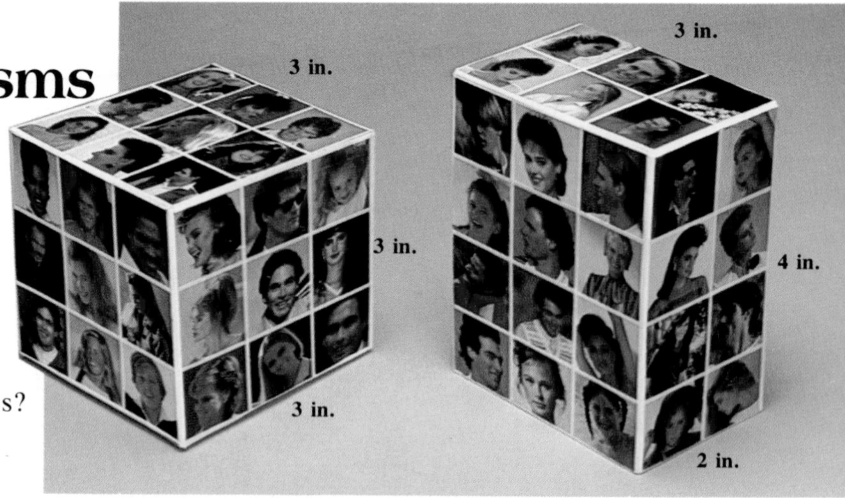

Photo box A   Photo box B

Here's how *to find the surface area of a rectangular prism.*

Think about unfolding **photo box B.** To find the surface area, compute the area of each face by multiplying its length by its width. Then add all six areas.

	Top (2″ × 3″)		
Left side (2″ × 4″)	Front (3″ × 4″)	Right side (2″ × 4″)	Back (3″ × 4″)
	Bottom (2″ × 3″)		

Area of front .... 12 in.^{2}
back .... 12 in.^{2}
top........... 6 in.^{2}
bottom .... 6 in.^{2}
left side ...... 8 in.^{2}
right side ..... 8 in.^{2}
Surface area = 52 in.^{2}

2. Look at the *Here's how.*
   a. The area of the front is the same as the area of the ?.
   b. The area of the top is the same as the area of the ?.
   c. The area of the left side is the same as the area of the ? side.
3. Look at photo box A. If the area of each face is 9 square inches, then the surface area of the cube is ? square inches.
4. Which photo box has the greater surface area?

EXERCISES

Find the surface area of each box.

5. 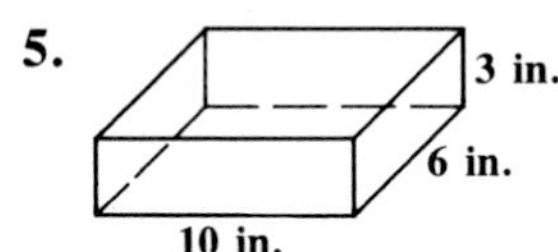

front: ? in.^{2}
back: ? in.^{2}
top: ? in.^{2}
bottom: ? in.^{2}
left side: ? in.^{2}
right side: ? in.^{2}
Surface area = ? in.^{2}

6. 2 ft, 2 ft, 2 ft

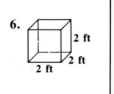

Hint: To find the surface area of a cube, first find the area of one face, then multiply by 6.

7. 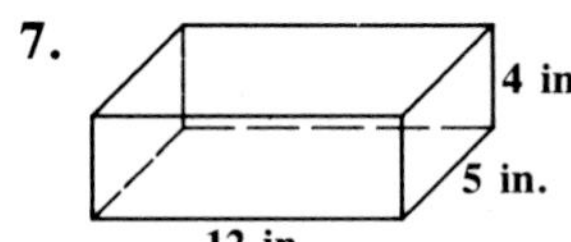
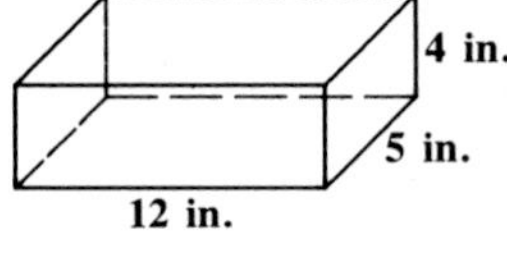

8. 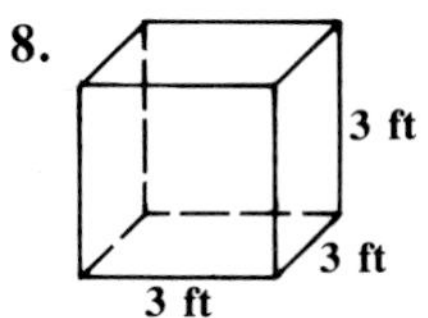

9. 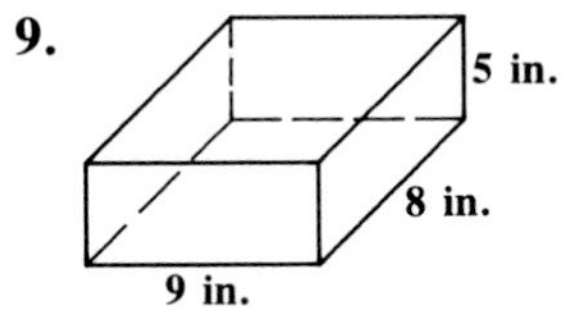

10. 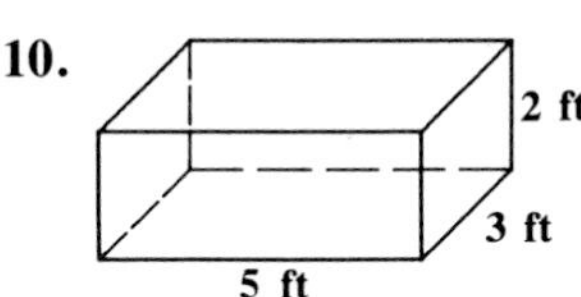

11. 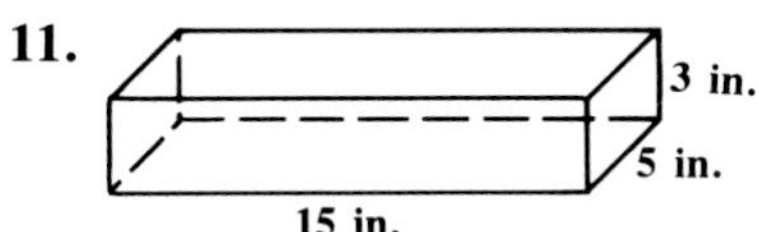

12. 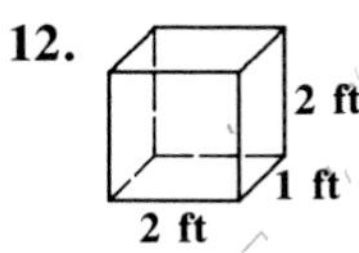

Solve.

13. How many 1-inch-square pictures are needed to cover a photo box 5 inches long, 4 inches wide, and 6 inches tall?

14. How many 1-inch-square pictures are needed to cover a photo cube that is 5 inches on an edge?

Blockheads

15. This 3-inch photo cube is cut into 27 1-inch cubes. How many of the 1-inch cubes will have
    - **a.** photos on 3 of the faces?
    - **b.** photos on 2 of the faces?
    - **c.** photos on 1 of the faces?
    - **d.** no photos on any of the faces?

Cumulative Skill Practice

Give the product. *(page 64)*

1. 5.1×0.4 **2.** 6.3×0.42 **3.** 0.59×0.8

4. 45×2.7 **5.** 0.82×6.2 **6.** 2.18×4.9

7. 7.94×6 **8.** 52.6×9.1 **9.** 53.1×0.62

10. 6.59×12 **11.** 31.6×5.8 **12.** 207×1.5

13. 3.04×0.06 **14.** 51.3×30.8 **15.** 6.42×3.05

Give the quotient rounded to the nearest tenth. *(page 96)*

16. $17.4 \div 0.9$ **17.** $4.65 \div 0.2$ **18.** $6.47 \div 0.03$

19. $5.27 \div 1.6$ **20.** $3.059 \div 2.1$ **21.** $6.07 \div 0.35$

22. $16.083 \div 0.39$ **23.** $4.003 \div 0.26$ **24.** $7.03 \div 5.4$

25. $7.94 \div 6.5$ **26.** $3.849 \div 5.7$ **27.** $41 \div 3.2$

Change to a decimal rounded to the nearest hundredth. *(page 146)*

28. $\frac{1}{3}$ **29.** $\frac{1}{6}$ **30.** $\frac{1}{9}$ **31.** $\frac{2}{3}$ **32.** $\frac{2}{9}$ **33.** $\frac{5}{6}$ **34.** $\frac{1}{8}$

35. $\frac{1}{12}$ **36.** $\frac{11}{6}$ **37.** $\frac{5}{12}$ **38.** $\frac{5}{3}$ **39.** $\frac{5}{8}$ **40.** $\frac{13}{6}$ **41.** $\frac{20}{6}$

42. $\frac{4}{3}$ **43.** $\frac{10}{9}$ **44.** $\frac{3}{8}$ **45.** $\frac{7}{3}$ **46.** $\frac{7}{12}$ **47.** $\frac{11}{3}$ **48.** $\frac{10}{3}$

Subtract. Give the difference in simplest form. *(page 170)*

49. $3\frac{5}{6} - 1\frac{1}{6}$ **50.** $5\frac{3}{4} - 3\frac{1}{4}$ **51.** $7 - 2\frac{1}{2}$ **52.** $8\frac{1}{3} - 3\frac{3}{8}$ **53.** $6 - 4\frac{3}{4}$ **54.** $9\frac{2}{5} - 1\frac{7}{10}$

55. $10 - 5\frac{3}{4}$ **56.** $12\frac{1}{3} - 8\frac{5}{6}$ **57.** $15\frac{2}{5} - 4\frac{3}{4}$ **58.** $16\frac{3}{4} - 11\frac{7}{8}$ **59.** $22\frac{3}{10} - 18\frac{5}{6}$ **60.** $25\frac{3}{4} - 5\frac{1}{2}$

Give the quotient in simplest form. *(page 190)*

61. $1\frac{1}{3} \div 4$ **62.** $4\frac{1}{2} \div 2$ **63.** $3 \div 1\frac{1}{2}$ **64.** $4 \div 1\frac{1}{4}$ **65.** $8 \div 1\frac{1}{2}$

66. $2\frac{5}{6} \div 1\frac{1}{8}$ **67.** $5\frac{7}{8} \div 4$ **68.** $12\frac{1}{2} \div 2\frac{1}{2}$ **69.** $6\frac{2}{3} \div 3\frac{1}{3}$ **70.** $2\frac{1}{2} \div 3\frac{1}{2}$

Problem solving

YOU'RE THE ROOFER!

SHINGLE SALE

Asphalt shingles . . **\$59.90** per square
Shake shingles . . . **\$89.90** per square

Each "square" of shingles will cover 100 square feet of roof.

Use the newspaper ad to answer these customers' questions.

1. *How many square feet will a square of shingles cover?*

2. *Can I buy 6 squares of asphalt shingles for \$350?*

3. *Are 7 squares of shingles enough to shingle my house? My roof has an area of 720 square feet.*

4. *My roof has an area of 900 square feet. How much will it cost to shingle my roof with shakes?*

Use the pictures to answer these questions.

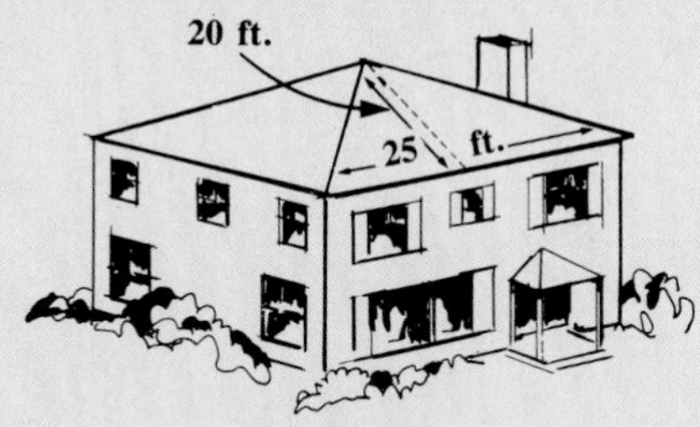

5. a. What is the area of the roof? Remember: There are two parts to the roof.

b. How many squares of shingles will it take to cover the roof?

c. How much will it cost to shingle the roof with asphalt shingles?

6. a. Each side of the roof is a triangle with a base of 25 feet and a height of 20 feet. What is the area of the roof?

b. How many squares of shingles will it take to cover the roof?

c. How much will it cost to shingle the roof with shake shingles?

Volume—rectangular prisms and cubes

WHAT'S THE VOLUME?

The amount that a space figure holds is called its **volume.** Volume is measured in cubic units.

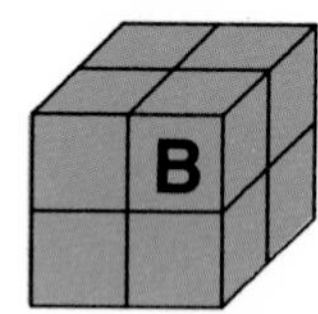

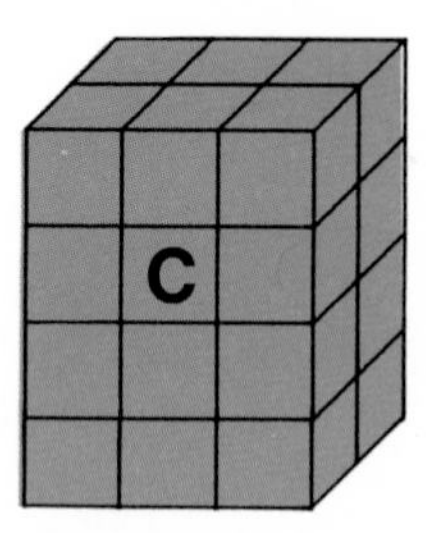

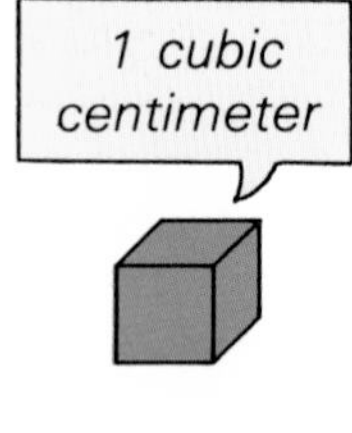

1. Count the cubes. Which prism has a volume of 6 cubic centimeters?
2. Which prism has a volume of 8 cubic centimeters?
3. What is the volume of prism C?

Here's how *to use a formula to find the volume of a prism.*

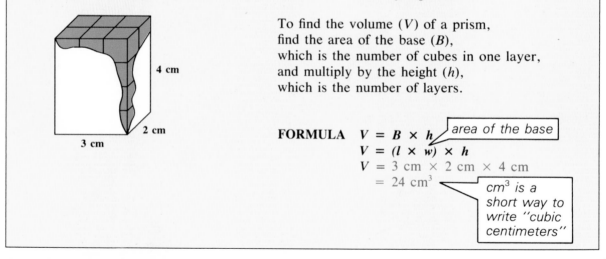

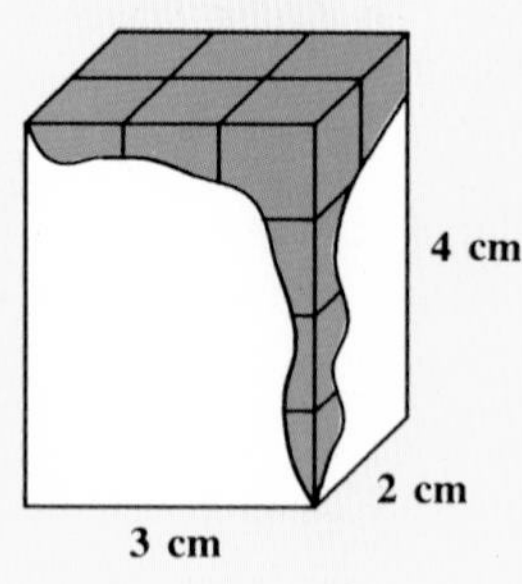

To find the volume (V) of a prism, find the area of the base (B), which is the number of cubes in one layer, and multiply by the height (h), which is the number of layers.

FORMULA $V = B \times h$ (area of the base)

$V = (l \times w) \times h$

$V = 3 \text{ cm} \times 2 \text{ cm} \times 4 \text{ cm}$

$= 24 \text{ cm}^3$

cm^3 is a short way to write "cubic centimeters"

4. Look at the *Here's how*. What is the formula for the volume of a rectangular prism? What does each letter stand for?
5. If the length, width, and height of a rectangular prism are 4 centimeters, 5 centimeters, and 6 centimeters, the volume is 120 [?] centimeters.
6. If the edge of a cube is 5 inches long, its volume is 125 cubic [?].

EXERCISES

Use the formula* V = B × h. *Find the volume.

7. 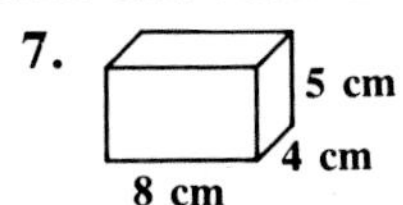

8. 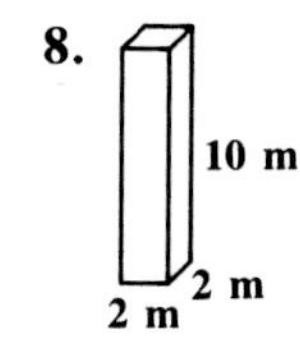

9. 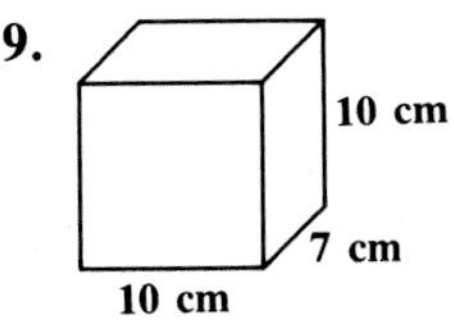

10. 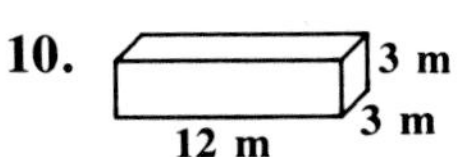

11. 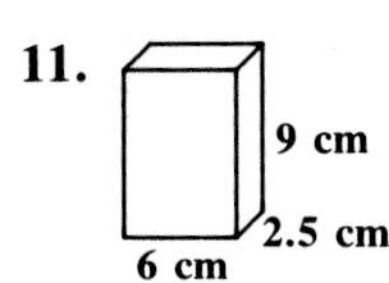

12. 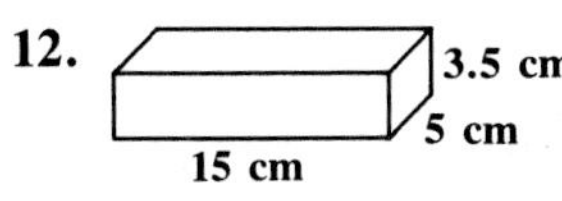

13. 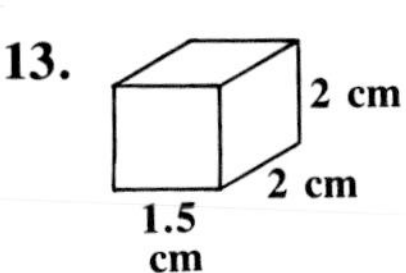

14. 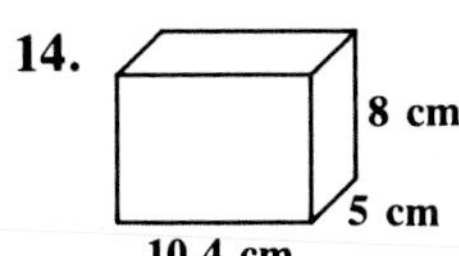

15. 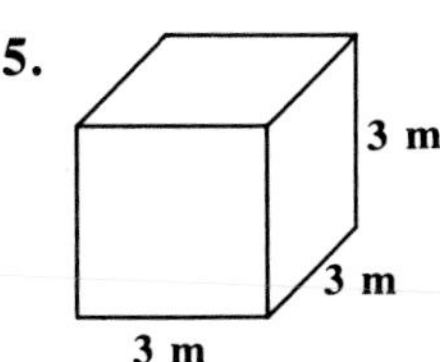

Solve.

16. Which box above has a surface area of 88 square meters?

17. Which box above has a surface area of 54 square meters?

Math on the job

Your job is to take an inventory of all the nails. There are three stacks of boxes.

18. **a.** How many boxes?
b. How many nails?

19. **a.** How many boxes?
b. How many nails?

20. **a.** How many boxes?
b. How many nails?

Check your calculations. Your inventory should total 13,050 nails.

Volume—cylinders

ROLL IT UP!

Here are two ways to roll a sheet of paper to make a cylinder.

Which cylinder do you think has the greater volume?

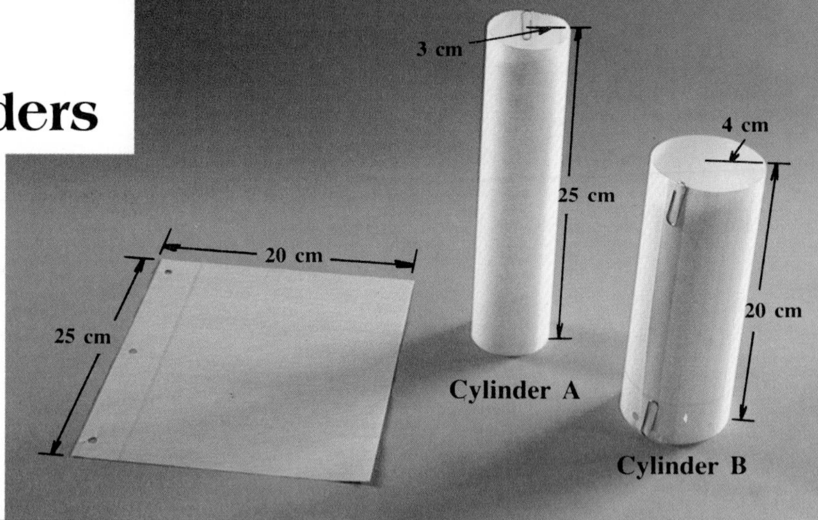

Here's how *to use a formula to find the volume of a cylinder.*

Cylinder A

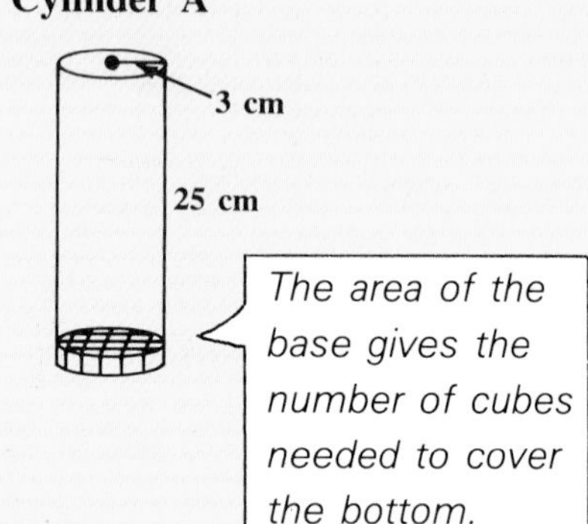

3 cm
25 cm
The area of the base gives the number of cubes needed to cover the bottom.

To find the volume (V) of a cylinder, multiply the area of the base (B) times the height (h).

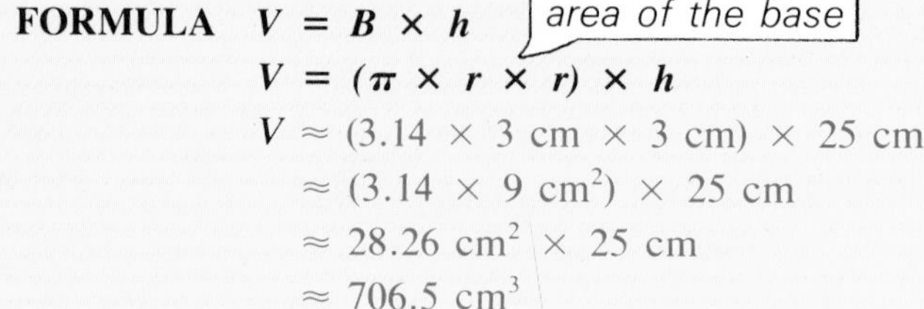

FORMULA $V = B \times h$ (area of the base)

$V = (\pi \times r \times r) \times h$

$V \approx (3.14 \times 3 \text{ cm} \times 3 \text{ cm}) \times 25 \text{ cm}$

$\approx (3.14 \times 9 \text{ cm}^2) \times 25 \text{ cm}$

$\approx 28.26 \text{ cm}^2 \times 25 \text{ cm}$

$\approx 706.5 \text{ cm}^3$

Cylinder B

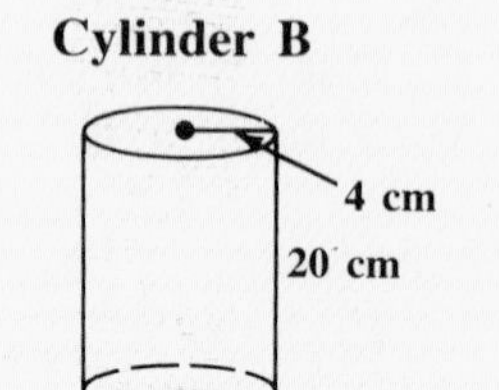

FORMULA $V = B \times h$

$V = (\pi \times r \times r) \times h$

$V \approx (3.14 \times 4 \text{ cm} \times 4 \text{ cm}) \times 20 \text{ cm}$

$\approx (3.14 \times 16 \text{ cm}^2) \times 20 \text{ cm}$

$\approx 1004.8 \text{ cm}^3$

1. In the formula $V = (\pi \times r \times r) \times h$, what do the letters V, π, r, and h stand for?
2. Look at the *Here's how*. If the radius and height of a cylinder are 3 centimeters and 25 centimeters, the volume is approximately [?] cubic centimeters.
3. If the radius and height of a cylinder are 4 centimeters and 20 centimeters, the volume is approximately [?] cubic centimeters.
4. Which has the greater volume, Cylinder A or Cylinder B?

EXERCISES

The area of each base is given. Use V = B × h ***to find the volume.***

5.

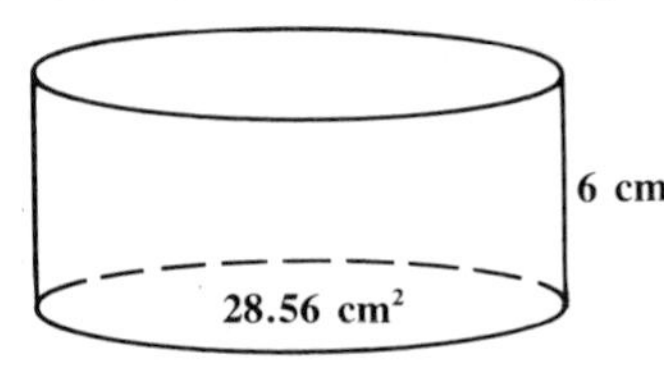

6.

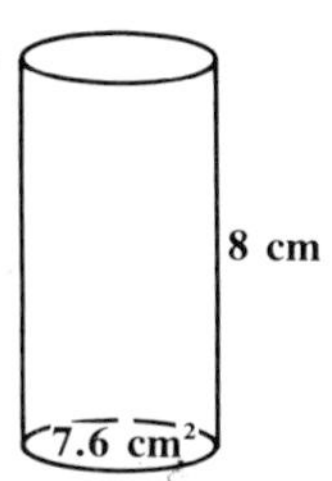

7.

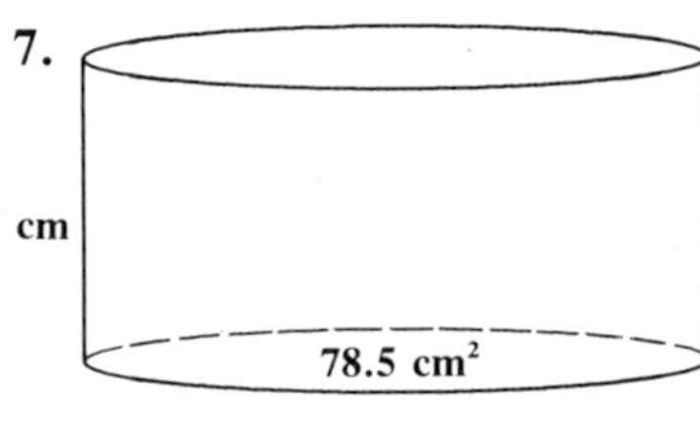

The radius and height are given. Use V = π × r × r × h ***to find the volume. Use 3.14 as an approximation for*** π***.***

8.

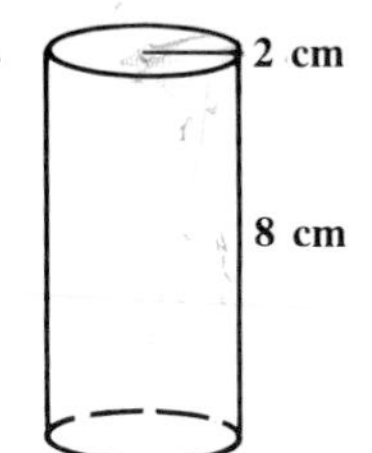

9.

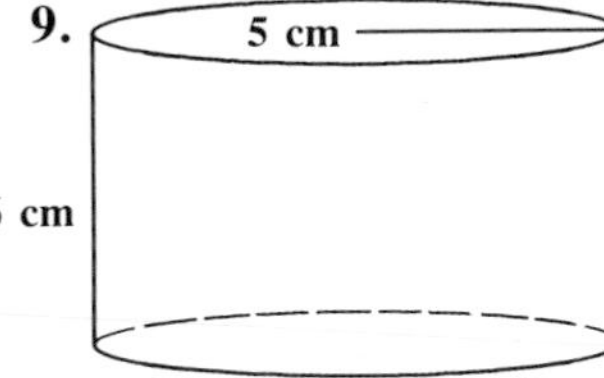

10.

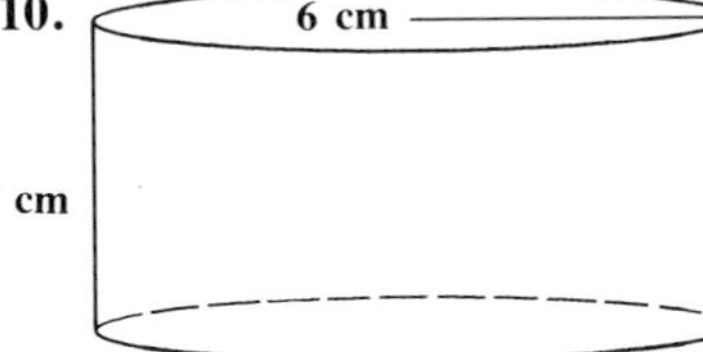

11.

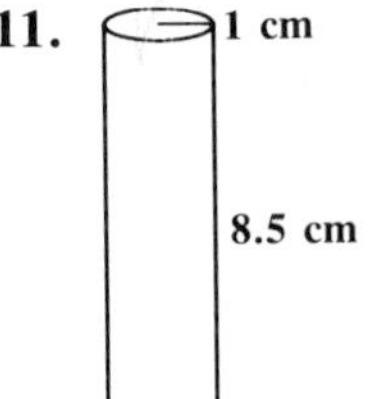

12.

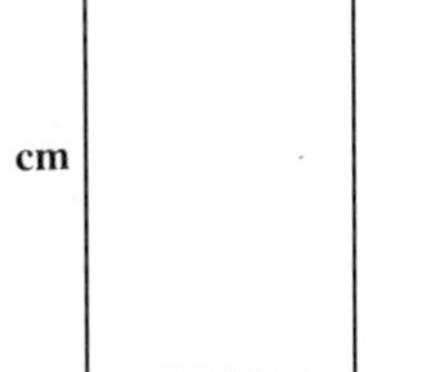

13.

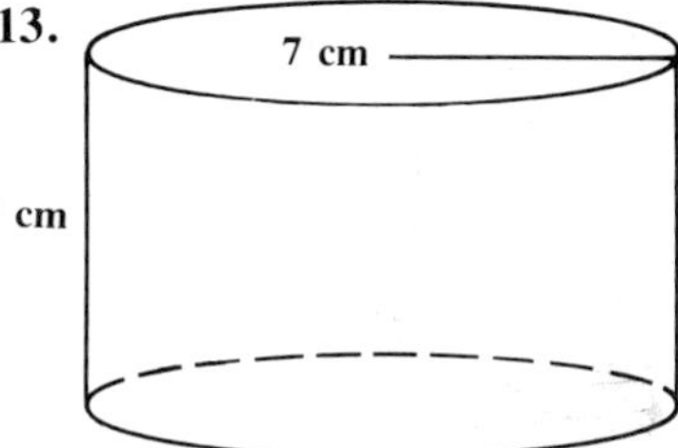

You decide!

Is the question about perimeter, area, or volume?

14. *How much fencing is needed to fence a patio?*

15. *How many flowers are needed to border a garden?*

16. "How much paper is needed to gift-wrap a box?"

17. "How much space is needed to store a corn harvest?"

Volume—pyramids and cones

1. It takes 3 pyramids of sand to fill the prism. So, the volume of a pyramid is ? the volume of a prism having the same base and height.
2. It takes 3 cones of sand to fill the cylinder. So, the volume of a cone is ? the volume of a cylinder having the same base and height.

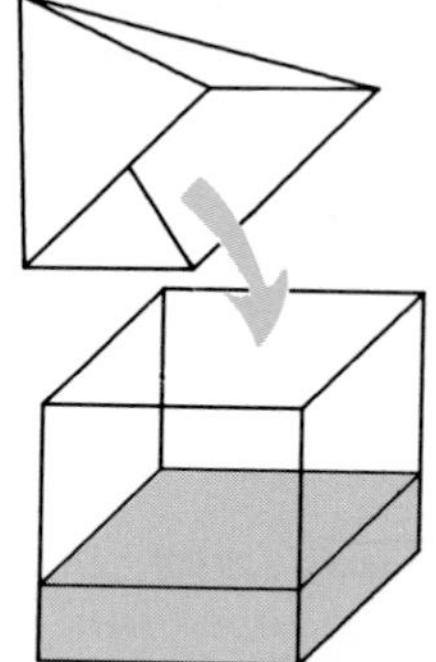

Here's how *to use a formula to find the volume of a pyramid or a cone.*

Pyramid

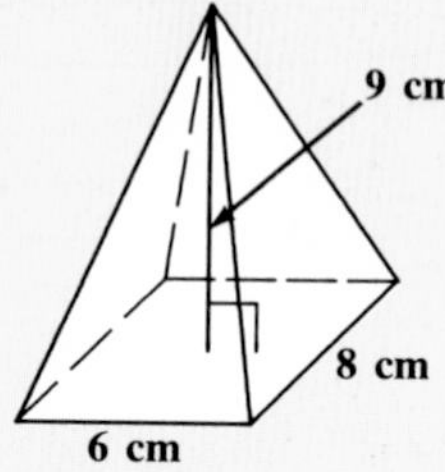

Rectangular Base

The volume (V) of a pyramid is $\frac{1}{3}$ times the area of the base (B) times the height (h).

FORMULA $V = \frac{1}{3} \times B \times h$ (area of the base)

$V = \frac{1}{3} \times (l \times w) \times h$

$V = \frac{1}{3} \times 6\text{ cm} \times 8\text{ cm} \times 9\text{ cm}$

$= 144\text{ cm}^3$

Cone

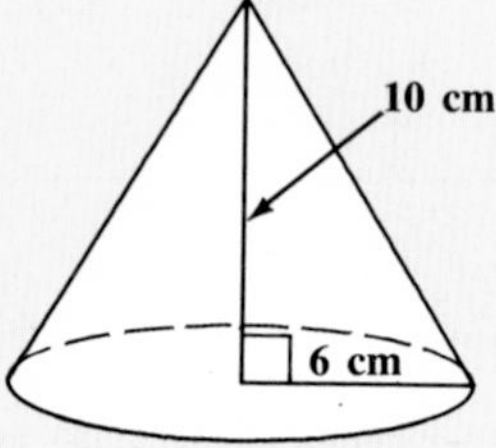

The volume (V) of a cone is $\frac{1}{3}$ times the area of the base (B) times the height (h).

FORMULA $V = \frac{1}{3} \times B \times h$ (area of the base)

$V = \frac{1}{3} \times (\pi \times r \times r) \times h$

$V \approx \frac{1}{3} \times 3.14 \times 6\text{ cm} \times 6\text{ cm} \times 10\text{ cm}$

$\approx \frac{1}{3} \times 1130.4\text{ cm}^3$

$\approx 376.8\text{ cm}^3$

3. Look at the *Here's how*. If the area of the base of a pyramid is 48 square centimeters and the height is 9 centimeters, the volume is ? cubic centimeters.
4. If the radius and height of a cone are 6 centimeters and 10 centimeters, the volume is approximately 376.8 cubic ?.

EXERCISES

The area of each base is given. Use the formula $V = \frac{1}{3} \times B \times h$ ***to find the volume.***

5\.
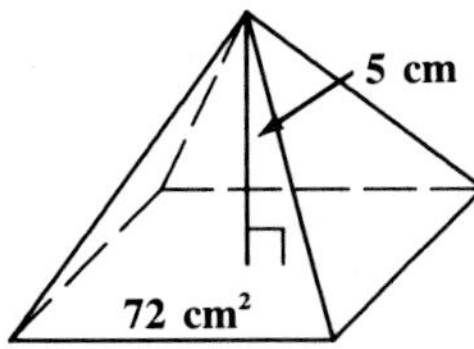

6\.
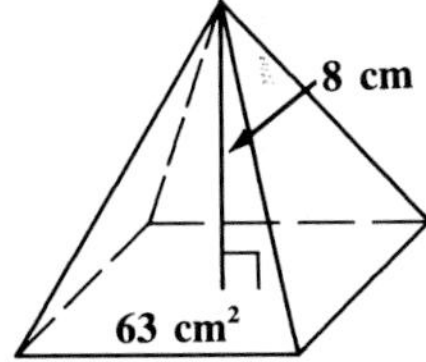

7\.
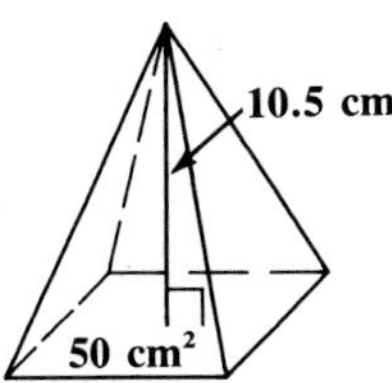

8\.
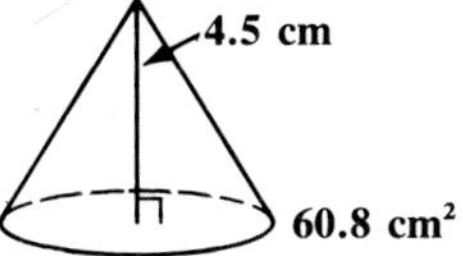

9\.
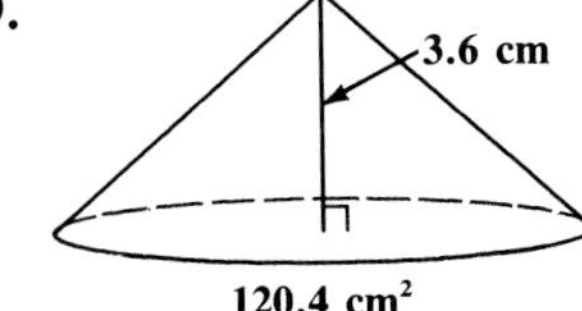

10\.

Each pyramid described below has a rectangular base. Find the volume.

11. $l = 4$ m, $w = 6$ m, $h = 3$ m

12. $l = 6$ m, $w = 5$ m, $h = 8$ m

13. $l = 2$ m, $w = 12$ m, $h = 11$ m

14. $l = 2.5$ m, $w = 4$ m, $h = 6$ m

15. $l = 7$ m, $w = 4.5$ m, $h = 8$ m

16. $l = 1.5$ m, $w = 10$ m, $h = 4.2$ m

Find the volume of each cone. Round the answer to the nearest tenth.

17. $r = 2$ cm, $h = 5$ cm

18. $r = 3$ cm, $h = 4$ cm

19. $r = 4$ cm, $h = 6$ cm

20. $r = 6$ cm, $h = 10$ cm

21. $r = 8$ cm, $h = 5$ cm

22. $r = 10$ cm, $h = 10$ cm

Volume hunt

23. *What size cube would have a volume of this many cubic meters?*

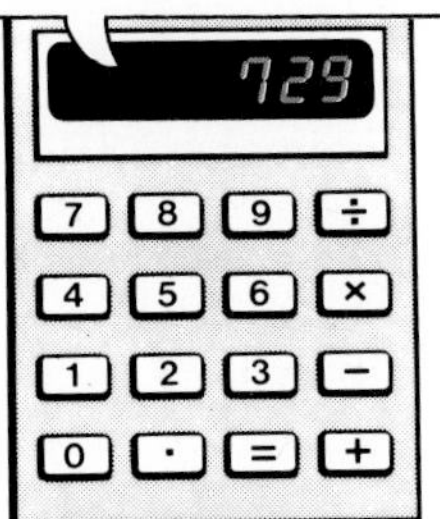

24. *What size cube would have a volume of this many cubic meters?*

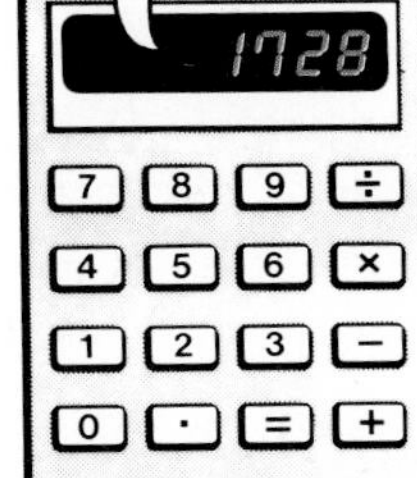

25. *What size cube would have a volume of this many cubic meters?*

Cumulative Skill Practice

Complete. *(page 206)*

1. 5000 mg = ? g
2. 3452 mg = ? g
3. 845 mg = ? g
4. 2000 g = ? kg
5. 6428 g = ? kg
6. 425 g = ? kg
7. 6.3 kg = ? g
8. 275 g = ? kg
9. 444 mg = ? g

Change to a decimal. *(page 252)*

10. 6%
11. 9%
12. 25%
13. 48%
14. 62%
15. 125%
16. 150%
17. 175%
18. 185%
19. 225%
20. 0.4%
21. 0.9%
22. 67.8%
23. 5.2%
24. 0.05%
25. $33\frac{1}{3}\%$
26. $37\frac{1}{2}\%$
27. $16\frac{2}{3}\%$
28. $162\frac{1}{2}\%$
29. $166\frac{2}{3}\%$

Solve. *(page 258)*

30. 10% of 60 = n
31. 25% of 96 = n
32. 20% of 60 = n
33. 16% of 40 = n
34. 7% of 23.5 = n
35. 150% of 72 = n
36. 8.5% of 110 = n
37. 22.4% of 80 = n
38. 36.5% of 62.5 = n
39. $33\frac{1}{3}\%$ of 81 = n
40. $62\frac{1}{2}\%$ of 74 = n
41. $66\frac{2}{3}\%$ of 171 = n

Solve. *(page 260)*

42. 20% of n = 15
43. 10% of n = 16
44. 40% of n = 60
45. 6% of n = 24
46. 80% of n = 20
47. 12% of n = 3

Solve. Round each answer to the nearest tenth. *(page 260)*

48. 12.5% of n = 8.4
49. 8.5% of n = 11.2
50. 9.6% of n = 15
51. 1.4% of n = 2.6
52. 125% of n = 43
53. 132% of n = 7.5
54. 12.5% of n = 9
55. 100% of n = 56
56. 105% of n = 63

Compute the interest. Round to the nearest cent. *(page 284)*

57. Principal = \$1000
Rate = 15% per year
Time = 3 years
58. Principal = \$700
Rate = 12% per year
Time = 6 months
59. Principal = \$100
Rate = 1.5% per month
Time = 3 months
60. Principal = \$350
Rate = 1% per month
Time = 5 months
61. Principal = \$900
Rate = 16% per year
Time = 9 months
62. Principal = \$250
Rate = 15.5% per year
Time = 18 months

Problem solving

COMPUTER GRAPHICS A computer can be programmed to sketch a space figure. These sketches were generated by a computer:

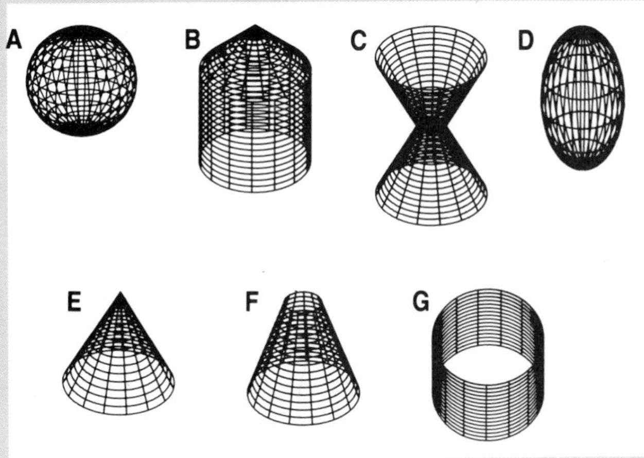

A computer can also be programmed to show several views of the same space figure.

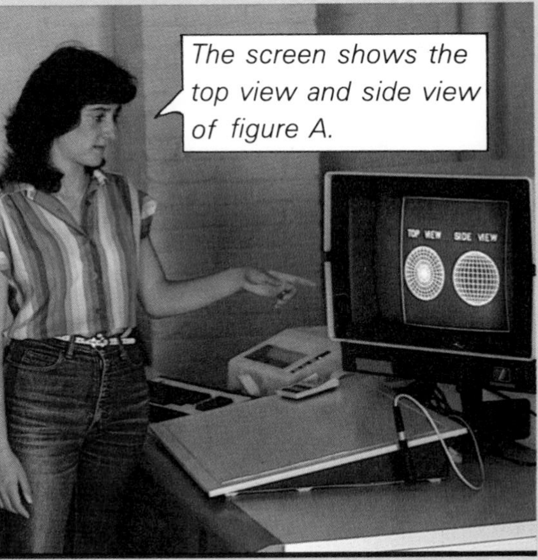

The screen shows the top view and side view of figure A.

Match the top and side views with one of the figures shown above.

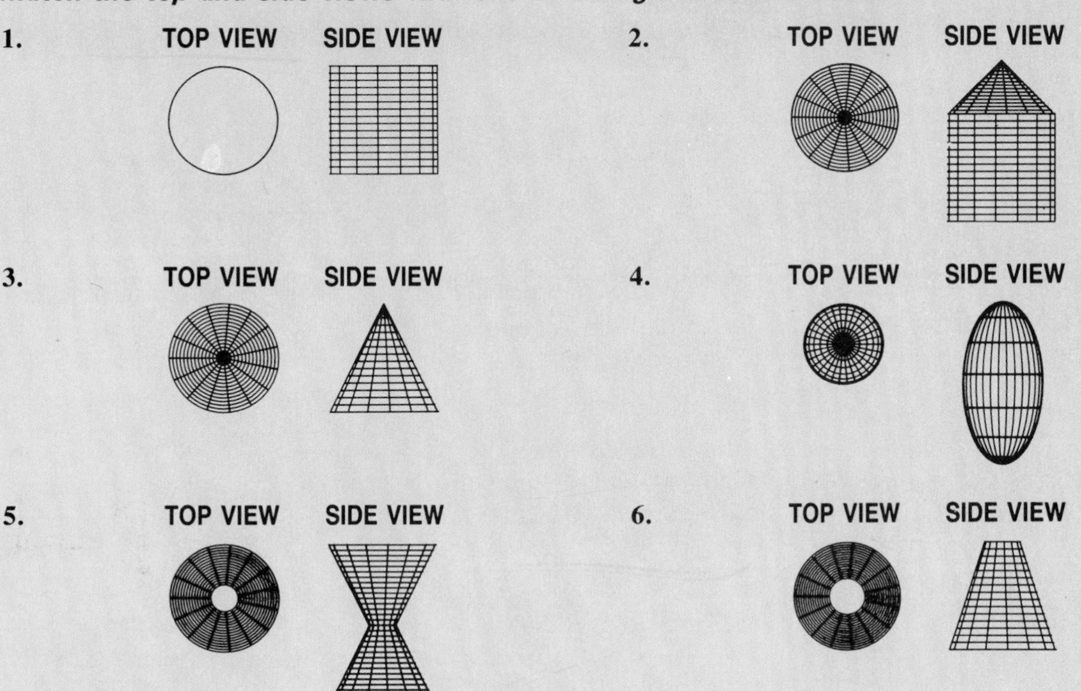

Chapter REVIEW

Here are scrambled answers for the review exercises:

12	125	add	cylinder	sphere
36	209	area	height	square pyramid
90	314	cone	rectangular prism	triangular prism

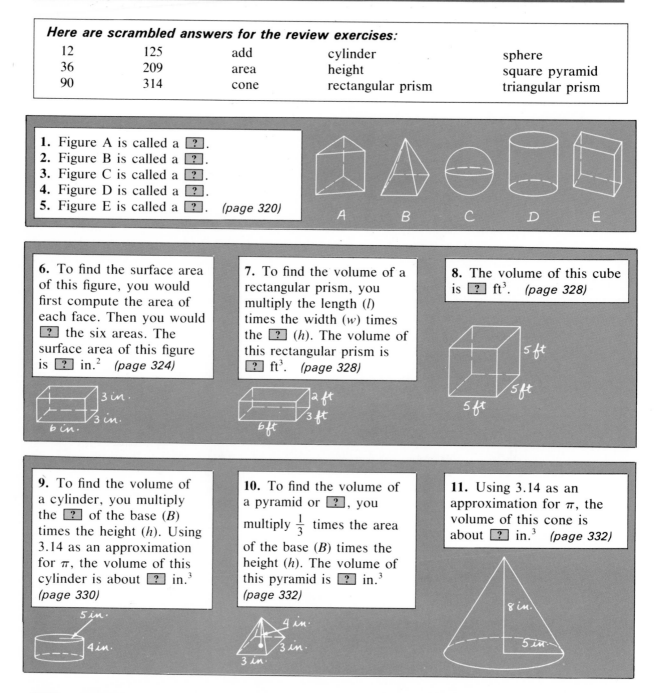

1. Figure A is called a [?].
2. Figure B is called a [?].
3. Figure C is called a [?].
4. Figure D is called a [?].
5. Figure E is called a [?]. *(page 320)*

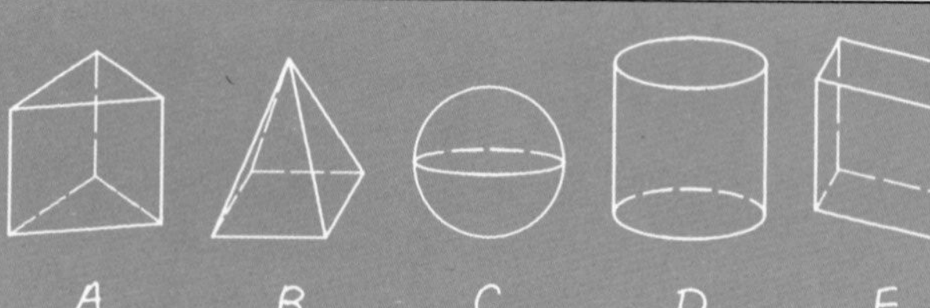

6. To find the surface area of this figure, you would first compute the area of each face. Then you would [?] the six areas. The surface area of this figure is [?] in.^{2} *(page 324)*

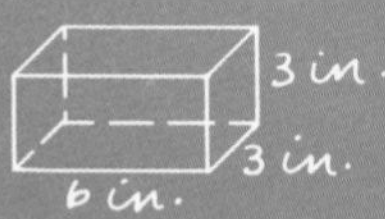

7. To find the volume of a rectangular prism, you multiply the length (l) times the width (w) times the [?] (h). The volume of this rectangular prism is [?] ft^3. *(page 328)*

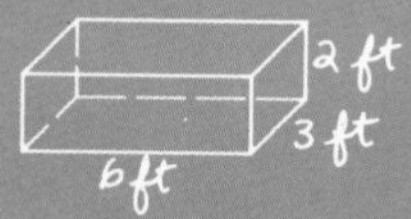

8. The volume of this cube is [?] ft^3. *(page 328)*

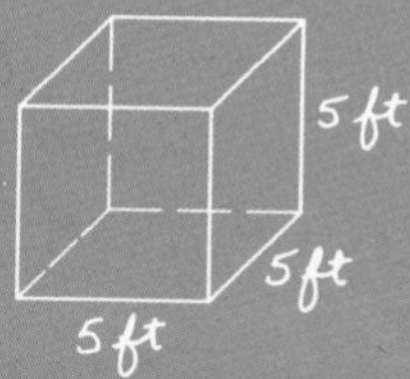

9. To find the volume of a cylinder, you multiply the [?] of the base (B) times the height (h). Using 3.14 as an approximation for π, the volume of this cylinder is about [?] in.^{3} *(page 330)*

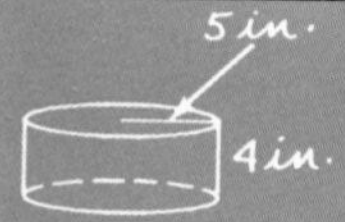

10. To find the volume of a pyramid or [?], you multiply $\frac{1}{3}$ times the area of the base (B) times the height (h). The volume of this pyramid is [?] in.^{3} *(page 332)*

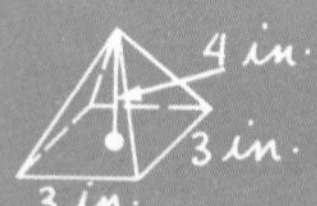

11. Using 3.14 as an approximation for π, the volume of this cone is about [?] in.^{3} *(page 332)*

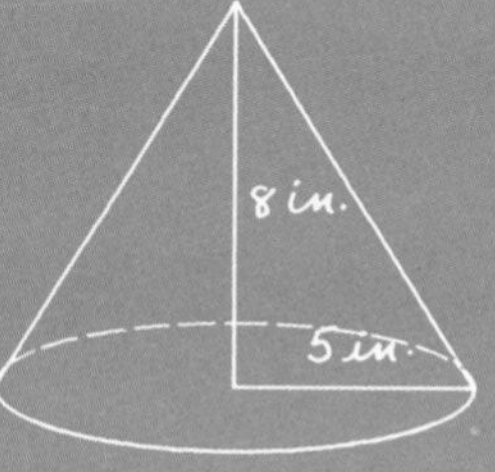

Chapter TEST

Match each space figure with its name. *(page 320)*

1. 
2. 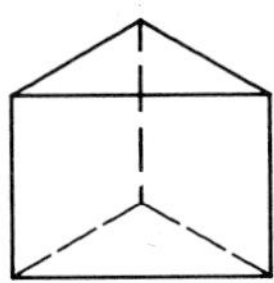
3. 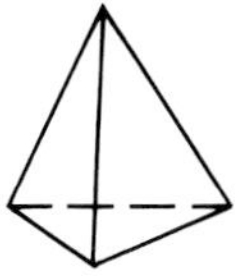 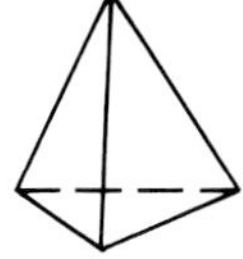 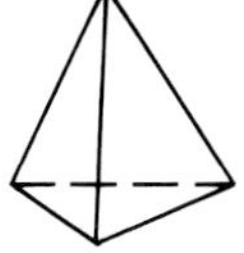 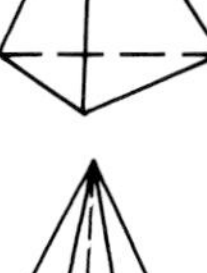
4. 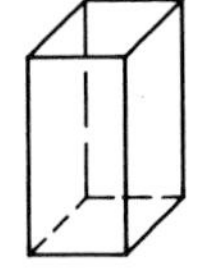
5. 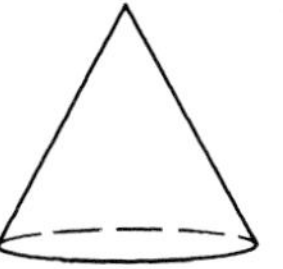
6. 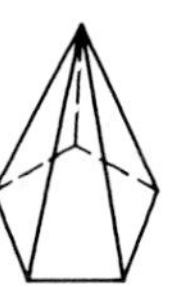
7. 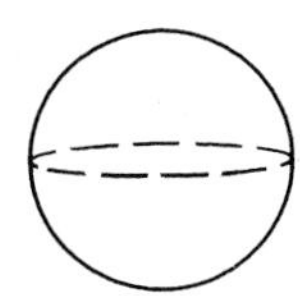
8. 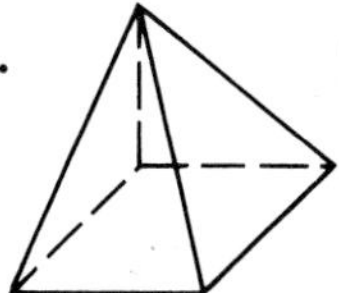
9. 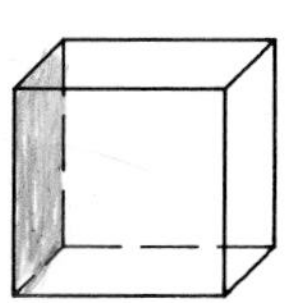

A. Cone
B. Cube
C. Cylinder
D. Pentagonal pyramid
E. Rectangular prism
F. Sphere
G. Square pyramid
H. Triangular prism
I. Triangular pyramid

Find the surface area. *(page 324)*

10. 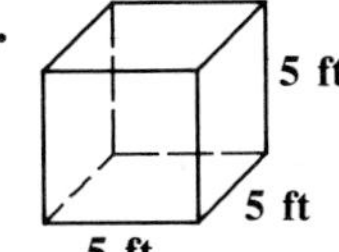

11. 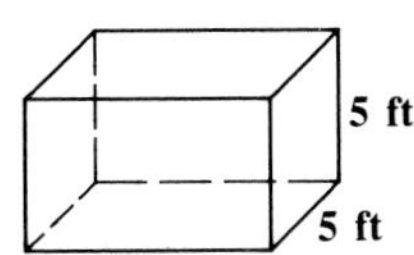

12. 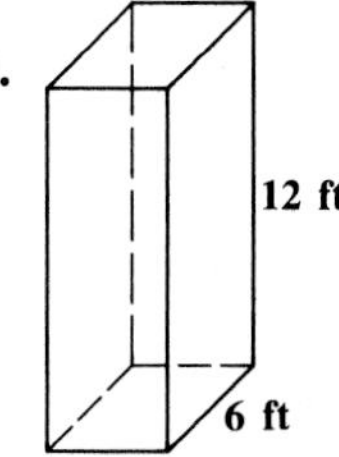

Find the volume. Use 3.14 as an approximation for π. *(pages 328, 330, 332)*

13. 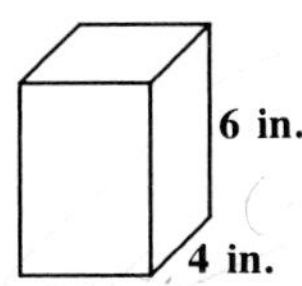

14. 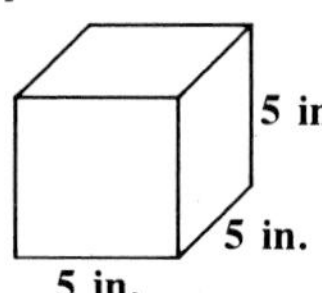

15. 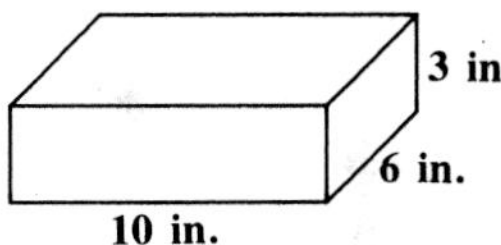

16. 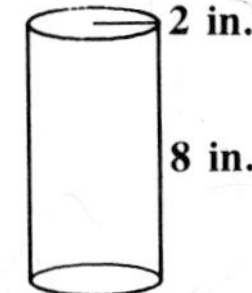

17. 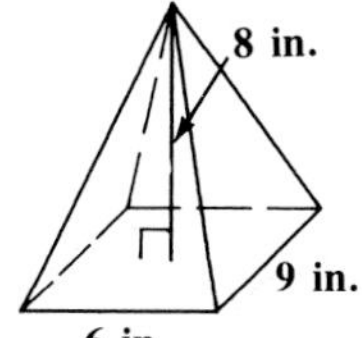

18. 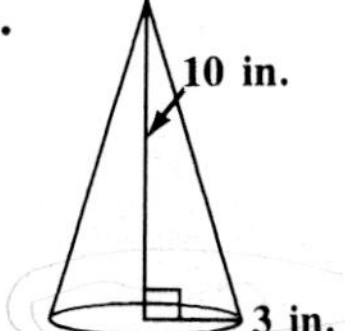

Cumulative TEST Standardized Format

Choose the correct letter.

1. Give the product.

   29.04×1.09

   A. 31.6536
   B. 55.1760
   C. 29.2506
   D. none of these

2. Give the quotient rounded to the nearest tenth.

   $64.08 \div 3.1$

   A. 20.67 B. 20.6
   C. 20.7 D. none of these

3. Change to a decimal rounded to the nearest hundredth.

   $\frac{5}{12} = ?$

   A. 2.40 B. 0.42
   C. 0.41 D. none of these

4. Subtract. $4\frac{1}{3} - 2\frac{3}{4}$

   A. $2\frac{5}{12}$ B. $2\frac{7}{12}$
   C. $1\frac{7}{12}$ D. none of these

5. Give the quotient.

   $3\frac{1}{4} \div 1\frac{1}{2}$

   A. $2\frac{1}{6}$ B. $4\frac{7}{8}$
   C. $\frac{6}{13}$ D. none of these

6. 525 mg = ___?___ g

   A. 5.25
   B. 52.5
   C. 5250
   D. none of these

7. Change to a decimal.

   $37\frac{1}{2}\% = ?$

   A. 37.5
   B. 3.75
   C. 0.375
   D. none of these

8. Solve.

   $33\frac{1}{3}\%$ of $45 = n$

   A. 15
   B. 30
   C. 135
   D. none of these

9. Solve.

   25% of $n = 17$

   A. 4.25
   B. 68
   C. 12.75
   D. none of these

10. Compute the interest.

    Principal = $820
    Rate = 14% per year
    Time = 9 months

    A. $114.80
    B. $28.70
    C. $1033.20
    D. none of these

11. Find the area of this parallelogram.

    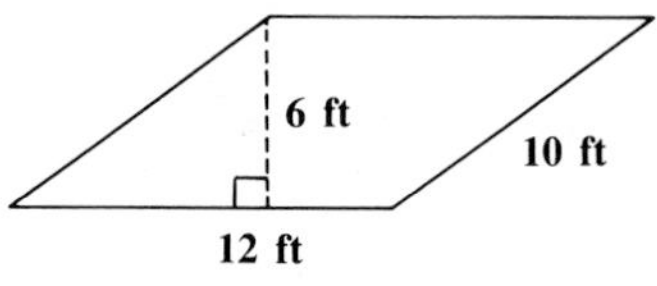

    A. 72 ft^2
    B. 120 ft^2
    C. 44 ft^2
    D. none of these

12. Find the volume of this rectangular prism.

    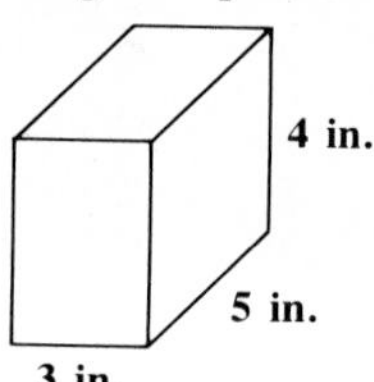

    A. 12 $in.^3$
    B. 35 $in.^3$
    C. 60 $in.^3$
    D. none of these

Chapter 15
Probability

A basic counting principle

DECISIONS, DECISIONS!

1. How many different outfits (a skirt and a blouse) can be made if the blue skirt is worn?
2. How many different outfits can be made if the gray skirt is worn?
3. How many different outfits are there in all?

Here's how *to show all the possible outfits with a* **tree diagram.**

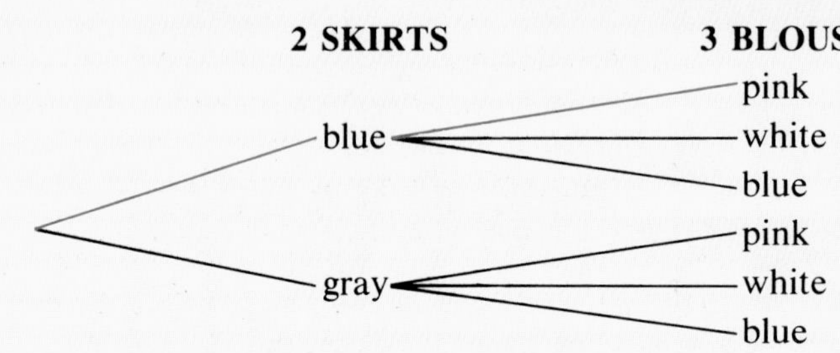

The red "branch" represents a blue skirt and a pink blouse.
You can determine the number of outfits by counting the branches of the tree diagram.

4. Look at the *Here's how*. What outfit is represented by the top branch? The bottom branch?
5. How many possible outfits are there? *Hint: Count the branches.*

Here's how *to use a* **basic counting principle** *to compute the total number of outfits.*

To compute the total number of ways that several decisions can be made, multiply the number of choices for each of the decisions.

Choices in First Decision (skirts)		Choices in Second Decision (blouses)		Total Choices (outfits)
2	×	3	=	6

EXERCISES

Solve.

6. a. How many choices of pants are there? How many choices of sweaters are there?
   b. Draw a tree diagram to show all possible outfits.
   c. How many possible outfits are there?
   d. How many different outfits can be made if the black pants are worn?
   e. How many different outfits can be made if the red sweater is not worn?

7. You decide to wear a pair of corduroys and a sweater. How many outfits do you have if you have 4 pairs of corduroys and 5 sweaters?

8. How many outfits can you make from 3 pairs of pants, 4 shirts, and 2 sweaters if each outfit consists of pants, a shirt, and a sweater?

9. In an election of your class officers, 3 students are running for president, 3 for vice president, 2 for secretary, and 2 for treasurer. How many different combinations are possible?

10. You decide to buy a stereo system. You can choose from 5 amplifiers, 6 kinds of speakers, and 4 turntables. How many different systems are possible?

11. You are in Chicago and win a free trip to Waikiki Beach in Honolulu. The "map" shows the choices of ways to travel.
    a. How many ways can you travel from Chicago to Los Angeles?
    b. How many ways can you travel from Chicago to Honolulu?
    c. How many ways can you travel from Chicago to Waikiki Beach?
    d. How many choices would you have for making the round trip?

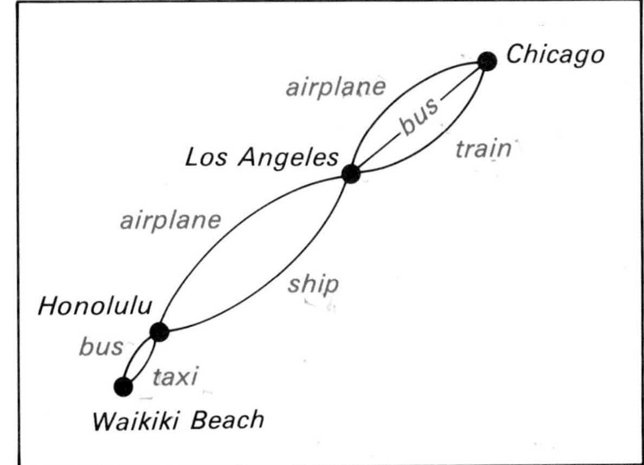

You're the detective!

12. A witness observed a speeding car leaving the scene of an accident. One digit and two letters on the license plate were covered with mud.

    What is the greatest number of license plates that you would have to check to find the owner of the car?

Permutations

Bob, Ann, and Mary had this photograph taken at an amusement park.

1. Who is on the left? The right? Who is in the middle?
2. The letters BAM may be used to describe the order they were in when the photo was taken. Use the letters to list all possible orders.
3. How many ways can the 3 people be arranged for the photograph?

An arrangement of things in a **definite order** is called a **permutation**.

Here's how *to compute the number of permutations (possible arrangements).*

Number of people to choose from for first position		Number left to choose from for second position		Number left to choose from for third position		Number of possible arrangements
↓		↓		↓		↓
3	×	2	×	1	=	6

4. Look at the *Here's how*. To compute the number of permutations (possible arrangements) of 3 things, you would multiply what three numbers?
5. Think about 4 people and a comic photo scene that requires 4 faces.
   a. How many people would there be to choose from for the first position?
   b. How many people would there be left to choose from for the second position? The third position? The fourth position?
   c. What four numbers would you multiply to compute the number of permutations (possible arrangements) of 4 things?
   d. How many ways can the 4 people be arranged for the photograph?

EXERCISES

Solve.

6. Bob, Ann, and Mary decided to buy some ride tickets at the amusement park. How many ways could they line up to purchase their tickets?

7. Bob bought the tickets shown.
   a. For how many rides did he buy tickets?
   b. What was the average price of the tickets?
   c. In how many different orders could Bob take the 5 rides?

8. Each bobsled seated 4 people in a row. In how many ways could 4 people be seated on a bobsled?

9. a. Ann decided to buy a sandwich and a drink for lunch. How many different lunches could she buy?
   b. Mary decided to buy a sandwich and a dessert for lunch. How many different lunches could she buy?
   c. Suppose that you wanted to buy a sandwich and a drink and that you decided not to order a fish sandwich. How many different lunches could you buy?
   d. How many different lunches could Bob order if he decided to order a sandwich, a drink, and a dessert?
   e. Bob ordered a cheeseburger, milk, and a dessert. He gave the clerk $5 and got $1.90 in change. What dessert did he order?

JOYLAND SNACK BAR	
SANDWICHES	
Hamburger	$1.45
Cheeseburger	1.65
Hot Dog	1.30
Fish	1.45
DRINKS	
Coffee	.60
Cola	.65
Root Beer	.65
Lemonade	.75
Milk	.70
DESSERTS	
Ice Cream	.95
Brownie	.75
Apple Pie	1.30

Please be seated!

10. Each car on the Grand Canyon Railroad holds 10 people. Suppose that you and 9 of your friends were in one of the cars.
   a. How many ways could the group be seated?
   b. Suppose that the group could change the seating order every 5 seconds. How many seconds would it take for the group to sit in all possible orders?
   c. How many minutes would it take? How many hours? How many days?

Probability

WHAT ARE YOUR CHANCES?

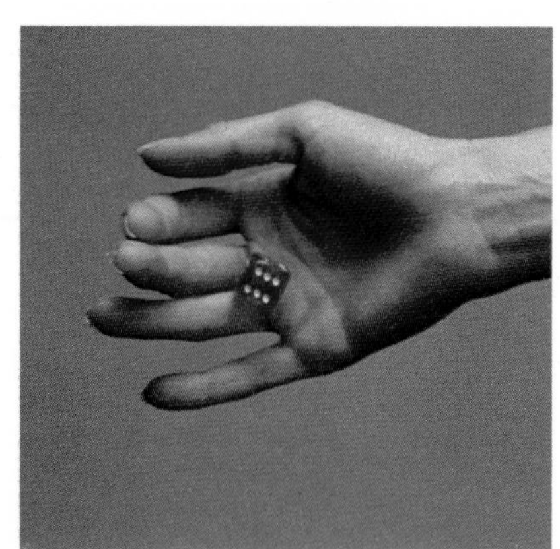

1. Suppose that you rolled the die. How many different outcomes would be possible? (How many different numbers could possibly land facing up?)
2. Would the possible outcomes be equally likely? (Would all numbers have the same chance of landing facing up?)

Here's how ***to find the probability (the chance) of a given outcome when all the outcomes are equally likely.***

Probability of rolling a 1

$$P(1) = \frac{\text{number of ways of rolling a 1}}{\text{number of possible outcomes}}$$

$$P(1) = \frac{1}{6}$$

The probability of 1 equals $\frac{1}{6}$.

Probability of rolling either a 5 or a 6

$$P(5 \text{ or } 6) = \frac{2}{6}$$

There are two ways to get either a 5 or a 6.

$$P(5 \text{ or } 6) = \frac{1}{3}$$

3. Look at the *Here's how*. What is the probability of rolling a 1?
4. What is the probability of rolling a 5 or a 6?

EXERCISES

Give each probability as a fraction in simplest form.

Think about rolling a die.

5. P(3)	**6.** P(6)	**7.** P(1 or 2)
8. P(even)	**9.** P(odd)	**10.** P(1, 2, or 3)
11. P(3 or less)	**12.** P(greater than 2)	**13.** P(not 1)
14. P(not 5)	**15.** P(7)	**16.** P(6 or less)

17. Look at your answer to exercise 15. What is the probability of an impossible outcome?
18. Look at your answer to exercise 16. What is the probability of an outcome that is certain to occur?

Give each probability as a fraction in simplest form.

Think about spinning this spinner.

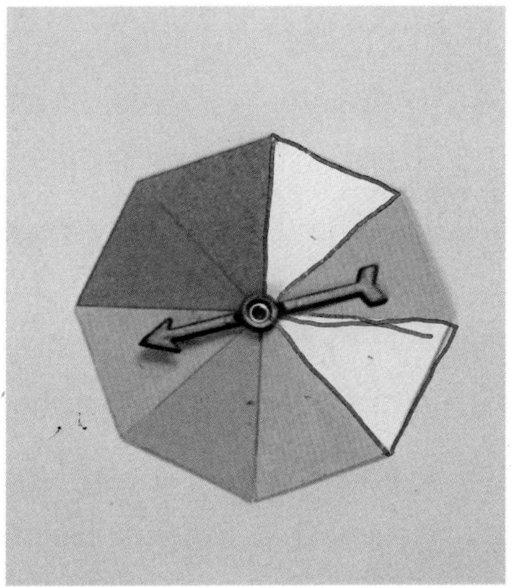

19. P(red)
20. P(not red)
21. P(blue)
22. P(not blue)
23. P(yellow)
24. P(not yellow)
25. P(green)
26. P(not green)
27. P(black)
28. P(not black)
29. P(brown or red)
30. P(yellow or blue)
31. P(yellow or green)
32. P(red or green)
33. P(blue or green)
34. P(black or yellow)
35. P(yellow, blue, or green)
36. P(brown, blue, or red)

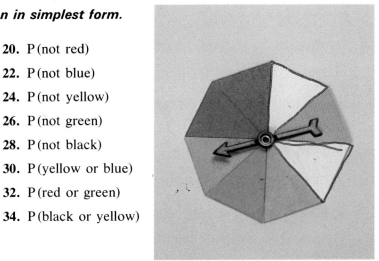

Think about shuffling these cards and then turning one of the cards face up.

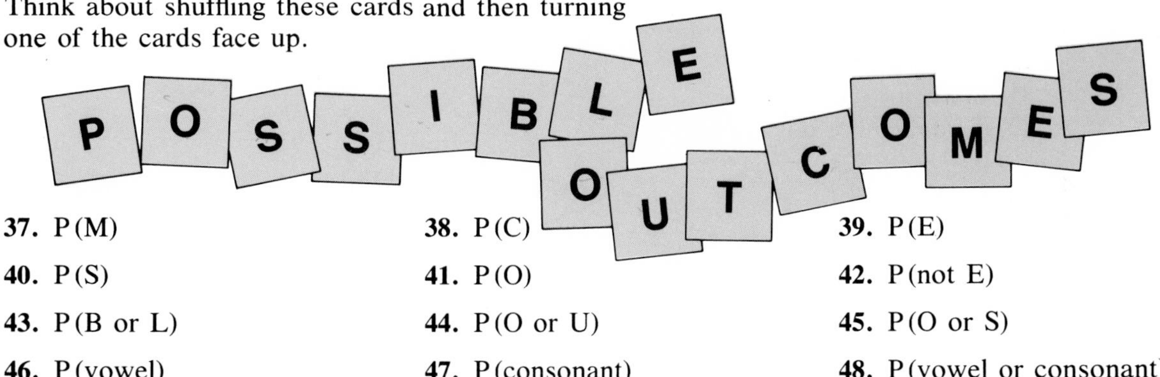

37. P(M)
38. P(C)
39. P(E)
40. P(S)
41. P(O)
42. P(not E)
43. P(B or L)
44. P(O or U)
45. P(O or S)
46. P(vowel)
47. P(consonant)
48. P(vowel or consonant)

Tack toss

When you toss a thumbtack, there are two possible outcomes: landing point up or landing point down.

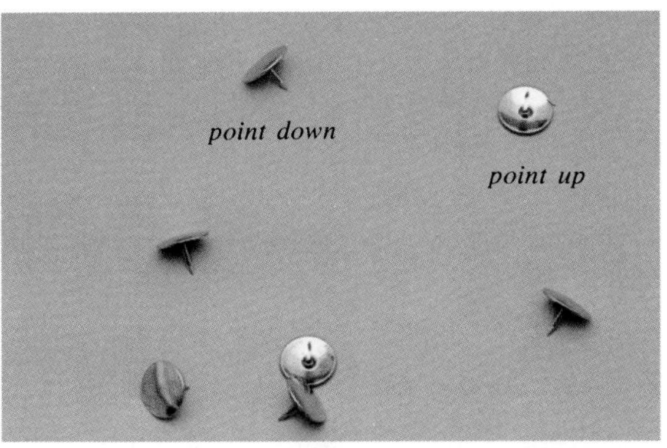

49. Do you think that the outcomes are equally likely?
50. Toss a thumbtack 50 times and keep a record of the outcomes.
51. From the results of your experiment, do you think a thumbtack has a greater chance of landing point up or landing point down?

Sample spaces

FREE FRIES!

BOB'S BURGER HOUSE
Rub each square.
If all pictures match,
you get a free order of fries!

Each time you buy a hamburger or hot dog at BOB'S BURGER HOUSE, you get a card like the one shown. When you rub each square on your card, a picture of a hamburger is as likely to appear as a picture of a hot dog.

1. What is the prize for a winning card?
2. Is the card shown above a winning card?

To find how many different kinds of cards are possible, you can list the **sample space** (all possible outcomes).

Here's how *to use a tree diagram to show the sample space.*

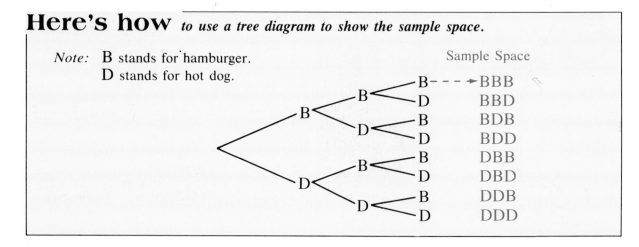

Note: B stands for hamburger.
D stands for hot dog.

First	Second	Third	Sample Space
B	B	B	BBB
		D	BBD
	D	B	BDB
		D	BDD
D	B	B	DBB
		D	DBD
	D	B	DDB
		D	DDD

3. Look at the *Here's how*. How many outcomes are in the sample space?
4. How many of the outcomes are winners (all of the pictures match)?
5. What is the probability (in simplest form) of getting a winning card?

EXERCISES

Use the sample space above. Give each probability in simplest form.

What is the probability of getting a card having

6. exactly 1 hamburger?
7. exactly 2 hamburgers?
8. a hot dog in the first square?
9. a hamburger in the middle square?
10. What is the probability of getting a losing card?

Solve.

11. a. One day BOB'S BURGER HOUSE gave away 296 cards. Suppose that one fourth of the cards were winning cards. How many orders of fries were given away?

b. It costs BOB'S BURGER HOUSE 23¢ to buy, prepare, and serve an order of fries. How much did the winning cards cost BOB'S?

12. a. Of the 296 hamburgers and hot dogs sold that day, 183 were hamburgers. If each hamburger sold for \$1.35, how much money did BOB'S get from the sale of hamburgers?

b. How many hot dogs were sold?

c. If \$107.35 was received from the sale of hot dogs, what was the price of each hot dog?

If you buy an ice cream cone at BOB'S BURGER HOUSE you get one of the cards shown below. When you rub each square on your card, a vanilla, chocolate, or strawberry cone will appear. Each flavor is equally likely to appear.

13. Copy and complete the tree diagram to show the sample space.

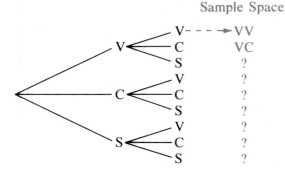

		Sample Space
V	V	VV
	C	VC
	S	?
C	V	?
	C	?
	S	?
S	V	?
	C	?
	S	?

14. Use the sample space from exercise 13. Give each probability in simplest form.

a. P(exactly 1 vanilla)
b. P(2 strawberry)
c. P(no chocolate)
d. P(winning)
e. P(losing)

15. a. During one day, 141 cones were sold. If one third of the cards were winners, how many cones were sold for 25¢ off the regular price?

b. The regular price for a cone is 75¢. How much money was received from cone sales that day?

Cone count

16. A certain ice-cream store sells 31 flavors. A customer decides to order a 3-dip cone. He first orders the flavor of the bottom dip, next orders the flavor of the middle dip, and last orders the flavor of the top dip. How many different such orders could he give? *Hint: He may order 3 scoops of the same flavor.*

Cumulative Skill Practice

Round to the nearest ten thousand. *(page 12)*

1. 12,750 **2.** 46,394 **3.** 75,008 **4.** 45,000 **5.** 59,981

6. 56,000 **7.** 94,999 **8.** 95,000 **9.** 97,074 **10.** 98,241

11. 386,381 **12.** 283,077 **13.** 439,500 **14.** 705,000 **15.** 164,138

16. 526,000 **17.** 664,990 **18.** 837,911 **19.** 895,000 **20.** 306,241

Give the product. *(page 64)*

21. 4.6×0.7 **22.** 3.9×0.31 **23.** 0.65×0.6 **24.** 4.5×3.1

25. 52×2.6 **26.** 0.74×8.1 **27.** 5.13×1.4 **28.** 2.04×0.1

29. 8.72×16 **30.** 38.5×7.4 **31.** 56.3×0.75 **32.** 62.3×6.3

33. 8.58×8 **34.** 23.3×5.6 **35.** 403×2.9 **36.** 124×8.4

37. 2.01×0.08 **38.** 52.3×60.4 **39.** 5.92×22.9 **40.** 4.7×3.08

Give the quotient rounded to the nearest tenth. *(page 96)*

41. $18.2 \div 0.6$ **42.** $2.95 \div 0.2$ **43.** $8.3 \div 0.03$ **44.** $16.4 \div 0.2$

45. $34.1 \div 0.5$ **46.** $8.64 \div 0.07$ **47.** $9.2 \div 0.08$ **48.** $3.95 \div 0.03$

49. $6.23 \div 1.4$ **50.** $2.036 \div 3.1$ **51.** $5.02 \div 0.35$ **52.** $4.61 \div 0.21$

53. $14.071 \div 0.33$ **54.** $5.003 \div 0.54$ **55.** $7.51 \div 8.2$ **56.** $8.34 \div 2.4$

57. $6.71 \div 8.03$ **58.** $2759 \div 4.8$ **59.** $37.7 \div 3.09$ **60.** $46.3 \div 2.01$

Give the sum in simplest form. *(page 158)*

61. $\frac{2}{9} + \frac{4}{9}$ **62.** $\frac{1}{8} + \frac{3}{8}$ **63.** $\frac{1}{2} + \frac{1}{4}$ **64.** $\frac{1}{2} + \frac{1}{3}$ **65.** $\frac{3}{8} + \frac{1}{4}$

66. $\frac{1}{4} + \frac{1}{3}$ **67.** $\frac{2}{5} + \frac{1}{2}$ **68.** $\frac{1}{6} + \frac{1}{8}$ **69.** $\frac{1}{5} + \frac{3}{4}$ **70.** $\frac{1}{6} + \frac{4}{5}$

71. $\frac{3}{10} + \frac{3}{10}$ **72.** $\frac{5}{12} + \frac{3}{4}$ **73.** $\frac{9}{16} + \frac{7}{8}$ **74.** $\frac{4}{5} + \frac{3}{4}$ **75.** $\frac{8}{15} + \frac{9}{10}$

Give the difference in simplest form. *(page 166)*

76. $\frac{1}{2} - \frac{1}{4}$ **77.** $\frac{2}{3} - \frac{1}{4}$ **78.** $\frac{1}{2} - \frac{1}{3}$ **79.** $\frac{2}{5} - \frac{1}{4}$ **80.** $\frac{3}{4} - \frac{2}{3}$

81. $\frac{2}{3} - \frac{1}{8}$ **82.** $\frac{1}{2} - \frac{2}{5}$ **83.** $\frac{7}{8} - \frac{3}{4}$ **84.** $\frac{4}{5} - \frac{3}{10}$ **85.** $\frac{3}{8} - \frac{1}{6}$

86. $3 - \frac{9}{10}$ **87.** $\frac{11}{16} - \frac{1}{2}$ **88.** $\frac{11}{12} - \frac{5}{8}$ **89.** $\frac{7}{10} - \frac{1}{4}$ **90.** $\frac{9}{16} - \frac{3}{8}$

Problem solving

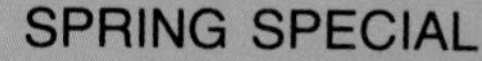

SPRING SPECIAL **ONLY $900**

INSTALLMENT PLAN

$228 down payment
$65 per month for 12 months

SALE

SHADE TREES	Regular Price	THIS WEEK ONLY
Pin Oak	$24	25% OFF
Red Oak	$30	30% OFF
Sugar Maple	$40	20% OFF
Sweet Gum	$28	25% OFF
White Birch	$36	25% OFF

Grass Seed .... $1.65 per lb
Fertilizer .... 10 lb for $9.60

You are the clerk. Answer each customer's question.

1. *What is the sale price of a white birch tree?*

2. *How much do I save by buying a pin oak on sale?*

3. "How much will 8 pounds of grass seed and 20 pounds of fertilizer cost?"

4. "How much do I save if I buy a sugar maple and a sweet gum on sale?"

5. "If I use 2 pounds of grass seed for every 600 square feet, how many pounds will I need to seed a square lawn that measures 60 feet on a side?"

6. "If I use 4 pounds of grass seed for every 1000 square feet, how much will it cost to seed a rectangular yard that is 50 feet by 80 feet?"

7. "What is the total cost of a red oak, a sweet gum, and a sugar maple on sale?"

8. "How much is the total installment cost for the lawn tractor?"

9. "If I could borrow $900 at 12% per year for 1 year, would that be less expensive than buying the tractor on your installment plan?"

10. "If 10 pounds of fertilizer will cover 5000 square feet of lawn, how many pounds will I use to fertilize a lawn that is 50 feet by 70 feet?"

Probability—more than 1 event

The tree diagram shows all possible outcomes of a first event (rolling a die) followed by a second event (tossing a coin).

1. Think about the first event, rolling a die. What is the probability of rolling a 1?
2. Think about the second event, tossing a coin. What is the probability of tossing heads (H)?
3. Now look at the tree diagram. What is the probability of first rolling a 1 and then tossing heads (H)?

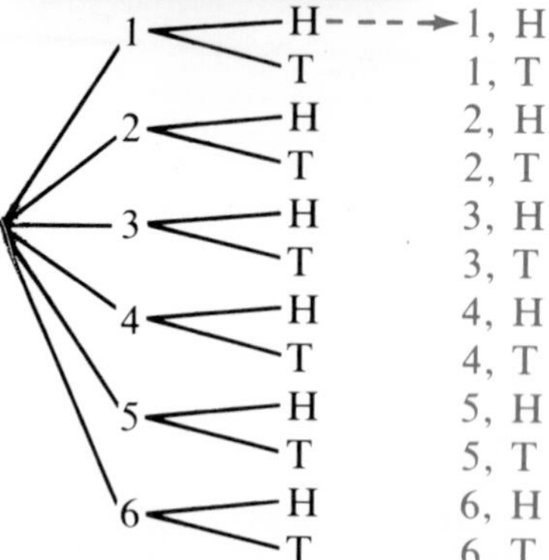

Here's how *to compute the probability of rolling a 1 and then tossing heads (H).*

Multiply the probability of the first outcome's occurring by the probability of the second outcome's occurring.

the probability of 1 and then heads

$$P(1, H) = \underset{P(1)}{\frac{1}{6}} \times \underset{P(H)}{\frac{1}{2}}$$

$$= \frac{1}{12}$$

4. Look at the *Here's how*. What is P(1)? What is P(H)?
5. What is P(1, H)?

EXERCISES

Give each probability as a fraction in simplest form.

Think about first rolling a die and then tossing a coin.

6. **a.** P(2)
   b. P(T)
   c. P(2, T)
7. **a.** P(even number)
   b. P(H)
   c. P(even number, H)
8. P(number less than 3, T)
9. P(not 5, T)

Think about first rolling the die and then spinning the spinner.

10. P(4, red)
11. P(6, yellow)
12. P(even number, yellow)
13. P(not 6, blue)
14. P(2, not yellow)
15. P(not 1, not brown)
16. P(number greater than 2, green)

Think about spinning the above spinner once and then spinning it again.

17. P(red, red)
18. P(yellow, yellow)
19. P(green, green)
20. P(brown, blue)
21. P(red, yellow)
22. P(yellow, green)
23. P(not red, green)
24. P(yellow, not yellow)
25. P(not green, not blue)
26. P(not green, not yellow)

Think about placing the 6 marbles in a bag and thoroughly mixing them up. Suppose that, without looking, you picked out a first marble, **put it back into the bag,** and then picked out a second marble.

27. P(green, blue)
28. P(orange, green)
29. P(blue, red)
30. P(green, not orange)
31. P(not orange, green)
32. P(blue, not blue)

Think about placing the 6 marbles in a bag and thoroughly mixing them up. Suppose that without looking, you picked out a first marble, **left it out of the bag,** and then picked out a second marble.

33. P(green, blue) $= \frac{1}{6} \times \frac{2}{5}$
$= ?$

There are 2 blue marbles among the 5 remaining marbles.

34. P(orange, green)
35. P(blue, orange)
36. P(orange, orange)
37. P(green, blue)
38. P(blue, blue)
39. P(green, green)

Seven up!

Think about tossing 2 dice.

40. How many ways can you get a sum of 7?
41. What is the probability of getting a sum of 7?

Odds

COLOR	NUMBER OF GUM BALLS
Green	80
Blue	90
White	70
Yellow	140
Red	100
Orange	120

The table shows the contents of the gum-ball machine.

1. Suppose that the gum balls have been thoroughly mixed. Which color do you have the best chance of getting? The worst chance of getting?
2. How many gum balls are red?
3. How many gum balls are not red?

Here's how *to find the odds in favor of getting a red gum ball with your first penny.*

To find the **odds in favor of an outcome,** write the ratio of the number of ways the outcome can occur to the number of ways that the outcome cannot occur.

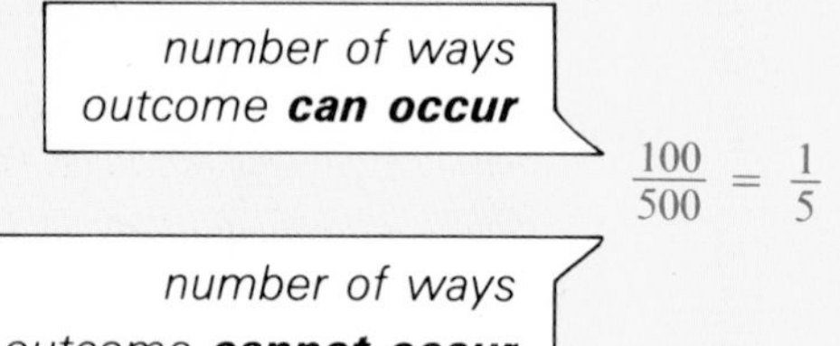

$$\frac{100}{500} = \frac{1}{5}$$

The odds in favor of getting a red gum ball are 1 to 5.

4. Look at the *Here's how*. What is the number of ways the outcome can occur? Cannot occur?
5. What are the odds in favor of getting a red gum ball?

EXERCISES

Give the odds as a fraction in lowest terms.

Think about putting your first penny into the gum-ball machine.

6. Odds in favor of getting a green
7. Odds in favor of getting a blue
8. Odds in favor of getting a white
9. Odds in favor of getting a yellow
10. Odds in favor of getting either a red or an orange
11. Odds in favor of getting either a green or a white

Here's how *to find the odds against getting a red gum ball with your first penny.*

To find the **odds against an outcome,** write the ratio of the number of ways that the outcome cannot occur to the number of ways that the outcome can occur.

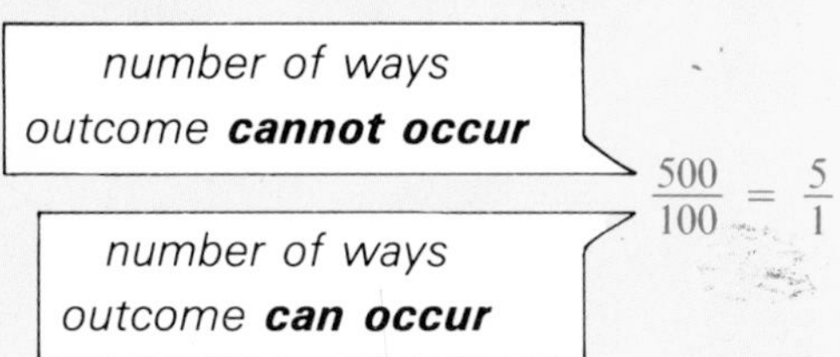

The odds against getting a red gum ball are 5 to 1.

Give the odds in lowest terms.

Think about putting your first penny into the gum-ball machine.

12. Odds against getting red

13. Odds against getting blue

14. Odds against getting white

15. Odds against getting yellow

16. Odds against getting either a blue or a white

17. Odds against getting either a yellow or a red

18. Suppose that your favorite color is yellow. What are the odds in favor of your getting your favorite color? The odds against?

19. A friend likes either white or orange. What are the odds in favor of your friend's getting one of his favorite colors? The odds against?

Solve.

20. Suppose that in another gum-ball machine the odds in favor of your getting your favorite color are 1 to 7. What would be the odds against your getting your favorite color?

21. If the odds against getting a black gum ball are 11 to 3, what are the odds in favor of getting a black gum ball?

Something to chew on!

22. The odds in favor of getting a red gum ball are 5 to 23. What is the probability of getting a red gum ball?

23. The odds against getting a green gum ball are 25 to 3. What is the probability of getting a green gum ball?

Expectation

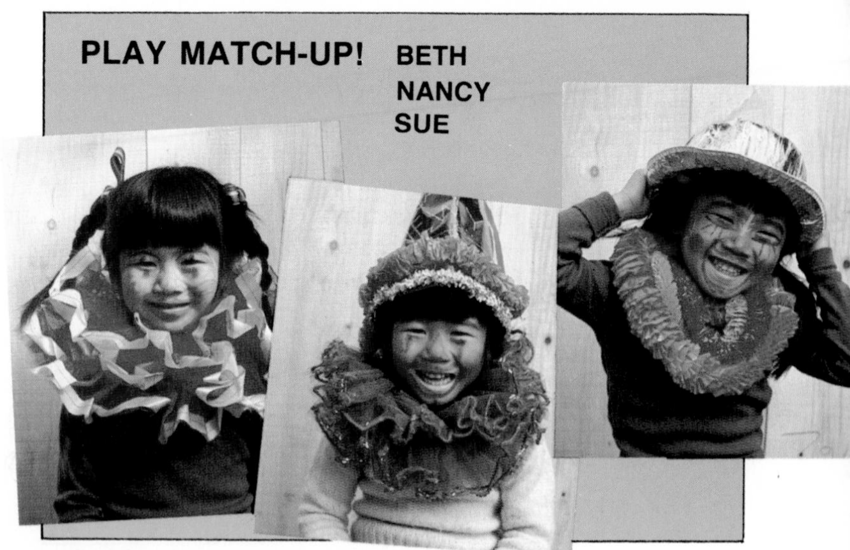

A set of triplets gave these childhood pictures to their school carnival committee. Each contestant is charged \$2 to match the pictures with the names.

At the end of the carnival, each contestant who correctly matchs all three pictures wins an \$8 calculator.

1. How much does it cost to play MATCH-UP?
2. How many ways can the pictures be matched with the names?
3. What is the probability of winning (matching all the pictures with the right names)? Assume that all matchings are equally likely.
4. What is the value of the prize?

Here's how *to compute the* **expectation** *for a game of MATCH-UP.*

To find the expectation, multiply the probability of winning the prize times the value of the prize.

	P(winning)		Value of Prize	
Expectation =	$\frac{1}{6}$	×	\$8	= \$1.33

The expectation for a game of MATCH-UP is \$1.33.

5. Look at the *Here's how*. What is the expectation for a game of MATCH-UP?
6. To decide whether such a game is a good deal for the player, you compare the cost of playing with the expectation. Is the expectation less than or greater than the cost of playing?
7. If the expectation is less than the cost of playing, then such a game is a "bad deal" for the player. Is the game MATCH-UP a "bad deal" for the player?
8. How much would the expectation have to be for the game to be considered a "good deal" for the player?

EXERCISES

Here is another game that was played at the school carnival. A player pays $1.50 to spin this wheel. If the wheel stops on yellow, the player wins a $4.00 movie ticket.

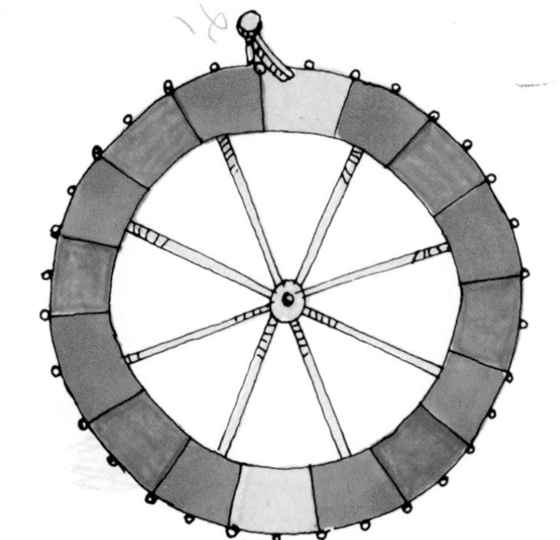

9. What is the probability (in simplest form) of winning?
10. What is the value of the movie ticket?
11. How much is the expectation?
12. How much does it cost to play?
13. Is the expectation less than or greater than the cost of playing the game?
14. Is the game a good deal or a bad deal?

BUY A CHANCE
ON A UNICYCLE WORTH $220!

A local merchant donated this unicycle to the school carnival. The carnival committee decided to sell 135 chances on it, at $2 each.

15. What is the cost of one chance?
16. If a person bought one chance, what would be that person's probability of winning?
17. What is the value of the unicycle?
18. What is the expectation rounded to the nearest cent?
19. Is the expectation less than or greater than the cost of a chance?
20. Is buying a chance a good deal or a bad deal?

Which for what?

21. John bought 2 chances on the watch and 1 chance on the radio. He spent $4.00. Sue bought 1 chance on the watch and 2 chances on the radio. She spent $3.50. How much would one chance on each have cost?

Cumulative Skill Practice

Give the product in simplest form. (page 178)

1. $\frac{1}{2} \times \frac{1}{4}$
2. $\frac{1}{3} \times \frac{1}{3}$
3. $\frac{7}{8} \times \frac{4}{5}$
4. $\frac{3}{8} \times \frac{2}{3}$
5. $\frac{2}{5} \times \frac{2}{5}$
6. $\frac{9}{10} \times \frac{1}{3}$
7. $\frac{5}{6} \times \frac{3}{3}$
8. $\frac{4}{5} \times \frac{1}{2}$
9. $\frac{5}{6} \times \frac{0}{2}$
10. $\frac{3}{8} \times \frac{3}{8}$
11. $\frac{5}{9} \times \frac{3}{10}$
12. $3 \times \frac{1}{3}$
13. $\frac{0}{3} \times \frac{5}{6}$
14. $\frac{3}{8} \times 4$
15. $\frac{4}{4} \times \frac{7}{8}$

Give the quotient in simplest form. (page 188)

16. $3 \div \frac{1}{2}$
17. $4 \div \frac{1}{3}$
18. $\frac{1}{2} \div \frac{2}{3}$
19. $\frac{2}{3} \div \frac{1}{2}$
20. $3 \div \frac{2}{3}$
21. $\frac{2}{3} \div \frac{1}{2}$
22. $\frac{3}{4} \div \frac{3}{8}$
23. $\frac{3}{5} \div \frac{3}{8}$
24. $\frac{3}{8} \div \frac{3}{4}$
25. $\frac{5}{8} \div \frac{1}{4}$
26. $\frac{4}{5} \div 3$
27. $\frac{9}{10} \div \frac{3}{5}$
28. $\frac{5}{16} \div \frac{3}{8}$
29. $\frac{2}{3} \div \frac{3}{4}$
30. $\frac{7}{12} \div \frac{5}{6}$

Solve. (page 230)

31. $\frac{5}{n} = \frac{2}{7}$
32. $\frac{n}{3} = \frac{5}{2}$
33. $\frac{1}{4} = \frac{n}{6}$
34. $\frac{10}{n} = \frac{3}{5}$
35. $\frac{3}{8} = \frac{n}{12}$
36. $\frac{11}{n} = \frac{8}{21}$
37. $\frac{3}{15} = \frac{5}{n}$
38. $\frac{2}{3} = \frac{9}{n}$
39. $\frac{n}{9} = \frac{5}{12}$
40. $\frac{6}{15} = \frac{4}{n}$
41. $\frac{n}{16} = \frac{13}{10}$
42. $\frac{3}{16} = \frac{8}{n}$
43. $\frac{15}{6} = \frac{n}{4}$
44. $\frac{9}{n} = \frac{8}{5}$
45. $\frac{9}{4} = \frac{18}{n}$

Change to a percent. (page 250)

46. $\frac{1}{10}$
47. $\frac{2}{5}$
48. $\frac{1}{4}$
49. $\frac{1}{5}$
50. $\frac{1}{2}$
51. $\frac{1}{7}$
52. $\frac{3}{4}$
53. $\frac{1}{3}$
54. 2
55. $\frac{1}{6}$
56. $\frac{7}{8}$
57. $\frac{2}{9}$
58. $\frac{3}{2}$
59. $\frac{4}{3}$
60. 3
61. $\frac{7}{4}$
62. $\frac{9}{5}$
63. $\frac{1}{8}$

Solve. (page 258)

64. 10% of 80 = n
65. 20% of 45 = n
66. 25% of 52 = n
67. 15% of 46 = n
68. 9% of 36.5 = n
69. 125% of 64 = n
70. 7.5% of 112 = n
71. 12.3% of 60 = n
72. 22.5% of 72.5 = n
73. $62\frac{1}{2}$% of 62 = n
74. $33\frac{1}{3}$% of 126 = n
75. $66\frac{2}{3}$% of 159 = n

Problem solving

COMPUTERS AND ARCHITECTS

Computers are used to draw "blueprints" of an architect's design. The computer can be programmed to display a floor plan on a screen or printout.

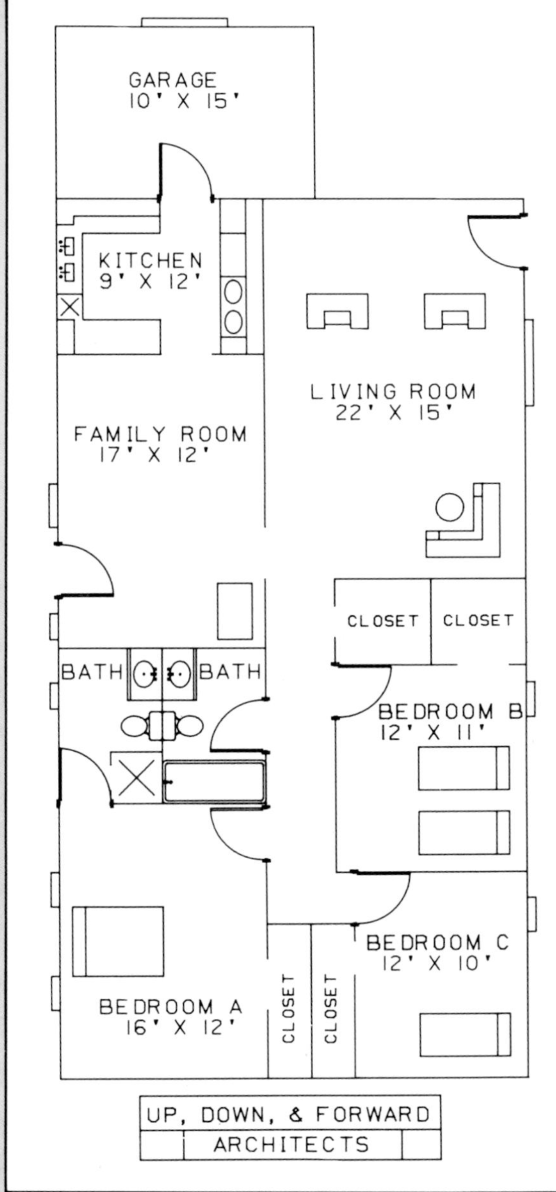

Use the floor plan to answer the questions.

1. Which room is 17 feet by 12 feet?
2. Which room is 16 feet by 12 feet?
3. What are the length and width of the living room?
4. What are the dimensions of the kitchen?
5. Which room has an area of 132 square feet?
6. What is the area of the smallest bedroom?
7. What is the area of the largest bedroom?
8. Carpet costs \$1.50 per square foot. How much will it cost to carpet bedroom B? *Hint: First find the area; then find the cost.*
9. At \$1.75 per square foot, how much will it cost to carpet the living room?
10. A floor tile 1 foot by 1 foot costs \$.49. How much will it cost to tile the family-room floor?
11. A contractor said this house could be built for \$50 per square foot. Would you expect the cost to be more or less than \$60,000?

Chapter REVIEW

Here are scrambled answers for the review exercises:

$\frac{1}{12}$	$\frac{1}{3}$	5	18	permutation	sample
$\frac{3}{10}$	1	8	24	possible	value

1. A certain automobile is available in 3 different models, and each model comes in 6 different colors. If you decided to order such an automobile, you would have [?] choices. *(page 340)*

2. An arrangement of things in a definite order is called a [?]. Four students decide to go to lunch. They can line up in [?] different ways. *(page 342)*

3. If you roll a die, the probability of rolling a 2 is equal to

$$\frac{\text{number of ways of rolling a 2}}{\text{number of [?] outcomes}}$$

(page 344)

4. If you roll a die, the probability of rolling a number greater than 4 is [?]. *(page 344)*

5. A [?] space is the set of all possible outcomes. If you listed the sample space for tossing a coin 3 times, the sample space would have [?] outcomes. *(page 346)*

6. Think about first rolling a die and then tossing a coin. P(6, H) = [?]. *(page 350)*

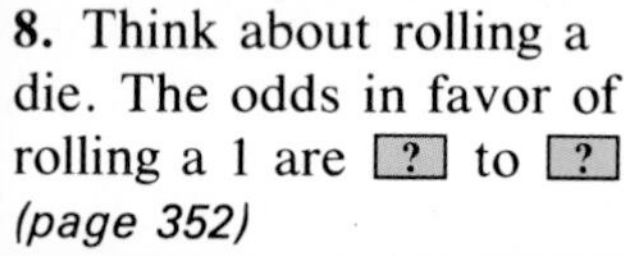

7. Think about placing these marbles in a bag, thoroughly mixing them up, picking a marble, not replacing it, and then picking a second marble. P(red, blue) = [?]. *(page 350)*

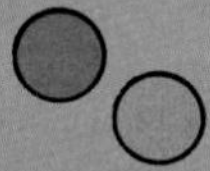

8. Think about rolling a die. The odds in favor of rolling a 1 are [?] to [?]. *(page 352)*

9. You can find the expectation by multiplying the probability of winning a prize by the [?] of the prize. *(page 354)*

Chapter TEST

Solve. *(page 340, 342)*

1. You have 4 different colors of slacks and 6 different colors of shirts. How many different outfits can you make?

2. You and 5 friends decide to go to a movie. How many ways can you line up at the ticket office?

Give each probability in simplest form. *(page 344)*

Think about spinning this spinner.

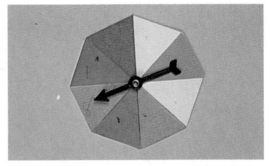

3. P(red)

4. P(yellow)

5. P(green)

6. P(blue)

7. P(red or brown)

8. P(green or blue)

9. P(not brown)

10. P(not yellow)

Solve. *(page 346)*

Think about a family with 3 children.

11. List the sample space for the children in the family. *Hint: Use GBB to represent a girl as the oldest, a boy as the "middle" child, and a boy as the youngest child.*

12. a. What is the probability that in a family with 3 children, exactly 2 will be girls?

b. What is the probability that in a family with 3 children, exactly 1 will be a girl?

Give each probability in simplest form. *(page 350)*

Think about first flipping the coin and then tossing the die.

13. P(H, 3)

14. P(T, 4)

15. P(H, even number)

16. P(T, number greater than 3)

Give the odds as a fraction in lowest terms. *(pages 352, 353)*

Think about spinning the spinner shown above.

17. Odds in favor of spinning red

18. Odds in favor of spinning green

19. Odds against spinning blue

20. Odds against spinning yellow

Solve. *(page 354)*

21. a. Eighty chances were sold for $2 each. Suppose you bought a chance. What would be your expectation?

b. Is buying a chance on the binoculars a good deal?

BUY A CHANCE!
BINOCULARS
WORTH $120

Cumulative TEST Standardized Format

Choose the correct letter.

1. 398,520 rounded to the nearest ten thousand is

A. 399,000
B. 390,000
C. 398,500
D. 400,000

2. Give the product.
52.4 × 2.07

A. 141.48
B. 108.468
C. 14.288
D. none of these

3. Give the quotient rounded to the nearest tenth.
30.89 ÷ 3.7

A. 8.35
B. 8.4
C. 8.3
D. none of these

4. Give the sum.
$\frac{7}{16} + \frac{5}{8}$

A. $1\frac{1}{16}$
B. $\frac{1}{2}$
C. $\frac{3}{4}$
D. none of these

5. Give the difference.
$\frac{5}{6} - \frac{2}{3}$

A. 1
B. $\frac{1}{6}$
C. $\frac{1}{2}$
D. none of these

6. Give the product.
$\frac{5}{12} \times \frac{3}{4}$

A. $\frac{5}{9}$
B. $1\frac{1}{4}$
C. $\frac{5}{16}$
D. none of these

7. Give the quotient.
$\frac{9}{10} \div \frac{3}{2}$

A. $\frac{3}{5}$
B. $1\frac{2}{3}$
C. $1\frac{7}{20}$
D. none of these

8. Solve.
$\frac{5}{8} = \frac{n}{6}$

A. 3.75
B. 9.6
C. 240
D. none of these

9. Change to a percent.
$\frac{3}{8} = ?$

A. $33\frac{1}{3}\%$
B. $38\frac{1}{2}\%$
C. $62\frac{1}{2}\%$
D. none of these

10. Solve.
32% of 18 = n

A. 56.25
B. 5.76
C. 57.6
D. none of these

11. How many feet of fencing will it take to go around a circular garden that has a radius of 7 feet? Use 3.14 for π.

A. 21.98
B. 153.86
C. 43.96
D. none of these

12. If you toss a penny and a dime, what is the probability that both will land heads?

A. $\frac{1}{2}$
B. $\frac{1}{4}$
C. $\frac{1}{3}$
D. none of these

Chapter 16
Integers

Ordering and comparing integers

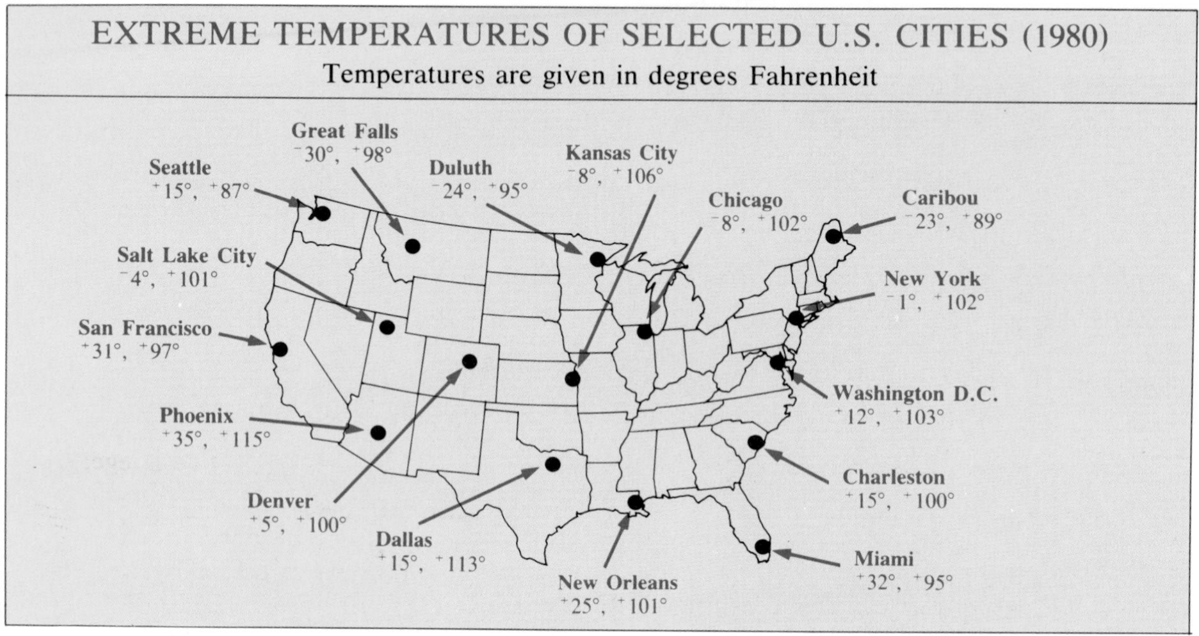

1. The low temperature for Seattle is 15 degrees above 0, which can be written as $^{+}15^\circ$ (“positive fifteen degrees”). What is the low temperature for San Francisco?

2. The low temperature for Chicago is 8 degrees below 0, which can be written as $^{-}8^\circ$ (“negative eight degrees”). What is the low temperature for Great Falls?

Here’s how *to use the number line to compare two integers.*

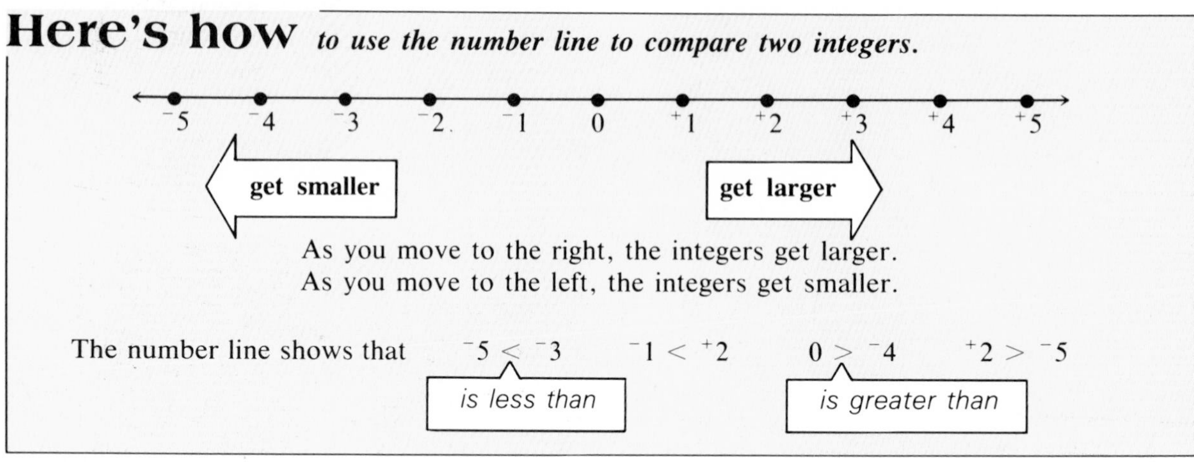

As you move to the right, the integers get larger.
As you move to the left, the integers get smaller.

The number line shows that $^{-}5 < {}^{-}3$ $\quad$ $^{-}1 < {}^{+}2$ $\quad$ $0 > {}^{-}4$ $\quad$ $^{+}2 > {}^{-}5$

3. Look at the *Here’s how*. Is $^{-}5$ less than or greater than $^{-}3$?

4. Is 0 less than or greater than $^{-}4$?

EXERCISES

$<$ or $>$?

5. $^{+}3$ ● $^{+}4$ 6. $^{+}3$ ● $^{-}4$ 7. $^{-}3$ ● $^{+}4$ 8. $^{-}3$ ● $^{-}4$ 9. $^{-}8$ ● $^{+}9$

10. $^{+}5$ ● $^{-}2$ 11. $^{-}5$ ● $^{+}2$ 12. $^{-}5$ ● $^{-}2$ 13. $^{+}5$ ● $^{+}2$ 14. $^{-}2$ ● 0

15. $^{-}10$ ● $^{+}6$ 16. 0 ● $^{+}6$ 17. 0 ● $^{-}6$ 18. $^{+}10$ ● $^{-}6$ 19. $^{-}4$ ● $^{-}8$

20. $^{-}7$ ● $^{+}9$ 21. $^{+}7$ ● $^{-}9$ 22. $^{+}7$ ● $^{+}9$ 23. $^{-}7$ ● $^{-}9$ 24. $^{+}7$ ● $^{-}4$

25. $^{+}8$ ● $^{+}11$ 26. $^{-}12$ ● $^{+}10$ 27. $^{+}15$ ● $^{-}19$ 28. $^{-}20$ ● 0 29. 0 ● $^{+}15$

30. $^{-}21$ ● $^{+}12$ 31. $^{+}24$ ● $^{-}27$ 32. $^{-}32$ ● $^{-}25$ 33. $^{+}30$ ● $^{+}25$ 34. $^{-}30$ ● $^{+}8$

35. 0 ● $^{-}56$ 36. $^{-}25$ ● $^{+}25$ 37. $^{-}32$ ● $^{+}8$ 38. $^{-}19$ ● 0 39. $^{+}32$ ● $^{+}23$

Complete.

40. All [?] integers are greater than 0.
41. All [?] integers are less than 0.
42. [?] is neither positive nor negative.
43. Zero is [?] than any negative integer.
44. A negative integer is [?] than any positive integer.
45. A positive integer is [?] than any negative integer.

Solve. Use the information on page 362.

46. Which city has the highest high temperature?
47. Which city has the lowest low temperature?
48. Which city has the highest low temperature?
49. Which city has the lowest high temperature?
50. List the low temperatures in order from least to greatest. (If two or more cities have the same low temperature, tell the number of cities with that low temperature.)
51. List the high temperatures in order from least to greatest. (If two or more cities have the same high temperature, tell the number of cities with that high temperature.)
52. How many cities listed have low temperatures that are less than the low for Denver?
53. Which cities have high temperatures that are higher than the high for Washington, D.C.?

It was a record!

54. A record for extreme temperatures in a 24-hour period was set at Browning, Montana, in 1916. The high was 44°F. During the next 24 hours the temperature dropped 100 degrees. What was the low?

Adding integers

Imagine some small particles that have either a positive electrical charge or a negative electrical charge. The positive charges and negative charges are opposites. This means that when one positive charge and one negative charge are put together, the result is no charge, or a charge of 0.

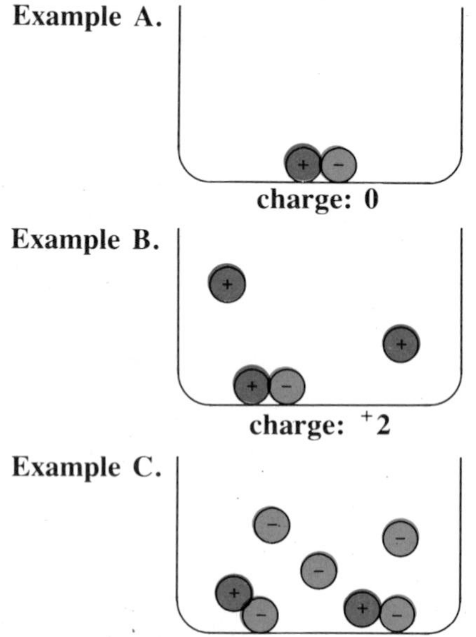

1. Look at Example A. What is the charge when one positive charge and one negative charge are combined?
2. Look at Example B. What is the charge when three positive charges and one negative charge are combined?
3. Look at Example C. What is the charge when two positive charges and five negative charges are combined?

Here's how *to add integers by thinking about combining charges.*

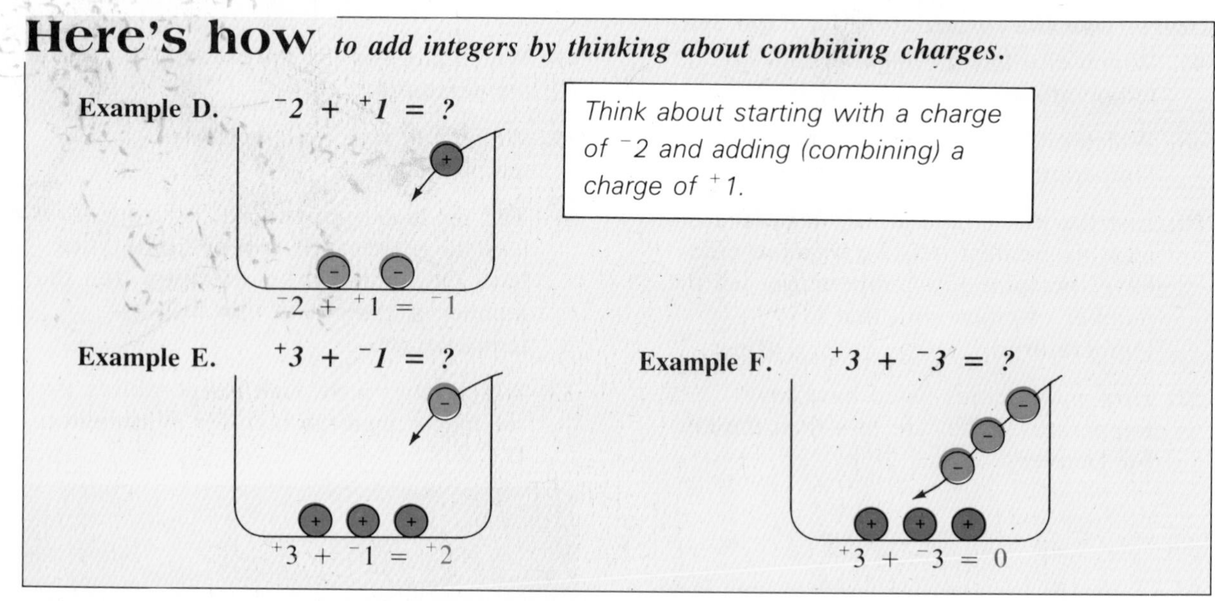

Example D. $^{-}2 + {}^{+}1 = ?$
Think about starting with a charge of $^{-}2$ and adding (combining) a charge of $^{+}1$.
$^{-}2 + {}^{+}1 = {}^{-}1$
Example E. $^{+}3 + {}^{-}1 = ?$
$^{+}3 + {}^{-}1 = {}^{+}2$
Example F. $^{+}3 + {}^{-}3 = ?$
$^{+}3 + {}^{-}3 = 0$

4. Look at the *Here's how*. What is the sum of $^{-}2$ and $^{+}1$? What is the sum of $^{+}3$ and $^{-}1$?
5. If the sum of the two numbers is 0, then one number is the **opposite** of the other. Look at Example F. Since the sum of the two numbers is 0, you know that the opposite of $^{+}3$ is what number? What is the opposite of $^{-}3$?

EXERCISES

Give each sum.

Here are scrambled answers for the next row of exercises: $0 \quad ^{+}5 \quad ^{+}4 \quad ^{+}2 \quad ^{-}6$

6. $^{+}3 + ^{+}2$	**7.** $^{+}4 + ^{-}2$	**8.** $^{-}3 + ^{+}3$	**9.** $^{-}1 + ^{-}5$	**10.** $^{+}5 + ^{-}1$
11. $^{+}6 + ^{-}1$	**12.** $^{-}6 + ^{+}1$	**13.** $^{-}6 + ^{-}1$	**14.** $^{+}6 + ^{+}1$	**15.** $^{+}6 + ^{-}6$
16. $^{-}5 + ^{+}4$	**17.** $^{+}5 + ^{+}4$	**18.** $^{-}5 + ^{-}4$	**19.** $^{+}5 + ^{-}4$	**20.** $^{+}4 + ^{-}9$
21. $^{+}7 + ^{-}3$	**22.** $^{-}7 + ^{-}3$	**23.** $^{+}7 + ^{+}3$	**24.** $^{-}7 + ^{+}3$	**25.** $^{+}5 + ^{-}8$
26. $^{+}4 + ^{-}4$	**27.** $^{-}5 + ^{+}5$	**28.** $^{+}8 + ^{-}8$	**29.** $^{-}9 + ^{+}9$	**30.** $^{-}2 + ^{-}2$
31. $^{+}7 + 0$	**32.** $^{-}6 + 0$	**33.** $0 + ^{+}5$	**34.** $0 + 0$	**35.** $^{-}7 + ^{+}7$
36. $^{-}12 + ^{-}10$	**37.** $^{+}15 + ^{+}18$	**38.** $^{+}17 + ^{-}11$	**39.** $^{-}16 + ^{+}19$	**40.** $^{+}13 + ^{-}19$
41. $^{-}20 + ^{+}12$	**42.** $^{-}24 + ^{-}24$	**43.** $^{+}28 + ^{+}21$	**44.** $^{+}26 + ^{-}28$	**45.** $^{-}34 + ^{-}11$
46. $^{+}30 + ^{-}24$	**47.** $^{+}24 + ^{+}30$	**48.** $^{-}36 + ^{+}32$	**49.** $^{-}36 + ^{-}32$	**50.** $^{+}46 + ^{-}18$
51. $^{-}35 + 0$	**52.** $^{-}37 + ^{+}37$	**53.** $^{+}39 + ^{-}30$	**54.** $^{-}38 + ^{+}34$	**55.** $^{+}25 + ^{-}25$
56. $^{-}40 + ^{-}48$	**57.** $^{+}40 + ^{-}48$	**58.** $^{-}40 + ^{+}48$	**59.** $^{+}40 + ^{+}48$	**60.** $0 + ^{-}88$

True or false?

61. The sum of two positive numbers is always positive.

62. The sum of two negative numbers is always positive.

63. The sum of a positive number and a negative number is always positive.

64. The sum of a positive number and a negative number is always negative.

65. The sum of a positive number and a negative number may be positive, may be negative, or may be 0.

66. The sum of two opposites is 0.

Magic squares

67. Add the numbers in each row, column, and diagonal. If the sums are the same, the square is a Magic Square. Is this a Magic Square?

$^{+}5$	$^{-}2$	$^{+}3$
0	$^{+}2$	$^{+}4$
$^{+}1$	$^{+}6$	$^{-}1$

68. Copy and complete this Magic Square.

?	$^{-}6$	?
$^{-}4$	$^{-}2$	0
$^{-}3$	?	$^{-}5$

Subtracting integers

Look at the picture at the right to answer the following questions.

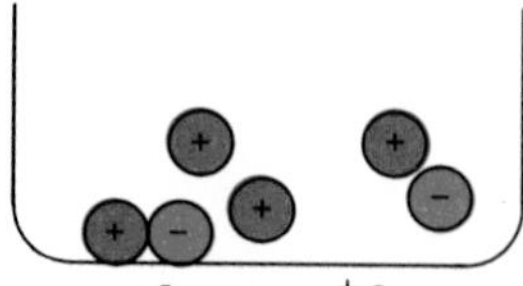

charge: $^{+}2$

1. What is the charge of the particles in the container?
2. Suppose that you removed a charge of $^{+}1$. What would the charge be then?
3. Suppose instead that you removed a charge of $^{-}2$. What would the charge be then?

Here's how *to subtract integers by thinking about removing charges.*

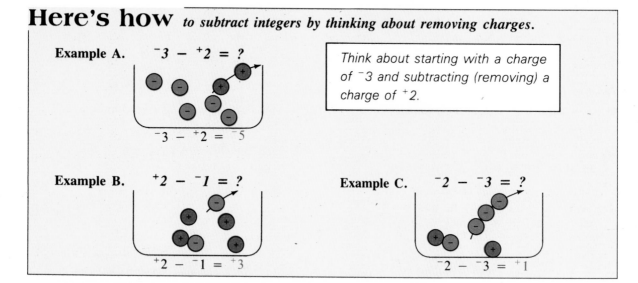

Example A. $^{-}3 - {}^{+}2 = ?$

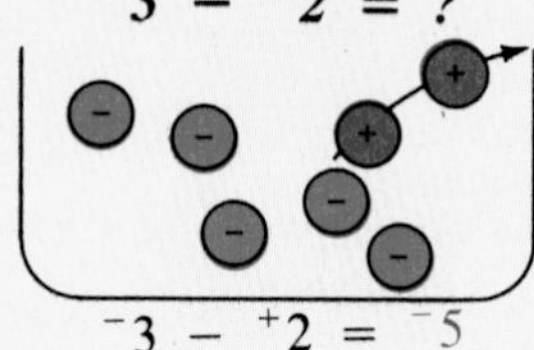

$^{-}3 - {}^{+}2 = {}^{-}5$

Think about starting with a charge of $^{-}3$ and subtracting (removing) a charge of $^{+}2$.

Example B. $^{+}2 - {}^{-}1 = ?$

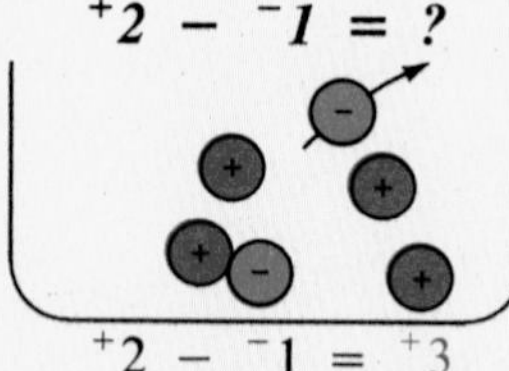

$^{+}2 - {}^{-}1 = {}^{+}3$

Example C. $^{-}2 - {}^{-}3 = ?$

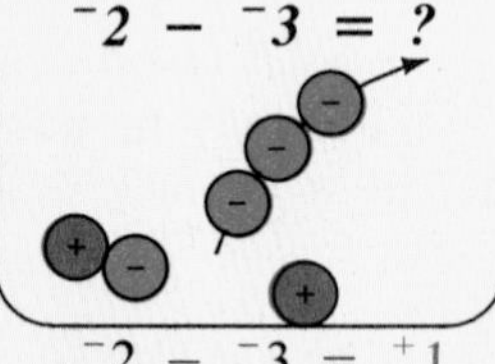

$^{-}2 - {}^{-}3 = {}^{+}1$

4. Look at Example A in the *Here's how.* Adding a charge of $^{-}2$ would give the same result as subtracting a charge of $^{+}2$.

   $^{-}3 - {}^{+}2 = {}^{-}5$

   $^{-}3 + \boxed{?} = {}^{-}5$

5. Look at Example B. Adding a charge of $^{+}1$ would give the same result as subtracting a charge of $^{-}1$.

   $^{+}2 - {}^{-}1 = {}^{+}3$

   $^{+}2 + \boxed{?} = {}^{+}3$

6. Look at Example C.

   $^{-}2 - {}^{-}3 = {}^{+}1$

   $^{-}2 + \boxed{?} = {}^{+}1$

Here's how *to subtract integers.*

To subtract an integer, add the opposite of the integer.

$^{+}5 - {}^{-}4 = {}^{+}5 + {}^{+}4$
$= {}^{+}9$

$^{-}6 - {}^{+}2 = {}^{-}6 + {}^{-}2$
$= {}^{-}8$

$^{+}3 - {}^{+}7 = {}^{+}3 + {}^{-}7$
$= {}^{-}4$

EXERCISES

7. The result of subtracting $^{-}4$ is the same as adding ?.
8. The result of subtracting $^{+}2$ is the same as adding ?.
9. To subtract $^{+}7$, you would add ?.
10. To subtract $^{-}9$, you would add ?.

Give each difference.

Here are scrambled answers for the next row of exercises: $^{-}3$ $^{+}10$ $^{-}8$ $^{-}15$ $^{-}4$

11. $^{+}7 - {}^{-}3$ **12.** $^{-}9 - {}^{-}5$ **13.** $^{-}2 - {}^{+}6$ **14.** $^{+}4 - {}^{+}7$ **15.** $^{-}10 - {}^{+}5$

16. $^{-}4 - {}^{-}9$ **17.** $^{+}6 - {}^{+}2$ **18.** $^{-}6 - {}^{+}6$ **19.** $^{+}7 - 0$ **20.** $0 - {}^{+}8$

21. $^{+}7 - {}^{-}5$ **22.** $0 - {}^{-}6$ **23.** $^{+}1 - {}^{+}9$ **24.** $^{-}4 - {}^{+}4$ **25.** $^{-}3 - {}^{+}4$

26. $^{-}6 - {}^{+}3$ **27.** $^{+}6 - {}^{+}3$ **28.** $^{+}6 - {}^{-}3$ **29.** $^{-}6 - {}^{-}3$ **30.** $^{-}9 - {}^{+}5$

31. $^{+}6 - 0$ **32.** $0 - {}^{+}6$ **33.** $^{-}7 - {}^{+}4$ **34.** $^{+}4 - {}^{+}9$ **35.** $^{-}11 - {}^{-}4$

36. $^{-}4 - {}^{+}9$ **37.** $^{-}9 - {}^{+}4$ **38.** $^{+}8 - {}^{-}3$ **39.** $^{+}3 - {}^{+}8$ **40.** $^{-}14 - {}^{+}8$

41. $^{-}10 - {}^{+}13$ **42.** $^{+}11 - {}^{-}12$ **43.** $^{-}14 - {}^{-}16$ **44.** $^{+}12 - {}^{+}12$ **45.** $^{-}21 - {}^{-}3$

46. $^{+}16 - {}^{+}18$ **47.** $^{+}18 - {}^{+}16$ **48.** $^{-}17 - {}^{+}11$ **49.** $^{+}17 - {}^{-}11$ **50.** $^{-}14 - {}^{+}18$

Give each sum or difference.

51. $^{+}10 + {}^{+}11$ **52.** $^{-}12 - {}^{+}15$ **53.** $^{-}16 - {}^{-}14$ **54.** $^{+}18 + {}^{-}12$ **55.** $^{+}13 - {}^{-}12$

56. $^{-}14 + 0$ **57.** $0 + {}^{+}17$ **58.** $^{-}11 + {}^{-}11$ **59.** $^{-}11 - {}^{-}11$ **60.** $^{-}30 + {}^{-}15$

61. $^{+}20 - {}^{-}16$ **62.** $^{-}23 - {}^{+}23$ **63.** $^{+}24 + {}^{+}16$ **64.** $^{-}25 + {}^{+}25$ **65.** $^{-}24 - {}^{+}18$

Add across. Subtract down.

Copy and complete these addition-subtraction boxes.

66.

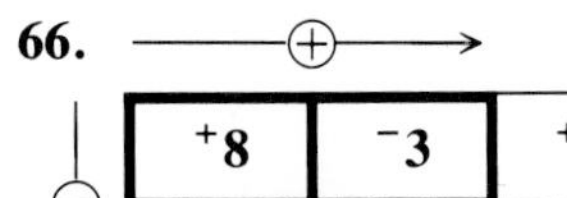

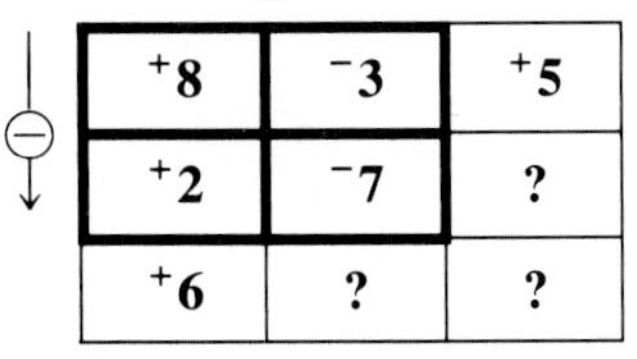

$^{+}8$	$^{-}3$	$^{+}5$
$^{+}2$	$^{-}7$	?
$^{+}6$	?	?

67.

$^{+}4$	$^{+}7$	?
$^{-}6$	$^{-}1$	?
?	?	?

68.

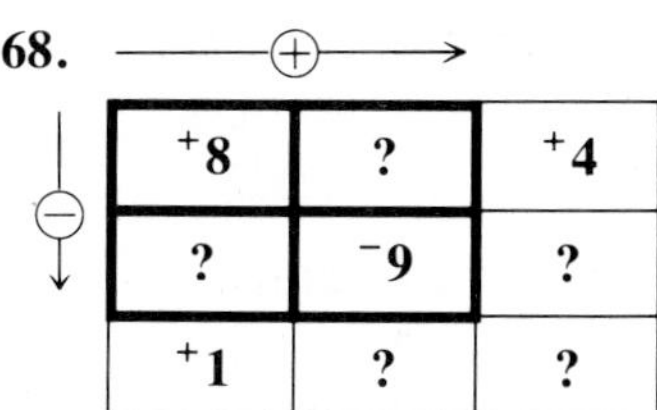

$^{+}8$	?	$^{+}4$
?	$^{-}9$	?
$^{+}1$	?	?

Cumulative Skill Practice

Give the product. *(page 68)*

1. 8.23×10 **2.** 8.23×100 **3.** 8.23×1000

4. 45×1000 **5.** 45×10 **6.** 45×100

7. 0.004×100 **8.** 0.004×10 **9.** 0.004×1000

10. 9.1×1000 **11.** 9.1×10 **12.** 9.1×100

Give the quotient. *(page 92)*

13. $789.5 \div 10$ **14.** $789.5 \div 100$ **15.** $789.5 \div 1000$

16. $297 \div 100$ **17.** $297 \div 10$ **18.** $297 \div 1000$

19. $7.1 \div 100$ **20.** $7.1 \div 10$ **21.** $7.1 \div 1000$

22. $9 \div 10$ **23.** $9 \div 100$ **24.** $9 \div 1000$

Change to a decimal rounded to the nearest hundredth. *(page 146)*

25. $\frac{1}{3}$ **26.** $\frac{1}{6}$ **27.** $\frac{1}{8}$ **28.** $\frac{1}{12}$ **29.** $\frac{5}{6}$ **30.** $\frac{3}{8}$ **31.** $\frac{7}{9}$

32. $\frac{5}{12}$ **33.** $\frac{11}{12}$ **34.** $\frac{2}{3}$ **35.** $\frac{1}{16}$ **36.** $\frac{7}{8}$ **37.** $\frac{9}{16}$ **38.** $\frac{1}{11}$

39. $\frac{5}{3}$ **40.** $\frac{7}{6}$ **41.** $\frac{5}{8}$ **42.** $\frac{16}{9}$ **43.** $\frac{4}{3}$ **44.** $\frac{11}{8}$ **45.** $\frac{13}{3}$

Give the sum in simplest form. *(page 160)*

46. $2\frac{1}{2} + 3$ **47.** $5 + 2\frac{2}{3}$ **48.** $1\frac{1}{4} + 2\frac{1}{2}$ **49.** $2\frac{1}{3} + 1\frac{1}{3}$ **50.** $3\frac{5}{8} + \frac{1}{4}$ **51.** $4\frac{2}{3} + 3\frac{1}{5}$

52. $5\frac{1}{2} + 4\frac{1}{3}$ **53.** $6\frac{2}{3} + 3\frac{1}{2}$ **54.** $5\frac{5}{8} + 1\frac{3}{4}$ **55.** $7\frac{5}{6} + 7\frac{2}{3}$ **56.** $9\frac{3}{4} + 8\frac{2}{5}$ **57.** $6\frac{1}{4} + 3\frac{1}{2}$

Give the product in simplest form. *(page 182)*

58. $3 \times 1\frac{1}{3}$ **59.** $2 \times 2\frac{1}{2}$ **60.** $1\frac{3}{4} \times 4$ **61.** $3\frac{1}{3} \times 3$

62. $1\frac{1}{3} \times 1\frac{1}{2}$ **63.** $2\frac{1}{2} \times 2\frac{1}{3}$ **64.** $3\frac{1}{2} \times 2\frac{1}{4}$ **65.** $3\frac{1}{2} \times 2\frac{1}{2}$

66. $1\frac{1}{6} \times 2\frac{3}{4}$ **67.** $3\frac{1}{2} \times 1\frac{1}{4}$ **68.** $1\frac{2}{3} \times 2\frac{1}{2}$ **69.** $4\frac{1}{2} \times 2\frac{1}{3}$

Problem solving

YOU'RE THE PIZZA MAKER!

THE PIZZA WITH PIZZAZZ!

	small *10-inch diameter*	**medium** *12-inch diameter*	**large** *14-inch diameter*
CHEESE	**$3.00**	**$4.50**	**$5.50**
BACON	**$3.60**	**$4.80**	**$6.25**
PEPPERONI	**$4.00**	**$5.25**	**$6.75**
SAUSAGE	**$3.75**	**$5.00**	**$6.50**

Add **50¢** for each topping:
chili peppers
green peppers
mushrooms
onions

Use the information on the sign to answer these customers' questions.

1. *How much will a large pepperoni pizza with mushrooms cost?*

2. *I have $10. Do I have enough to buy 2 small cheese pizzas and 1 small sausage pizza with onions?*

3. "What will 2 medium bacon and 3 large sausage pizzas cost?"

4. "We have $20. How much more will we need to buy 3 large pepperoni pizzas with green peppers and mushrooms?"

Solve.

5. On Wednesday, all large pizzas are 20% off. What would you charge a customer who orders a large bacon, a large cheese, and a small pepperoni pizza?

6. You get a special order for 18 medium pepperoni pizzas. It costs you $43.20 to make the pizzas. How much profit do you make?

7. You hire 2 part-time employees to work from 4:00 to 8:00 each day. If you pay each $4.50 an hour, how much does your part-time help cost per day?

8. You borrow $1150 for a pizza oven. How much interest will you have to pay if you borrow the money for 9 months at the yearly rate of 16%?

9. a. What is the area of a 10-inch pizza? Use 3.14 for π.

b. What is the price per square inch of a small cheese pizza? Give the answer to the nearest tenth of a cent.

10. Which pizza is the better deal (costs less per square inch), a medium sausage or a large sausage?

Multiplying integers

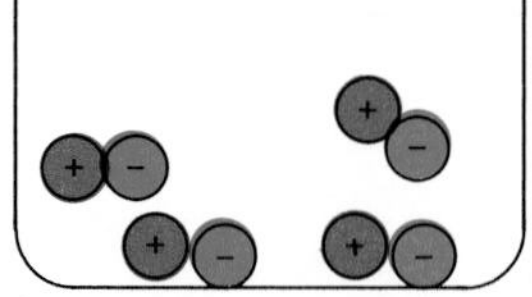

Look at the picture at the right to answer the following questions.

1. What is the charge of the particles in the container?
2. Suppose that you put in 2 sets of $^{+}2$ charges. What would the charge be then?

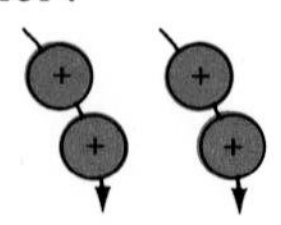

Look again at the container with a charge of 0.

3. Suppose that you took out 2 sets of $^{+}2$ charges. What would the charge be then?
4. What would the charge be if instead you put in 2 sets of $^{-}2$?
5. What would the charge be if instead you took out 2 sets of $^{-}2$?

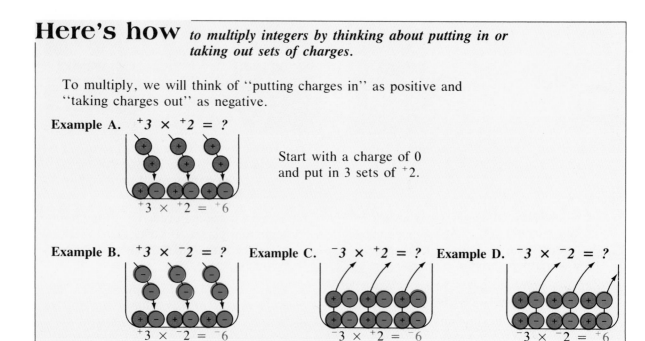

Here's how *to multiply integers by thinking about putting in or taking out sets of charges.*

To multiply, we will think of "putting charges in" as positive and "taking charges out" as negative.

Example A. $^{+}3 \times {}^{+}2 = ?$

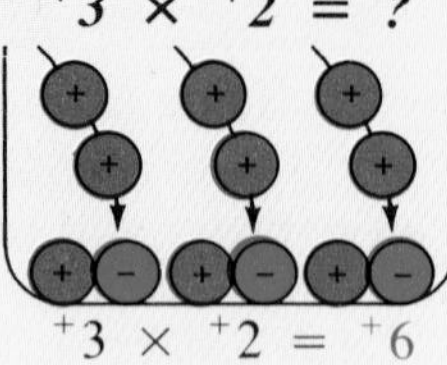

Start with a charge of 0 and put in 3 sets of $^{+}2$.

Example B. $^{+}3 \times {}^{-}2 = ?$

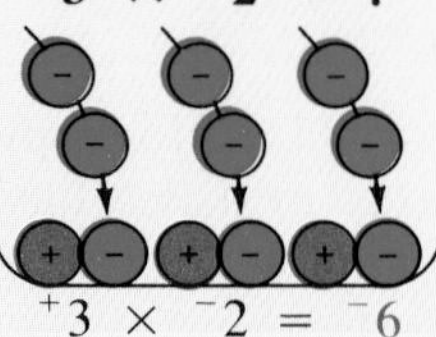

Example C. $^{-}3 \times {}^{+}2 = ?$

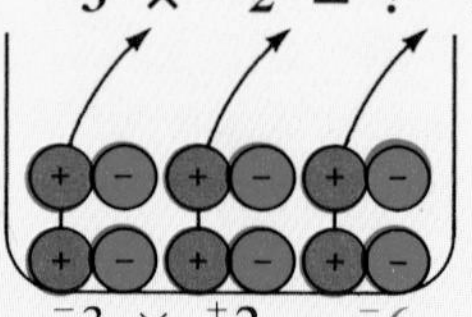

Example D. $^{-}3 \times {}^{-}2 = ?$

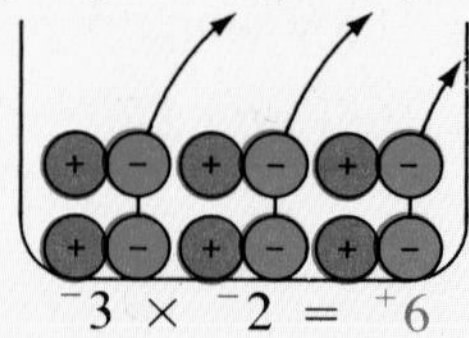

6. Look at the *Here's how*. In Examples A and D, we multiplied two integers with the same signs (both positive or both negative). Was the product positive or negative?
7. In Examples B and C, we multiplied two integers with different signs. Was the product positive or negative?

Here's how *to multiply integers.*

The product of two integers with the **same** signs is **positive.**

The product of two integers with **different** signs is **negative.**

The product of any integer and 0 is 0.

EXERCISES

Positive, negative, or zero?

8. The product of a positive integer and a positive integer is a [?] integer.

9. The product of a positive integer and a negative integer is a [?] integer.

10. The product of a negative integer and a negative integer is a [?] integer.

11. The product of an integer and 0 is [?].

Give each product.

Here are scrambled answers for the next row of exercises: $^{-}12$ $^{+}8$ $^{+}9$ $^{-}12$ $^{-}10$

12. $^{-}2 \times {}^{+}5$	**13.** $^{+}4 \times {}^{+}2$	**14.** $^{-}3 \times {}^{-}3$	**15.** $^{+}2 \times {}^{-}6$	**16.** $^{-}3 \times {}^{+}4$
17. $^{+}3 \times {}^{+}5$	**18.** $^{+}3 \times {}^{-}5$	**19.** $^{-}3 \times {}^{+}5$	**20.** $^{-}3 \times {}^{-}5$	**21.** $^{+}1 \times {}^{-}8$
22. $^{-}6 \times {}^{+}4$	**23.** $^{+}6 \times {}^{+}4$	**24.** $^{-}6 \times {}^{-}4$	**25.** $^{+}6 \times {}^{-}4$	**26.** $^{-}4 \times {}^{-}7$
27. $^{-}6 \times 0$	**28.** $0 \times {}^{+}4$	**29.** $^{+}8 \times 0$	**30.** 0×0	**31.** $0 \times {}^{-}3$
32. $^{-}5 \times {}^{+}5$	**33.** $^{+}7 \times {}^{+}6$	**34.** $^{-}6 \times {}^{-}6$	**35.** $^{+}5 \times {}^{-}9$	**36.** $^{-}3 \times {}^{+}8$
37. $^{-}8 \times {}^{-}6$	**38.** $^{+}9 \times {}^{-}6$	**39.** $0 \times {}^{+}3$	**40.** $^{+}9 \times {}^{+}5$	**41.** $^{+}4 \times {}^{+}8$
42. $^{+}12 \times {}^{+}12$	**43.** $^{+}12 \times {}^{-}12$	**44.** $^{-}12 \times {}^{+}12$	**45.** $^{-}12 \times {}^{-}12$	**46.** $^{-}11 \times {}^{-}11$
47. $^{-}11 \times {}^{+}11$	**48.** $^{+}15 \times 0$	**49.** $^{-}16 \times {}^{-}14$	**50.** $^{+}20 \times {}^{-}12$	**51.** $^{-}4 \times {}^{+}8$

Build an expression

Use all the cards to build an expression for each of the following numbers.

52. $^{-}9$ ⟨ $^{+}3 \times ({}^{-}2 + {}^{-}1)$

53. $^{+}5$

54. $^{-}4$

55. $^{-}7$

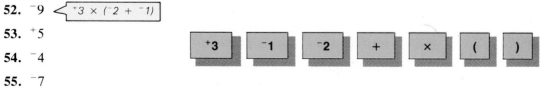

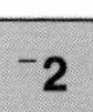

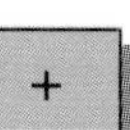

Dividing integers

1. What would you multiply by $^{+}3$ to get $^{+}18$?
2. What would you multiply by $^{-}4$ to get $^{+}28$?
3. What would you multiply by $^{-}9$ to get 0?

Here's how *to divide integers by finding a missing factor.*

Example A. $^{+}18 \div {}^{+}3 = ?$

$^{+}18 \div {}^{+}3 = {}^{+}6$
because
$^{+}3 \times {}^{+}6 = {}^{+}18$

Example B. $^{+}18 \div {}^{-}3 = ?$

$^{+}18 \div {}^{-}3 = {}^{-}6$
because
$^{-}3 \times {}^{-}6 = {}^{+}18$

Example C. $^{-}18 \div {}^{+}3 = ?$

$^{-}18 \div {}^{+}3 = {}^{-}6$
because
$^{+}3 \times {}^{-}6 = {}^{-}18$

Example D. $^{-}18 \div {}^{-}3 = ?$

$^{-}18 \div {}^{-}3 = {}^{+}6$
because
$^{-}3 \times {}^{+}6 = {}^{-}18$

4. Look at the *Here's how*. In Example A, we divided a positive integer by a positive integer. Was the quotient positive or negative?
5. If you divide a positive integer by a negative integer, will the quotient be positive or negative?
6. If you divide a negative integer by a positive integer, will the quotient be positive or negative?
7. If you divide a negative integer by a negative integer, will the quotient be positive or negative?

Here's how *to divide integers.*

The quotient of two integers with the **same** signs is **positive.**

The quotient of two integers with **different** signs is **negative.**

The quotient of 0 divided by any nonzero integer is 0.

EXERCISES

Give each quotient.

Here are scrambled answers for the next row of exercises: $^{+}8$ $^{+}4$ $^{-}10$ $^{-}6$ $^{-}8$

8. $^{+}20 \div {}^{-}2$ **9.** $^{+}24 \div {}^{+}3$ **10.** $^{-}30 \div {}^{+}5$ **11.** $^{-}36 \div {}^{-}9$ **12.** $^{-}56 \div {}^{+}7$

13. $^{+}14 \div {}^{+}2$ **14.** $^{+}14 \div {}^{-}2$ **15.** $^{-}14 \div {}^{+}2$ **16.** $^{-}14 \div {}^{-}2$ **17.** $^{+}15 \div {}^{-}5$

18. $^{+}15 \div {}^{-}3$ **19.** $^{-}15 \div {}^{+}3$ **20.** $^{-}18 \div {}^{-}6$ **21.** $^{+}15 \div {}^{+}3$ **22.** $^{-}15 \div {}^{-}3$

23. $^{+}24 \div {}^{+}6$ **24.** $^{+}24 \div {}^{-}6$ **25.** $^{+}12 \div {}^{+}6$ **26.** $^{-}24 \div {}^{+}6$ **27.** $^{-}24 \div {}^{-}6$

28. $^{-}30 \div {}^{+}6$ **29.** $0 \div {}^{-}6$ **30.** $^{+}18 \div {}^{-}6$ **31.** $^{-}30 \div {}^{-}5$ **32.** $^{+}30 \div {}^{+}5$

33. $^{+}30 \div {}^{-}5$ **34.** $0 \div {}^{+}8$ **35.** $^{-}12 \div {}^{-}4$ **36.** $^{+}10 \div {}^{-}2$ **37.** $^{-}16 \div {}^{+}4$

38. $^{-}24 \div {}^{+}8$ **39.** $^{+}28 \div {}^{-}4$ **40.** $^{+}32 \div {}^{-}8$ **41.** $^{+}25 \div {}^{+}5$ **42.** $^{-}27 \div {}^{-}3$

43. $^{-}45 \div {}^{-}5$ **44.** $^{+}54 \div {}^{-}6$ **45.** $^{+}36 \div {}^{-}6$ **46.** $^{-}48 \div {}^{+}8$ **47.** $^{+}56 \div {}^{+}7$

48. $^{+}81 \div {}^{+}9$ **49.** $0 \div {}^{-}12$ **50.** $^{+}81 \div {}^{-}9$ **51.** $^{-}64 \div {}^{+}8$ **52.** $^{+}54 \div {}^{+}9$

53. $^{-}72 \div {}^{-}9$ **54.** $^{+}121 \div {}^{+}11$ **55.** $^{+}144 \div {}^{+}12$ **56.** $^{+}150 \div {}^{-}10$ **57.** $^{-}132 \div {}^{-}12$

58. $^{+}124 \div {}^{-}4$ **59.** $^{-}176 \div {}^{-}16$ **60.** $^{-}120 \div {}^{+}20$ **61.** $^{+}162 \div {}^{+}18$ **62.** $^{-}147 \div {}^{+}21$

Simplify.

Here are scrambled answers for the next row of exercises: $^{-}3$ $^{+}4$ $^{+}3$ $^{+}12$ $^{+}8$

63. $^{+}6 + {}^{+}2$ **64.** $^{+}6 - {}^{+}2$ **65.** $^{-}6 \div {}^{+}2$ **66.** $^{+}6 \times {}^{+}2$ **67.** $^{+}6 \div {}^{+}2$

68. $^{+}8 + {}^{-}4$ **69.** $^{+}8 - {}^{-}4$ **70.** $^{-}8 - {}^{+}4$ **71.** $^{+}8 \times {}^{-}4$ **72.** $^{+}8 \div {}^{-}4$

73. $^{-}15 + {}^{+}3$ **74.** $^{-}15 - {}^{+}3$ **75.** $^{+}15 \div {}^{-}3$ **76.** $^{-}15 \times {}^{+}3$ **77.** $^{-}15 \div {}^{+}3$

78. $^{+}8 + 0$ **79.** $^{+}8 - 0$ **80.** $0 \times {}^{-}8$ **81.** $^{+}8 \times 0$ **82.** $0 \div {}^{+}8$

83. $^{-}24 + {}^{-}6$ **84.** $^{-}24 - {}^{-}6$ **85.** $^{+}24 + {}^{-}6$ **86.** $^{-}24 \times {}^{-}6$ **87.** $^{-}24 \div {}^{-}6$

88. $^{+}18 + {}^{-}9$ **89.** $^{+}18 - {}^{-}9$ **90.** $^{+}18 \div {}^{+}9$ **91.** $^{+}18 \times {}^{-}9$ **92.** $^{+}18 \div {}^{-}9$

93. $^{-}21 + {}^{+}3$ **94.** $^{-}21 - {}^{+}3$ **95.** $^{+}21 \div {}^{-}3$ **96.** $^{-}21 \times {}^{+}3$ **97.** $^{-}21 \div {}^{+}3$

98. $^{+}20 + {}^{+}5$ **99.** $^{+}20 - {}^{+}5$ **100.** $^{+}20 \times {}^{-}5$ **101.** $^{+}20 \times {}^{+}5$ **102.** $^{+}20 \div {}^{+}5$

Multiply across. Divide down.

Copy and complete these multiplication-division boxes.

103.

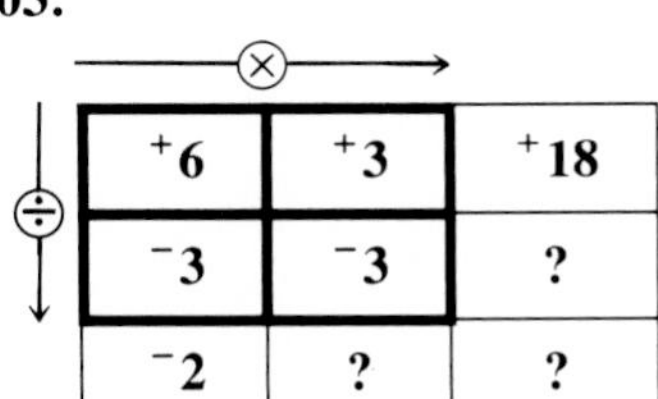

$^{+}6$	$^{+}3$	$^{+}18$
$^{-}3$	$^{-}3$	?
$^{-}2$	?	?

104.

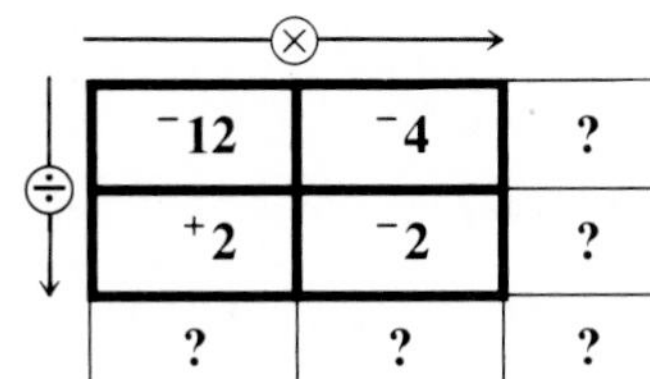

$^{-}12$	$^{-}4$	?
$^{+}2$	$^{-}2$	?
?	?	?

105.

$^{+}24$	?	$^{-}144$
?	$^{+}2$	?
$^{-}8$	?	?

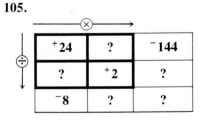

Graphing ordered pairs

Look at the picture on the right to answer the following questions.

1. What is the red number line called?
2. What is the blue number line called?
3. What is the point called where the two axes intersect?

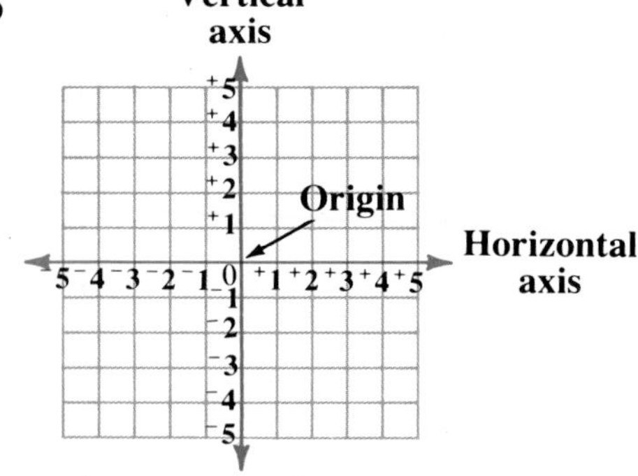

Here's how *to graph ordered pairs of integers.*

Example A. Graph the ordered pair ($^+4$, $^-3$).

Step 1. Start at the origin.
Go 4 units to the right ($^+4$).

Step 2. Now go 3 units down ($^-3$).

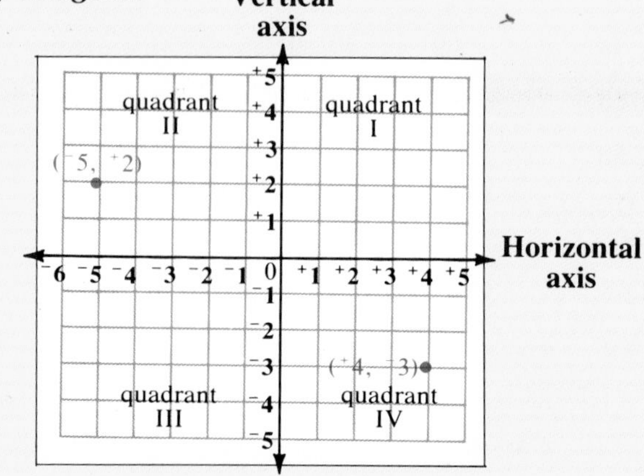

Example B. Graph the ordered pair ($^-5$, $^+2$).

Step 1. Start at the origin.
Go 5 units to the left ($^-5$).

Step 2. Now go 2 units up ($^+2$).

4. Look at the *Here's how*. Which ordered pair is graphed in quadrant II?
5. Which ordered pair is graphed in quadrant IV?
6. The ordered pair ($^+4$, $^+5$) would be graphed in quadrant [?].
7. The ordered pair ($^-3$, $^-4$) would be graphed in quadrant [?].
8. (0, $^+4$) would be graphed on the [?] axis.
9. Where would the ordered pair (0, 0) be graphed?

EXERCISES

Give the ordered pair for each point.

10. *A* **11.** *B* **12.** *C*

13. *D* **14.** *E* **15.** *F*

16. *G* **17.** *H* **18.** *I*

19. *J* **20.** *K* **21.** *L*

22. *M* **23.** *N* **24.** *P*

25. *Q* **26.** *R* **27.** *S*

28. *T* **29.** *U* **30.** *V*

31. *W* **32.** *X* **33.** *Y*

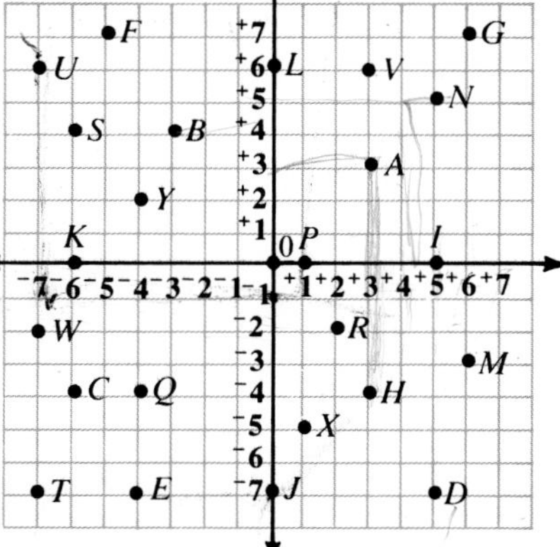

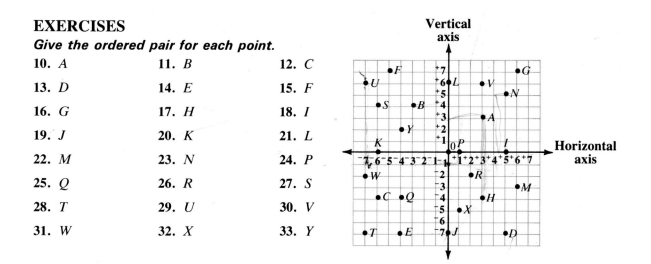

Graph these ordered pairs. Label each point with its ordered pair.

34. $(^{+}5, ^{+}4)$ **35.** $(^{+}5, ^{-}4)$ **36.** $(^{-}5, ^{+}4)$ **37.** $(^{-}5, ^{-}4)$ **38.** $(^{+}5, 0)$ **39.** $(0, ^{+}5)$

40. $(^{+}3, ^{+}2)$ **41.** $(^{+}3, ^{-}2)$ **42.** $(^{-}3, ^{+}2)$ **43.** $(^{-}3, ^{-}2)$ **44.** $(^{-}3, 0)$ **45.** $(0, ^{-}3)$

46. $(^{+}6, 0)$ **47.** $(^{-}6, 0)$ **48.** $(0, ^{+}6)$ **49.** $(0, ^{-}6)$ **50.** $(^{+}4, ^{-}2)$ **51.** $(^{-}2, ^{+}4)$

52. $(^{-}1, ^{+}7)$ **53.** $(^{+}1, ^{-}7)$ **54.** $(0, 0)$ **55.** $(^{-}7, ^{+}1)$ **56.** $(^{-}5, ^{+}3)$ **57.** $(^{+}3, ^{-}5)$

Triangle tricks

58. Copy the triangle on graph paper and give the ordered pairs for points *A*, *B*, and *C*.

59. Add $^{+}3$ to the second number of each ordered pair. Graph the new ordered pairs. Connect the points to make a new triangle.

60. Multiply the second number of each ordered pair (for points *A*, *B*, and *C*) by $^{-}1$. Graph the ordered pairs and draw the triangle.

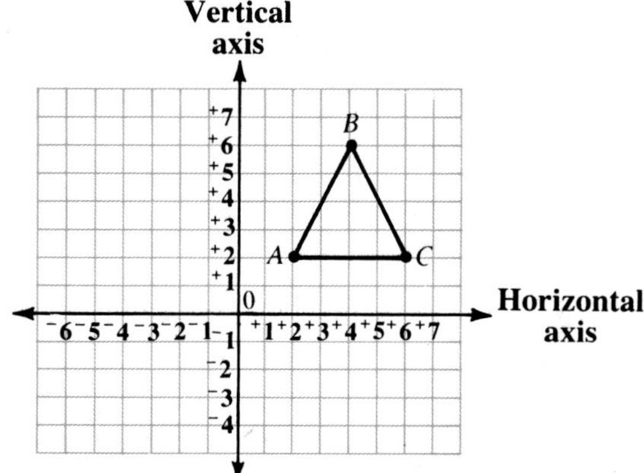

Cumulative Skill Practice

Complete. *(page 202)*

1. 49 cm = ? m **2.** 58 mm = ? cm **3.** 36 km = ? m

4. 2250 m = ? km **5.** 9.6 km = ? m **6.** 7.4 cm = ? mm

7. 68 cm = ? mm **8.** 16 m = ? cm **9.** 5.3 m = ? cm

10. 342 km = ? m **11.** 700 mm = ? m **12.** 0.8 m = ? mm

Solve. *(page 230)*

13. $\frac{n}{8} = \frac{3}{4}$ **14.** $\frac{9}{n} = \frac{8}{5}$ **15.** $\frac{16}{5} = \frac{n}{3}$ **16.** $\frac{4}{12} = \frac{3}{n}$ **17.** $\frac{5}{n} = \frac{10}{6}$

18. $\frac{7}{n} = \frac{3}{5}$ **19.** $\frac{n}{4} = \frac{13}{10}$ **20.** $\frac{15}{8} = \frac{n}{6}$ **21.** $\frac{2}{3} = \frac{11}{n}$ **22.** $\frac{3}{5} = \frac{30}{n}$

23. $\frac{3}{7} = \frac{12}{n}$ **24.** $\frac{11}{6} = \frac{n}{12}$ **25.** $\frac{n}{21} = \frac{11}{7}$ **26.** $\frac{9}{n} = \frac{3}{4}$ **27.** $\frac{8}{6} = \frac{2}{n}$

Change to a fraction, whole number, or mixed number in simplest form. *(page 248)*

28. 10% **29.** 20% **30.** 25% **31.** 40% **32.** 50% **33.** 95%

34. 80% **35.** 125% **36.** 175% **37.** 150% **38.** 100% **39.** 55%

40. $12\frac{1}{2}\%$ **41.** $33\frac{1}{3}\%$ **42.** $37\frac{1}{2}\%$ **43.** $87\frac{1}{2}\%$ **44.** $166\frac{2}{3}\%$ **45.** $66\frac{2}{3}\%$

Solve. *(page 258)*

46. 10% of 40 = n **47.** 25% of 36 = n **48.** 125% of 44 = n

49. 9% of 79 = n **50.** 8.5% of 23 = n **51.** 12.4% of 144 = n

52. 37.5% of 15.4 = n **53.** 0.5% of 140 = n **54.** 0.08% of 300 = n

55. $33\frac{1}{3}\%$ of 78 = n **56.** $16\frac{2}{3}\%$ of 84 = n **57.** $66\frac{2}{3}\%$ of 141 = n

Solve. *(page 260)*

58. 20% of n = 19 **59.** 25% of n = 23 **60.** 50% of n = 37

61. 8% of n = 24 **62.** 12% of n = 84 **63.** 40% of n = 28

64. 75% of n = 51 **65.** 125% of n = 75 **66.** 150% of n = 81

Solve. Round each answer to the nearest tenth. *(page 260)*

67. 18% of n = 37 **68.** 21% of n = 45 **69.** 35% of n = 29

70. 42% of n = 53 **71.** 12% of n = 25 **72.** 15% of n = 41

Problem solving

COMPUTERS AND PHOTOGRAPHY

Look at the two photographs. The top photograph was altered to produce the bottom photograph. This "trick" photography was performed by an image processor, a special machine that uses a large computer.

The computer divides the photograph into tiny squares called pixels. (If you take a close look at a television screen, you can see large pixels that make up a TV image.) Each of the pixels in the photograph is given a number. The numbers can then be rearranged to create a new photograph.

Use the two photographs to answer these questions.

1. Can you find seven ways that the bottom photograph differs from the top photograph? (*Hint: Look at each building identified by a letter.*)

2. What is the area of the original photograph? Give the answer to the nearest square inch.

3. There are more than 100,000 pixels in each square inch of the photograph. Does the photograph have more or less than 1 million pixels?

4. To change each square inch of the photograph, the computer used 360,000 bytes (parts) of its memory.

- **a.** How many bytes of the computer's memory were used to change the entire photograph?
- **b.** How many bytes of the computer's memory would be used to change an 8-inch by 10-inch photograph?

Chapter REVIEW

Here are scrambled answers for the review exercises:

$^{-}3$	$^{+}3$	different	less	opposite	right
$^{-}1$	$^{+}4$	down	negative	origin	same
0	add	greater	nonzero	positive	

1. As you move to the [?] on this number line, the numbers get larger. *(page 362)*

2. The number line shows that negative 3 is [?] than positive one. *(page 362)*

3. The number line also shows that zero is [?] than negative two. *(page 362)*

−4 −3 −2 −1 0 +1 +2 +3 +4

4. The picture shows that $^{-}2 + {}^{+}1 =$ [?].
If the sum of two numbers is 0, then one number is the [?] of the other.
The opposite of $^{+}3$ is [?]. *(page 364)*

5. The picture shows that $^{+}2 - {}^{-}1 =$ [?].
To subtract an integer, you [?] the opposite of the integer. *(pages 366, 367)*

6. The picture shows that $^{-}2 \times {}^{-}2 =$ [?]. *(page 370)*

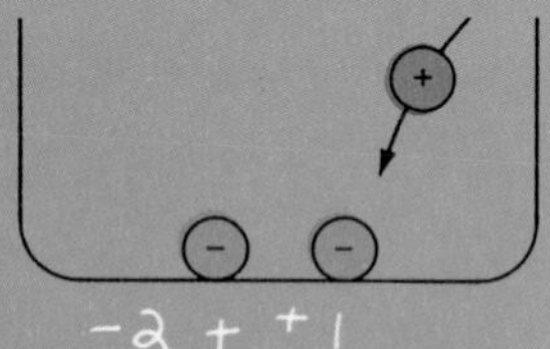

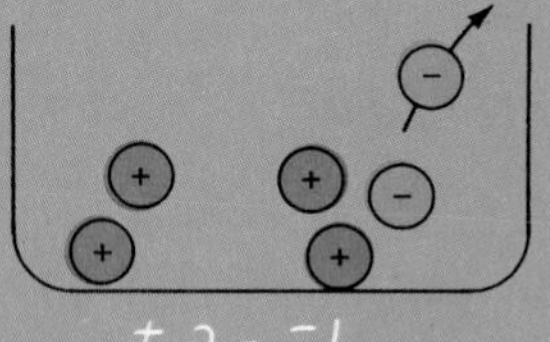

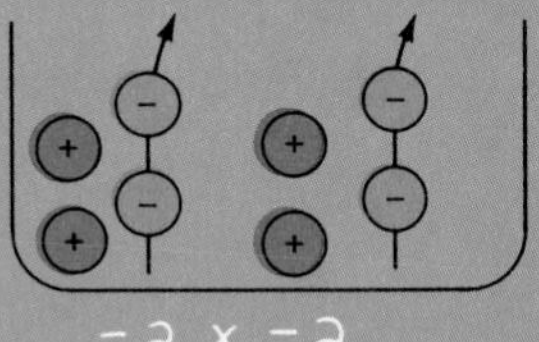

7. The product of two integers with the same signs is [?].
The product of two integers with different signs is [?].
The product of any integer and 0 is [?]. *(page 371)*

8. The quotient of two integers with the [?] signs is positive.
The quotient of two integers with [?] signs is negative.
The quotient of 0 divided by any [?] integer is 0. *(page 372)*

9. To graph the ordered pair $(^{+}3, {}^{-}2)$ you would start at the [?] and go 3 units to the right ($^{+}3$).
Then you would go 2 units [?] ($^{-}2$). *(page 374)*

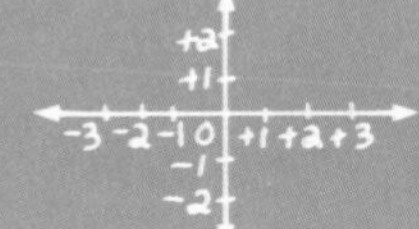

Chapter TEST

< or >? *(page 362)*

1. $^{+}4$ ● $^{+}5$	**2.** $^{+}3$ ● $^{-}6$	**3.** $^{-}6$ ● $^{+}2$	**4.** $^{-}8$ ● $^{-}1$	**5.** $^{-}6$ ● $^{+}3$
6. $^{+}20$ ● $^{-}23$	**7.** $^{-}25$ ● $^{-}22$	**8.** $^{-}26$ ● $^{+}21$	**9.** $^{+}24$ ● $^{-}24$	**10.** $^{-}2$ ● 0

Give each sum. *(page 364)*

11. $^{+}6 + {}^{+}2$	**12.** $^{+}6 + {}^{-}2$	**13.** $0 + {}^{-}2$	**14.** $^{-}4 + {}^{-}8$	**15.** $^{-}4 + {}^{+}8$
16. $^{-}5 + 0$	**17.** $0 + {}^{+}7$	**18.** $0 + 0$	**19.** $^{-}9 + {}^{+}9$	**20.** $^{-}9 + {}^{-}9$
21. $^{-}7 + {}^{-}10$	**22.** $^{+}12 + {}^{-}12$	**23.** $^{+}15 + {}^{+}11$	**24.** $^{-}18 + {}^{+}16$	**25.** $^{-}18 + {}^{-}16$

Give each difference. *(pages 366, 367)*

26. $^{+}4 - {}^{-}2$	**27.** $^{+}4 - {}^{+}2$	**28.** $^{-}5 - {}^{+}8$	**29.** $^{+}5 - {}^{+}8$	**30.** $^{-}8 - 0$
31. $^{+}9 - 0$	**32.** $0 - {}^{-}7$	**33.** $0 - 0$	**34.** $^{+}7 - {}^{-}7$	**35.** $^{-}6 - {}^{-}3$
36. $^{-}12 - {}^{+}10$	**37.** $^{-}13 - {}^{-}13$	**38.** $^{+}18 - {}^{-}11$	**39.** $^{+}15 - {}^{+}19$	**40.** $^{+}21 - {}^{-}3$

Give each product. *(pages 370, 371)*

41. $^{+}3 \times {}^{+}5$	**42.** $^{+}3 \times {}^{-}5$	**43.** $^{-}7 \times {}^{-}4$	**44.** $^{+}7 \times {}^{+}4$	**45.** $^{+}7 \times {}^{-}1$
46. $^{-}9 \times 0$	**47.** $0 \times {}^{+}7$	**48.** 0×0	**49.** $^{+}6 \times {}^{-}7$	**50.** $^{-}4 \times {}^{-}3$
51. $^{-}11 \times {}^{+}8$	**52.** $^{-}12 \times {}^{-}12$	**53.** $^{+}15 \times {}^{-}6$	**54.** $^{+}16 \times {}^{+}10$	**55.** $^{-}21 \times {}^{+}10$

Give each quotient. *(page 372)*

56. $^{+}12 \div {}^{+}3$	**57.** $^{+}12 \div {}^{-}3$	**58.** $^{-}12 \div {}^{+}3$	**59.** $^{+}8 \div {}^{+}1$	**60.** $^{+}16 \div {}^{+}2$
61. $^{-}16 \div {}^{+}2$	**62.** $0 \div {}^{-}8$	**63.** $^{-}20 \div {}^{+}5$	**64.** $^{+}24 \div {}^{-}6$	**65.** $^{-}12 \div {}^{+}6$
66. $^{-}32 \div {}^{-}4$	**67.** $^{-}36 \div {}^{+}9$	**68.** $^{+}45 \div {}^{+}5$	**69.** $^{+}54 \div {}^{-}9$	**70.** $^{-}63 \div {}^{-}9$

Give the ordered pair for each point. *(page 374)*

71. *A*
72. *B*
73. *C*
74. *D*
75. *E*
76. *F*
77. *G*
78. *H*

Vertical axis

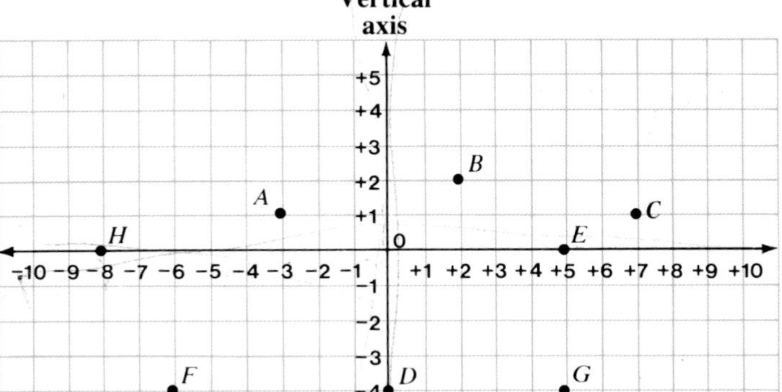

Horizontal axis

Cumulative TEST Standardized Format

Choose the correct letter.

1. Give the product.

2.408×100

A. 24.08
B. 0.02408
C. 2408
D. none of these

2. Give the quotient.

$78.95 \div 1000$

A. 78950
B. 0.7895
C. 0.07895
D. none of these

3. Change to a decimal rounded to the nearest hundredth.

$\frac{5}{6} = ?$

A. 0.17
B. 0.83
C. 0.67
D. none of these

4. Add.

$$\begin{array}{r} 3\frac{1}{2} \\ +2\frac{2}{3} \\ \hline \end{array}$$

A. $5\frac{3}{5}$
B. $5\frac{1}{6}$
C. $6\frac{1}{6}$
D. none of these

5. Give the product.

$2\frac{2}{3} \times 1\frac{3}{4}$

A. $4\frac{2}{3}$
B. $\frac{21}{32}$
C. $1\frac{11}{32}$
D. none of these

6. 345 cm = __?__ m

A. 34.5
B. 3.45
C. 345
D. none of these

7. Solve.

$\frac{n}{3} = \frac{11}{4}$

A. 3.5
B. 14.7
C. 8.25
D. none of these

8. Change to a fraction.

$37\frac{1}{2}\% = ?$

A. $\frac{1}{3}$
B. $\frac{5}{8}$
C. $\frac{2}{5}$
D. none of these

9. Solve.

25% of $24.5 = n$

A. 98
B. 6.125
C. 61.25
D. none of these

10. Solve.

40% of $n = 36$

A. 90
B. 14.4
C. 9.0
D. none of these

11. Find the surface area.

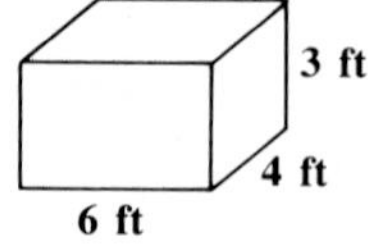

A. 54 ft^2
B. 72 ft^2
C. 108 ft^2
D. none of these

12. Give the difference.

$^{+}12 - {}^{-}10$

A. $^{+}2$
B. $^{-}2$
C. $^{+}22$
D. none of these

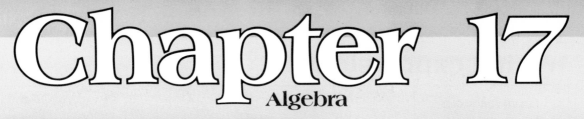

Chapter 17

Algebra

Writing expressions

I'm **n** years old.
If you're **n** years old, then I'm **n + 2** years old.
I'm **n ÷ 2** years old.
I'm **2n** years old.
I'm **n − 2** years old.
Ann
David
Chris
Craig
Beth

Who's the oldest? Who's the youngest?

The letter ***n*** is a variable. It represents Ann's age in years.

Variables, numbers, and operation signs can be combined to form **mathematical expressions.** Look at the cards below. First a mathematical expression is given in red. Then several different word expressions are given for the mathematical expression.

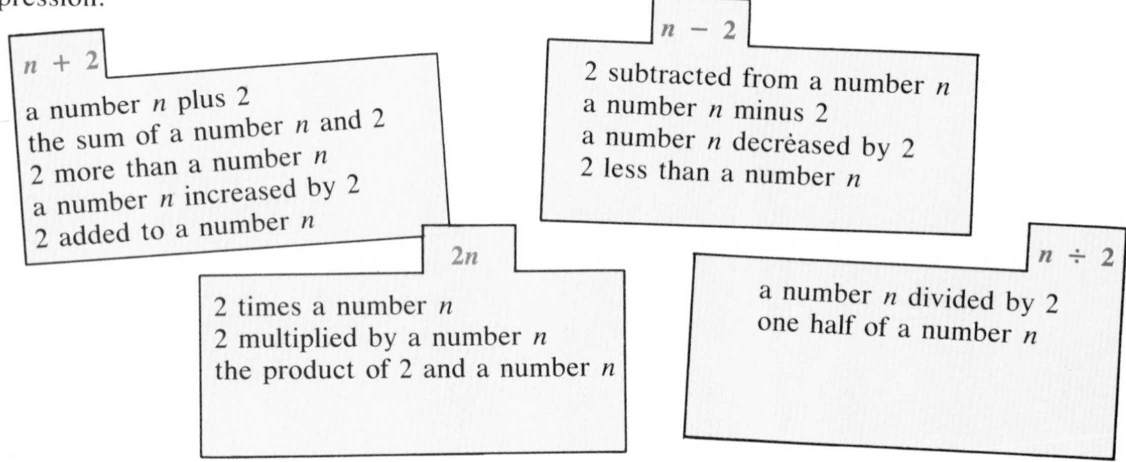

$n + 2$
a number n plus 2
the sum of a number n and 2
2 more than a number n
a number n increased by 2
2 added to a number n
$n - 2$
2 subtracted from a number n
a number n minus 2
a number n decreased by 2
2 less than a number n
$2n$
2 times a number n
2 multiplied by a number n
the product of 2 and a number n
$n \div 2$
a number n divided by 2
one half of a number n

Other examples:

Word Expression		Mathematical Expression
a number s increased by 6	⟶	$s + 6$
9 less than a number h	⟶	$h - 9$
4 times a number d	⟶	$4d$
one third of a number r	⟶	$r \div 3$ or $\frac{r}{3}$ or $\frac{1}{3}r$
5 times a number x, plus 4	⟶	$5x + 4$

EXERCISES

Write a mathematical expression for each word expression.

1. 5 more than a number n
2. 10 more than a number r
3. 11 times a number t
4. a number x minus 6
5. the sum of a number y and 4
6. a number b divided by 4
7. 15 times a number c
8. a number t decreased by 4
9. a number d increased by 6
10. 15 less than a number x
11. 40 divided by a number s
12. the product of 2 and a number n
13. 3 times a number m, plus 2
14. 4 times a number c, minus 6
15. 6 multiplied by a number r, plus 8
16. a number e divided by 5, minus 3

Let* n *be the number of letters you wrote last year. Write a mathematical expression for the number of letters that is

17. 2 more than your number of letters.
18. 5 letters less than your number of letters.
19. one third the number of your letters.
20. your number of letters decreased by 8.
21. one fourth the number of your letters.
22. 4 less than your number of letters.
23. your number of letters increased by 3 letters.
24. your number of letters divided by 9.
25. 4 times the number of your letters, plus 5 more letters.
26. 3 times the number of your letters, plus 2 more letters.

Who is it?

27. One of these people is not telling his/her true age. Who is it?
Hint: Use the clues at the top of page 382.

I'm 22 years old.
I'm 24 years old.
I'm 11 years old.
I'm 44 years old.
I'm 18 years old.
Ann
David
Chris
Craig
Beth

Evaluating expressions

WHAT DO YOU THINK?

Which is the cheapest plan?

JIFFY CAR RENTAL		
Plan A $.30 per mile	**Plan B** $40 per day	**Plan C** $10 per day plus $.20 per mile

1. Let d be the number of days and m be the number of miles. Which rental plan would cost $10d + .20m$ dollars?
2. Which plan would cost $.30m$ dollars?
3. What expression would you use for the cost of Plan B?

Here's how *to evaluate mathematical expressions.*

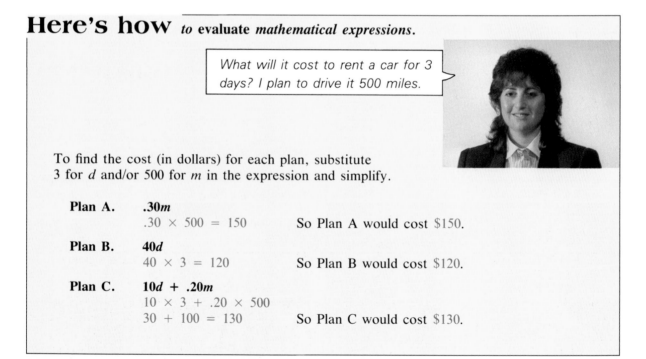

What will it cost to rent a car for 3 days? I plan to drive it 500 miles.

To find the cost (in dollars) for each plan, substitute 3 for d and/or 500 for m in the expression and simplify.

Plan A. $.30m$

$.30 \times 500 = 150$ So Plan A would cost $150.

Plan B. $40d$

$40 \times 3 = 120$ So Plan B would cost $120.

Plan C. $10d + .20m$

$10 \times 3 + .20 \times 500$

$30 + 100 = 130$ So Plan C would cost $130.

4. Look at the *Here's how*. Which is the cheapest plan for renting a car for 3 days and 500 miles?

EXERCISES

Evaluate each expression for n = 12.

Here are scrambled answers for the next row of exercises: 47 31 38 22 6

5. $n + 10$ 6. $3n - 5$ 7. $4n - 1$ 8. $n \div 2$ 9. $3n + 2$

From now on, let's agree not to write the raised plus sign when writing a positive number.

10. $2n + 1$ 11. $4 + n$ 12. $n - 11$ 13. $n + 12$

14. $8n$ 15. $2n - 20$ 16. $n \div 12$ 17. $12n + 6$

Evaluate each expression for r = 6 and s = 5.

Here are scrambled answers for the next row of exercises: 28 27 30 11 1

18. $r + s$ 19. $r - s$ 20. rs [$r \times s$] 21. $2r + 3s$ 22. $rs - 2$

23. $3r$ 24. $4s$ 25. $r \div 3$ 26. $\frac{10}{s}$ 27. $\frac{15}{s}$

28. $r + s + 5$ 29. $2rs$ 30. $3r - 2s$ 31. $12s - r$ 32. $14r - 3$

Evaluate each expression for a = 10 and b = ⁻2.

Here are scrambled answers for the next row of exercises: ⁻6 8 ⁻20 28 12

33. $a + b$ 34. ab 35. $3a + b$ 36. $3b$ 37. $a - b$

38. $4a$ 39. $5a + 10$ 40. $b + a$ 41. $\frac{20}{a}$ 42. $ab - 5$

43. $10 \div b$ 44. $ab + 20$ 45. $4a + 2b$ 46. $3ab$ 47. $4ab - 8$

Solve. Use the car rental plans on page 384.

48. Using Plan A, how much would it cost to rent a car for 600 miles?

49. Using Plan B, how much would it cost to rent a car for 6 days?

50. Using Plan C, how much would it cost to rent a car for 4 days and drive it 1000 miles?

51. You want to rent a car for 5 days and drive it 2000 miles. Which is the cheapest plan for you?

Name the rental plan

52. *Which rental plan did I use? It cost me $80 to rent a car for 2 days and 100 miles.*

53. *Which rental plan did I use? I paid $100 to rent a car for 4 days. I drove it 300 miles.*

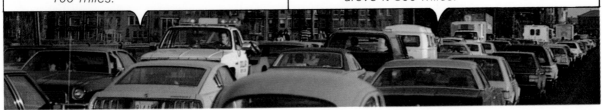

Solving addition equations

A BALANCING ACT!

Each of the marbles weighs the same.

1. The marbles in the red box plus the 4 extra marbles weigh the same as how many marbles?

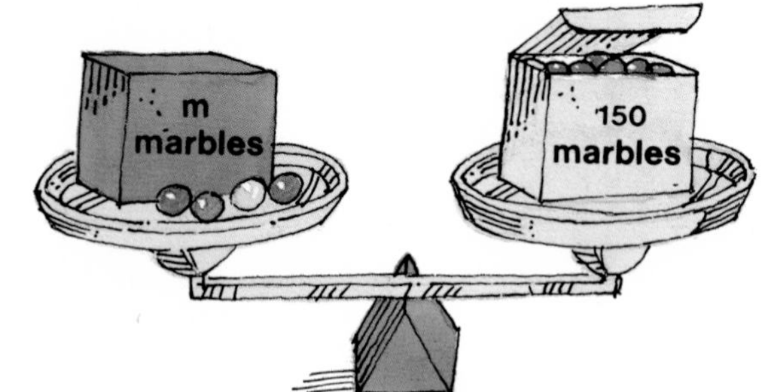

If we let m be the number of marbles in the red box, we can write the equation

$$m + 4 = 150$$

To **solve the equation** is to find the number that we can substitute for m to make the equation true.

Here's how *to solve an addition equation.*

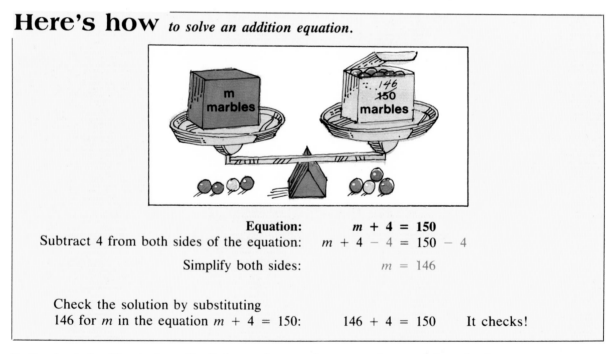

Equation:	$m + 4 = 150$
Subtract 4 from both sides of the equation:	$m + 4 - 4 = 150 - 4$
Simplify both sides:	$m = 146$

Check the solution by substituting 146 for m in the equation $m + 4 = 150$: $146 + 4 = 150$ It checks!

2. Look at the *Here's how*. To find m, what number was subtracted from both sides of the equation? How many marbles are in the red box?

3. Check these examples. Has each equation been solved correctly?

a.
$$a + 7 = 20$$
$$a + 7 - 7 = 20 - 7$$
$$a = 13$$

b.
$$b + 8 = 2$$
$$b + 8 - 8 = 2 - 8$$
$$b = {}^{-}6$$

c.
$$c + 10 = {}^{-}6$$
$$c + 10 - 10 = {}^{-}6 - 10$$
$$c = {}^{-}16$$

EXERCISES

Solve and check.

Here are scrambled answers for the next 2 rows of exercises:

2 13 ${}^-14$ 25 ${}^-1$ 22 ${}^-10$ ${}^-21$

4. $n + 16 = 38$	**5.** $r + 10 = {}^-4$	**6.** $x + {}^-8 = 5$	**7.** $t + {}^-2 = {}^-3$
Hint: Subtract 16 from both sides.	Hint: Subtract 10 from both sides.	Hint: Subtract ${}^-8$ from both sides.	Hint: Subtract ${}^-2$ from both sides.
8. $n + 28 = 30$	**9.** $y + {}^-20 = 5$	**10.** $x + {}^-15 = {}^-25$	**11.** $z + 13 = {}^-8$
12. $m + 9 = 19$	**13.** $r + {}^-6 = {}^-4$	**14.** $w + 7 = {}^-9$	**15.** $m + 4 = 26$
16. $y + {}^-5 = {}^-1$	**17.** $d + {}^-15 = {}^-10$	**18.** $x + 18 = 25$	**19.** $y + {}^-5 = {}^-8$
20. $27 + x = 68$	**21.** $42 + p = 40$	**22.** $19 + s = 11$	**23.** $g + 8 = {}^-7$
24. $x + 4 = {}^-6$	**25.** $m + {}^-11 = 40$	**26.** $t + 5 = {}^-7$	**27.** $h + {}^-3 = {}^-3$
28. $g + {}^-8 = {}^-10$	**29.** $s + {}^-3 = {}^-4$	**30.** $r + 15 = {}^-50$	**31.** $b + 4 = 10$
32. $m + {}^-8 = 50$	**33.** $x + 16 = 14$	**34.** $g + {}^-20 = {}^-21$	**35.** $n + 6 = 6$
36. $t + 97 = 80$	**37.** $c + 46 = 58$	**38.** $x + 24 = 24$	**39.** $f + 21 = {}^-2$
40. $a + 62 = 75$	**41.** $y + {}^-10 = {}^-10$	**42.** $k + 3 = {}^-32$	**43.** $c + {}^-4 = 5$
44. $r + 15 = {}^-25$	**45.** $k + 20 = 0$	**46.** $c + {}^-46 = 0$	**47.** $p + 5 = {}^-8$
48. $x + 16 = 9$	**49.** $f + 17 = 17$	**50.** $d + {}^-18 = 4$	**51.** $k + 4 = 4$
52. $t + 12 = 15$	**53.** $r + {}^-9 = {}^-10$	**54.** $6 + k = {}^-5$	**55.** $a + 18 = {}^-15$
56. $d + 0 = 9$	**57.** $w + 7 = 23$	**58.** $n + {}^-4 = {}^-9$	**59.** $t + {}^-14 = 7$
60. $m + 6 = {}^-8$	**61.** $q + {}^-9 = {}^-1$	**62.** $b + {}^-32 = 0$	**63.** $e + 10 = 3$
64. $v + {}^-15 = 7$	**65.** $n + 18 = 18$	**66.** $s + 8 = {}^-2$	**67.** $r + {}^-2 = {}^-21$
68. $a + 24 = 0$	**69.** $s + 9 = {}^-17$	**70.** $p + 14 = {}^-5$	**71.** $m + {}^-8 = 2$
72. $w + {}^-3 = {}^-9$	**73.** $6 + y = {}^-2$	**74.** $y + {}^-10 = 10$	**75.** $s + 14 = {}^-13$
76. $t + 5 = 1$	**77.** $c + 0 = {}^-7$	**78.** $k + {}^-1 = 6$	**79.** ${}^-20 + d = {}^-1$

Balance it!

Find the weight* n *that is needed to make each scale balance.

80.

81.

Solving subtraction equations

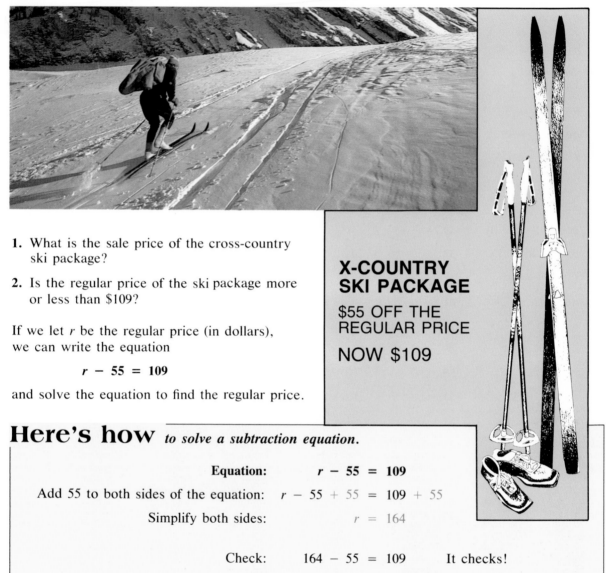

X-COUNTRY
SKI PACKAGE
$55 OFF THE
REGULAR PRICE
NOW $109

1. What is the sale price of the cross-country ski package?
2. Is the regular price of the ski package more or less than $109?

If we let r be the regular price (in dollars), we can write the equation

$$r - 55 = 109$$

and solve the equation to find the regular price.

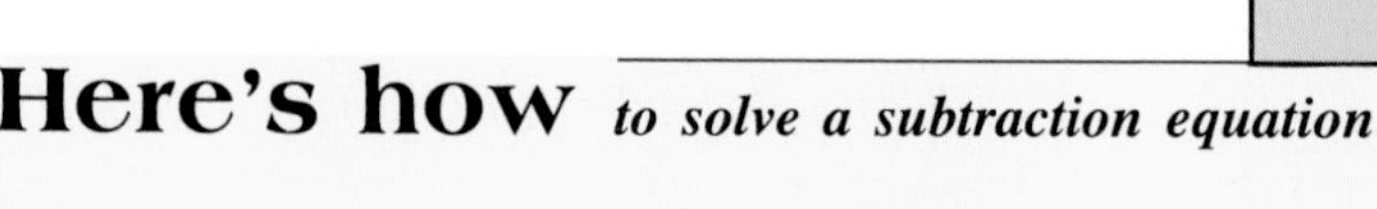

Here's how *to solve a subtraction equation.*

Equation:	$\mathbf{r - 55 = 109}$
Add 55 to both sides of the equation:	$r - 55 + 55 = 109 + 55$
Simplify both sides:	$r = 164$
Check:	$164 - 55 = 109$ It checks!

3. Look at the *Here's how*. To find r, what number was added to both sides of the equation? What is the regular price of the ski package?
4. Check these examples. Has each equation been solved correctly?

a. $\mathbf{a - 5 = 12}$
$a - 5 + 5 = 12 + 5$
$a = 17$

b. $\mathbf{b - 6 = {}^-2}$
$b - 6 + 6 = {}^-2 + 6$
$b = 4$

c. $\mathbf{c - {}^-4 = {}^-1}$
$c - {}^-4 + {}^-4 = {}^-1 + {}^-4$
$c = {}^-5$

EXERCISES

Solve and check. *Here are scrambled answers for the next two rows of exercises:* $3 \quad {}^-1 \quad {}^-5 \quad 40 \quad 37 \quad 70 \quad 41 \quad 63$

5. $n - 15 = 25$

Hint: Add 15 to both sides.

6. $r - 46 = {}^-5$

Hint: Add 46 to both sides.

7. $n - 10 = 60$

Hint: Add 10 to both sides.

8. $p - {}^-3 = 6$

Hint: Add ⁻3 to both sides.

9. $s - 19 = 18$ **10.** $g - 5 = {}^-6$ **11.** $b - 35 = {}^-40$ **12.** $n - 25 = 38$

13. $m - 23 = 49$ **14.** $n - 42 = 76$ **15.** $a - 65 = 61$ **16.** $r - 24 = {}^-8$

17. $x - 6 = 2$ **18.** $d - 9 = {}^-1$ **19.** $y - 20 = 7$ **20.** $k - 125 = 0$

21. $x - 18 = {}^-2$ **22.** $b - 33 = 33$ **23.** $s - 5 = {}^-5$ **24.** $n - 2 = 5$

25. $c - 61 = 62$ **26.** $x - 2 = {}^-8$ **27.** $y - 17 = 20$ **28.** $t - 14 = 2$

29. $y - 17 = 14$ **30.** $b - 3 = {}^-4$ **31.** $y - 20 = 1$ **32.** $n - 4 = {}^-1$

33. $p - 8 = {}^-3$ **34.** $m - 8 = {}^-2$ **35.** $t - 1 = 5$ **36.** $x - 45 = 54$

37. $c - {}^-7 = {}^-3$ **38.** $m - 100 = 0$ **39.** $a - {}^-2 = 9$ **40.** $y - 6 = {}^-11$

41. $c - {}^-4 = 10$ **42.** $x - 12 = 6$ **43.** $e - 9 = 0$ **44.** $t - 16 = {}^-8$

45. $n - {}^-7 = 16$ **46.** $z - 5 = 4$ **47.** $d - {}^-8 = 0$ **48.** $w - 6 = 20$

You decide!

Decide whether Equation A or B would be used to solve each problem. Then solve the problem.

Equation A: $n + 15 = 66$
Equation B: $n - 15 = 66$

49. *$15 off the regular price is $66. What is the regular price?*

50. $15 more than the sale price is $66. What is the sale price?

51. The regular price decreased by $15 is $66. What is the regular price?

52. The sum of the sale price and a $15 discount is $66. What is the sale price?

53. Sarah gave her brother $15. She then had $66. How much money did Sarah have before she gave her brother the money?

54. James got paid $15. He then had $66. How much money did he have before he got paid?

Cumulative Skill Practice

Give the product. *(page 64)*

1. 6.2×0.5 **2.** 8.4×0.61 **3.** 0.72×0.4 **4.** 6.2×0.83

5. 32×5.3 **6.** 0.79×5.3 **7.** 2.05×1.7 **8.** 3.01×1.5

9. 9.46×8 **10.** 47.1×6.2 **11.** 47.9×0.38 **12.** 48.6×0.11

13. 5.78×13 **14.** 33.4×4.7 **15.** 309×1.5 **16.** 403×1.8

17. 2.09×0.03 **18.** 35.3×20.5 **19.** 9.36×2.04 **20.** 2.98×0.05

Give the quotient rounded to the nearest tenth. *(page 96)*

21. $19.3 \div 0.9$ **22.** $5.47 \div 0.2$ **23.** $8.09 \div 0.03$ **24.** $8.65 \div 0.2$

25. $15.7 \div 0.5$ **26.** $8.43 \div 0.07$ **27.** $5.405 \div 0.08$ **28.** $3.09 \div 0.04$

29. $8.41 \div 1.7$ **30.** $3.047 \div 2.9$ **31.** $5.09 \div 0.35$ **32.** $4.65 \div 0.21$

33. $15.085 \div 0.33$ **34.** $8.001 \div 0.27$ **35.** $5.05 \div 7.4$ **36.** $5.006 \div 0.12$

37. $5.92 \div 3.8$ **38.** $7.397 \div 8.1$ **39.** $38 \div 7.3$ **40.** $46 \div 8.12$

Give the sum in simplest form. *(page 158)*

41. $\frac{1}{2} + \frac{1}{4}$ **42.** $\frac{1}{4} + \frac{5}{8}$ **43.** $\frac{1}{5} + \frac{3}{10}$ **44.** $\frac{2}{3} + \frac{1}{3}$ **45.** $\frac{1}{3} + \frac{2}{5}$ **46.** $\frac{3}{7} + \frac{4}{7}$

47. $\frac{1}{2} + \frac{5}{8}$ **48.** $\frac{7}{8} + \frac{3}{5}$ **49.** $\frac{1}{2} + \frac{3}{8}$ **50.** $\frac{7}{8} + 0$ **51.** $\frac{6}{11} + \frac{3}{11}$ **52.** $\frac{3}{5} + \frac{1}{2}$

53. $\frac{1}{4} + \frac{3}{5}$ **54.** $\frac{2}{3} + \frac{3}{7}$ **55.** $\frac{2}{3} + \frac{5}{6}$ **56.** $\frac{2}{5} + \frac{3}{4}$ **57.** $\frac{3}{5} + \frac{1}{3}$ **58.** $\frac{4}{9} + \frac{1}{3}$

Give the difference in simplest form. *(page 166)*

59. $\frac{3}{4} - \frac{1}{4}$ **60.** $\frac{3}{4} - \frac{1}{8}$ **61.** $\frac{1}{2} - \frac{1}{3}$ **62.** $\frac{5}{8} - \frac{1}{2}$ **63.** $\frac{6}{7} - \frac{1}{2}$ **64.** $\frac{1}{2} - \frac{1}{4}$

65. $\frac{3}{5} - \frac{1}{4}$ **66.** $\frac{3}{2} - \frac{2}{3}$ **67.** $\frac{3}{4} - \frac{1}{2}$ **68.** $\frac{9}{10} - \frac{1}{5}$ **69.** $\frac{4}{5} - \frac{1}{10}$ **70.** $\frac{2}{3} - \frac{1}{9}$

71. $\frac{2}{3} - \frac{5}{8}$ **72.** $\frac{7}{8} - \frac{3}{4}$ **73.** $\frac{4}{5} - \frac{3}{8}$ **74.** $\frac{5}{6} - \frac{1}{3}$ **75.** $\frac{9}{10} - \frac{1}{2}$ **76.** $\frac{3}{7} - \frac{1}{14}$

Give the product in simplest form. *(page 178)*

77. $\frac{1}{2} \times \frac{1}{3}$ **78.** $\frac{1}{2} \times \frac{1}{4}$ **79.** $\frac{1}{3} \times \frac{3}{5}$ **80.** $\frac{3}{4} \times \frac{2}{3}$ **81.** $\frac{2}{3} \times \frac{1}{5}$ **82.** $\frac{2}{7} \times \frac{1}{2}$

83. $\frac{3}{2} \times \frac{3}{4}$ **84.** $\frac{5}{9} \times \frac{3}{8}$ **85.** $\frac{1}{2} \times \frac{2}{5}$ **86.** $2 \times \frac{7}{8}$ **87.** $3 \times \frac{5}{9}$ **88.** $\frac{3}{5} \times \frac{1}{4}$

89. $\frac{5}{2} \times \frac{3}{10}$ **90.** $\frac{1}{3} \times \frac{3}{8}$ **91.** $3 \times \frac{3}{4}$ **92.** $\frac{1}{6} \times \frac{1}{6}$ **93.** $\frac{1}{7} \times \frac{1}{7}$ **94.** $\frac{5}{6} \times \frac{1}{2}$

Problem solving

Decide which operation sign (+, −, ×, ÷) should replace the question mark to give the correct equation. Then solve the equation.

1. One long-stemmed rose costs \$2. What is the price (p) of 12 long-stemmed roses?

$$2 \boxed{?}\ 12 = p$$

2. Six carnations cost \$4.50. What is the price (p) of one carnation?

$$4.50 \boxed{?}\ 6 = p$$

3. A dozen strawflowers cost \$2.40. What is the price (p) of each flower?

$$2.40 \boxed{?}\ 12 = p$$

4. Five tulips cost \$1.50. What is the price (p) of 3 tulips?

$$(1.50 \boxed{?}\ 5) \boxed{?}\ 3 = p$$

5. A customer bought 2 bunches of baby's breath at \$.89 per bunch. How much change (c) should he get from a \$10 bill?

$$10 \boxed{?}\ (2 \boxed{?}\ .89) = c$$

Solve.

6. Mini carnations are priced at \$3.89 per bunch. How much would you pay for 3 bunches of mini carnations?

7. A bunch of 15 daisies costs \$3.45. What is the cost per daisy?

8. A mixed bouquet costs \$4.95. What is the cost of 2 mixed bouquets?

9. A customer bought 4 mixed bouquets at \$4.95 each. How much change should she get from a \$20 bill?

10. Three dozen daffodils cost \$9.60. What is the cost of 4 dozen daffodils?

11. Gladioli are selling at 3 for \$2.37. How much would you expect to pay for 5 gladioli?

12. Marcia bought 3 dozen chrysanthemums at \$10.50 per dozen and some fern for \$1.25. How much did she spend in all?

13. Marty paid \$3.30 for some sweetheart roses. If 3 sweetheart roses cost \$1.65, how many did Marty buy?

Solving multiplication equations

ANOTHER BALANCING ACT!

Each box contains the same number of marbles.

1. Three times the number of marbles in 1 box weighs the same as how many marbles?

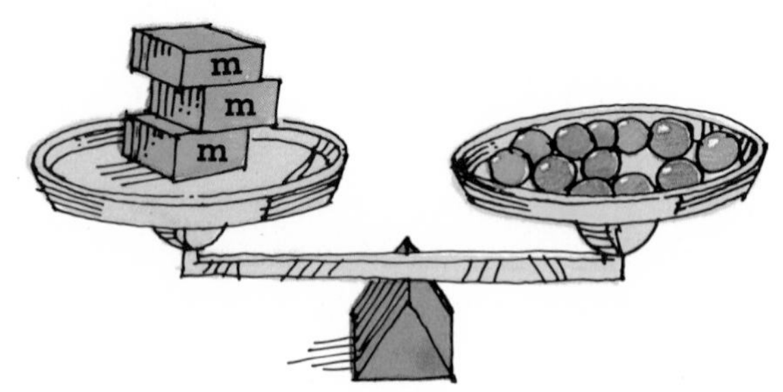

If we let m be the number of marbles in each box, we can write the equation

$$3m = 12$$

Here's how *to solve a multiplication equation.*

Equation: $3m = 12$

Divide both sides of the equation by 3: $\frac{3m}{3} = \frac{12}{3}$

Simplify both sides: $m = 4$

Remember that a fraction bar can be used to show division.

Check the solution by substituting 4 for m in the equation $3m = 12$: $3 \times 4 = 12$ It checks!

2. Look at the *Here's how*. To find m, both sides of the equation were divided by what number? How many marbles are in each box?

3. Check these examples. Has each equation been solved correctly?

a. $5a = 60$

$\frac{5a}{5} = \frac{60}{5}$

$a = 12$

b. $3b = {}^-30$

$\frac{3b}{3} = \frac{{}^-30}{3}$

$b = {}^-10$

c. ${}^-2c = 14$

$\frac{{}^-2c}{{}^-2} = \frac{14}{{}^-2}$

$c = {}^-7$

EXERCISES

Solve and check.

Here are scrambled answers for the next row of exercises: $^-7$ 5 6 $^-3$

4. $4n = 24$	**5.** $^-5t = 35$	**6.** $2r = {}^-6$	**7.** $^-3x = {}^-15$
Hint: Divide both sides by 4.	Hint: Divide both sides by $^-5$.	Hint: Divide both sides by 2.	Hint: Divide both sides by $^-3$.
8. $9n = 27$	**9.** $^-7n = 14$	**10.** $5s = 55$	**11.** $3y = {}^-21$
12. $4t = 48$	**13.** $8w = 120$	**14.** $^-6n = 42$	**15.** $^-2r = {}^-22$
16. $9a = 108$	**17.** $12n = 240$	**18.** $^-3x = 15$	**19.** $9y = {}^-27$
20. $^-2x = 6$	**21.** $30t = 30$	**22.** $7x = {}^-21$	**23.** $^-15a = 30$
24. $^-4s = 40$	**25.** $3s = 57$	**26.** $6c = 66$	**27.** $11n = 88$
28. $^-4c = {}^-40$	**29.** $8n = {}^-16$	**30.** $^-2x = {}^-2$	**31.** $7n = 7$
32. $^-3b = {}^-33$	**33.** $9y = 189$	**34.** $25t = 100$	**35.** $20n = {}^-60$
36. $7h = {}^-77$	**37.** $^-5s = {}^-5$	**38.** $15t = 30$	**39.** $25a = 0$
40. $^-15x = {}^-15$	**41.** $12y = 132$	**42.** $^-20a = {}^-100$	**43.** $25c = 175$
44. $10w = 130$	**45.** $^-16r = 0$	**46.** $14x = {}^-154$	**47.** $^-9w = 270$
48. $^-8b = 168$	**49.** $11v = 165$	**50.** $7r = {}^-84$	**51.** $^-16n = 224$
52. $30t = {}^-210$	**53.** $^-15y = {}^-330$	**54.** $32k = 0$	**55.** $^-24w = {}^-192$
56. $^-17x = 153$	**57.** $16c = {}^-272$	**58.** $15y = 15$	**59.** $^-26s = 0$

You decide!

Decide whether Equation A, B, or C could be used to solve each problem. Then solve the problem.

Equation A: $s + .99 = 1.65$
Equation B: $3s = 5.28$
Equation C: $2s = 1.14$

60. What is the price of a box of cereal? Clue: 3 boxes of cereal would cost \$5.28.

61. What is the price of a can of soup? Clue: A can of soup and a jar of pickles cost a total of \$1.65.

62. What is the price of a can of juice? Clue: 2 cans of juice cost \$.15 more than a jar of pickles.

Solving division equations

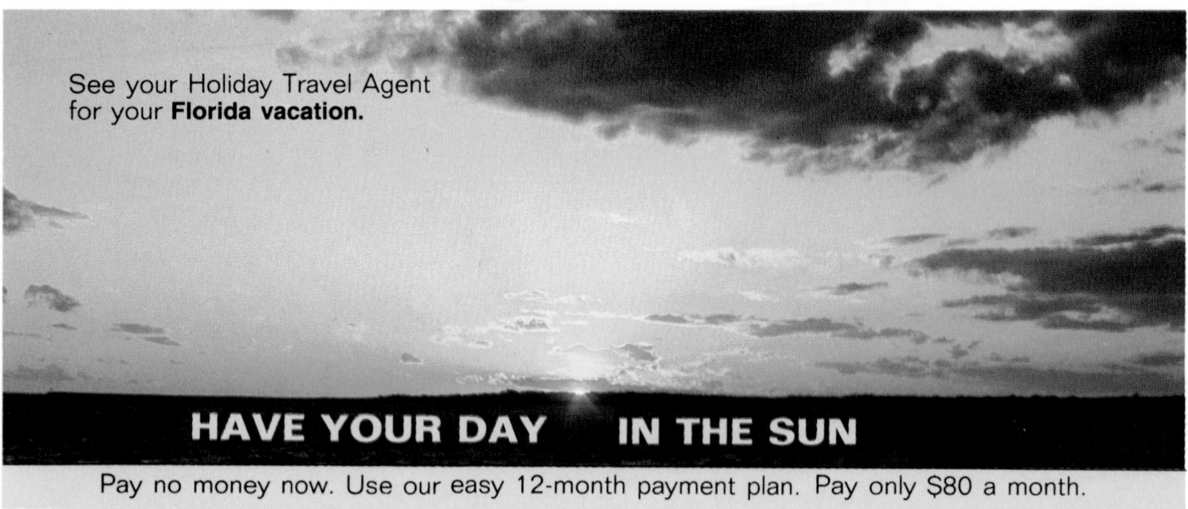

See your Holiday Travel Agent
for your **Florida vacation.**
HAVE YOUR DAY IN THE SUN
Pay no money now. Use our easy 12-month payment plan. Pay only $80 a month.

1. How many monthly payments are there?

2. How much is each monthly payment?

If we let t be the total cost (in dollars) of the Florida vacation, we can write the equation $\frac{t}{12} = 80$

Here's how *to solve a division equation.*

Equation:	$\frac{t}{12} = 80$	
Multiply both sides by 12:	$12 \times \frac{t}{12} = 12 \times 80$	
Simplify both sides:	$t = 960$	
Check:	$\frac{960}{12} = 80$	It checks!

3. Look at the *Here's how*. To find t, both sides of the equation were multiplied by what number? What is the total cost of the Florida vacation?

4. Check these examples. Has each equation been solved correctly?

a.
$$\frac{a}{4} = 20$$
$$4 \times \frac{a}{4} = 4 \times 20$$
$$a = 80$$

b.
$$\frac{b}{^-2} = 16$$
$$^-2 \times \frac{b}{^-2} = {}^-2 \times 16$$
$$b = {}^-32$$

c.
$$\frac{c}{^-5} = {}^-4$$
$$^-5 \times \frac{c}{^-5} = {}^-5 \times {}^-4$$
$$c = 20$$

EXERCISES

Solve and check.

Here are scrambled answers for the next row of exercises: 10 ${}^-18$ ${}^-12$ 64 35

5. $\frac{x}{2} = 32$ **6.** $\frac{b}{{}^-3} = 4$ **7.** $\frac{n}{6} = {}^-3$ **8.** $\frac{n}{{}^-2} = {}^-5$ **9.** $\frac{d}{7} = 5$

10. $\frac{y}{5} = 3$ **11.** $\frac{m}{9} = {}^-3$ **12.** $\frac{k}{10} = 15$ **13.** $\frac{n}{5} = 12$ **14.** $\frac{a}{20} = 2$

15. $\frac{h}{15} = 3$ **16.** $\frac{c}{{}^-3} = {}^-4$ **17.** $\frac{t}{12} = {}^-6$ **18.** $\frac{x}{10} = {}^-8$ **19.** $\frac{a}{2} = 15$

20. $\frac{x}{4} = {}^-9$ **21.** $\frac{n}{7} = 9$ **22.** $\frac{y}{100} = 5$ **23.** $\frac{t}{{}^-8} = {}^-1$ **24.** $\frac{n}{50} = 6$

25. $\frac{c}{{}^-3} = {}^-40$ **26.** $\frac{n}{30} = 4$ **27.** $\frac{x}{4} = {}^-7$ **28.** $\frac{n}{{}^-8} = {}^-2$ **29.** $\frac{x}{4} = {}^-10$

30. $\frac{f}{15} = 8$ **31.** $\frac{c}{{}^-7} = 1$ **32.** $\frac{r}{5} = {}^-25$ **33.** $\frac{y}{{}^-5} = {}^-2$ **34.** $\frac{a}{4} = 300$

35. $\frac{x}{{}^-9} = {}^-2$ **36.** $\frac{b}{50} = 1$ **37.** $\frac{a}{{}^-8} = {}^-9$ **38.** $\frac{n}{6} = 0$ **39.** $\frac{x}{{}^-9} = {}^-11$

40. $\frac{t}{4} = {}^-5$ **41.** $\frac{r}{3} = 12$ **42.** $\frac{b}{{}^-10} = 10$ **43.** $\frac{n}{12} = {}^-3$ **44.** $\frac{c}{{}^-7} = {}^-15$

45. $\frac{k}{9} = 0$ **46.** $\frac{y}{{}^-6} = {}^-11$ **47.** $\frac{w}{{}^-5} = 20$ **48.** $\frac{s}{8} = 21$ **49.** $\frac{m}{18} = {}^-13$

You decide!

Decide whether Equation A, B, C, or D could be used to solve each problem. Then solve the problem.

50. *I spent $450 for 5 nights' lodging at the resort. How much was it for 1 night's lodging?*

Equation A:	$5n = 450$
Equation B:	$\frac{n}{5} = 450$
Equation C:	$n + 50 = 450$
Equation D:	$n - 50 = 450$

51. Karen spent $50 more for her trip than Alan did. She spent $450. How much did Alan spend?

52. After spending $50 at the ski resort, Brian had $450 left. How much money did he have to start with?

53. A vacation cottage at the ocean rents for $450 a week. How much rent is paid in 5 weeks?

Solving two-step equations

To find the number of reprints he can get for \$20, solve this two-step equation:

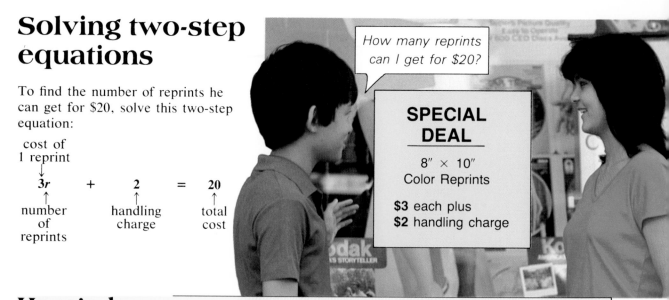

cost of 1 reprint ↓

$3r$	$+$	2	$=$	20
↑ number of reprints		↑ handling charge		↑ total cost

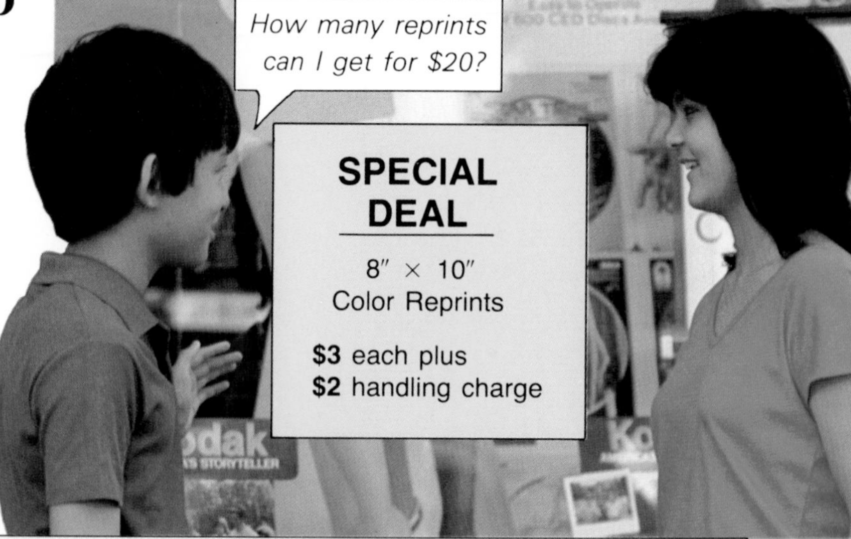
How many reprints can I get for $20?
SPECIAL DEAL
8" × 10" Color Reprints
$3 each plus
$2 handling charge

Here's how *to solve a two-step equation.*

To solve the equation, get an equation with only the variable r on one side of the equal sign.

Equation: $3r + 2 = 20$

First subtract 2 from both sides: $3r + 2 - 2 = 20 - 2$

Then divide both sides by 3: $\frac{3r}{3} = \frac{18}{3}$

$r = 6$

Check: $3 \times 6 + 2 = 20$ It checks!

1. Look at the *Here's how*. To find r, first subtract [?] from both sides of the equation and then divide both sides by [?].
2. Check the solution. How many reprints can be bought for \$20?
3. Check these examples. Has each two-step equation been solved correctly?

a.
$$\mathbf{2a + 4 = 26}$$
$$2a + 4 - 4 = 26 - 4$$
$$2a = 22$$
$$\frac{2a}{2} = \frac{22}{2}$$
$$a = 11$$

b.
$$\mathbf{4b - 3 = 21}$$
$$4b - 3 + 3 = 21 + 3$$
$$4b = 24$$
$$\frac{4b}{4} = \frac{24}{4}$$
$$b = 6$$

c.
$$\mathbf{\frac{c}{2} + 7 = 18}$$
$$\frac{c}{2} + 7 - 7 = 18 - 7$$
$$\frac{c}{2} = 11$$
$$2 \times \frac{c}{2} = 2 \times 11$$
$$c = 22$$

EXERCISES

Copy and finish solving each equation. Check your solution.

4. $2y + 8 = 14$

$2y + 8 - 8 = 14 - ?$

$2y = ?$

$y = ?$

5. $5t - 7 = 28$

$5t - 7 + 7 = 28 + ?$

$5t = ?$

$t = ?$

6. $\frac{n}{3} + 6 = 12$

$\frac{n}{3} + 6 - 6 = 12 - ?$

$\frac{n}{3} = ?$

$n = ?$

Solve and check.

Here are scrambled answers for the next two rows of exercises: 17 9 4 11 5 2 6 7

7. $4x + 3 = 27$	**8.** $2n + 5 = 39$	**9.** $4t + 8 = 28$	**10.** $3m - 2 = 25$
11. $6y - 4 = 20$	**12.** $6k - 3 = 39$	**13.** $2y + 10 = 32$	**14.** $8y - 2 = 14$
15. $6a + 4 = 28$	**16.** $3y - 5 = 7$	**17.** $5t + 7 = 52$	**18.** $5c - 2 = 33$
19. $\frac{m}{3} + 7 = 9$	**20.** $\frac{n}{2} + 2 = 5$	**21.** $\frac{t}{7} + 4 = 6$	**22.** $\frac{d}{3} - 4 = 5$
23. $\frac{n}{3} + 20 = 21$	**24.** $5n + {}^{-}3 = 7$	**25.** $\frac{t}{6} - 9 = {}^{-}3$	**26.** $6a - 12 = 30$
27. $\frac{c}{{}^{-}3} + 7 = {}^{-}8$	**28.** ${}^{-}7x + 4 = 32$	**29.** $\frac{y}{{}^{-}4} - {}^{-}2 = 10$	**30.** $9a - 4 = 23$
31. $\frac{d}{9} + 9 = 0$	**32.** $8r + {}^{-}5 = 11$	**33.** ${}^{-}10y + 6 = {}^{-}14$	**34.** $\frac{s}{{}^{-}7} - 3 = 8$
35. ${}^{-}4x + 8 = 0$	**36.** $\frac{n}{{}^{-}4} + {}^{-}6 = 1$	**37.** $12s - {}^{-}3 = {}^{-}9$	**38.** $\frac{n}{7} + {}^{-}5 = 0$

Mystery numbers

Decide whether Equation A, B, C, or D would be used to solve each problem. Then solve the problem.

Equation A: $6y + 3 = 33$

Equation B: $6y - 3 = 33$

Equation C: $\frac{y}{6} + 3 = 33$

Equation D: $\frac{y}{6} - 3 = 33$

39. *I'm thinking of a number. If I multiply it by 6 and then subtract 3, I get 33. What's my number?*

40. If you multiply a number by 6 and then add 3, you get 33. What is the number?

41. A number divided by 6 and then decreased by 3 is 33. What is the number?

42. If you divide a number by 6 and then add 3, you get 33. What is the number?

Cumulative Skill Practice

Give the quotient in simplest form. *(page 188)*

1. $\frac{1}{2} \div \frac{1}{4}$ **2.** $\frac{1}{6} \div \frac{1}{2}$ **3.** $\frac{3}{5} \div \frac{3}{2}$ **4.** $\frac{3}{4} \div \frac{2}{3}$ **5.** $\frac{2}{3} \div 2$ **6.** $\frac{4}{5} \div \frac{1}{2}$

7. $\frac{3}{5} \div \frac{3}{8}$ **8.** $0 \div \frac{2}{3}$ **9.** $\frac{9}{10} \div \frac{4}{5}$ **10.** $\frac{5}{8} \div 2$ **11.** $\frac{2}{5} \div 5$ **12.** $4 \div \frac{1}{8}$

13. $2 \div \frac{7}{8}$ **14.** $\frac{9}{10} \div \frac{3}{2}$ **15.** $3 \div \frac{3}{4}$ **16.** $\frac{5}{4} \div \frac{5}{2}$ **17.** $\frac{5}{6} \div \frac{1}{3}$ **18.** $\frac{3}{7} \div \frac{6}{7}$

Solve. *(page 258)*

19. 10% of 70 = n **20.** 25% of 48 = n **21.** 40% of 65 = n

22. 14% of 58 = n **23.** 8% of 36.5 = n **24.** 125% of 52 = n

25. 6.5% of 147 = n **26.** 13.2% of 60 = n **27.** 22.6% of 34.7 = n

28. $16\frac{2}{3}$% of 78 = n **29.** $66\frac{2}{3}$% of 81 = n **30.** $62\frac{1}{2}$% of 120 = n

31. 16.4% of 8.2 = n **32.** 9.6% of 59.3 = n **33.** 8.9% of 238.3 = n

Solve. *(page 260)*

34. 10% of n = 18 **35.** 20% of n = 20 **36.** 25% of n = 16

37. 50% of n = 26 **38.** 75% of n = 60 **39.** 150% of n = 90

40. 6% of n = 21 **41.** 60% of n = 51 **42.** 15% of n = 30

Solve. Round each number to the nearest tenth. *(page 260)*

43. 3.5% of n = 8 **44.** 8.4% of n = 10 **45.** 6.2% of n = 11

46. 9.5% of n = 12 **47.** 32.4% of n = 12.4 **48.** 16.8% of n = 9.7

Compute the interest. *(page 284)*

49. Principal = \$1000
Rate = 12% per year
Time = 4 years

50. Principal = \$900
Rate = 15% per year
Time = 4 months

51. Principal = \$150
Rate = 1.5% per month
Time = 3 months

52. Principal = \$450
Rate = 1% per month
Time = 7 months

53. Principal = \$800
Rate = 14% per year
Time = 9 months

54. Principal = \$500
Rate = 13.5% per year
Time = 18 months

Give the sum. *(page 364)*

55. ${}^{+}4 + {}^{+}6$ **56.** ${}^{+}4 + {}^{-}6$ **57.** ${}^{-}4 + {}^{+}6$ **58.** ${}^{-}4 + {}^{-}6$ **59.** ${}^{-}6 + 0$

60. $0 + {}^{+}9$ **61.** $0 + {}^{-}9$ **62.** ${}^{-}6 + {}^{-}7$ **63.** $0 + 0$ **64.** ${}^{-}7 + {}^{+}7$

Problem solving

LOGO—A COMPUTER LANGUAGE

Logo is a popular **computer language** that allows students to use a computer as a tool in learning, playing, and exploring. Many students learn Logo by starting with "turtle graphics." The "turtle" is a small triangular printer on the computer screen that responds to commands. Study these examples.

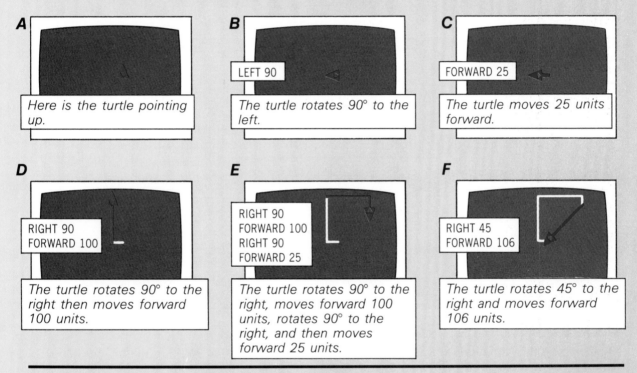

A

Here is the turtle pointing up.

B

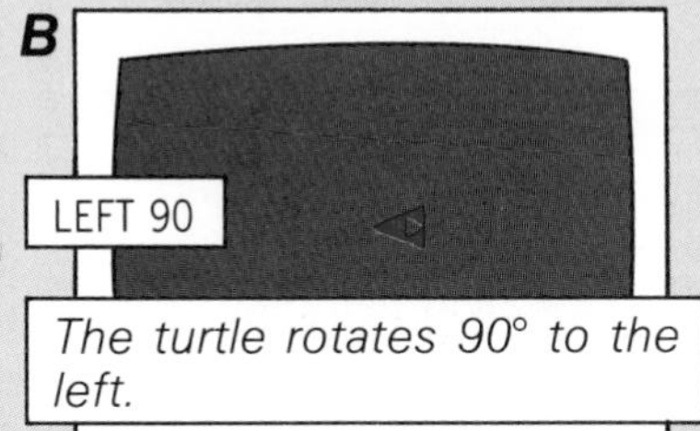

The turtle rotates 90° to the left.

C

The turtle moves 25 units forward.

D

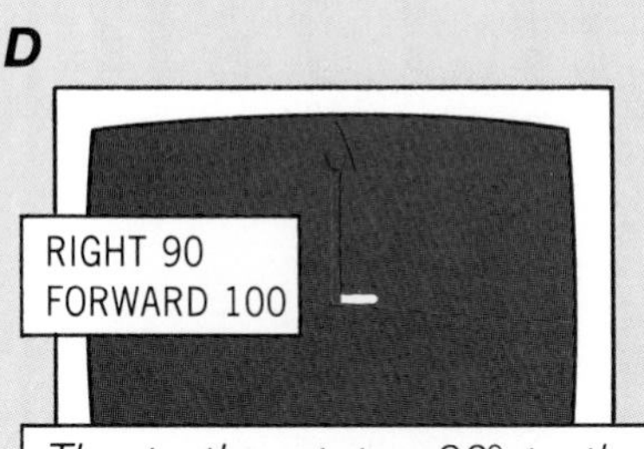

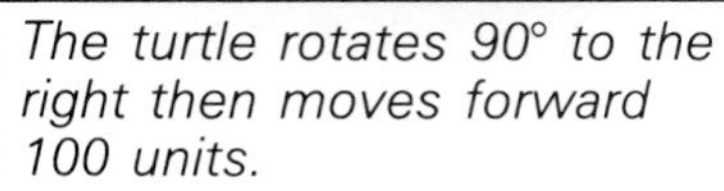

The turtle rotates 90° to the right then moves forward 100 units.

E

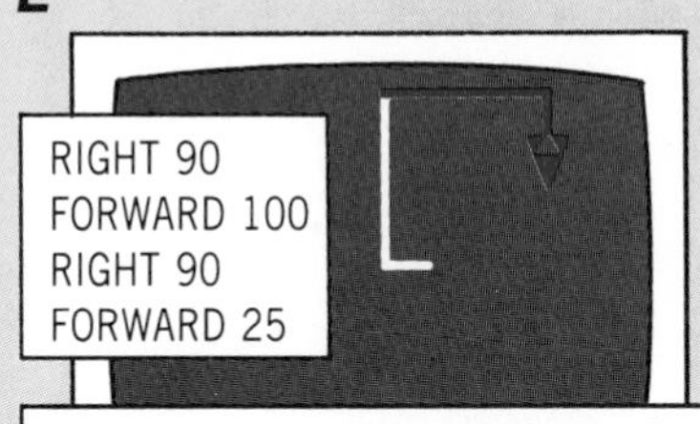

The turtle rotates 90° to the right, moves forward 100 units, rotates 90° to the right, and then moves forward 25 units.

F

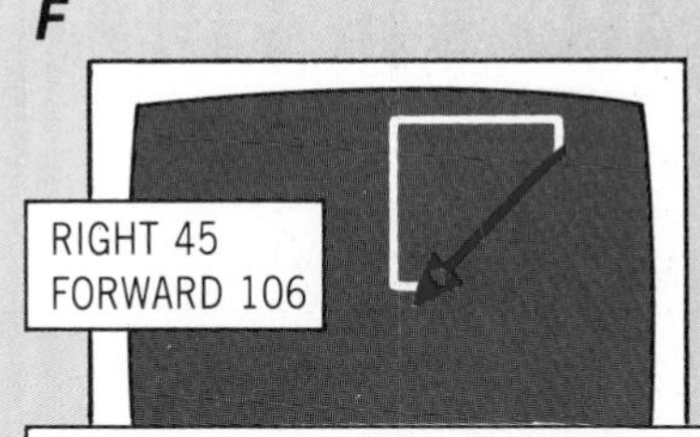

The turtle rotates 45° to the right and moves forward 106 units.

Match each of the turtle graphics with its set of Logo commands. Assume that the turtle starts pointing up.

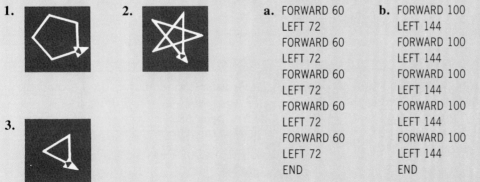

1. 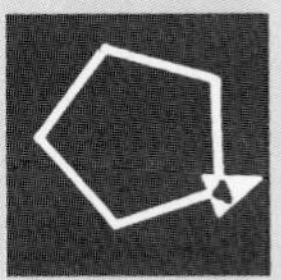

2. 

3. 

a.
```
FORWARD 60
LEFT 72
FORWARD 60
LEFT 72
FORWARD 60
LEFT 72
FORWARD 60
LEFT 72
FORWARD 60
LEFT 72
END
```

b.
```
FORWARD 100
LEFT 144
FORWARD 100
LEFT 144
FORWARD 100
LEFT 144
FORWARD 100
LEFT 144
FORWARD 100
LEFT 144
END
```

c.
```
FORWARD 60
LEFT 120
FORWARD 60
LEFT 120
FORWARD 60
END
```

Chapter REVIEW

Here are scrambled answers for the review exercises:

$^-2$	5	add	more	variable
$^-7$	35	divide	multiply	
3	48	expressions	simplified	

1. Variables, numbers, and operation signs can be combined to form mathematical [?]. In this expression, the letter n is called a [?]. A word expression for this mathematical expression is 6 [?] than a number n. *(page 382)*

$n + 6$

2. If you evaluate this expression for $a = 6$ and $b = 9$, you get [?]. If you evaluate this expression for $a = 3$ and $b = 10$, you get [?]. *(page 384)*

$5a + 2b$

3. To solve the equation, [?] was subtracted from both sides of the equation. Then both sides were [?]. To check the solution, [?] was substituted for x in the equation $x + 5 = {}^-2$. *(page 386)*

$$x + 5 = {}^-2$$
$$x + 5 - 5 = {}^-2 - 5$$
$$x = {}^-7$$
$$\text{Check: } {}^-7 + 5 = {}^-2$$

4. To solve this equation, you would first add [?] to both sides of the equation and then simplify both sides. *(page 388)*

$c - {}^-2 = 7$

5. To find the solution of this equation, you would [?] both sides by 9 and then simplify both sides. *(page 392)*

$9d = {}^-45$

6. To find the solution of this equation, you would [?] both sides by $^-4$ and then simplify both sides. *(page 394)*

$\frac{t}{-4} = 7$

7. To solve this equation, you would first [?] 4 to both sides and then divide by [?]. *(page 396)*

$3y - 4 = 14$

Chapter TEST

Write a mathematical expression. *(page 382)*

1. 7 more than a number n
2. 11 times a number n
3. the sum of a number n and 3
4. a number n divided by 6
5. 12 times a number n
6. 8 less than a number n
7. 2 more than 4 times a number n
8. a number n divided by 5, minus 6

Evaluate each expression for a = 2 and b = $^{-}3$. *(page 384)*

9. $a + b$ **10.** $a - b$ **11.** $b - a$ **12.** ab **13.** $^{-}5ab$

14. $4a$ **15.** $ab + 10$ **16.** $16 \div a$ **17.** $3ab$ **18.** $^{-}8ab$

19. $2a + b$ **20.** $a + 4b$ **21.** $4a + 3b$ **22.** $3a + 4b$ **23.** $4a + 5b + 6$

Solve and check. *(pages 386, 388)*

24. $n + 7 = 4$ **25.** $x + 9 = {}^{-}3$ **26.** $a + 6 = 6$ **27.** $y + 8 = 8$

28. $r + 9 = 5$ **29.** $l - 12 = 7$ **30.** $12 + v = {}^{-}1$ **31.** $m - 9 = {}^{-}8$

32. $a - 3 = 6$ **33.** $c - 7 = {}^{-}2$ **34.** $y - 5 = 5$ **35.** $n - 8 = 16$

36. $x - 8 = 0$ **37.** $h - 11 = 3$ **38.** $t - 15 = {}^{-}10$ **39.** $6 + r = 12$

Solve and check. *(pages 392, 394)*

40. $6n = 42$ **41.** $5c = {}^{-}35$ **42.** $8d = 24$ **43.** $^{-}9x = 81$

44. $9y = {}^{-}27$ **45.** $^{-}7x = 49$ **46.** $6k = 54$ **47.** $6m = 42$

48. $^{-}5g = 55$ **49.** $10w = 40$ **50.** $^{-}12t = {}^{-}60$ **51.** $^{-}3h = {}^{-}33$

52. $\frac{x}{3} = 6$ **53.** $\frac{y}{^{-}4} = 9$ **54.** $\frac{j}{3} = {}^{-}10$ **55.** $\frac{f}{4} = 20$

56. $\frac{r}{^{-}5} = 7$ **57.** $\frac{t}{9} = 11$ **58.** $\frac{d}{7} = {}^{-}6$ **59.** $\frac{y}{8} = {}^{-}64$

60. $\frac{s}{3} = 12$ **61.** $\frac{v}{^{-}6} = 8$ **62.** $\frac{y}{^{-}10} = {}^{-}20$ **63.** $\frac{x}{^{-}30} = {}^{-}90$

Solve and check. *(page 396)*

64. $3n + 6 = 30$ **65.** $4k + 2 = 34$ **66.** $7j + 3 = 52$ **67.** $7m + 2 = 51$

68. $5x - 6 = 34$ **69.** $6r - 8 = 46$ **70.** $9t - 10 = 44$ **71.** $12a - 3 = 45$

72. $\frac{x}{3} + 2 = 6$ **73.** $\frac{n}{4} + 3 = 9$ **74.** $\frac{c}{7} - 6 = 0$ **75.** $\frac{r}{4} - 8 = 12$

Cumulative TEST Standardized Format

Choose the correct letter.

1. Give the product.

0.26×0.031

A. 0.0806
B. 0.00806
C. 0.00104
D. none of these

2. Give the quotient rounded to the nearest tenth.

$17.43 \div 2.9$

A. 6.0
B. 6.1
C. 0.61
D. none of these

3. Give the sum.

$\frac{4}{9} + \frac{5}{6}$

A. $\frac{3}{5}$
B. 1
C. $1\frac{5}{18}$
D. none of these

4. Give the difference.

$\frac{7}{8} - \frac{2}{3}$

A. 1
B. $\frac{5}{8}$
C. $\frac{5}{24}$
D. none of these

5. Give the product.

$\frac{4}{5} \times \frac{3}{2}$

A. $1\frac{1}{5}$
B. $\frac{8}{15}$
C. $1\frac{7}{8}$
D. none of these

6. Give the quotient.

$\frac{5}{6} \div \frac{2}{3}$

A. $\frac{5}{9}$
B. $1\frac{1}{4}$
C. $\frac{4}{5}$
D. none of these

7. Solve.

$66\frac{2}{3}\%$ of $42 = n$

A. 63
B. 28
C. 14
D. none of these

8. Solve.

20% of $n = 15$

A. 75
B. 3
C. 150
D. none of these

9. Compute the interest.

Principal = \$720
Rate = 12% per year
Time = 4 months

A. \$86.40
B. \$43.20
C. \$1036.80
D. none of these

10. Give the sum.

$^{-}9 + {}^{+}7$

A. $^{-}2$
B. $^{+}2$
C. $^{-}16$
D. $^{+}16$

11. Find the volume of this cone. Use 3.14 for π.

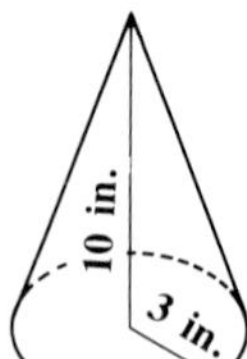

A. 62.8 in.^{3}
B. 282.6 in.^{3}
C. 94.2 in.^{3}
D. none of these these

12. Solve.

$2b + 8 = 32$

A. 20
B. 12
C. 24
D. none of these

SKILL TEST
EXTRA PRACTICE
EXTRA PROBLEM SOLVING

SKILL TEST

Pages 404–411

This test will help you find out which skills you know well and which skills you need to practice more.

EXTRA PRACTICE

Pages 412–443

These practice sets cover the skills tested on the SKILL TEST. Each set practices one skill. The skills are presented in the same order as they are in the book. Page references will help you and your teacher decide when to use them.

EXTRA PROBLEM SOLVING

Pages 444–460

These lessons provide additional opportunities to apply what you learn in the book to situations you will encounter in everyday life.

SKILL TEST

SKILL	TEST ITEMS				EXTRA PRACTICE
1 Adding whole numbers *page 6*	78 +35	396 +672	56 37 +92	406 328 78 +281	*page 412*
2 Adding whole numbers *page 8*	7549 + 4261 496 + 3081 + 2566		80,665 + 24,364 26,245 + 6518 + 276		*page 412*
3 Rounding whole numbers *page 12*	Round to the nearest ten. 63	125	682	598	*page 413*
	Round to the nearest hundred. 446	967	2809	650	
4 Rounding decimals *page 20*	Round to the nearest tenth. 1.38	2.50	63.05	36.95	*page 413*
	Round to the nearest hundredth. 18.342	0.375	0.496	8.640	
5 Adding decimals *page 22*	3.8 +2.3	5.62 +2.94	7.46 2.18 +6.53	4.71 0.39 9.24 +1.68	*page 414*
6 Adding decimals *page 24*	2.34 + 1.7 8.04 + 7 + 9.6		5.62 + 2.94 0.483 + 1.56 + 4.4		*page 414*
7 Comparing whole numbers *page 32*	< or >? 743 ● 734 42,382 ● 42,328		3321 ● 3400 599,999 ● 600,000		*page 415*
8 Subtracting whole numbers *page 34*	89 −37	90 −41	763 −280	846 −198	*page 415*

SKILL TEST

	SKILL	TEST ITEMS				EXTRA PRACTICE
9	**Subtracting whole numbers** *page 36*	70 − 37	80 − 19	900 − 514		*page 416*
		802 − 378	600 − 374	4500 − 3492		
		500 − 142	300 − 62	3800 − 1452		
10	**Subtracting whole numbers** *page 38*	50,341 − 28,220	83,510 − 27,496	573,017 − 77,480	800,356 − 366,082	*page 416*
11	**Comparing decimals** *page 42*	< or >?				*page 417*
		3.57 ● 3.75	4.2 ● 3.21	0.2 ● 0.19		
		0.345 ● 0.3366	0.4 ● 4.0	0.031 ● 0.13		
12	**Subtracting decimals** *page 44*	43.6 − 6.4	9.15 − 2.08	6.02 − 3.96	14.00 − 0.65	*page 417*
13	**Subtracting decimals** *page 46*	5 − 2.7	7 − 2.4	25.3 − 6		*page 418*
		4.23 − 2.849	13 − 6.7	16.2 − 3.571		
14	**Multiplying by multiples of 10, 100, 1000** *page 54*	35 × 100	40 × 60	324 × 10		*page 418*
		78 × 1000	70 × 500	500 × 600		
		92 × 10	90 × 60	300 × 40		
15	**Multiplying whole numbers** *page 56*	42 × 3	426 × 8	608 × 6	4815 × 7	*page 419*
16	**Multiplying whole numbers** *page 58*	58 × 35	304 × 62	879 × 28	2836 × 81	*page 419*
17	**Multiplying whole numbers** *page 60*	248 × 112	644 × 306	1320 × 638	4801 × 709	*page 420*

SKILL TEST

	SKILL	TEST ITEMS			EXTRA PRACTICE
18	**Multiplying decimals** *page 64*	5.4 × 0.36	6.3 × 1.2	34 × 0.88	*page 420*
		6.05 × 0.39	2.04 × 1.6	8.25 × 2.06	
19	**Simplifying expressions** *page 66*	12 − (2.8 + 7.4)		5.6 × (9.9 − 3.8)	*page 421*
		(23.97 × 1.6) + 17.4		5 − (3.07 × 0.44)	
20	**Multiplying decimals by 10, 100, 1000** *page 68*	0.93 × 100	0.3 × 10	4.7 × 10	*page 421*
		5.28 × 1000	4.1 × 1000	0.004 × 100	
		3.8 × 10	5.22 × 100	0.03 × 1000	
21	**Dividing whole numbers** *page 76*	$4\overline{)96}$	$5\overline{)85}$	$6\overline{)384}$	*page 422*
		$8\overline{)784}$	$3\overline{)678}$	$7\overline{)833}$	
22	**Dividing whole numbers** *page 78*	618 ÷ 6	104 ÷ 2	1505 ÷ 5	*page 422*
		8514 ÷ 9	404 ÷ 4	7595 ÷ 7	
23	**Dividing whole numbers** *page 80*	$12\overline{)5842}$	$25\overline{)5750}$	$26\overline{)4097}$	*page 423*
		$52\overline{)45,388}$	$50\overline{)7500}$	$78\overline{)60,411}$	
24	**Dividing whole numbers** *page 84*	Round each quotient to the nearest whole number.			*page 423*
		$125\overline{)83,772}$	$101\overline{)68,204}$	$245\overline{)89,447}$	
		$372\overline{)386,945}$	$400\overline{)682,140}$	$466\overline{)631,100}$	
25	**Simplifying expressions** *page 86*	12 − 8 + 4		18 ÷ 6 × 2	*page 424*
		24 × (12 − 2)		16 + 3 × 4 ÷ 2	
26	**Dividing decimals** *page 88*	Round each quotient to the nearest hundredth.			*page 424*
		$8\overline{)12.17}$	$3\overline{)6.34}$	$9\overline{)27.62}$	
		$24\overline{)6.335}$	$25\overline{)7.873}$	$44\overline{)1.6238}$	

SKILL TEST

	SKILL	TEST ITEMS				EXTRA PRACTICE
27	**Dividing decimals by 10, 100, 1000** *page 92*	$9.45 \div 10$ $53.5 \div 1000$	$8.3 \div 10$ $6.94 \div 1000$	$450.5 \div 100$ $0.84 \div 100$		*page 425*
28	**Dividing decimals** *page 94*	$0.6\overline{)2.04}$ $0.18\overline{)0.1206}$	$0.4\overline{)1.64}$ $0.21\overline{)4.221}$	$0.04\overline{)0.0644}$ $5.3\overline{)0.3233}$		*page 425*
29	**Dividing decimals** *page 96*	Round each quotient to the nearest tenth. $0.3\overline{)1.7}$ $2.6\overline{)3.79}$	 $0.2\overline{)3.7}$ $1.3\overline{)6.21}$	 $0.06\overline{)0.574}$ $0.82\overline{)0.097}$		*page 426*
30	**Finding equivalent fractions** *page 126*	$\frac{1}{4} = \frac{?}{8}$ $\frac{1}{3} = \frac{?}{9}$	$\frac{3}{9} = \frac{?}{3}$ $\frac{4}{8} = \frac{?}{2}$	$\frac{8}{12} = \frac{?}{6}$ $\frac{4}{5} = \frac{?}{10}$	$\frac{5}{8} = \frac{?}{24}$ $\frac{5}{12} = \frac{?}{24}$	*page 426*
31	**Writing fractions in lowest terms** *page 128*	$\frac{3}{12} = ?$ $\frac{2}{6} = ?$	$\frac{15}{20} = ?$ $\frac{3}{9} = ?$	$\frac{9}{6} = ?$ $\frac{8}{7} = ?$	$\frac{18}{10} = ?$ $\frac{15}{10} = ?$	*page 427*
32	**Find the least common denominator** *page 130*	Find the least common denominator. $\frac{1}{3}$ $\frac{1}{2}$	 $\frac{1}{4}$ $\frac{3}{4}$	 $\frac{3}{4}$ $\frac{5}{6}$	 $\frac{5}{6}$ $\frac{5}{8}$	*page 427*
33	**Comparing fractions** *page 132*	< or >? $\frac{4}{5}$ ● $\frac{3}{5}$	 $\frac{1}{4}$ ● $\frac{3}{8}$	 $\frac{3}{4}$ ● $\frac{2}{3}$	 $\frac{5}{6}$ ● $\frac{7}{8}$	*page 428*
34	**Writing whole and mixed numbers as fractions** *page 136*	Change to fourths. $2 = ?$ Change to a fraction. $1\frac{1}{4} = ?$	 $4 = ?$ $1\frac{2}{3} = ?$	 $6 = ?$ $2\frac{3}{4} = ?$	 $3 = ?$ $3\frac{5}{6} = ?$	*page 428*

SKILL TEST

	SKILL	TEST ITEMS	EXTRA PRACTICE
35	**Writing fractions as whole or mixed numbers** *page 138*	Change to a whole number. $\frac{8}{2} = ?$ $\frac{9}{3} = ?$ $\frac{16}{4} = ?$ $\frac{18}{6} = ?$ Change to a mixed number. $\frac{4}{3} = ?$ $\frac{5}{2} = ?$ $\frac{13}{5} = ?$ $\frac{11}{4} = ?$	*page 429*
36	**Writing fractions and mixed numbers in simplest form** *page 140*	Write in simplest form. $\frac{6}{9} = ?$ $3\frac{2}{4} = ?$ $\frac{15}{3} = ?$ $\frac{14}{6} = ?$	*page 429*
37	**Writing fractions and mixed numbers as decimals** *page 146*	Change to a decimal. $\frac{2}{5} = ?$ $\frac{3}{2} = ?$ $1\frac{3}{4} = ?$ $2\frac{3}{8} = ?$ Change to a decimal rounded to the nearest hundredth. $\frac{1}{3} = ?$ $\frac{5}{6} = ?$ $\frac{10}{9} = ?$ $\frac{20}{3} = ?$	*page 430*
38	**Writing decimals as fractions or mixed numbers** *page 148*	Change to a fraction in simplest form. 0.4 = ? 0.75 = ? 0.375 = ? 0.36 = ? Change to a mixed number in simplest form. 1.25 = ? 3.5 = ? 1.625 = ? 2.08 = ?	*page 430*
39	**Adding fractions** *page 156*	Give the sum in simplest form. $\frac{1}{8} + \frac{3}{8}$ $\frac{1}{3} + \frac{2}{3}$ $\frac{4}{5} + \frac{3}{5}$ $\frac{7}{16} + \frac{5}{16}$	*page 431*
40	**Adding fractions** *page 158*	Give each sum in simplest form. $\frac{1}{6} + \frac{1}{3}$ $\frac{1}{3} + \frac{1}{2}$ $\frac{5}{6} + \frac{3}{4}$ $\frac{9}{16} + \frac{5}{8}$	*page 431*

SKILL TEST

	SKILL	TEST ITEMS				EXTRA PRACTICE
41	**Adding mixed numbers** *page 160*	Give the sum in simplest form.				*page 432*
		$3\frac{1}{4} + 2\frac{1}{2}$	$4\frac{3}{4} + 3\frac{1}{8}$	$2\frac{2}{3} + 2\frac{1}{2}$	$4\frac{1}{4} + 3\frac{7}{8}$	
42	**Subtracting fractions** *page 164*	Give the difference in simplest form.				*page 432*
		$\frac{4}{5} - \frac{1}{5}$	$\frac{3}{4} - \frac{1}{4}$	$\frac{5}{6} - \frac{1}{6}$	$\frac{11}{8} - \frac{5}{8}$	
43	**Subtracting fractions** *page 166*	Give the difference in simplest form.				*page 433*
		$\frac{3}{4} - \frac{1}{2}$	$\frac{5}{8} - \frac{1}{3}$	$\frac{5}{6} - \frac{1}{4}$	$\frac{7}{6} - \frac{5}{9}$	
44	**Subtracting mixed numbers** *page 168*	Give the difference in simplest form.				*page 433*
		$4\frac{3}{4} - 2\frac{1}{2}$	$5\frac{3}{5} - 1\frac{1}{3}$	$6\frac{2}{3} - 4\frac{1}{6}$	$4\frac{7}{8} - 3\frac{5}{16}$	
45	**Subtracting mixed numbers** *page 170*	Give the difference in simplest form.				*page 434*
		$4\frac{1}{8} - 1\frac{3}{8}$	$6 - 2\frac{1}{2}$	$8\frac{1}{4} - 3\frac{2}{3}$	$5\frac{1}{4} - 4\frac{2}{5}$	
46	**Multiplying fractions** *page 178*	Give the product in simplest form.				*page 434*
		$\frac{1}{2} \times \frac{1}{3}$	$\frac{2}{3} \times \frac{3}{4}$	$3 \times \frac{3}{4}$	$\frac{5}{6} \times \frac{6}{5}$	
47	**Finding a fraction of a number** *page 180*	$\frac{1}{2}$ of 24 = ?	$\frac{1}{3}$ of 18 = ?	$\frac{2}{3}$ of 42 = ?		*page 435*
		$\frac{3}{5}$ of 60 = ?	$\frac{2}{7}$ of 21 = ?	$\frac{3}{4}$ of 72 = ?		

SKILL TEST

	SKILL	TEST ITEMS	EXTRA PRACTICE
48	**Multiplying mixed numbers** *page 182*	Give the product in simplest form. $1\frac{1}{4} \times 1\frac{1}{2}$ $2 \times 2\frac{1}{2}$ $1\frac{2}{3} \times 1\frac{3}{4}$ $3\frac{1}{5} \times 2\frac{3}{8}$	*page 435*
49	**Finding a fraction of a number** *pages 184, 185*	$1\frac{2}{3}$ h = ? min $2\frac{1}{2}$ ft = ? in. $2\frac{2}{3}$ yd = ? ft $1\frac{3}{4}$ gal = ? qt	*page 436*
50	**Dividing fractions** *page 188*	Give the quotient in simplest form. $\frac{2}{3} \div 4$ $\frac{3}{4} \div \frac{3}{2}$ $\frac{4}{9} \div \frac{1}{3}$ $\frac{5}{2} \div \frac{3}{4}$	*page 436*
51	**Dividing mixed numbers** *page 190*	Give the quotient in simplest form. $3 \div 2\frac{1}{3}$ $3\frac{2}{3} \div 1\frac{1}{2}$ $4\frac{3}{4} \div 2$ $4\frac{1}{5} \div 2\frac{5}{8}$	*page 437*
52	**Solving proportions** *page 230*	$\frac{12}{n} = \frac{1}{4}$ $\frac{n}{8} = \frac{4}{5}$ $\frac{2}{3} = \frac{3}{n}$ $\frac{7}{10} = \frac{n}{8}$	*page 437*
53	**Writing percents as fractions or mixed numbers** *page 248*	Change to a fraction or mixed number in simplest form. 25% = ? 150% = ? $33\frac{1}{3}$ % = ? $62\frac{1}{2}$ % = ?	*page 438*
54	**Writing fractions as percents** *page 250*	Change to a percent. $\frac{3}{5}$ = ? $\frac{3}{2}$ = ? $\frac{1}{6}$ = ? $\frac{2}{3}$ = ?	*page 438*
55	**Writing percents as decimals** *page 252*	Change to a decimal. 8% = ? 32% = ? 37.5% = ? 5.6% = ?	*page 439*

SKILL TEST

	SKILL	TEST ITEMS	EXTRA PRACTICE
56	**Writing decimals as percents** *page 253*	Change to a percent. $0.05 = ?$ $0.9 = ?$ $1.375 = ?$ $0.12\frac{1}{2} = ?$	*page 439*
57	**Finding a percent of a number** *page 256*	25% of $44 = n$ 9% of $37 = n$ 6.5% of $38 = n$ 0.5% of $60 = n$	*page 440*
58	**Finding a percent of a number** *page 258*	$33\frac{1}{3}\%$ of $81 = n$ $12\frac{1}{2}\%$ of $48 = n$ $66\frac{2}{3}\%$ of $96 = n$ $16\frac{2}{3}\%$ of $72 = n$	*page 440*
59	**Finding the number when a percent is given** *page 260*	20% of $n = 16$ 75% of $n = 48$ Round each answer to the nearest tenth. 8.5% of $n = 12.5$ 32.2% of $n = 34.6$	*page 441*
60	**Comparing integers** *page 362*	$<$ or $>$? $^{-}3 \bullet {}^{-}2$ $^{+}9 \bullet 0$ $^{+}12 \bullet {}^{+}11$ $^{+}10 \bullet {}^{-}13$	*page 441*
61	**Adding integers** *page 364*	$^{+}4 + {}^{+}7$ $^{+}9 + {}^{-}3$ $^{-}8 + {}^{+}8$ $^{-}12 + {}^{-}15$	*page 442*
62	**Subtracting integers** *pages 366, 367*	$^{-}7 - {}^{+}3$ $^{+}8 - {}^{-}9$ $^{+}14 - {}^{+}14$ $^{-}16 - {}^{-}20$	*page 442*
63	**Multiplying integers** *pages 370, 371*	$^{+}6 \times {}^{-}7$ $^{+}8 \times {}^{+}3$ $^{-}5 \times {}^{+}9$ $^{-}7 \times 0$	*page 443*
64	**Dividing integers** *page 372*	$^{-}24 \div {}^{+}8$ $^{+}54 \div {}^{-}9$ $^{-}45 \div {}^{-}5$ $^{+}72 \div {}^{+}8$	*page 443*

EXTRA PRACTICE

SKILL 1 *(Use after page 6.)*

Here's how

Add ones and regroup.

$$\begin{array}{r} {\scriptstyle 1} \\ \mathbf{96} \\ \mathbf{284} \\ \mathbf{+163} \\ \hline 3 \end{array}$$

Add tens and regroup.

$$\begin{array}{r} {\scriptstyle 1} \\ {\scriptstyle 2}96 \\ 284 \\ +163 \\ \hline 43 \end{array}$$

Add hundreds.

$$\begin{array}{r} 1 \\ 296 \\ 284 \\ +163 \\ \hline 543 \end{array}$$

Add.

1. $\begin{array}{r} 84 \\ +15 \\ \hline \end{array}$
2. $\begin{array}{r} 50 \\ +38 \\ \hline \end{array}$
3. $\begin{array}{r} 63 \\ +28 \\ \hline \end{array}$
4. $\begin{array}{r} 65 \\ +27 \\ \hline \end{array}$
5. $\begin{array}{r} 29 \\ +48 \\ \hline \end{array}$
6. $\begin{array}{r} 47 \\ +27 \\ \hline \end{array}$
7. $\begin{array}{r} 68 \\ +68 \\ \hline \end{array}$
8. $\begin{array}{r} 93 \\ +49 \\ \hline \end{array}$
9. $\begin{array}{r} 356 \\ +\ 82 \\ \hline \end{array}$
10. $\begin{array}{r} 483 \\ +\ 56 \\ \hline \end{array}$
11. $\begin{array}{r} 297 \\ +240 \\ \hline \end{array}$
12. $\begin{array}{r} 839 \\ +374 \\ \hline \end{array}$
13. $\begin{array}{r} 74 \\ 29 \\ +38 \\ \hline \end{array}$
14. $\begin{array}{r} 82 \\ 30 \\ +56 \\ \hline \end{array}$
15. $\begin{array}{r} 534 \\ 217 \\ +\ 92 \\ \hline \end{array}$
16. $\begin{array}{r} 611 \\ 309 \\ +200 \\ \hline \end{array}$
17. $\begin{array}{r} 516 \\ 86 \\ 129 \\ +202 \\ \hline \end{array}$
18. $\begin{array}{r} 892 \\ 114 \\ 63 \\ +\ 29 \\ \hline \end{array}$
19. $\begin{array}{r} 331 \\ 75 \\ 209 \\ +113 \\ \hline \end{array}$
20. $\begin{array}{r} 455 \\ 333 \\ 86 \\ +264 \\ \hline \end{array}$

SKILL 2 *(Use after page 8.)*

Here's how

245 + 92 + 3916 = ?

Line up the digits that are in the same place.

$$\begin{array}{r} 245 \\ 92 \\ +3916 \\ \hline \end{array}$$

Add.

$$\begin{array}{r} {\scriptstyle 11} \\ 245 \\ {\scriptstyle 1}\ 92 \\ +3916 \\ \hline 4253 \end{array}$$

Give the sum.

1. 6438 + 8310
2. 5832 + 694
3. 966 + 2947
4. 3370 + 1938
5. 34,006 + 8825
6. 4721 + 76,082
7. 12,500 + 38,926
8. 38,842 + 27,111
9. 493 + 3493 + 977
10. 8218 + 739 + 1005
11. 182 + 4200 + 3628
12. 7467 + 941 + 604
13. 593 + 444 + 1660
14. 2741 + 8009 + 476
15. 4850 + 1188 + 2055
16. 1748 + 2966 + 1826
17. 54,388 + 2112 + 599
18. 4368 + 829 + 12,477
19. 29,006 + 2704 + 1822
20. 2864 + 31,000 + 8002
21. 458 + 359 + 1642 + 28
22. 56 + 2516 + 929 + 311

SKILL 3 *(Use after page 12.)*

Here's how

Round 45,359 to the nearest hundred.

Rounding to this place
↓
45,359
↑
When the next digit to the right is 5 or greater, round up.

45,359 rounds to 45,400.

Round to the nearest ten.

1. 74	**2.** 37	**3.** 42	**4.** 75
5. 183	**6.** 366	**7.** 805	**8.** 411
9. 4336	**10.** 3721	**11.** 3605	**12.** 2398

Round to the nearest hundred.

13. 276	**14.** 550	**15.** 743	**16.** 849
17. 3408	**18.** 3423	**19.** 6660	**20.** 8050
21. 20,305	**22.** 32,780	**23.** 42,912	**24.** 62,950

Round to the nearest thousand.

25. 4841	**26.** 6851	**27.** 9310	**28.** 6500
29. 35,431	**30.** 42,573	**31.** 719,527	**32.** 273,500

Round to the nearest ten thousand.

33. 24,146	**34.** 52,700	**35.** 56,913	**36.** 49,430
37. 92,604	**38.** 28,911	**39.** 249,300	**40.** 613,812

SKILL 4 *(Use after page 20.)*

Here's how

Round 36.417 to the nearest tenth.

Rounding to this place
↓
36.417
↑
When the next digit to the right is 5 or greater, round up.

36.417 rounds to 36.4.

Round to the nearest whole number.

1. 16.6	**2.** 38.3	**3.** 92.4	**4.** 35.5
5. 51.27	**6.** 38.93	**7.** 0.025	**8.** 20.19
9. 327.04	**10.** 118.40	**11.** 0.500	**12.** 12.099

Round to the nearest tenth.

13. 403.38	**14.** 26.10	**15.** 5.25	**16.** 3.95
17. 21.39	**18.** 24.188	**19.** 22.06	**20.** 7.472
21. 204.29	**22.** 444.484	**23.** 0.0592	**24.** 0.95

Round to the nearest hundredth.

25. 22.317	**26.** 56.208	**27.** 5.531	**28.** 54.325
29. 71.594	**30.** 6.30196	**31.** 0.0518	**32.** 1.065
33. 0.0946	**34.** 11.269	**35.** 3.9421	**36.** 0.097
37. 42.3381	**38.** 28.095	**39.** 0.6422	**40.** 1.4920

Here's how

Add hundredths and regroup.

```
    1
  4.74
 +2.38
     2
```

Add tenths and regroup.

```
  1 1
  4.74
 +2.38
   .12
```

Add ones.

```
  1 1
  4.74
 +2.38
  7.12
```

SKILL 5 *(Use after page 22.)*

Add.

1. 5.1 + 2.3	**2.** 6.3 + 1.6	**3.** 4.8 + 4.0	**4.** 9.7 + 0.2
5. 5.9 + 2.6	**6.** 7.7 + 1.8	**7.** 8.6 + 2.5	**8.** 4.2 + 6.6
9. 6.06 + 2.75	**10.** 5.55 + 4.88	**11.** 6.73 + 0.95	**12.** 8.33 + 1.78
13. 22.68 + 8.66	**14.** 18.93 + 9.22	**15.** 11.06 + 10.47	**16.** 32.55 + 13.78
17. 8.4, 0.6, + 7.5	**18.** 9.6, 3.5, + 0.4	**19.** 8.59, 2.22, + 1.47	**20.** 5.07, 3.06, + 2.81
21. 21.74, 12.08, 32.68, + 12.12	**22.** 35.06, 31.88, 19.75, + 10.74	**23.** 8.59, 19.23, 25.75, + 9.09	**24.** 46.66, 7.42, 31.66, + 7.00

Here's how

3 + 2.51 + 8.6 = ?

Line up the decimal points.

```
   3
   2.51
  +8.6
```

Add.

```
   1
   3
   2.51
  +8.6
  14.11
```

SKILL 6 *(Use after page 24.)*

Give the sum.

1. 4.64 + 3.08

2. 7.564 + 3.806

3. 6.3521 + 0.5821

4. 721.6 + 38.4

5. 2.35 + 4.829

6. 5.008 + 3.62

7. 43.6 + 27.48

8. 10.88 + 9.3

9. 5.6 + 3.04 + 2.7

10. 2.64 + 5.7 + 8.8

11. 4.20 + 9.2 + 3.65

12. 6.1 + 2.22 + 6.83

13. 2.641 + 0.75 + 3.58

14. 5.34 + 0.756 + 2.84

15. 9.3645 + 2.055 + 0.221

16. 8.471 + 0.4911 + 3.300

17. 7.4 + 4.611 + 8.5

18. 15.966 + 8.4 + 4.8

19. 32 + 3.4 + 2.08

20. 5.7 + 41 + 6.63

SKILL 7 *(Use after page 32.)*

Here's how

54,375 ● 54,491

Start at the left and compare digits that are in the same place.

54,375 —is less than→ 54,491

So

54,375 < 54,491

< or >?

1. 93 ● 90
2. 74 ● 79
3. 376 ● 388
4. 200 ● 186
5. 565 ● 566
6. 496 ● 490
7. 567 ● 576
8. 699 ● 700
9. 950 ● 1000
10. 1503 ● 999
11. 875 ● 1100
12. 1224 ● 899
13. 3721 ● 3615
14. 6732 ● 6655
15. 8472 ● 8427
16. 3818 ● 3811
17. 57,352 ● 58,410
18. 29,435 ● 29,400
19. 88,642 ● 89,000
20. 49,462 ● 50,362
21. 74,000 ● 73,999
22. 53,078 ● 53,780
23. 480,000 ● 479,000
24. 799,999 ● 800,000

SKILL 8 *(Use after page 34.)*

Here's how

Regroup and subtract ones.

```
    5
 5 6 ¹4
−2 9 7
     7
```

Regroup and tens.

```
 4 15
 5 6 ¹4
−2 9 7
   6 7
```

Subtract hundreds.

```
 4 15
 5 6 ¹4
−2 9 7
 2 6 7
```

Subtract.

1. 82 − 21
2. 75 − 33
3. 94 − 40
4. 88 − 65
5. 91 − 24
6. 80 − 54
7. 52 − 19
8. 46 − 27
9. 462 − 36
10. 350 − 18
11. 274 − 59
12. 783 − 47
13. 832 − 258
14. 856 − 193
15. 470 − 295
16. 673 − 488
17. 629 − 274
18. 900 − 366
19. 531 − 295
20. 842 − 416
21. 631 − 289
22. 497 − 179
23. 469 − 293
24. 259 − 140

SKILL 9 *(Use after page 36.)*

Here's how

No tens! Regroup 1 hundred for 10 tens.

```
   2
 8 3̸ ¹0 5
-4 0  7 8
```

Regroup 1 ten for 10 ones.

```
   2  9
 8 3̸ ¹0̸ ¹5
-4 0  7  8
```

Subtract.

```
   2  9
 8 3̸ ¹0̸ ¹5
-4 0  7  8
 4 2  2  7
```

Give the difference.

1. 828 − 411
2. 594 − 221
3. 710 − 463
4. 824 − 258
5. 504 − 356
6. 701 − 588
7. 806 − 529
8. 903 − 165
9. 800 − 361
10. 400 − 249
11. 700 − 318
12. 600 − 233
13. 800 − 444
14. 500 − 381
15. 4916 − 2854
16. 5874 − 2222
17. 3406 − 2153
18. 7112 − 4338
19. 2502 − 458
20. 3701 − 229
21. 5205 − 1286
22. 6101 − 2255
23. 3111 − 2478
24. 9055 − 3861

SKILL 10 *(Use after page 38.)*

Here's how

Subtract.

```
  5 0, 4 5 3
- 4 6, 4 7 3
           0
```

Regroup and subtract.

```
        3
  5 0, 4̸ ¹5 3
- 4 6, 4  7 3
          8 0
```

Regroup twice and subtract.

```
  4  9   13
  5̸ ¹0̸, 4̸ ¹5 3
- 4  6,  4  7 3
     3,  9  8 0
```

Subtract.

1. 5831 − 2127
2. 6427 − 3408
3. 5377 − 1724
4. 8212 − 3001
5. 6811 − 2366
6. 3422 − 1830
7. 5136 − 2209
8. 4725 − 3546
9. 7038 − 4152
10. 3206 − 1137
11. 5013 − 2963
12. 8607 − 4359
13. 9003 − 2814
14. 4006 − 1759
15. 7000 − 3644
16. 4000 − 1842
17. 42,583 − 8,077
18. 29,531 − 6,499
19. 56,031 − 23,740
20. 38,205 − 13,418
21. 38,003 − 27,584
22. 51,009 − 29,446
23. 345,729 − 158,362
24. 841,371 − 158,492

SKILL 11 *(Use after page 42.)*

Here's how

82.64 ● 82.39

Start at the left and compare digits that are in the same place.

82.64 — is greater than — 82.39

So

82.64 > 82.39

< or >?

1. 0.3 ● 0.8	**2.** 0.6 ● 0.1
3. 0.04 ● 0.03	**4.** 0.06 ● 0.07
5. 0.004 ● 0.002	**6.** 0.008 ● 0.009
7. 15.5 ● 15.0	**8.** 8.43 ● 8.34
9. 0.57 ● 0.5	**10.** 0.007 ● 0.06
11. 0.6 ● 0.07	**12.** 9.73 ● 9.37
13. 42.89 ● 42.9	**14.** 5.1 ● 4.99
15. 4.352 ● 43.52	**16.** 0.625 ● 1.2
17. 3.08 ● 3.008	**18.** 0.715 ● 0.72
19. 51.86 ● 51.87	**20.** 33.78 ● 31.88

SKILL 12 *(Use after page 44.)*

Here's how

Regroup and subtract hundredths.

$$\begin{array}{r} \overset{1}{\cancel{2}}\ {}^{1}4 \\ 6. \end{array}$$

$$\begin{array}{r} 6.\overset{1}{\cancel{2}}{}^{1}4 \\ -1.4\,7 \\ \hline 7 \end{array}$$

Regroup and subtract tenths.

$$\begin{array}{r} \overset{5}{\cancel{6}}.\overset{11}{\cancel{2}}{}^{1}4 \\ -1.4\,7 \\ \hline .7\,7 \end{array}$$

Subtract ones.

$$\begin{array}{r} \overset{5}{\cancel{6}}.\overset{11}{\cancel{2}}{}^{1}4 \\ -1.4\,7 \\ \hline 4.7\,7 \end{array}$$

Subtract.

1. $8.5 - 0.4$	**2.** $7.4 - 3.2$	**3.** $6.3 - 1.5$	**4.** $5.2 - 3.3$
5. $47.3 - 9.2$	**6.** $58.4 - 6.6$	**7.** $60.2 - 7.1$	**8.** $71.5 - 8.4$
9. $5.12 - 0.58$	**10.** $6.93 - 0.95$	**11.** $8.44 - 2.86$	**12.** $7.43 - 1.66$
13. $8.11 - 2.88$	**14.** $7.23 - 3.45$	**15.** $5.46 - 0.67$	**16.** $9.71 - 4.86$
17. $39.3 - 22.3$	**18.** $42.1 - 34.7$	**19.** $53.2 - 52.9$	**20.** $74.5 - 15.8$
21. $112.3 - 24.6$	**22.** $15.53 - 8.66$	**23.** $321.6 - 21.8$	**24.** $25.34 - 7.65$
25. $43.56 - 29.38$	**26.** $38.44 - 10.74$	**27.** $284.3 - 147.9$	**28.** $583.5 - 265.3$

SKILL 13 *(Use after page 46.)*

Here's how

20 − 14.38 = ?

Line up the decimal points. Write the zeros.

```
  20.00
- 14.38
```

Regroup.

```
  1 9 9
  2 ¹0.¹0 ¹0
- 1 4 . 3 8
```

Subtract.

```
  1 9 9
  2 ¹0.¹0 ¹0
- 1 4 . 3 8
      5 . 6 2
```

Give the difference.

1. 9 − 3.2
2. 8 − 4.6
3. 15 − 7.2
4. 23 − 8.6
5. 18.01 − 9.45
6. 14.05 − 7.75
7. 9.4 − 6.73
8. 8.5 − 4.55
9. 8.3 − 6
10. 7.4 − 2
11. 10.3 − 8.4
12. 30.1 − 9.7
13. 7 − 3.44
14. 8 − 6.45
15. 8.23 − 0.749
16. 6.729 − 0.88
17. 8.5 − 3.692
18. 5.1 − 0.651
19. 42 − 8.2
20. 34 − 9.5
21. 81.64 − 33
22. 63.89 − 18
23. 100 − 44.63
24. 200 − 53.87
25. 102 − 9.4
26. 105 − 49.7

SKILL 14 *(Use after page 54.)*

Here's how

30 × 200 = ?

Multiply 3 × 2.

30 × 200 = 6

Copy all the zeros.

30 × 200 = 6000

Give the product.

1. 9 × 10
2. 6 × 100
3. 5 × 1000
4. 3 × 100
5. 8 × 20
6. 8 × 200
7. 12 × 10
8. 15 × 1000
9. 20 × 30
10. 80 × 300
11. 3 × 800
12. 20 × 40
13. 30 × 2000
14. 40 × 400
15. 50 × 100
16. 50 × 1000
17. 40 × 200
18. 20 × 3000
19. 30 × 20
20. 40 × 300
21. 400 × 30
22. 145 × 100
23. 256 × 1000
24. 100 × 300

SKILL 15 *(Use after page 56.)*

Here's how

Multiply ones.

```
 564
×  2
   8
```

Multiply tens and regroup.

```
  1
 564
×  2
  28
```

Multiply hundreds and add.

```
  1
 564
×  2
1128
```

Multiply.

1. 23 × 3
2. 12 × 4
3. 44 × 2
4. 11 × 6
5. 56 × 5
6. 70 × 7
7. 39 × 9
8. 82 × 4
9. 142 × 3
10. 481 × 6
11. 330 × 2
12. 511 × 5
13. 309 × 8
14. 622 × 7
15. 711 × 4
16. 961 × 9
17. 446 × 6
18. 705 × 5
19. 512 × 4
20. 878 × 6
21. 2103 × 2
22. 3854 × 4
23. 6007 × 6
24. 8615 × 3

SKILL 16 *(Use after page 58.)*

Here's how

Multiply by 3.

```
 145
× 23
 435
```

Multiply by 20.

```
 145
× 23
 435
2900
```

Add.

```
 145
× 23
 435
2900
3335
```

Multiply.

1. 34 × 12
2. 26 × 20
3. 40 × 41
4. 51 × 33
5. 75 × 18
6. 84 × 25
7. 59 × 36
8. 47 × 29
9. 43 × 55
10. 50 × 62
11. 78 × 18
12. 95 × 77
13. 125 × 31
14. 236 × 22
15. 304 × 58
16. 411 × 70
17. 638 × 63
18. 905 × 85
19. 731 × 17
20. 592 × 46
21. 3015 × 33
22. 4628 × 60
23. 5911 × 45
24. 6408 × 28

Here's how

Start each product directly below the digit you are multiplying by.

```
    3 5 8
  × 2 3 9
  -------
    3 2 2 2
  1 0 7 4
  7 1 6
  -------
  8 5,5 6 2
```

SKILL 17 *(Use after page 60.)*

Multiply.

1. 456 × 122	**2.** 311 × 232	**3.** 506 × 456	**4.** 811 × 348
5. 630 × 505	**6.** 910 × 644	**7.** 713 × 309	**8.** 298 × 400
9. 542 × 550	**10.** 491 × 389	**11.** 670 × 507	**12.** 384 × 229
13. 2043 × 150	**14.** 4951 × 238	**15.** 6004 × 356	**16.** 5101 × 474

Here's how

3.08 × 4.2 = ?

Multiply as whole numbers.

```
     3.0 8
  ×    4.2
  --------
     6 1 6
   1 2 3 2
  --------
   1 2 9 3 6
```

Count the digits to the right of the decimal points.

```
     3.0 8
     × 4.2    [3]
  --------
     6 1 6
   1 2 3 2
  --------
   1 2.9 3 6
```

Count off the same number of digits in the product.

SKILL 18 *(Use after page 64.)*

Give the product.

1. 4.2 × 12	**2.** 3.8 × 10
3. 2.6 × 2.6	**4.** 5.9 × 8.7
5. 4.06 × 0.8	**6.** 2.05 × 5.5
7. 0.94 × 0.34	**8.** 0.95 × 0.55
9. 58 × 0.25	**10.** 74 × 0.78
11. 221 × 4.6	**12.** 360 × 8.2
13. 3.62 × 0.95	**14.** 2.88 × 0.47
15. 6.16 × 7.5	**16.** 2.09 × 0.8
17. 5.4 × 0.06	**18.** 8.8 × 0.07
19. 6.25 × 0.56	**20.** 8.65 × 0.44
21. 30.5 × 20.2	**22.** 56.7 × 18.4
23. 55.5 × 21.6	**24.** 63.2 × 8.94
25. 300 × 4.8	**26.** 600 × 0.52
27. 2.54 × 2.54	**28.** 3.08 × 3.08
29. 298 × 16.1	**30.** 315 × 22.5

SKILL 19 *(Use after page 66.)*

Here's how

2.8 + (0.2 × 0.3) = ?

Work inside the grouping symbols first.

First multiply.

$$\begin{array}{r} 0.2 \\ \times 0.3 \\ \hline 0.06 \end{array}$$

Then add.

$$\begin{array}{r} 0.2 \\ \times 0.3 \\ \hline 0.06 \\ +2.8 \\ \hline 2.86 \end{array}$$

Simplify.

1. 4.1 + (0.2 × 0.3)
2. 12 − (4.3 + 2.8)
3. 5.2 × (6.1 + 3.8)
4. (8.2 × 0.7) + 4.11
5. (0.5 × 0.04) + 2.49
6. 8 − (0.3 × 0.06)
7. (5.3 − 1.4) × 0.08
8. (9.22 + 4.1) − 1.82
9. (23 − 15.5) × 2.1
10. (17.9 + 8.4) + 0.9
11. 18.3 + (8.6 + 7.7)
12. (11.34 − 6.91) − 2.08
13. 14.37 − (6.02 − 3.11)
14. (7.4 × 2.3) × 1.7
15. 3.5 × (9.1 − 2.03)
16. (3.5 × 9.1) − 2.03
17. 4.2 × (3.1 × 6)
18. (4.2 × 3.1) × 6
19. 6.01 + (2.5 + 3.7)
20. (6.01 + 2.5) + 3.7
21. 22 − (6.6 + 1.9)
22. (22 − 6.6) + 1.9
23. 12 + (4.5 × 0.5)
24. (12 + 4.5) × 0.5
25. 10 − (2.4 × 0.06)
26. (10 − 2.4) × 0.06

SKILL 20 *(Use after page 68.)*

Here's how

Multiplying by 10 moves the decimal point 1 place to the right.

2.47 × 10 = 24.7

Multiplying by 100 moves the decimal point 2 places to the right.

2.47 × 100 = 247

Give the product.

1. 42 × 10
2. 38 × 100
3. 65 × 100
4. 125 × 100
5. 8.2 × 10
6. 0.05 × 1000
7. 4.7 × 100
8. 2.95 × 10
9. 220 × 1000
10. 300 × 10
11. 9.55 × 100
12. 8.74 × 1000
13. 0.005 × 10
14. 0.002 × 100
15. 8.4 × 1000
16. 7.2 × 100
17. 6.9 × 10
18. 3.74 × 100
19. 3.96 × 1000
20. 6.66 × 10
21. 4.798 × 100
22. 4.798 × 10
23. 2.655 × 1000
24. 148 × 100

Here's how

Not enough hundreds. Think 42 tens.

$$8\overline{)424}$$

Divide tens and subtract.

$$\begin{array}{r} 5 \\ 8\overline{)424} \\ -40 \\ \hline 2 \end{array}$$

Think 24 ones.

$$\begin{array}{r} 5 \\ 8\overline{)424} \\ -40 \\ \hline 24 \end{array}$$

Divide ones. Subtract.

$$\begin{array}{r} 53 \\ 8\overline{)424} \\ -40 \\ \hline 24 \\ -24 \\ \hline 0 \end{array}$$

SKILL 21 *(Use after page 76.)*

Divide.

1. $3\overline{)96}$	**2.** $4\overline{)84}$	**3.** $2\overline{)62}$	**4.** $3\overline{)63}$
5. $6\overline{)96}$	**6.** $8\overline{)88}$	**7.** $7\overline{)84}$	**8.** $9\overline{)99}$
9. $4\overline{)76}$	**10.** $5\overline{)90}$	**11.** $3\overline{)81}$	**12.** $6\overline{)84}$
13. $5\overline{)135}$	**14.** $7\overline{)245}$	**15.** $8\overline{)504}$	**16.** $4\overline{)352}$
17. $6\overline{)816}$	**18.** $4\overline{)588}$	**19.** $9\overline{)369}$	**20.** $5\overline{)295}$
21. $8\overline{)464}$	**22.** $3\overline{)207}$	**23.** $5\overline{)635}$	**24.** $6\overline{)450}$
25. $2\overline{)934}$	**26.** $9\overline{)513}$	**27.** $4\overline{)728}$	**28.** $7\overline{)812}$
29. $5\overline{)485}$	**30.** $6\overline{)558}$	**31.** $9\overline{)342}$	**32.** $8\overline{)952}$
33. $7\overline{)917}$	**34.** $4\overline{)696}$	**35.** $3\overline{)741}$	**36.** $6\overline{)498}$
37. $8\overline{)920}$	**38.** $2\overline{)584}$	**39.** $6\overline{)696}$	**40.** $5\overline{)950}$
41. $3\overline{)933}$	**42.** $5\overline{)675}$	**43.** $2\overline{)388}$	**44.** $7\overline{)819}$
45. $2\overline{)198}$	**46.** $5\overline{)695}$	**47.** $3\overline{)981}$	**48.** $6\overline{)366}$
49. $3\overline{)258}$	**50.** $4\overline{)508}$	**51.** $9\overline{)729}$	**52.** $4\overline{)896}$

Here's how

Don't forget to write this zero!

↓

$$\begin{array}{r} 109 \\ 4\overline{)436} \\ -4 \\ \hline 36 \\ -36 \\ \hline 0 \end{array}$$

SKILL 22 *(Use after page 78.)*

Divide.

1. 428 ÷ 4	**2.** 198 ÷ 9	**3.** 624 ÷ 6
4. 742 ÷ 7	**5.** 485 ÷ 5	**6.** 840 ÷ 8
7. 735 ÷ 7	**8.** 900 ÷ 3	**9.** 615 ÷ 5
10. 582 ÷ 6	**11.** 422 ÷ 2	**12.** 636 ÷ 6
13. 2016 ÷ 4	**14.** 5688 ÷ 8	**15.** 9396 ÷ 9
16. 8330 ÷ 7	**17.** 4656 ÷ 6	**18.** 4000 ÷ 8
19. 2945 ÷ 5	**20.** 3804 ÷ 4	**21.** 6210 ÷ 9

SKILL 23 *(Use after page 80.)*

Here's how

Think about dividing 39 by 4. So try 9.

$$\begin{array}{r} 48 \\ \times\ 9 \\ \hline 432 \end{array} \qquad 48\overline{)3999}$$

432 is too big!

Try 8.

$$\begin{array}{r} 48 \\ \times\ 8 \\ \hline 384 \end{array} \qquad \begin{array}{r} 8 \\ 48\overline{)3999} \\ -384 \\ \hline 15 \end{array}$$

Think about dividing 15 by 4. So try 3.

$$\begin{array}{r} 48 \\ \times\ 3 \\ \hline 144 \end{array} \qquad \begin{array}{r} 83\ \text{R15} \\ 48\overline{)3999} \\ -384 \\ \hline 159 \\ -144 \\ \hline 15 \end{array}$$

Divide.

1. $12\overline{)2946}$	**2.** $32\overline{)9375}$	**3.** $25\overline{)8611}$
4. $30\overline{)4789}$	**5.** $42\overline{)7194}$	**6.** $18\overline{)6978}$
7. $43\overline{)2589}$	**8.** $50\overline{)8526}$	**9.** $61\overline{)3810}$
10. $70\overline{)4490}$	**11.** $81\overline{)6351}$	**12.** $49\overline{)8555}$
13. $64\overline{)5773}$	**14.** $38\overline{)6310}$	**15.** $31\overline{)6000}$
16. $60\overline{)7008}$	**17.** $75\overline{)9362}$	**18.** $53\overline{)4867}$
19. $46\overline{)7351}$	**20.** $68\overline{)8022}$	**21.** $99\overline{)3366}$
22. $25\overline{)4875}$	**23.** $35\overline{)8610}$	**24.** $60\overline{)8614}$
25. $91\overline{)6235}$	**26.** $35\overline{)6842}$	**27.** $43\overline{)9286}$
28. $61\overline{)8642}$	**29.** $32\overline{)6192}$	**30.** $60\overline{)7815}$
31. $18\overline{)73{,}202}$	**32.** $35\overline{)20{,}496}$	**33.** $26\overline{)34{,}571}$
34. $83\overline{)62{,}440}$	**35.** $80\overline{)70{,}709}$	**36.** $44\overline{)82{,}522}$

SKILL 24 *(Use after page 84.)*

Here's how

Divide. Write a zero in the tenths place and carry out the division to that place.

$$\begin{array}{r} 42.8 \\ 124\overline{)5309.0} \\ -496 \\ \hline 349 \\ -248 \\ \hline 1010 \\ -992 \\ \hline 18 \end{array}$$

Divide.

1. $125\overline{)38{,}500}$	**2.** $150\overline{)67{,}800}$	**3.** $212\overline{)91{,}372}$
4. $318\overline{)57{,}558}$	**5.** $222\overline{)49{,}506}$	**6.** $300\overline{)56{,}100}$
7. $360\overline{)91{,}080}$	**8.** $436\overline{)57{,}988}$	**9.** $278\overline{)82{,}288}$

Divide. Round the quotient to the nearest whole number.

10. $516\overline{)81{,}088}$	**11.** $406\overline{)73{,}849}$	**12.** $616\overline{)47{,}321}$
13. $700\overline{)46{,}831}$	**14.** $688\overline{)91{,}156}$	**15.** $927\overline{)55{,}780}$
16. $250\overline{)465{,}890}$	**17.** $400\overline{)965{,}421}$	**18.** $536\overline{)571{,}903}$
19. $348\overline{)691{,}483}$	**20.** $198\overline{)485{,}579}$	**21.** $822\overline{)936{,}004}$

SKILL 25 *(Use after page 86.)*

Here's how

6 + 8 × (4 − 2) = ?

First, work within the grouping symbols.

6 + 8 × 2

Next, do the multiplication and division.

6 + 16

Last, do the addition and subtraction.

22

Simplify.

1. 6 ÷ 3 × 2

2. 12 − 8 + 4

3. 5 + 2 × 5 − 1

4. 5 × 2 + 10 ÷ 2

5. 5 + (3 + 9) ÷ 6

6. (4 + 5) × 2 − 8

7. 12 ÷ 4 − 1

8. 8 × 5 − 3

9. 24 − 4 ÷ 4

10. 30 − 12 − 6

11. 10 + 16 ÷ 4

12. 18 + 6 ÷ 3

13. 48 ÷ 8 × 2

14. 35 + 12 − 10

15. 18 − 6 + 6

16. 20 − 9 + 5

17. (12 + 18) ÷ 6

18. 34 × (8 − 3)

19. 16 + 8 ÷ 4 + 4

20. (16 + 8) ÷ 4 + 4

21. 16 + 8 ÷ (4 + 4)

22. 20 + 12 × 4 − 1

SKILL 26 *(Use after page 88.)*

Here's how

Divide.

```
      0.56
23 ) 12.99
    -11 5
      1 49
     -1 38
        11
```

Write a zero and carry out the division another place.

```
      0.564
23 ) 12.990
    -11 5
      1 49
     -1 38
       110
       -92
        18
```

Divide.

1. 5) 8.1

2. 7) 25.9

3. 8) 4.32

4. 2) 0.938

5. 9) 67.5

6. 7) 0.847

7. 12) 1.44

8. 23) 7.13

9. 36) 1.008

10. 47) 0.2491

11. 42) 16.212

12. 65) 352.95

Divide. Round the quotient to the nearest hundredth.

13. 3) 2.5

14. 6) 0.32

15. 9) 0.53

16. 25) 56.92

17. 14) 7.34

18. 49) 8.91

19. 39) 0.62

20. 53) 0.834

21. 26) 2.96

22. 57) 0.952

23. 48) 6.501

24. 32) 7.319

25. 71) 23.61

26. 42) 3.114

27. 29) 0.8113

28. 83) 72.9

29. 94) 89.1

30. 85) 5.347

SKILL 27 *(Use after page 92.)*

Here's how

Dividing by 10 moves the decimal point 1 place to the left.

5.2 ÷ 10 = 0.52

Dividing by 100 moves the decimal point 2 places to the left.

5.2 ÷ 100 = 0.052

Give the quotient.

1. 34.2 ÷ 10

2. 34.2 ÷ 100

3. 458 ÷ 100

4. 458 ÷ 1000

5. 252.5 ÷ 100

6. 252.5 ÷ 10

7. 80 ÷ 10

8. 80 ÷ 100

9. 23.94 ÷ 10

10. 23.94 ÷ 100

11. 2.8 ÷ 10

12. 2.8 ÷ 100

13. 2.8 ÷ 1000

14. 9.05 ÷ 10

15. 9.05 ÷ 100

16. 9.05 ÷ 1000

17. 325 ÷ 100

18. 325 ÷ 10

19. 325 ÷ 1000

20. 9 ÷ 10

21. 9 ÷ 1000

22. 9 ÷ 100

23. 26.7 ÷ 100

24. 26.7 ÷ 1000

25. 26.7 ÷ 10

26. 42.059 ÷ 100

27. 42.059 ÷ 10

28. 42.059 ÷ 1000

SKILL 28 *(Use after page 94.)*

Here's how

0.42) 0.5670

Move both decimal points two places to the right.

0.42.) 0.56.70

Divide.

```
        1.35
0.42.) 0.56.70
      -42
       147
      -126
        210
       -210
          0
```

Divide.

1. 0.7) 38.36

2. 0.6) 2.634

3. 0.9) 5.067

4. 0.08) 4.584

5. 0.03) 1.473

6. 0.005) 3.605

7. 0.004) 0.2656

8. 0.3) 96.30

9. 0.04) 6.400

10. 0.6) 350.4

11. 0.07) 0.0644

12. 0.9) 0.963

13. 0.005) 8.6055

14. 0.08) 0.0152

15. 0.4) 2.208

16. 0.002) 0.5978

17. 0.03) 2.0172

18. 0.7) 8.407

19. 1.2) 0.144

20. 0.15) 0.6075

21. 2.3) 28.52

22. 0.45) 1.3995

23. 2.4) 1.2912

24. 0.37) 0.22274

25. 6.7) 29.011

26. 5.3) 19.292

27. 0.86) 0.38442

SKILL 29 *(Use after page 96.)*

Here's how

Write a 0 in the dividend to place the decimal point.

$0.06\overline{)16.30}$

Divide.

$$\begin{array}{r} 271.66 \\ 0.06\overline{)16.30.00} \\ -12 \\ \hline 4\,3 \\ -4\,2 \\ \hline 10 \\ -6 \\ \hline 4\,0 \\ -3\,6 \\ \hline 40 \\ -36 \\ \hline 4 \end{array}$$

Divide.

1. $0.5\overline{)6.1}$
2. $0.2\overline{)8.7}$
3. $0.4\overline{)0.42}$
4. $0.08\overline{)0.052}$
5. $0.06\overline{)0.033}$
6. $0.05\overline{)0.17}$
7. $0.6\overline{)1.05}$
8. $0.4\overline{)3.1}$
9. $0.2\overline{)1.033}$
10. $0.05\overline{)0.4}$
11. $0.6\overline{)3}$
12. $0.4\overline{)9}$
13. $1.2\overline{)7.8}$
14. $3.1\overline{)124}$
15. $0.25\overline{)17.5}$
16. $0.42\overline{)159.6}$
17. $0.049\overline{)401.8}$
18. $0.066\overline{)48.84}$

Divide. Round each quotient to the nearest tenth.

19. $0.3\overline{)1.7}$
20. $0.6\overline{)1.02}$
21. $1.3\overline{)4.0}$
22. $2.5\overline{)9.1}$
23. $3.7\overline{)0.99}$
24. $7.1\overline{)52.8}$
25. $4.3\overline{)0.271}$
26. $0.55\overline{)0.382}$
27. $0.67\overline{)1.092}$
28. $0.59\overline{)0.377}$
29. $6.1\overline{)7.055}$
30. $5.2\overline{)8.033}$

SKILL 30 *(Use after page 126.)*

Here's how

$\frac{2}{5} = \frac{?}{15}$

Multiply numerator and denominator by 3.

$$\frac{2}{5} \overset{\times 3}{\underset{\times 3}{=}} \frac{6}{15}$$

$\frac{12}{20} = \frac{?}{5}$

Divide numerator and denominator by 4.

$$\frac{12}{20} \overset{\div 4}{\underset{\div 4}{=}} \frac{3}{5}$$

Complete.

1. $\frac{1}{2} = \frac{?}{4}$
2. $\frac{1}{3} = \frac{?}{6}$
3. $\frac{1}{4} = \frac{?}{12}$
4. $\frac{2}{3} = \frac{?}{6}$
5. $\frac{6}{8} = \frac{?}{4}$
6. $\frac{9}{24} = \frac{?}{8}$
7. $\frac{9}{6} = \frac{?}{2}$
8. $\frac{3}{9} = \frac{?}{3}$
9. $\frac{1}{4} = \frac{?}{20}$
10. $\frac{1}{2} = \frac{?}{6}$
11. $\frac{1}{5} = \frac{?}{10}$
12. $\frac{4}{5} = \frac{?}{15}$
13. $\frac{8}{12} = \frac{?}{3}$
14. $\frac{25}{10} = \frac{?}{2}$
15. $\frac{4}{16} = \frac{?}{4}$
16. $\frac{6}{9} = \frac{?}{3}$
17. $\frac{1}{3} = \frac{?}{15}$
18. $\frac{1}{6} = \frac{?}{18}$
19. $\frac{5}{8} = \frac{?}{16}$
20. $\frac{3}{4} = \frac{?}{16}$
21. $\frac{4}{24} = \frac{?}{6}$
22. $\frac{12}{10} = \frac{?}{5}$
23. $\frac{5}{10} = \frac{?}{2}$
24. $\frac{4}{20} = \frac{?}{5}$
25. $\frac{5}{2} = \frac{?}{10}$
26. $\frac{1}{4} = \frac{?}{8}$
27. $\frac{3}{2} = \frac{?}{10}$
28. $\frac{3}{5} = \frac{?}{20}$
29. $\frac{6}{12} = \frac{?}{2}$
30. $\frac{30}{18} = \frac{?}{3}$
31. $\frac{10}{15} = \frac{?}{3}$
32. $\frac{4}{12} = \frac{?}{3}$

SKILL 31 *(Use after page 128.)*

Here's how

To write a fraction in lowest terms, divide both terms by their greatest common divisor.

$$\frac{12}{18} \overset{\div 6}{\underset{\div 6}{=}} \frac{2}{3}$$

Write in lowest terms.

1. $\frac{3}{6}$	**2.** $\frac{3}{9}$	**3.** $\frac{2}{8}$	**4.** $\frac{6}{9}$
5. $\frac{9}{6}$	**6.** $\frac{14}{16}$	**7.** $\frac{9}{12}$	**8.** $\frac{10}{12}$
9. $\frac{8}{10}$	**10.** $\frac{5}{15}$	**11.** $\frac{6}{4}$	**12.** $\frac{7}{14}$
13. $\frac{8}{16}$	**14.** $\frac{15}{6}$	**15.** $\frac{2}{10}$	**16.** $\frac{16}{12}$
17. $\frac{21}{6}$	**18.** $\frac{4}{8}$	**19.** $\frac{6}{16}$	**20.** $\frac{4}{12}$
21. $\frac{3}{12}$	**22.** $\frac{4}{6}$	**23.** $\frac{3}{18}$	**24.** $\frac{15}{18}$
25. $\frac{10}{6}$	**26.** $\frac{15}{20}$	**27.** $\frac{5}{10}$	**28.** $\frac{10}{15}$
29. $\frac{6}{12}$	**30.** $\frac{4}{20}$	**31.** $\frac{18}{24}$	**32.** $\frac{6}{18}$

SKILL 32 *(Use after page 130.)*

Here's how

To find the least common denominator of two fractions, find the least common multiple of the denominators.

$\frac{2}{3}$	$\frac{3}{4}$
3	4
6	8
9	(12)
(12)	16
15	20

The least common denominator is 12.

Find the least common denominator.

1. $\frac{1}{6}$ $\frac{1}{5}$	**2.** $\frac{3}{4}$ $\frac{1}{2}$	**3.** $\frac{1}{5}$ $\frac{2}{9}$	**4.** $\frac{3}{7}$ $\frac{1}{6}$
5. $\frac{1}{10}$ $\frac{2}{5}$	**6.** $\frac{3}{20}$ $\frac{1}{10}$	**7.** $\frac{1}{4}$ $\frac{1}{6}$	**8.** $\frac{1}{2}$ $\frac{3}{7}$
9. $\frac{5}{6}$ $\frac{3}{8}$	**10.** $\frac{1}{6}$ $\frac{1}{8}$	**11.** $\frac{1}{8}$ $\frac{4}{3}$	**12.** $\frac{1}{10}$ $\frac{3}{4}$
13. $\frac{7}{8}$ $\frac{1}{12}$	**14.** $\frac{1}{6}$ $\frac{3}{4}$	**15.** $\frac{1}{5}$ $\frac{3}{7}$	**16.** $\frac{1}{3}$ $\frac{5}{6}$
17. $\frac{2}{5}$ $\frac{1}{4}$	**18.** $\frac{1}{10}$ $\frac{4}{5}$	**19.** $\frac{5}{9}$ $\frac{1}{2}$	**20.** $\frac{1}{4}$ $\frac{3}{5}$
21. $\frac{3}{10}$ $\frac{1}{4}$	**22.** $\frac{1}{6}$ $\frac{4}{5}$	**23.** $\frac{7}{6}$ $\frac{5}{9}$	**24.** $\frac{3}{8}$ $\frac{1}{9}$
25. $\frac{5}{6}$ $\frac{1}{15}$	**26.** $\frac{1}{7}$ $\frac{1}{3}$	**27.** $\frac{2}{5}$ $\frac{1}{8}$	**28.** $\frac{1}{12}$ $\frac{2}{3}$
29. $\frac{1}{4}$ $\frac{1}{7}$	**30.** $\frac{1}{9}$ $\frac{2}{3}$	**31.** $\frac{1}{3}$ $\frac{2}{9}$	**32.** $\frac{3}{8}$ $\frac{1}{7}$

SKILL 33 *(Use after page 132.)*

Here's how

Find the least common denominator.

$\frac{2}{3} \bullet \frac{3}{4}$

12

Change to equivalent fractions.

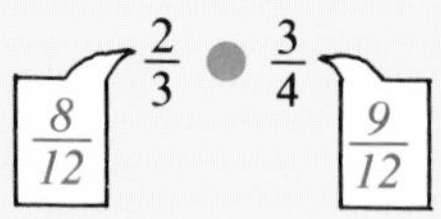

Compare.

$\frac{2}{3} < \frac{3}{4}$

< or >?

1. $\frac{1}{4} \bullet \frac{3}{4}$ **2.** $\frac{3}{5} \bullet \frac{2}{5}$ **3.** $\frac{3}{7} \bullet \frac{4}{7}$ **4.** $\frac{0}{8} \bullet \frac{5}{8}$

5. $\frac{5}{4} \bullet \frac{4}{4}$ **6.** $\frac{7}{5} \bullet \frac{9}{5}$ **7.** $\frac{5}{8} \bullet \frac{7}{8}$ **8.** $\frac{7}{3} \bullet \frac{5}{3}$

9. $\frac{2}{3} \bullet \frac{5}{6}$ **10.** $\frac{5}{4} \bullet \frac{3}{2}$ **11.** $\frac{2}{7} \bullet \frac{1}{3}$ **12.** $\frac{3}{4} \bullet \frac{3}{8}$

13. $\frac{1}{8} \bullet \frac{1}{6}$ **14.** $\frac{3}{8} \bullet \frac{1}{4}$ **15.** $\frac{3}{10} \bullet \frac{1}{3}$ **16.** $\frac{1}{4} \bullet \frac{2}{5}$

17. $\frac{1}{4} \bullet \frac{1}{3}$ **18.** $\frac{2}{9} \bullet \frac{3}{4}$ **19.** $\frac{2}{3} \bullet \frac{3}{4}$ **20.** $\frac{5}{8} \bullet \frac{4}{7}$

21. $\frac{3}{5} \bullet \frac{3}{7}$ **22.** $\frac{3}{4} \bullet \frac{5}{6}$ **23.** $\frac{8}{9} \bullet \frac{7}{8}$ **24.** $\frac{1}{3} \bullet \frac{5}{12}$

25. $\frac{7}{8} \bullet \frac{5}{6}$ **26.** $\frac{2}{3} \bullet \frac{7}{10}$ **27.** $\frac{7}{9} \bullet \frac{2}{3}$ **28.** $\frac{9}{2} \bullet \frac{9}{4}$

SKILL 34 *(Use after page 136.)*

Here's how

$4 = \frac{?}{3}$

Write the whole number over 1 and multiply both numerator and denominator by 3.

$\frac{4}{1} = \frac{12}{3}$

$2\frac{3}{4} = ?$

To change a mixed number to a fraction, multiply the denominator by the whole number and add the numerator.

$2\frac{3}{4} = \frac{11}{4}$

Change to thirds.

1. 2 **2.** 1 **3.** 4 **4.** 5

5. 3 **6.** 8 **7.** 10 **8.** 6

Change to fourths.

9. 3 **10.** 1 **11.** 4 **12.** 2

13. 7 **14.** 9 **15.** 10 **16.** 8

Change to a fraction.

17. $1\frac{1}{3}$ **18.** $2\frac{1}{4}$ **19.** $2\frac{1}{2}$ **20.** $1\frac{1}{5}$

21. $1\frac{2}{3}$ **22.** $2\frac{1}{3}$ **23.** $1\frac{1}{4}$ **24.** $3\frac{1}{4}$

25. $1\frac{1}{2}$ **26.** $2\frac{7}{8}$ **27.** $3\frac{3}{8}$ **28.** $2\frac{5}{6}$

29. $5\frac{1}{4}$ **30.** $2\frac{2}{3}$ **31.** $3\frac{1}{2}$ **32.** $4\frac{5}{8}$

33. $4\frac{4}{5}$ **34.** $3\frac{1}{3}$ **35.** $5\frac{3}{10}$ **36.** $4\frac{1}{5}$

SKILL 35 *(Use after page 138.)*

Here's how

To change a fraction to a whole number or mixed number, divide the numerator by the denominator.

$\frac{18}{3} = 6$

$\frac{19}{4} = 4\frac{3}{4}$

$$\begin{array}{r} 4 \\ 4 \overline{)19} \\ -16 \\ \hline 3 \end{array}$$

There are 3 fourths left over.

Change to a whole number.

1. $\frac{4}{2}$
2. $\frac{40}{5}$
3. $\frac{10}{2}$
4. $\frac{9}{3}$
5. $\frac{25}{5}$
6. $\frac{8}{2}$
7. $\frac{32}{4}$
8. $\frac{30}{3}$
9. $\frac{18}{3}$
10. $\frac{35}{5}$
11. $\frac{16}{4}$
12. $\frac{50}{5}$

Change to a mixed number.

13. $\frac{3}{2}$
14. $\frac{5}{4}$
15. $\frac{5}{3}$
16. $\frac{9}{2}$
17. $\frac{11}{4}$
18. $\frac{4}{3}$
19. $\frac{13}{5}$
20. $\frac{7}{6}$
21. $\frac{16}{3}$
22. $\frac{13}{10}$
23. $\frac{5}{2}$
24. $\frac{8}{3}$
25. $\frac{23}{10}$
26. $\frac{9}{5}$
27. $\frac{13}{12}$
28. $\frac{19}{6}$
29. $\frac{7}{2}$
30. $\frac{11}{3}$
31. $\frac{19}{4}$
32. $\frac{18}{5}$

SKILL 36 *(Use after page 140.)*

Here's how

simplest form ↓ $\frac{6}{9} = \frac{2}{3}$

simplest form ↓ $3\frac{4}{6} = 3\frac{2}{3}$

simplest form ↓ $\frac{18}{3} = 6$

simplest form ↓ $\frac{14}{4} = 3\frac{2}{4} = 3\frac{1}{2}$

Write in simplest form.

1. $\frac{8}{2}$
2. $\frac{6}{9}$
3. $\frac{10}{15}$
4. $\frac{15}{5}$
5. $\frac{10}{12}$
6. $\frac{6}{15}$
7. $\frac{4}{3}$
8. $\frac{4}{24}$
9. $\frac{9}{2}$
10. $1\frac{8}{12}$
11. $1\frac{3}{6}$
12. $2\frac{4}{6}$
13. $1\frac{2}{4}$
14. $\frac{10}{2}$
15. $\frac{11}{3}$
16. $3\frac{6}{16}$
17. $\frac{23}{4}$
18. $4\frac{4}{10}$
19. $5\frac{9}{24}$
20. $\frac{20}{24}$
21. $\frac{36}{6}$
22. $\frac{17}{2}$
23. $\frac{25}{5}$
24. $\frac{13}{3}$
25. $\frac{18}{5}$
26. $\frac{24}{3}$
27. $\frac{12}{15}$
28. $\frac{9}{12}$
29. $6\frac{10}{12}$
30. $\frac{19}{4}$
31. $8\frac{12}{16}$
32. $\frac{17}{5}$

Here's how

To change a fraction to a decimal, divide the numerator by the denominator.

$\frac{5}{8} = ?$

$$\begin{array}{r} 0.625 \\ 8\overline{)5.000} \\ -4\,8 \\ \hline 20 \\ -16 \\ \hline 40 \\ -40 \\ \hline 0 \end{array}$$

$\frac{5}{8} = 0.625$

$1\frac{5}{8} = ?$

$1\frac{5}{8} = 1.625$

SKILL 37 *(Use after page 146.)*

Change to a decimal.

1. $\frac{1}{4}$ **2.** $\frac{3}{4}$ **3.** $\frac{1}{5}$ **4.** $\frac{1}{2}$

5. $\frac{9}{10}$ **6.** $\frac{2}{5}$ **7.** $\frac{7}{10}$ **8.** $\frac{4}{5}$

9. $\frac{1}{8}$ **10.** $\frac{3}{10}$ **11.** $\frac{7}{4}$ **12.** $\frac{9}{8}$

13. $\frac{9}{2}$ **14.** $\frac{3}{8}$ **15.** $\frac{3}{5}$ **16.** $\frac{7}{8}$

17. $\frac{9}{4}$ **18.** $\frac{11}{2}$ **19.** $\frac{1}{16}$ **20.** $\frac{11}{8}$

21. $\frac{5}{16}$ **22.** $\frac{3}{2}$ **23.** $\frac{8}{5}$ **24.** $\frac{13}{5}$

25. $2\frac{1}{2}$ **26.** $3\frac{3}{4}$ **27.** $3\frac{4}{5}$ **28.** $2\frac{7}{8}$

Change to a decimal rounded to the nearest hundredth.

29. $\frac{1}{9}$ **30.** $\frac{1}{3}$ **31.** $\frac{4}{3}$ **32.** $\frac{1}{6}$

33. $\frac{11}{6}$ **34.** $\frac{3}{16}$ **35.** $\frac{5}{6}$ **36.** $\frac{5}{3}$

37. $\frac{7}{9}$ **38.** $\frac{17}{6}$ **39.** $\frac{9}{16}$ **40.** $\frac{21}{16}$

Here's how

Write as a fraction in simplest form.

0.75 $= \frac{75}{100} = \frac{3}{4}$

Write as a mixed number in simplest form.

3.4 $= 3\frac{4}{10} = 3\frac{2}{5}$

SKILL 38 *(Use after page 148.)*

Change to a fraction in simplest form.

1. 0.4 **2.** 0.8 **3.** 0.6 **4.** 0.1

5. 0.9 **6.** 0.5 **7.** 0.3 **8.** 0.2

9. 0.25 **10.** 0.75 **11.** 0.15 **12.** 0.45

13. 0.375 **14.** 0.625 **15.** 0.875 **16.** 0.125

Change to a mixed number in simplest form.

17. 1.2 **18.** 2.3 **19.** 1.6 **20.** 3.8

21. 2.4 **22.** 7.7 **23.** 4.5 **24.** 5.9

25. 3.25 **26.** 1.75 **27.** 2.12 **28.** 4.48

29. 4.625 **30.** 6.875 **31.** 2.125 **32.** 5.375

SKILL 39 *(Use after page 156.)*

Here's how

Add the numerators and use the common denominators.

$\frac{3}{8} + \frac{1}{8} = \frac{4}{8}$

Write in simplest form.

$\frac{3}{8} + \frac{1}{8} = \frac{4}{8}$

$= \frac{1}{2}$

Give the sum in simplest form.

1. $\frac{1}{4} + \frac{1}{4}$
2. $\frac{1}{5} + \frac{2}{5}$
3. $\frac{1}{4} + \frac{3}{4}$
4. $\frac{1}{6} + \frac{1}{6}$
5. $\frac{1}{9} + \frac{1}{9}$
6. $\frac{2}{7} + \frac{2}{7}$
7. $\frac{2}{9} + \frac{1}{9}$
8. $\frac{1}{8} + \frac{3}{8}$
9. $\frac{5}{8} + \frac{5}{8}$
10. $\frac{4}{9} + \frac{4}{9}$
11. $\frac{3}{10} + \frac{3}{10}$
12. $\frac{2}{5} + \frac{3}{5}$
13. $\frac{1}{6} + \frac{5}{6}$
14. $\frac{3}{4} + \frac{3}{4}$
15. $\frac{1}{8} + \frac{1}{8}$
16. $\frac{7}{10} + \frac{3}{10}$
17. $\frac{7}{12} + \frac{5}{12}$
18. $\frac{2}{9} + \frac{2}{9}$
19. $\frac{4}{5} + \frac{1}{5}$
20. $\frac{3}{8} + \frac{3}{8}$
21. $\frac{1}{5} + \frac{1}{5}$
22. $\frac{5}{7} + \frac{1}{7}$
23. $\frac{5}{16} + \frac{3}{16}$
24. $\frac{3}{7} + \frac{4}{7}$
25. $\frac{5}{12} + \frac{1}{12}$
26. $\frac{9}{16} + \frac{5}{16}$
27. $\frac{2}{5} + \frac{2}{5}$
28. $\frac{9}{16} + \frac{9}{16}$
29. $\frac{3}{5} + \frac{3}{5}$
30. $\frac{5}{9} + \frac{3}{9}$
31. $\frac{3}{8} + \frac{5}{8}$
32. $\frac{5}{9} + \frac{1}{9}$

SKILL 40 *(Use after page 158.)*

Here's how

Change to equivalent fractions with common denominators.

$\frac{2}{3} + \frac{3}{4} = \frac{8}{12} + \frac{9}{12}$

Add. Write in simplest form.

$\frac{2}{3} + \frac{3}{4} = \frac{8}{12} + \frac{9}{12}$

$= \frac{17}{12}$

$= 1\frac{5}{12}$

Give the sum in simplest form.

1. $\frac{1}{2} + \frac{1}{4}$
2. $\frac{1}{6} + \frac{2}{3}$
3. $\frac{3}{8} + \frac{1}{4}$
4. $\frac{1}{2} + \frac{3}{8}$
5. $\frac{1}{3} + \frac{1}{6}$
6. $\frac{2}{5} + \frac{3}{10}$
7. $\frac{1}{5} + \frac{3}{10}$
8. $\frac{1}{3} + \frac{1}{4}$
9. $\frac{1}{3} + \frac{3}{7}$
10. $\frac{5}{9} + \frac{1}{6}$
11. $\frac{1}{8} + \frac{3}{4}$
12. $\frac{2}{5} + \frac{1}{4}$
13. $\frac{2}{3} + \frac{1}{9}$
14. $\frac{1}{3} + \frac{1}{2}$
15. $\frac{2}{3} + \frac{1}{8}$
16. $\frac{1}{2} + \frac{1}{6}$
17. $\frac{3}{8} + \frac{1}{6}$
18. $\frac{1}{3} + \frac{2}{5}$
19. $\frac{1}{3} + \frac{5}{8}$
20. $\frac{1}{8} + \frac{1}{6}$
21. $\frac{3}{4} + \frac{1}{2}$
22. $\frac{1}{6} + \frac{2}{9}$
23. $\frac{5}{16} + \frac{1}{8}$
24. $\frac{1}{4} + \frac{2}{3}$
25. $\frac{5}{12} + \frac{1}{4}$
26. $\frac{2}{3} + \frac{11}{12}$
27. $\frac{3}{7} + \frac{1}{2}$
28. $\frac{7}{8} + \frac{5}{16}$
29. $\frac{2}{9} + \frac{2}{3}$
30. $\frac{1}{6} + \frac{4}{9}$
31. $\frac{1}{2} + \frac{2}{5}$
32. $\frac{9}{16} + \frac{1}{8}$

SKILL 41 *(Use after page 160.)*

Here's how

Write equivalent fractions with common denominators.

$$\begin{array}{rcr} 3\frac{2}{3} & = & 3\frac{8}{12} \\ +2\frac{3}{4} & = & +2\frac{9}{12} \\ \hline \end{array}$$

Add the fractions. Add the whole numbers. Write in simplest form.

$$\begin{array}{rcr} 3\frac{2}{3} & = & 3\frac{8}{12} \\ +2\frac{3}{4} & = & +2\frac{9}{12} \\ \hline & & 5\frac{17}{12} = 6\frac{5}{12} \end{array}$$

Give the sum in simplest form.

1. $2\frac{1}{4} + 3\frac{1}{2}$
2. $3\frac{1}{8} + 3\frac{3}{4}$
3. $1\frac{3}{8} + 4\frac{1}{4}$
4. $5\frac{1}{3} + 2\frac{1}{4}$
5. $8\frac{5}{9} + 2\frac{1}{6}$
6. $9\frac{1}{4} + 3\frac{2}{5}$
7. $6\frac{1}{9} + 8\frac{2}{3}$
8. $4\frac{1}{6} + 5\frac{1}{2}$
9. $7\frac{3}{8} + 4\frac{1}{6}$
10. $8\frac{1}{6} + 5\frac{2}{3}$
11. $9\frac{1}{2} + 9\frac{3}{8}$
12. $7\frac{1}{3} + 7\frac{1}{2}$
13. $6\frac{11}{12} + 8\frac{2}{3}$
14. $5\frac{1}{3} + 5\frac{2}{5}$
15. $7\frac{1}{8} + 8\frac{5}{16}$
16. $6\frac{2}{3} + 9\frac{1}{4}$
17. $9\frac{2}{5} + 3\frac{3}{10}$
18. $6\frac{1}{6} + 7\frac{1}{3}$
19. $8\frac{1}{4} + 6\frac{5}{12}$
20. $5\frac{1}{6} + 9\frac{2}{9}$

SKILL 42 *(Use after page 164.)*

Here's how

Subtract the numerators and use the common denominator.

$$\frac{5}{8} - \frac{1}{8} = \frac{4}{8}$$

Write in simplest form.

$$\frac{5}{8} - \frac{1}{8} = \frac{4}{8} = \frac{1}{2}$$

Give the difference in simplest form.

1. $\frac{3}{4} - \frac{1}{4}$
2. $\frac{1}{3} - \frac{1}{3}$
3. $\frac{3}{2} - \frac{1}{2}$
4. $\frac{4}{3} - \frac{1}{3}$
5. $\frac{4}{5} - \frac{1}{5}$
6. $\frac{5}{6} - \frac{1}{6}$
7. $\frac{5}{4} - \frac{3}{4}$
8. $\frac{1}{6} - \frac{1}{6}$
9. $\frac{5}{3} - \frac{2}{3}$
10. $\frac{5}{8} - \frac{1}{8}$
11. $\frac{4}{5} - \frac{2}{5}$
12. $\frac{7}{3} - \frac{3}{3}$
13. $\frac{3}{8} - \frac{3}{8}$
14. $\frac{7}{4} - \frac{3}{4}$
15. $\frac{5}{2} - \frac{1}{2}$
16. $\frac{5}{8} - \frac{3}{8}$
17. $\frac{2}{3} - \frac{0}{3}$
18. $\frac{3}{5} - \frac{1}{5}$
19. $\frac{7}{6} - \frac{3}{6}$
20. $\frac{7}{2} - \frac{1}{2}$
21. $\frac{9}{4} - \frac{3}{4}$
22. $\frac{5}{6} - \frac{0}{6}$
23. $\frac{5}{5} - \frac{3}{5}$
24. $\frac{7}{8} - \frac{3}{8}$
25. $\frac{9}{10} - \frac{1}{10}$
26. $\frac{9}{2} - \frac{3}{2}$
27. $\frac{11}{4} - \frac{7}{4}$
28. $\frac{11}{6} - \frac{5}{6}$

SKILL 43 *(Use after page 166.)*

Here's how

Write equivalent fractions with common denominators.

$\frac{2}{3} - \frac{1}{6} = \frac{4}{6} - \frac{1}{6}$

Subtract. Write in simplest form.

$\frac{2}{3} - \frac{1}{6} = \frac{4}{6} - \frac{1}{6}$

$= \frac{3}{6}$

$= \frac{1}{2}$

Give the difference in simplest form.

1. $\frac{1}{3} - \frac{1}{4}$	**2.** $\frac{1}{2} - \frac{1}{4}$	**3.** $\frac{3}{4} - \frac{1}{2}$	**4.** $\frac{5}{8} - \frac{1}{4}$
5. $\frac{3}{4} - \frac{0}{2}$	**6.** $\frac{2}{3} - \frac{1}{2}$	**7.** $\frac{1}{4} - \frac{1}{8}$	**8.** $\frac{1}{3} - \frac{1}{8}$
9. $\frac{3}{4} - \frac{3}{8}$	**10.** $\frac{7}{8} - \frac{2}{3}$	**11.** $\frac{1}{2} - \frac{1}{3}$	**12.** $\frac{2}{3} - \frac{5}{8}$
13. $\frac{5}{9} - \frac{1}{6}$	**14.** $\frac{1}{3} - \frac{1}{6}$	**15.** $\frac{5}{8} - \frac{2}{5}$	**16.** $\frac{7}{10} - \frac{2}{5}$
17. $\frac{1}{2} - \frac{3}{8}$	**18.** $\frac{9}{10} - \frac{2}{3}$	**19.** $\frac{3}{4} - \frac{2}{3}$	**20.** $\frac{2}{3} - \frac{2}{5}$
21. $\frac{11}{12} - \frac{3}{8}$	**22.** $\frac{2}{3} - \frac{1}{4}$	**23.** $\frac{1}{2} - \frac{5}{12}$	**24.** $\frac{7}{12} - \frac{3}{8}$
25. $\frac{5}{6} - \frac{5}{9}$	**26.** $\frac{7}{8} - \frac{5}{16}$	**27.** $\frac{8}{9} - \frac{5}{6}$	**28.** $\frac{3}{4} - \frac{1}{6}$
29. $\frac{1}{2} - \frac{7}{16}$	**30.** $\frac{1}{4} - \frac{3}{16}$	**31.** $\frac{11}{12} - \frac{5}{6}$	**32.** $\frac{11}{16} - \frac{3}{8}$

SKILL 44 *(Use after page 168.)*

Here's how

Write equivalent fractions with common denominators.

$8\frac{5}{6} = 8\frac{10}{12}$

$-2\frac{1}{12} = -2\frac{1}{12}$

Subtract the fractions. Subtract the whole numbers. Write in simplest form.

$8\frac{5}{6} = 8\frac{10}{12}$

$-2\frac{1}{12} = -2\frac{1}{12}$

$6\frac{9}{12} = 6\frac{3}{4}$

Give the difference in simplest form.

1. $3\frac{5}{8} - 2\frac{1}{4}$	**2.** $6\frac{3}{4} - 4\frac{3}{8}$	**3.** $4\frac{1}{2} - 2\frac{1}{4}$	**4.** $5\frac{5}{9} - 3\frac{1}{6}$
5. $8\frac{1}{3} - 4\frac{1}{6}$	**6.** $5\frac{3}{4} - 1\frac{1}{2}$	**7.** $9\frac{5}{8} - 3\frac{2}{5}$	**8.** $5\frac{7}{8} - 3\frac{2}{3}$
9. $7\frac{2}{3} - 6\frac{5}{8}$	**10.** $5\frac{7}{10} - 1\frac{2}{5}$	**11.** $6\frac{3}{4} - 1\frac{1}{8}$	**12.** $9\frac{2}{3} - 3\frac{1}{2}$
13. $6\frac{1}{3} - 4\frac{1}{4}$	**14.** $5\frac{1}{3} - 3\frac{1}{8}$	**15.** $7\frac{1}{2} - 2\frac{3}{8}$	**16.** $3\frac{9}{10} - 1\frac{2}{3}$

Here's how

Change to a common denominator.

$$5\frac{1}{3} = 5\frac{2}{6}$$
$$-2\frac{1}{2} = -2\frac{3}{6}$$

Regroup.

$$5\frac{1}{3} = 5\frac{2}{6} = 4\frac{8}{6}$$
$$-2\frac{1}{2} = -2\frac{3}{6} = -2\frac{3}{6}$$

Subtract.

$$5\frac{1}{3} = 5\frac{2}{6} = 4\frac{8}{6}$$
$$-2\frac{1}{2} = -2\frac{3}{6} = -2\frac{3}{6}$$
$$2\frac{5}{6}$$

SKILL 45 *(Use after page 170.)*

Give the difference in simplest form.

1. $4\frac{1}{2} - 3\frac{3}{4}$
2. $5\frac{5}{8} - 1\frac{3}{4}$
3. $7\frac{3}{4} - 4\frac{1}{2}$
4. $8\frac{2}{5} - 2\frac{1}{2}$
5. $9\frac{1}{3} - 6\frac{3}{4}$
6. $6\frac{1}{4} - 1\frac{3}{8}$
7. $8\frac{1}{8} - 3\frac{1}{3}$
8. $5\frac{2}{3} - 4\frac{7}{8}$
9. $7\frac{3}{8} - 2\frac{2}{3}$
10. $8\frac{5}{9} - 3\frac{1}{6}$
11. $6\frac{1}{6} - 4\frac{1}{3}$
12. $4\frac{3}{8} - 2\frac{1}{2}$
13. $6\frac{2}{3} - 5\frac{3}{4}$
14. $8\frac{2}{5} - 3\frac{2}{3}$
15. $7\frac{1}{4} - 6\frac{2}{3}$
16. $5\frac{5}{12} - 2\frac{1}{2}$
17. $9\frac{5}{9} - 4\frac{5}{6}$
18. $7\frac{5}{16} - 2\frac{7}{8}$
19. $6\frac{7}{16} - 3\frac{1}{2}$
20. $8\frac{3}{10} - 4\frac{4}{5}$

Here's how

Multiply numerators and denominators.

$$\frac{3}{4} \times \frac{4}{5} = \frac{12}{20}$$

Write in simplest form.

$$\frac{3}{4} \times \frac{4}{5} = \frac{12}{20} = \frac{3}{5}$$

SKILL 46 *(Use after page 178.)*

Give the product in simplest form.

1. $\frac{1}{2} \times \frac{1}{3}$
2. $\frac{3}{4} \times \frac{1}{4}$
3. $\frac{2}{3} \times \frac{4}{5}$
4. $\frac{3}{8} \times 2$
5. $3 \times \frac{1}{5}$
6. $\frac{1}{2} \times \frac{1}{4}$
7. $\frac{4}{3} \times \frac{3}{2}$
8. $\frac{3}{4} \times \frac{16}{3}$
9. $\frac{1}{3} \times \frac{3}{8}$
10. $\frac{7}{4} \times \frac{4}{3}$
11. $\frac{1}{3} \times \frac{4}{5}$
12. $\frac{1}{2} \times \frac{4}{9}$
13. $\frac{5}{8} \times \frac{4}{5}$
14. $\frac{1}{4} \times \frac{8}{5}$
15. $\frac{3}{2} \times \frac{2}{3}$
16. $5 \times \frac{4}{5}$
17. $\frac{5}{6} \times \frac{6}{5}$
18. $\frac{1}{2} \times \frac{2}{3}$
19. $\frac{3}{8} \times \frac{4}{3}$
20. $\frac{2}{3} \times 9$
21. $\frac{1}{3} \times 6$
22. $\frac{5}{8} \times \frac{4}{5}$
23. $\frac{1}{2} \times \frac{4}{5}$
24. $3 \times \frac{8}{3}$

SKILL 47 *(Use after page 180.)*

Here's how

Divide by the denominator and then multiply the result by the numerator.

$24 \div 4 \times 3 = 18$

$\frac{3}{4}$ **of 24** = 18

Complete.

1. $\frac{1}{4}$ of 12 = ?
2. $\frac{1}{2}$ of 18 = ?
3. $\frac{1}{3}$ of 24 = ?
4. $\frac{1}{5}$ of 30 = ?
5. $\frac{1}{8}$ of 72 = ?
6. $\frac{1}{6}$ of 42 = ?
7. $\frac{2}{3}$ of 18 = ?
8. $\frac{3}{4}$ of 20 = ?
9. $\frac{2}{5}$ of 10 = ?
10. $\frac{3}{8}$ of 32 = ?
11. $\frac{2}{3}$ of 24 = ?
12. $\frac{5}{6}$ of 30 = ?
13. $\frac{3}{4}$ of 32 = ?
14. $\frac{5}{8}$ of 40 = ?
15. $\frac{2}{5}$ of 40 = ?
16. $\frac{3}{5}$ of 25 = ?
17. $\frac{5}{6}$ of 42 = ?
18. $\frac{2}{3}$ of 36 = ?
19. $\frac{9}{10}$ of 90 = ?
20. $\frac{2}{3}$ of 21 = ?
21. $\frac{4}{5}$ of 45 = ?
22. $\frac{3}{4}$ of 36 = ?
23. $\frac{7}{10}$ of 40 = ?
24. $\frac{7}{8}$ of 56 = ?

SKILL 48 *(Use after page 182.)*

Here's how

Change to fractions.

$2\frac{1}{2} \times 1\frac{2}{3} = \frac{5}{2} \times \frac{5}{3}$

Multiply.

$2\frac{1}{2} \times 1\frac{2}{3} = \frac{5}{2} \times \frac{5}{3}$

$= \frac{25}{6}$

Write in simplest form.

$2\frac{1}{2} \times 1\frac{2}{3} = \frac{5}{2} \times \frac{5}{3}$

$= \frac{25}{6}$

$= 4\frac{1}{6}$

Give the product in simplest form.

1. $2 \times 1\frac{1}{2}$
2. $1\frac{1}{2} \times 1\frac{1}{3}$
3. $2\frac{2}{3} \times 1\frac{1}{4}$
4. $1\frac{3}{4} \times 1\frac{3}{4}$
5. $3 \times 2\frac{1}{3}$
6. $2\frac{1}{3} \times 2$
7. $2\frac{2}{5} \times 3$
8. $1\frac{5}{6} \times 2\frac{1}{3}$
9. $3\frac{1}{4} \times 3\frac{1}{4}$
10. $4\frac{1}{6} \times 2\frac{1}{3}$
11. $2\frac{2}{3} \times 2\frac{1}{2}$
12. $3 \times 4\frac{1}{2}$
13. $2 \times 1\frac{2}{3}$
14. $1\frac{1}{2} \times 2\frac{1}{2}$
15. $3\frac{3}{4} \times 2$
16. $1\frac{3}{8} \times 2\frac{1}{2}$
17. $3\frac{3}{4} \times 3\frac{1}{8}$
18. $1\frac{5}{8} \times 1\frac{5}{8}$
19. $1\frac{1}{2} \times 1\frac{3}{4}$
20. $2 \times 2\frac{3}{4}$
21. $2\frac{2}{3} \times 1\frac{3}{4}$
22. $4\frac{1}{2} \times 2\frac{3}{8}$
23. $1\frac{5}{8} \times 6$
24. $6\frac{3}{4} \times 3\frac{3}{8}$

SKILL 49 *(Use after page 185.)*

Here's how

$2\frac{3}{4}$ days = ? h

Find the hours in 2 days and $\frac{3}{4}$ of a day.

$2\frac{3}{4}$ days = 48 h + 18 h

Add.

$2\frac{3}{4}$ days = 48 h + 18 h
= 66 h

Complete.

1. $1\frac{1}{2}$ days = ? h
2. $1\frac{1}{4}$ h = ? min
3. $1\frac{3}{4}$ h = ? min
4. $2\frac{1}{2}$ min = ? sec
5. $2\frac{1}{4}$ min = ? sec
6. $2\frac{1}{3}$ days = ? h
7. $1\frac{2}{3}$ yd = ? ft
8. $1\frac{3}{4}$ ft = ? in.
9. $1\frac{1}{2}$ yd = ? in.
10. $2\frac{2}{3}$ ft = ? in.
11. $4\frac{1}{3}$ yd = ? ft
12. $1\frac{3}{4}$ yd = ? in.
13. $1\frac{1}{4}$ gal = ? qt
14. $2\frac{1}{2}$ qt = ? pt
15. $3\frac{1}{2}$ pt = ? c
16. $3\frac{1}{2}$ qt = ? pt

SKILL 50 *(Use after page 188.)*

Here's how

To divide by a fraction, multiply by its reciprocal.

$$\frac{5}{4} \div \frac{3}{2} = \frac{5}{4} \times \frac{2}{3} = \frac{10}{12}$$

Write in simplest form.

$$\frac{5}{4} \div \frac{3}{2} = \frac{5}{4} \times \frac{2}{3} = \frac{10}{12} = \frac{5}{6}$$

Give the quotient in lowest terms.

1. $\frac{3}{4} \div \frac{1}{4}$
2. $\frac{2}{3} \div \frac{1}{3}$
3. $\frac{1}{2} \div \frac{1}{3}$
4. $\frac{3}{5} \div \frac{1}{5}$
5. $\frac{4}{5} \div 3$
6. $\frac{7}{8} \div \frac{7}{8}$
7. $\frac{5}{6} \div \frac{2}{3}$
8. $\frac{2}{3} \div \frac{1}{2}$
9. $\frac{3}{10} \div \frac{4}{5}$
10. $\frac{3}{4} \div \frac{3}{2}$
11. $6 \div \frac{3}{4}$
12. $\frac{5}{8} \div 3$
13. $\frac{5}{6} \div \frac{5}{8}$
14. $\frac{5}{8} \div \frac{2}{3}$
15. $\frac{2}{3} \div \frac{4}{5}$
16. $\frac{7}{10} \div \frac{1}{5}$
17. $\frac{2}{3} \div \frac{5}{6}$
18. $\frac{3}{5} \div \frac{6}{1}$
19. $9 \div \frac{4}{3}$
20. $\frac{1}{2} \div \frac{5}{8}$
21. $\frac{5}{3} \div \frac{3}{2}$
22. $\frac{1}{2} \div \frac{5}{4}$
23. $\frac{3}{4} \div \frac{3}{8}$
24. $\frac{7}{4} \div \frac{2}{5}$
25. $6 \div \frac{2}{3}$
26. $\frac{5}{9} \div \frac{2}{3}$
27. $\frac{5}{8} \div \frac{3}{4}$
28. $\frac{3}{5} \div \frac{5}{4}$
29. $\frac{3}{4} \div \frac{5}{8}$
30. $\frac{9}{4} \div \frac{6}{5}$
31. $\frac{9}{10} \div \frac{5}{4}$
32. $\frac{8}{3} \div \frac{5}{6}$

SKILL 51 *(Use after page 190.)*

Here's how

Change to fractions.

$2\frac{1}{4} \div 4\frac{1}{2} = \frac{9}{4} \div \frac{9}{2}$

Divide. Write in simplest form.

$2\frac{1}{4} \div 4\frac{1}{2} = \frac{9}{4} \div \frac{9}{2}$
$= \frac{9}{4} \times \frac{2}{9}$
$= \frac{18}{36}$
$= \frac{1}{2}$

Give the quotient in simplest form.

1. $5 \div 2\frac{1}{2}$	**2.** $2\frac{1}{2} \div 1\frac{1}{4}$	**3.** $5 \div 1\frac{1}{4}$
4. $3\frac{1}{2} \div 2$	**5.** $10 \div 3\frac{1}{3}$	**6.** $5\frac{1}{4} \div 3$
7. $4\frac{1}{6} \div 5$	**8.** $4\frac{3}{4} \div 2$	**9.** $2\frac{1}{3} \div 1\frac{1}{4}$
10. $2\frac{1}{2} \div 2\frac{1}{2}$	**11.** $7\frac{1}{2} \div 2\frac{1}{2}$	**12.** $6\frac{3}{4} \div 3\frac{1}{2}$
13. $3\frac{1}{2} \div 1\frac{3}{4}$	**14.** $2\frac{7}{8} \div 3\frac{1}{4}$	**15.** $4\frac{5}{8} \div 2\frac{2}{3}$
16. $3\frac{5}{6} \div 2\frac{1}{3}$	**17.** $5 \div 1\frac{1}{4}$	**18.** $5\frac{3}{4} \div 2\frac{2}{3}$
19. $6\frac{2}{3} \div 5\frac{1}{3}$	**20.** $4\frac{7}{8} \div 6\frac{1}{4}$	**21.** $2\frac{3}{4} \div 5\frac{2}{3}$
22. $10 \div 3\frac{1}{3}$	**23.** $4\frac{1}{4} \div 3\frac{1}{8}$	**24.** $3\frac{1}{2} \div 1\frac{3}{4}$

SKILL 52 *(Use after page 230.)*

Here's how

$\frac{5}{3} = \frac{7}{n}$

Write the multiplication equation.

$\frac{5}{3} = \frac{7}{n}$
$5n = 21$

Solve the multiplication equation.

$\frac{5}{3} = \frac{7}{n}$
$5n = 21$
$n = 4\frac{1}{5}$

Solve.

1. $\frac{n}{6} = \frac{11}{4}$	**2.** $\frac{8}{n} = \frac{2}{9}$	**3.** $\frac{9}{8} = \frac{n}{7}$	**4.** $\frac{10}{7} = \frac{4}{n}$
5. $\frac{5}{n} = \frac{2}{9}$	**6.** $\frac{n}{13} = \frac{6}{5}$	**7.** $\frac{7}{4} = \frac{n}{6}$	**8.** $\frac{5}{8} = \frac{3}{n}$
9. $\frac{3}{7} = \frac{9}{n}$	**10.** $\frac{18}{n} = \frac{6}{5}$	**11.** $\frac{n}{21} = \frac{6}{7}$	**12.** $\frac{n}{6} = \frac{15}{8}$
13. $\frac{9}{n} = \frac{3}{13}$	**14.** $\frac{18}{n} = \frac{9}{16}$	**15.** $\frac{6}{11} = \frac{24}{n}$	**16.** $\frac{5}{7} = \frac{9}{n}$
17. $\frac{n}{7} = \frac{11}{4}$	**18.** $\frac{6}{n} = \frac{8}{3}$	**19.** $\frac{19}{2} = \frac{n}{5}$	**20.** $\frac{10}{13} = \frac{16}{n}$
21. $\frac{9}{n} = \frac{2}{15}$	**22.** $\frac{n}{9} = \frac{4}{3}$	**23.** $\frac{6}{15} = \frac{30}{n}$	**24.** $\frac{11}{4} = \frac{n}{8}$
25. $\frac{n}{4} = \frac{6}{8}$	**26.** $\frac{1}{n} = \frac{7}{21}$	**27.** $\frac{6}{9} = \frac{n}{3}$	**28.** $\frac{6}{10} = \frac{18}{n}$
29. $\frac{5}{15} = \frac{3}{n}$	**30.** $\frac{10}{3} = \frac{n}{12}$	**31.** $\frac{7}{n} = \frac{10}{9}$	**32.** $\frac{n}{8} = \frac{7}{4}$

SKILL 53 *(Use after page 248.)*

Here's how

Write the percent as a fraction with a denominator of 100. Write the fraction in simplest form.

$$25\% = \frac{25}{100} = \frac{1}{4}$$

$$33\frac{1}{3}\% = \frac{33\frac{1}{3}}{100} = 33\frac{1}{3} \div 100 = \frac{100}{3} \times \frac{1}{100} = \frac{100}{300} = \frac{1}{3}$$

Change to a fraction in simplest form.

1. 10%	**2.** 15%	**3.** 40%	**4.** 50%
5. 90%	**6.** 60%	**7.** 25%	**8.** 75%
9. 20%	**10.** 30%	**11.** 45%	**12.** 85%
13. 80%	**14.** 40%	**15.** 48%	**16.** 96%
17. 18%	**18.** 24%	**19.** 72%	**20.** 84%
21. 150%	**22.** 125%	**23.** 175%	**24.** 120%
25. 180%	**26.** 250%	**27.** 275%	**28.** 225%
29. 160%	**30.** 200%	**31.** 300%	**32.** 320%
33. $33\frac{1}{3}\%$	**34.** $66\frac{2}{3}\%$	**35.** $37\frac{1}{2}\%$	**36.** $16\frac{2}{3}\%$
37. $87\frac{1}{2}\%$	**38.** $81\frac{1}{4}\%$	**39.** $162\frac{1}{2}\%$	**40.** $118\frac{3}{4}\%$

SKILL 54 *(Use after page 250.)*

Here's how

Change to an equivalent fraction with a denominator of 100. Write as a percent.

$$\frac{1}{2} = \frac{50}{100} = 50\%$$

Solve a proportion.

$$\frac{1}{6} = \frac{n}{100}$$

$$6n = 100$$

$$n = 16\frac{2}{3}$$

$$\text{So } \frac{1}{6} = \frac{16\frac{2}{3}}{100} = 16\frac{2}{3}\%$$

Change to a percent.

1. $\frac{1}{5}$	**2.** $\frac{1}{4}$	**3.** $\frac{1}{2}$	**4.** $\frac{4}{5}$
5. $\frac{3}{4}$	**6.** $\frac{1}{3}$	**7.** $\frac{2}{5}$	**8.** $\frac{2}{3}$
9. $\frac{1}{8}$	**10.** $\frac{3}{5}$	**11.** $\frac{3}{8}$	**12.** $\frac{3}{2}$
13. $\frac{6}{5}$	**14.** $\frac{1}{6}$	**15.** $\frac{5}{4}$	**16.** $\frac{7}{5}$
17. $\frac{1}{10}$	**18.** $\frac{8}{5}$	**19.** $\frac{3}{10}$	**20.** $\frac{1}{12}$
21. $\frac{5}{2}$	**22.** 3	**23.** $\frac{7}{4}$	**24.** $\frac{1}{20}$
25. $\frac{5}{8}$	**26.** $\frac{7}{10}$	**27.** $\frac{11}{8}$	**28.** $\frac{7}{3}$
29. $\frac{5}{12}$	**30.** $\frac{5}{3}$	**31.** 2	**32.** $\frac{7}{12}$

SKILL 55 *(Use after page 252.)*

Here's how

To change a percent to a decimal, move the decimal point two places to the left and remove the percent sign.

3% = 0.03

17% = 0.17

15.2% = 0.152

$66\frac{2}{3}$% = $0.66\frac{2}{3}$

112% = 1.12

Change to a decimal.

1. 25%	**2.** 20%	**3.** 45%	**4.** 82%
5. 34%	**6.** 65%	**7.** 80%	**8.** 56%
9. 75%	**10.** 12%	**11.** 81%	**12.** 62%
13. 5%	**14.** 8%	**15.** 2%	**16.** 4%
17. 1%	**18.** 3%	**19.** 7%	**20.** 6%
21. 150%	**22.** 125%	**23.** 173%	**24.** 225%
25. 160%	**26.** 250%	**27.** 300%	**28.** 500%
29. 28.5%	**30.** 16.2%	**31.** 34.6%	**32.** 56.8%
33. 47.2%	**34.** 93.9%	**35.** 60.5%	**36.** 85.2%
37. $33\frac{1}{3}$%	**38.** $87\frac{1}{2}$%	**39.** $16\frac{2}{3}$%	**40.** $37\frac{1}{2}$%

SKILL 56 *(Use after page 253.)*

Here's how

To change a decimal to a percent, move the decimal point two places to the right and write the percent sign.

0.5 = 50%

0.125 = 12.5%

$0.87\frac{1}{2}$ = $87\frac{1}{2}$%

1.475 = 147.5%

Change to a percent.

1. 0.04	**2.** 0.07	**3.** 0.02	**4.** 0.06
5. 0.08	**6.** 0.01	**7.** 0.05	**8.** 0.03
9. 0.09	**10.** 0.56	**11.** 0.49	**12.** 0.66
13. 0.71	**14.** 0.11	**15.** 0.98	**16.** 0.38
17. 0.5	**18.** 0.4	**19.** 0.3	**20.** 0.8
21. 0.2	**22.** 0.6	**23.** 0.1	**24.** 0.9
25. 2.25	**26.** 1.58	**27.** 1.55	**28.** 2.75
29. 3.46	**30.** 8.25	**31.** 7.52	**32.** 5.37
33. $0.12\frac{1}{2}$	**34.** $0.33\frac{1}{3}$	**35.** $0.62\frac{1}{2}$	**36.** $0.16\frac{2}{3}$
37. $1.37\frac{1}{2}$	**38.** $1.66\frac{2}{3}$	**39.** $2.33\frac{1}{3}$	**40.** $2.83\frac{1}{3}$

SKILL 57 *(Use after page 256.)*

Here's how

First change the percent to a fraction or decimal. Then multiply.

75% of 36 $= \frac{3}{4} \times 36$
$= 27$

6.5% of 9 $= 0.065 \times 9$
$= 0.585$

Solve.

1. 50% of 28 = n
2. 25% of 24 = n
3. 40% of 60 = n
4. 20% of 45 = n
5. 80% of 40 = n
6. 10% of 50 = n
7. 75% of 48 = n
8. 25% of 64 = n
9. 100% of 56 = n
10. 150% of 18 = n
11. 125% of 40 = n
12. 250% of 72 = n
13. 14% of 26 = n
14. 23% of 75 = n
15. 56% of 29 = n
16. 41% of 83 = n
17. 5.4% of 60 = n
18. 6.5% of 47 = n
19. 0.25% of 160 = n
20. 0.6% of 314 = n

SKILL 58 *(Use after page 258.)*

Here's how

Change to a fraction or decimal and multiply.

20% of 45 $= \frac{1}{5} \times 45$
$= 9$

8.2% of 6 $= 0.082 \times 6$
$= 0.492$

Solve a proportion.

$16\frac{2}{3}$ % of 72 = n

$$\frac{16\frac{2}{3}}{100} = \frac{n}{72}$$

$$100n = 16\frac{2}{3} \times 72$$

$$= \frac{50}{3} \times 72$$

$$= 1200$$

$$n = 12$$

Solve.

1. 25% of 116 = n
2. 60% of 60 = n
3. 100% of 73 = n
4. 75% of 12 = n
5. 20% of 95 = n
6. $87\frac{1}{2}$% of 88 = n
7. 8.2% of 50 = n
8. 6.5% of 35 = n
9. 2.25% of 304 = n
10. $37\frac{1}{2}$% of 104 = n
11. $62\frac{1}{2}$% of 72 = n
12. 3.45% of 156 = n
13. 7.5% of 56 = n
14. $33\frac{1}{3}$% of 81 = n
15. 0.36% of 100 = n
16. 0.25% of 200 = n
17. $66\frac{2}{3}$% of 63 = n
18. $8\frac{1}{3}$% of 96 = n
19. 0.5% of 38 = n
20. $16\frac{2}{3}$% of 48 = n

Here's how

60% of n = 27

Solve a proportion.

$$\frac{\text{part}}{\text{whole}} \quad \frac{60}{100} = \frac{27}{n} \quad \frac{\text{part}}{\text{whole}}$$

$$60n = 2700$$

$$n = 45$$

SKILL 59 *(Use after page 260.)*

Solve.

1. 25% of n = 14
2. 50% of n = 19
3. 75% of n = 33
4. 60% of n = 48
5. 80% of n = 64
6. 40% of n = 46
7. 10% of n = 16
8. 5% of n = 120
9. 30% of n = 57
10. 20% of n = 65

Solve. Round each answer to the nearest tenth.

11. 8.5% of n = 6
12. 7.5% of n = 11
13. 20.5% of n = 16.2
14. 14.2% of n = 37
15. 34.6% of n = 18.5
16. 42.8% of n = 10.3
17. 1.8% of n = 2.4
18. 4.7% of n = 2.9
19. 125% of n = 17.6
20. 250% of n = 31.3

Here's how

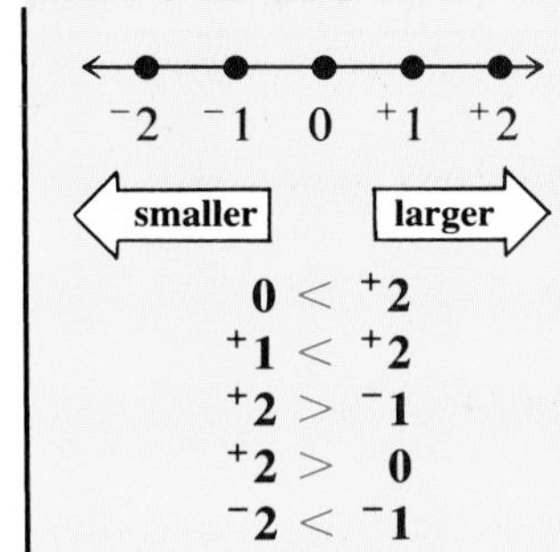

SKILL 60 *(Use after page 362.)*

< or >?

1. $^{+}5$ ● $^{+}8$
2. $^{+}5$ ● $^{-}8$
3. $^{-}5$ ● $^{-}8$
4. $^{-}6$ ● $^{+}1$
5. $^{+}6$ ● $^{-}1$
6. $^{+}6$ ● $^{+}1$
7. 0 ● $^{-}5$
8. 0 ● $^{+}5$
9. $^{-}7$ ● 0
10. $^{+}9$ ● $^{-}4$
11. $^{-}9$ ● $^{+}4$
12. $^{+}9$ ● $^{+}4$
13. $^{-}7$ ● $^{-}2$
14. $^{-}8$ ● $^{+}3$
15. 0 ● $^{+}6$
16. $^{+}9$ ● $^{+}4$
17. $^{-}6$ ● $^{+}6$
18. $^{-}3$ ● $^{-}5$
19. $^{-}11$ ● $^{+}10$
20. $^{+}16$ ● $^{-}17$
21. $^{+}15$ ● $^{+}17$
22. 0 ● $^{-}12$
23. $^{+}15$ ● $^{-}15$
24. $^{-}19$ ● $^{-}13$
25. $^{-}16$ ● $^{+}11$
26. $^{-}19$ ● $^{-}18$
27. $^{+}14$ ● $^{+}17$
28. $^{-}22$ ● $^{+}22$
29. $^{-}26$ ● $^{-}21$
30. $^{+}23$ ● $^{+}24$
31. $^{+}27$ ● $^{-}20$
32. $^{-}29$ ● $^{+}23$
33. $^{-}28$ ● $^{-}26$
34. 0 ● $^{+}32$
35. $^{-}36$ ● 0
36. $^{+}37$ ● $^{-}31$

SKILL 61 *(Use after page 364.)*

Here's how

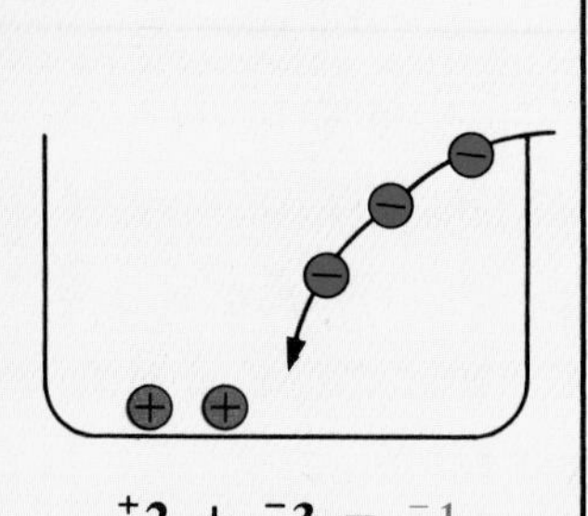

$^{+}2 + ^{-}3 = ^{-}1$

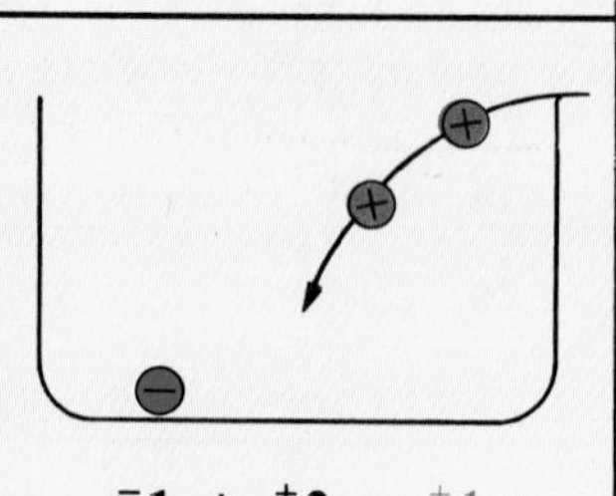

$^{-}1 + ^{+}2 = ^{+}1$

Give the sum.

1. $^{+}3 + ^{+}2$
2. $^{+}3 + ^{-}2$
3. $^{-}3 + ^{-}2$
4. $^{-}1 + ^{+}5$
5. $^{-}1 + ^{-}5$
6. $^{+}1 + ^{-}5$
7. $0 + ^{-}8$
8. $0 + ^{+}8$
9. $^{-}6 + 0$
10. $^{+}4 + ^{-}4$
11. $^{-}4 + ^{+}4$
12. $^{+}4 + ^{+}4$
13. $^{+}7 + ^{-}3$
14. $^{-}7 + ^{+}3$
15. $^{-}7 + ^{-}3$
16. $^{-}6 + ^{+}9$
17. $^{+}6 + ^{-}9$
18. $^{-}6 + ^{-}9$
19. $^{+}10 + ^{+}12$
20. $^{+}11 + ^{-}11$
21. $^{-}17 + ^{+}14$
22. $^{-}19 + ^{-}13$
23. $^{+}18 + ^{-}19$
24. $^{-}16 + ^{+}11$
25. $^{+}15 + ^{+}14$
26. $^{-}18 + ^{-}12$
27. $^{-}11 + ^{+}19$
28. $^{+}17 + ^{-}17$
29. $^{-}19 + ^{+}14$
30. $^{+}12 + ^{+}15$
31. $^{-}20 + ^{-}20$
32. $^{-}21 + ^{+}25$
33. $^{+}27 + ^{-}22$
34. $^{-}31 + ^{+}31$
35. $0 + ^{+}34$
36. $^{-}32 + ^{-}36$

SKILL 62 *(Use after page 367.)*

Here's how

To subtract an integer, add the opposite of the integer.

$^{+}5 - ^{+}2 = ^{+}5 + ^{-}2$
$= ^{+}3$

$^{-}5 - ^{+}2 = ^{-}5 + ^{-}2$
$= ^{-}7$

$^{+}5 - ^{-}2 = ^{+}5 + ^{+}2$
$= ^{+}7$

$^{-}5 - ^{-}2 = ^{-}5 + ^{+}2$
$= ^{-}3$

Give the difference.

1. $^{+}4 - ^{-}6$
2. $^{-}4 - ^{+}6$
3. $^{+}4 - ^{+}6$
4. $^{-}7 - ^{-}3$
5. $^{+}7 - ^{-}3$
6. $^{-}7 - ^{+}3$
7. $^{+}8 - ^{+}1$
8. $^{-}8 - ^{+}1$
9. $^{+}8 - ^{-}1$
10. $^{-}7 - 0$
11. $0 - ^{+}7$
12. $0 - ^{-}7$
13. $^{+}5 - ^{+}9$
14. $^{+}5 - ^{-}9$
15. $^{-}5 - ^{+}9$
16. $^{-}5 - ^{-}5$
17. $^{+}5 - ^{+}5$
18. $^{-}5 - ^{+}5$
19. $^{+}12 - ^{-}11$
20. $^{-}13 - ^{+}16$
21. $^{-}14 - ^{-}14$
22. $^{-}16 - ^{+}19$
23. $^{+}18 - ^{+}11$
24. $^{+}19 - ^{+}14$
25. $^{+}17 - ^{-}10$
26. $^{-}10 - ^{+}17$
27. $^{-}16 - ^{-}16$
28. $^{+}11 - ^{+}15$
29. $^{-}15 - ^{+}18$
30. $^{+}17 - ^{-}14$
31. $^{-}23 - ^{-}27$
32. $^{+}25 - ^{+}25$
33. $^{-}28 - ^{+}24$
34. $0 - ^{-}34$
35. $^{-}36 - ^{+}32$
36. $^{+}33 - ^{-}38$

SKILL 63 *(Use after page 371.)*

Here's how

The product of two integers with the same signs is positive.

$^{+}2 \times {}^{+}3 = {}^{+}6$
$^{-}4 \times {}^{-}5 = {}^{+}20$

The product of two integers with different signs is negative.

$^{+}6 \times {}^{-}3 = {}^{-}18$
$^{-}5 \times {}^{+}6 = {}^{-}30$

The product of any integer and 0 is 0.

$^{+}7 \times 0 = 0$
$0 \times {}^{-}4 = 0$

Give the product.

1. $^{+}3 \times {}^{+}4$	**2.** $^{+}3 \times {}^{-}4$	**3.** $^{-}3 \times {}^{-}4$
4. $^{-}6 \times {}^{+}5$	**5.** $^{+}6 \times {}^{+}5$	**6.** $^{+}6 \times {}^{-}5$
7. $^{-}5 \times {}^{+}7$	**8.** $^{-}5 \times {}^{-}7$	**9.** $^{+}5 \times {}^{+}7$
10. $^{+}2 \times {}^{-}6$	**11.** $^{-}6 \times {}^{+}2$	**12.** $^{-}6 \times {}^{-}2$
13. $^{+}7 \times 0$	**14.** $^{-}7 \times 0$	**15.** 0×0
16. $^{-}9 \times {}^{-}8$	**17.** $^{+}8 \times {}^{-}8$	**18.** $^{-}6 \times {}^{+}5$
19. $^{+}4 \times {}^{+}6$	**20.** $^{-}5 \times {}^{+}5$	**21.** $^{+}6 \times {}^{-}6$
22. $^{-}5 \times {}^{-}9$	**23.** $^{+}7 \times {}^{-}8$	**24.** $^{-}8 \times {}^{+}7$
25. $^{+}9 \times {}^{+}7$	**26.** $^{-}7 \times {}^{-}7$	**27.** $0 \times {}^{+}8$
28. $^{+}10 \times {}^{-}6$	**29.** $^{-}10 \times {}^{+}6$	**30.** $^{+}10 \times {}^{+}6$
31. $^{-}11 \times {}^{-}11$	**32.** $^{+}11 \times {}^{-}11$	**33.** $^{+}11 \times {}^{+}11$
34. $^{-}13 \times {}^{+}14$	**35.** $^{+}18 \times {}^{+}15$	**36.** $^{-}19 \times {}^{-}13$

SKILL 64 *(Use after page 372.)*

Here's how

The quotient of two integers with the same signs is positive.

$^{+}12 \div {}^{+}6 = {}^{+}2$
$^{-}21 \div {}^{-}7 = {}^{+}3$

The quotient of two integers with different signs is negative.

$^{+}20 \div {}^{-}4 = {}^{-}5$
$^{-}32 \div {}^{+}8 = {}^{-}4$

The quotient of 0 divided by any non-zero integer is 0.

$0 \div {}^{-}6 = 0$
$0 \div {}^{+}7 = 0$

Give the quotient.

1. $^{+}12 \div {}^{+}3$	**2.** $^{+}12 \div {}^{-}3$	**3.** $^{-}12 \div {}^{-}3$
4. $^{-}8 \div {}^{+}2$	**5.** $^{+}8 \div {}^{+}2$	**6.** $^{+}8 \div {}^{-}2$
7. $^{-}16 \div {}^{+}4$	**8.** $^{-}16 \div {}^{-}4$	**9.** $^{+}16 \div {}^{-}4$
10. $^{-}18 \div {}^{+}6$	**11.** $^{+}18 \div {}^{+}6$	**12.** $^{+}18 \div {}^{-}6$
13. $^{-}25 \div {}^{+}5$	**14.** $^{-}25 \div {}^{-}5$	**15.** $^{+}25 \div {}^{-}5$
16. $0 \div {}^{+}4$	**17.** $0 \div {}^{-}4$	**18.** $0 \div {}^{-}9$
19. $^{+}49 \div {}^{-}7$	**20.** $^{-}42 \div {}^{+}6$	**21.** $^{-}45 \div {}^{-}5$
22. $^{+}36 \div {}^{+}6$	**23.** $^{-}32 \div {}^{+}8$	**24.** $^{+}35 \div {}^{-}7$
25. $^{-}36 \div {}^{-}9$	**26.** $^{+}54 \div {}^{+}6$	**27.** $^{-}64 \div {}^{+}8$
28. $^{+}72 \div {}^{-}9$	**29.** $^{-}81 \div {}^{-}9$	**30.** $^{+}63 \div {}^{-}7$
31. $^{-}70 \div {}^{+}10$	**32.** $^{+}90 \div {}^{+}10$	**33.** $^{-}60 \div {}^{-}10$
34. $^{-}132 \div {}^{+}12$	**35.** $^{+}182 \div {}^{-}13$	**36.** $^{+}224 \div {}^{+}16$

EXTRA PROBLEM SOLVING

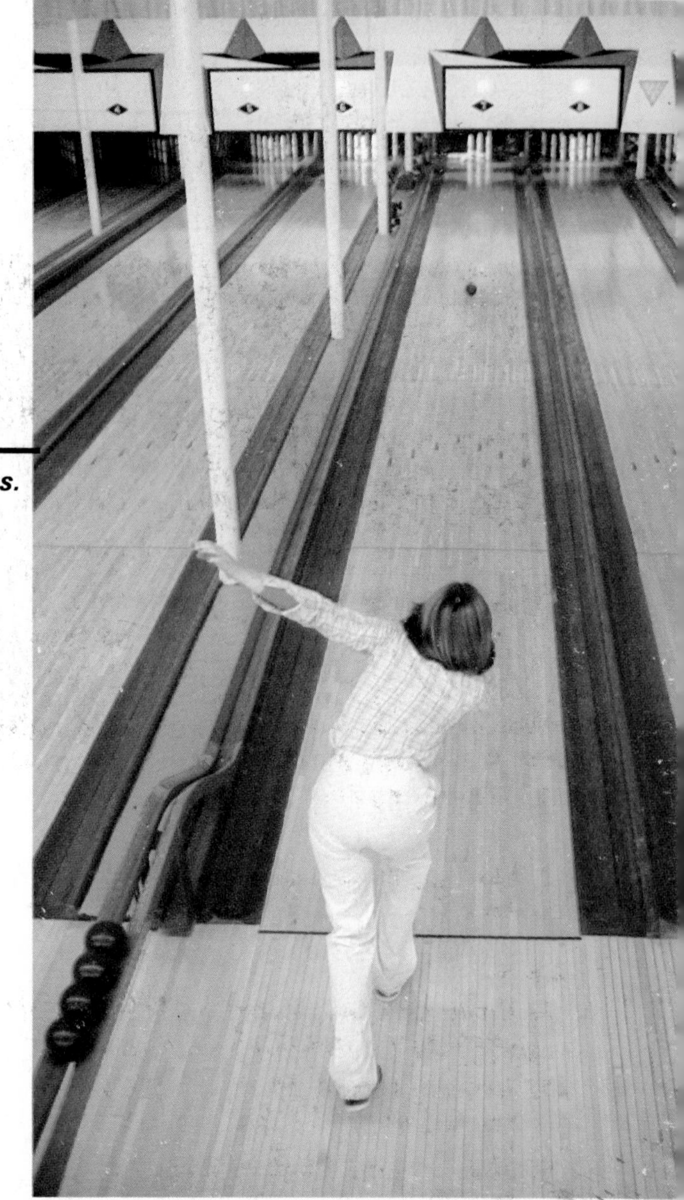

SET 1 *(Use after Chapter 1.)*

BOWLER	Scores		
	GAME 1	GAME 2	GAME 3
Robin	126	146	132
Jenny	125	163	140
Amy	113	123	145
Sarah	138	151	124

Use the bowling scores to solve these problems.

1. Who had a score of 138 in Game 1?
2. Who had the high score in Game 2?
3. What was Robin's high score?
4. What was Sarah's high score?
5. What was Jenny's low score?
6. In Game 1, who scored 12 more than Robin?
7. Whose high score was 27 more than her low score?
8. What was Sarah's total score for her first two games?
9. What was Amy's total score for her last two games?
10. Who had a total score of 289 for her first two games?
11. Who scored 38 more in her second game than in her first game?
12. In Game 3, did Sarah bowl better than Robin?
13. In Game 3, did Sarah and Amy together bowl better than Robin and Jenny?
14. Who had the lowest total score for all three games?
15. Who had the highest total score for all three games?

SET 2 *(Use after Chapter 2.)*

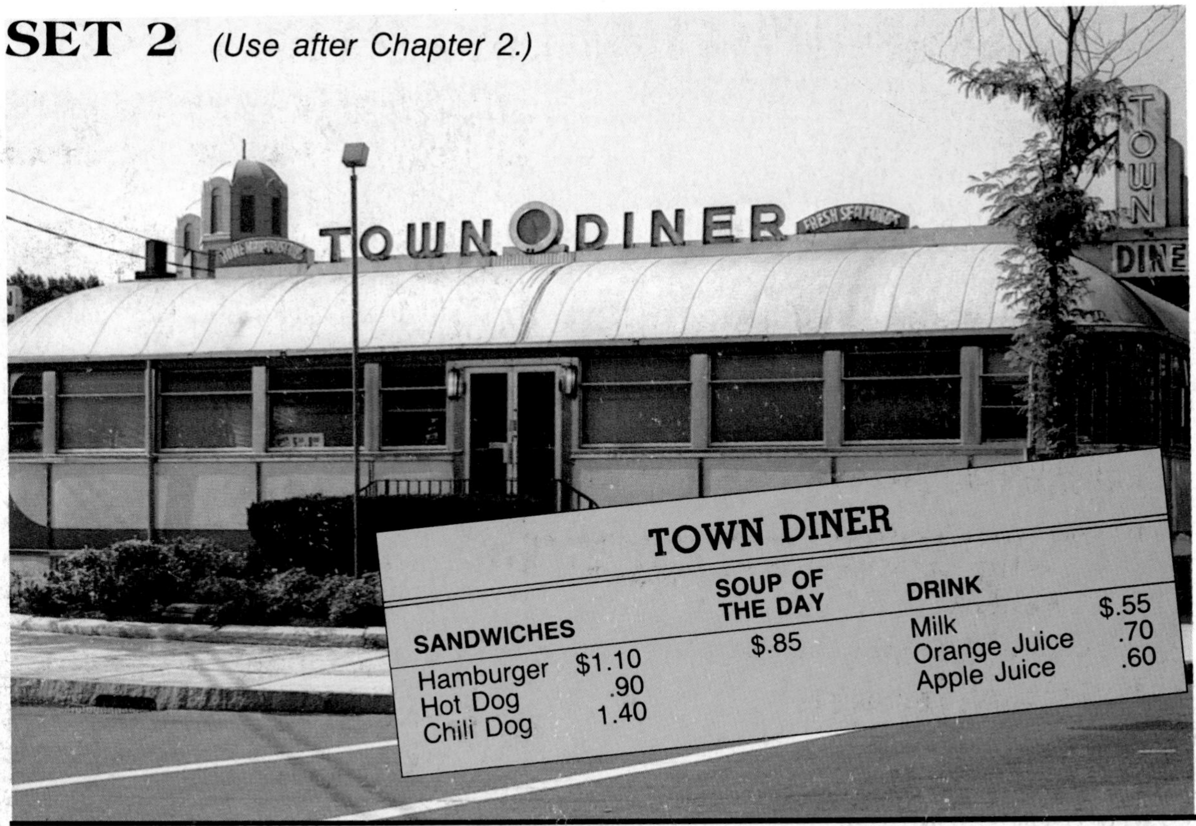

TOWN DINER
FRESH SEAFOODS
TOWN
DINE
TOWN DINER
SANDWICHES
Hamburger $1.10
Hot Dog .90
Chili Dog 1.40
SOUP OF THE DAY
$.85
DRINK
Milk $.55
Orange Juice .70
Apple Juice .60

Use the menu prices to answer each question.

1. What is the price of a hot dog?
2. Is $2 enough money to buy a chili dog and apple juice?
3. How many hamburgers can you buy for $5?
4. Can you buy a hot dog, bowl of soup, and milk for less than $2?

Solve.

5. Emily gave the cashier $5 and got $3.90 in change. She had a [?] for lunch.
6. Renée spent $1.45. She bought a bowl of soup and [?].
7. Joel spent $2.10. He bought a chili dog and [?].
8. Jeff's order cost $2.80. He had a chili dog, soup, and [?].
9. Heather spent $1.60. She bought a [?] and [?].
10. Amy spent $1.70. She had a [?] and [?].
11. Brian gave the cashier $2 and got a nickel in change. He had a [?] and [?].
12. Kevin ordered a [?] and [?]. He got $3.25 change from a five-dollar bill.

SET 3 *(Use after Chapter 3.)*

FIRST-CLASS STAMP FACTS

Before 1885, the first-class letter rate (cost for the first ounce) depended on distance traveled. On July 1, 1885, the national rate became 2 cents. Since then the rate has been changed several times. The following list shows these changes.

Date	*Rate*
November 3, 1917	3 cents
July 1, 1919	2 cents
July 6, 1932	3 cents
August 1, 1958	4 cents
January 7, 1963	5 cents
May 16, 1971	8 cents
March 2, 1974	10 cents
December 11, 1975	13 cents
May 29, 1978	15 cents
March 22, 1981	18 cents
November 1, 1981	20 cents

Use the information in the article to solve these problems.

1. What was the first-class letter rate on July 2, 1919?

2. What was the first-class letter rate in 1976?

3. On what date did the first-class letter rate increase from 13 cents to 15 cents?

4. On what date was there a decrease in the first-class letter rate?

5. How much more was the first-class letter rate on January 20, 1973, than on January 20, 1963?

6. How much was the increase in the first-class letter rate from November 10, 1977, to November 10, 1981?

7. What was the total cost of postage for mailing 15 one-ounce letters on July 5, 1971?

8. After July 5, 1932, a roll of 50 stamps cost $1.50. How much did a similar roll of 50 stamps cost 40 years later?

9. How much more did it cost to mail a Father's Day card in 1975 than it did in 1915? *Hint: Father's Day is always in June.*

10. How much more did it cost to mail 24 Valentine cards in 1980 than it did in 1950? *Hint: Valentine's Day is February 14.*

SET 4 *(Use after Chapter 4.)*

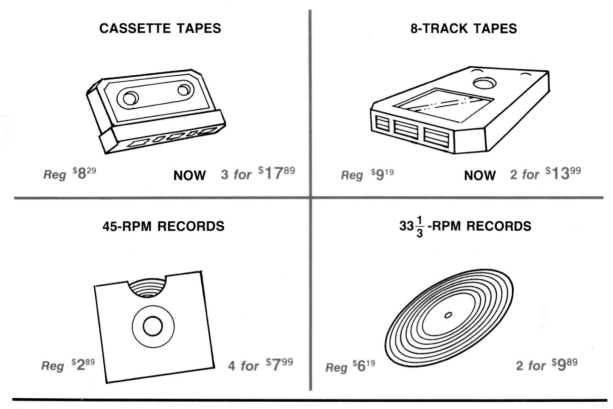

CASSETTE TAPES

Reg 8^{29} **NOW** *3 for* 17^{89}

8-TRACK TAPES

Reg 9^{19} **NOW** *2 for* 13^{99}

45-RPM RECORDS

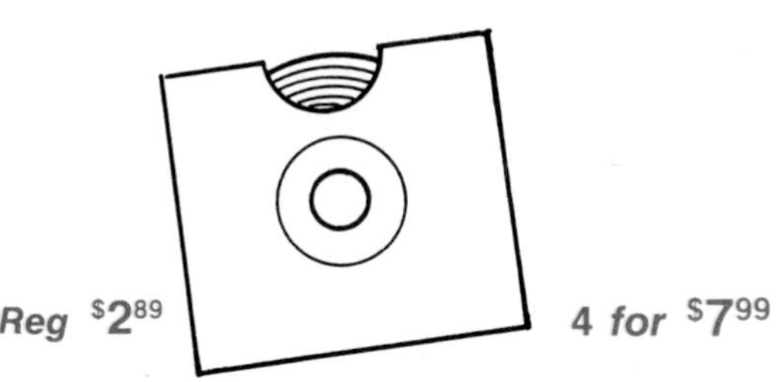

Reg 2^{89} *4 for* 7^{99}

$33\frac{1}{3}$-RPM RECORDS

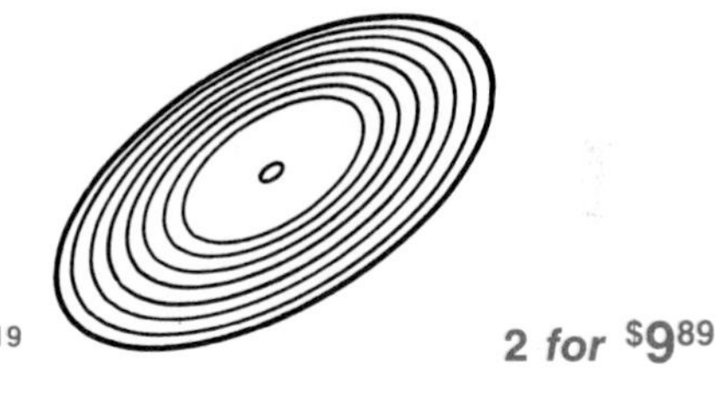

Reg 6^{19} *2 for* 9^{89}

Use the ad to solve these problems.

1. What was the regular price of the cassette tapes?
2. How many cassette tapes can you buy on sale for about $18?
3. How many $33\frac{1}{3}$-RPM records can you buy on sale for about $20?
4. Is $15 enough money to buy eight 45-RPM records at the sale price?
5. Alison spent about $5. She bought one [?] on sale.
6. Greg spent about $7. He bought one [?] on sale.
7. Ted spent about $4. He bought two [?] on sale.
8. Mike spent about $12. He bought two [?] on sale.
9. How much would you save if you bought 3 cassette tapes on sale?
10. Can you save more than $1.50 if you buy four 45-RPM records on sale?
11. If you pay the sale price, how much would a dozen cassette tapes cost?
12. How much would you have to pay for two 8-track tapes and four $33\frac{1}{3}$-RPM records on sale?

SET 5 *(Use after Chapter 5.)*

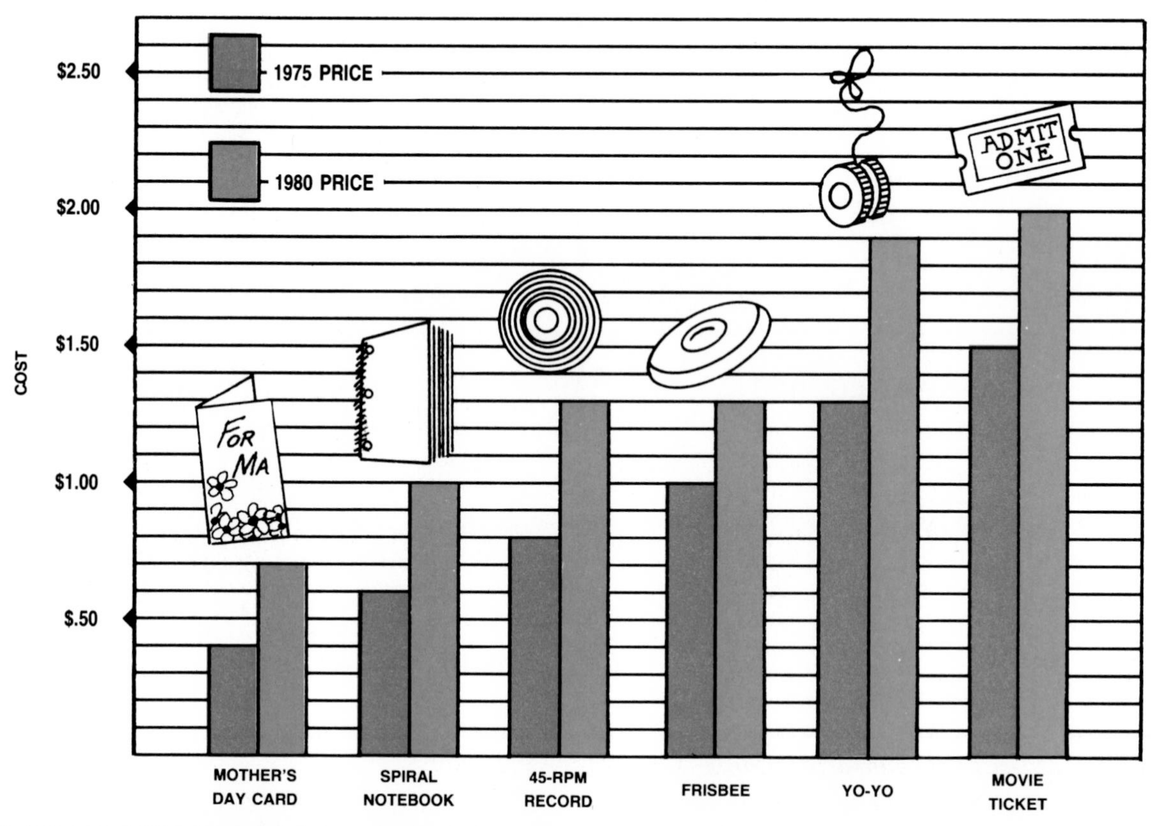

Use the bar graph to solve these problems.

1. Which of the items cost \$.60 in 1975?
2. Which of the items cost \$1.90 in 1980?
3. What was the cost of a Frisbee in 1975?
4. Which item cost \$.60 more in 1980 than it did in 1975?
5. Which items cost \$.30 less in 1975 than they did in 1980?
6. Which had the greater increase in price from 1975 to 1980, a 45 RPM record or a Frisbee?
7. In which year could you have bought 4 movie tickets for \$6.00?
8. In which year could you have paid for 2 yo-yos with a \$5 bill and received \$1.20 in change?
9. In 1975, would \$5.00 have been enough money to buy 3 movie tickets, a 45-RPM record, and a yo-yo?
10. In which year could you have bought a Frisbee, a 45-RPM record, and a Mother's Day card for \$2.20?

SET 6 *(Use after Chapter 6.)*

Here is a schedule for direct-dial telephone rates for calls made from Des Moines, Iowa, to other cities in the United States.

FROM DES MOINES TO	8 A.M.–5 P.M. Monday through Friday		5 P.M.–11 P.M. Sunday through Friday		11 P.M.–8 A.M. Every night 8 A.M.–11 P.M. Saturday 8 A.M.–5 P.M. Sunday	
	First Minute	Each Additional Minute	First Minute	Each Additional Minute	First Minute	Each Additional Minute
Atlanta	**$.66**	**$.46**	**$.42**	**$.30**	**$.26**	**$.19**
Boston	**.68**	**.48**	**.43**	**.31**	**.26**	**.19**
Chicago	**.64**	**.44**	**.41**	**.29**	**.25**	**.18**
Minneapolis	**.62**	**.42**	**.39**	**.28**	**.24**	**.17**
Omaha	**.59**	**.40**	**.37**	**.27**	**.23**	**.16**

Use the rate-schedule information to solve these problems.

1. Sandy called her sister in Atlanta. She called at 3 P.M. on Wednesday. They talked for 5 minutes.

- **a.** What was the cost for the first minute of their call?
- **b.** What was the cost for the next 4 minutes?
- **c.** What was the total cost of their 5-minute call?

2. David called his grandfather in Chicago. He called at 5:45 P.M. on Tuesday. They talked for 8 minutes.

- **a.** What was the cost for the first minute?
- **b.** What was the cost for the next 7 minutes?
- **c.** What was the total cost?

3. Kari called her brother in Boston. She called at 9 A.M. on Saturday. They talked for 11 minutes. What was the cost?

4. Robin called her friend in Minneapolis on Sunday. They talked from 9:10 A.M. to 9:17 A.M. What was the cost?

5. Mr. Bix called his son in Omaha at 1:30 P.M. on Monday. The charge was $1.79. How many minutes did they talk?

6. A 20-minute call to Atlanta on a weekday before 5 P.M. costs $9.40. How much money can you save if you wait until after 5 P.M. to make the call?

SET 7 *(Use after Chapter 7.)*

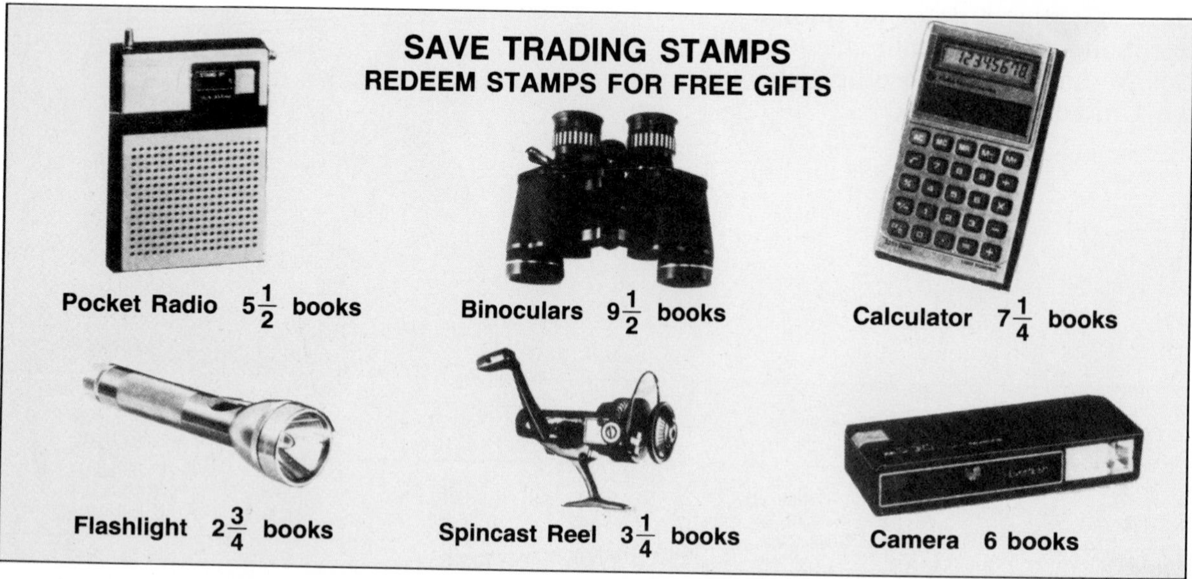

SAVE TRADING STAMPS
REDEEM STAMPS FOR FREE GIFTS
Pocket Radio $5\frac{1}{2}$ books
Binoculars $9\frac{1}{2}$ books
Calculator $7\frac{1}{4}$ books
Flashlight $2\frac{3}{4}$ books
Spincast Reel $3\frac{1}{4}$ books
Camera 6 books

Use the information in the ad to solve these problems.

1. How many books of trading stamps do you need to get a calculator?

2. Which item can you get for $9\frac{1}{2}$ books of trading stamps?

3. How many books of trading stamps do you need to get a Spincast reel and binoculars?

4. Charlene has $3\frac{1}{4}$ books of trading stamps. How many more books does she need to get a pocket radio?

5. If Sidney saves $\frac{1}{4}$ book of stamps each month, how many months will it take him to get a flashlight?

6. Randy saved $3\frac{1}{2}$ books of trading stamps and his sister saved $2\frac{1}{4}$ books. How many more books do they need to get a calculator?

7. Gina saved 12 books of trading stamps. Does she have enough stamps to get a Spincast reel, a flashlight, and a pocket radio?

8. If you have $4\frac{1}{4}$ books of trading stamps, how many more books do you need to get a camera?

9. It takes 1600 stamps to fill a trading-stamp book. Ted has 1200 stamps. What fraction of a book has he filled?

10. Rita has saved 4000 stamps. How many more stamps does she need to save in order to get a camera? (Remember—It takes 1600 stamps to fill a book.)

SET 8 *(Use after Chapter 8.)*

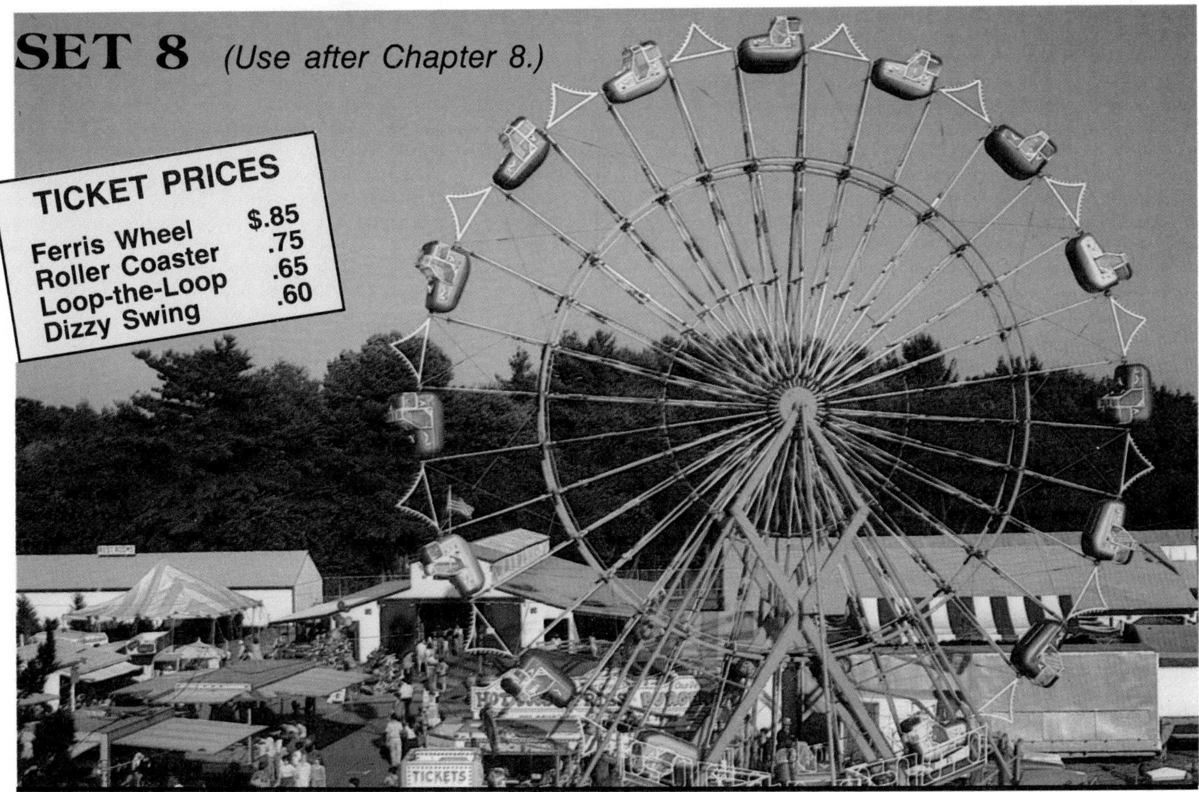

TICKET PRICES
Ferris Wheel $.85
Roller Coaster .75
Loop-the-Loop .65
Dizzy Swing .60
TICKETS

Use the ticket prices to solve these problems.

1. How much would 4 Ferris-wheel tickets cost?

2. Is $5 enough money to buy 8 roller-coaster tickets?

3. How much would you spend for 3 loop-the-loop tickets and 2 roller-coaster tickets?

4. Marcia spent $5.20 on Ferris-wheel tickets and dizzy-swing tickets. She had 3 rides on the dizzy swing. How many rides did she have on the Ferris wheel?

5. Wendy bought 5 roller-coaster tickets. She gave the clerk $10. How much change did she get?

6. Craig has $5. How many loop-the-loop tickets can he buy?

7. Dan bought 4 roller-coaster tickets. Melinda bought 5 loop-the-loop tickets. How much more did Melinda pay for her tickets than Dan?

8. Juan had $9. He spent $\frac{1}{3}$ of his money on dizzy-swing tickets. How many dizzy-swing tickets did he buy?

9. Anita had $6.80. She spent $\frac{1}{2}$ of her money for Ferris-wheel tickets. How many rides did she have on the Ferris wheel?

10. Lenny had $6. He spent $\frac{3}{4}$ of his money on roller-coaster tickets. How many rides did he have on the roller coaster?

SET 9 *(Use after Chapter 9.)*

SHIPPING COSTS FROM CHICAGO				
Shipping Weight*	Zone 1 Up to 150 miles**	Zone 2 151 to 300 miles	Zone 3 301 to 600 miles	Zone 4 601 to 1000 miles
1 oz to 8 oz	$ .50	$ .53	$ .56	$ .60
9 oz to 15 oz	.83	.86	.90	.94
1 lb to 2 lb	1.22	1.34	1.57	1.83
2 lb 1 oz to 3 lb	1.32	1.46	1.69	1.98
3 lb 1 oz to 4 lb	1.46	1.63	1.90	2.25
4 lb 1 oz to 5 lb	1.60	1.78	2.09	2.51

* Weight rounded to the nearest ounce ** Distance rounded to the nearest mile

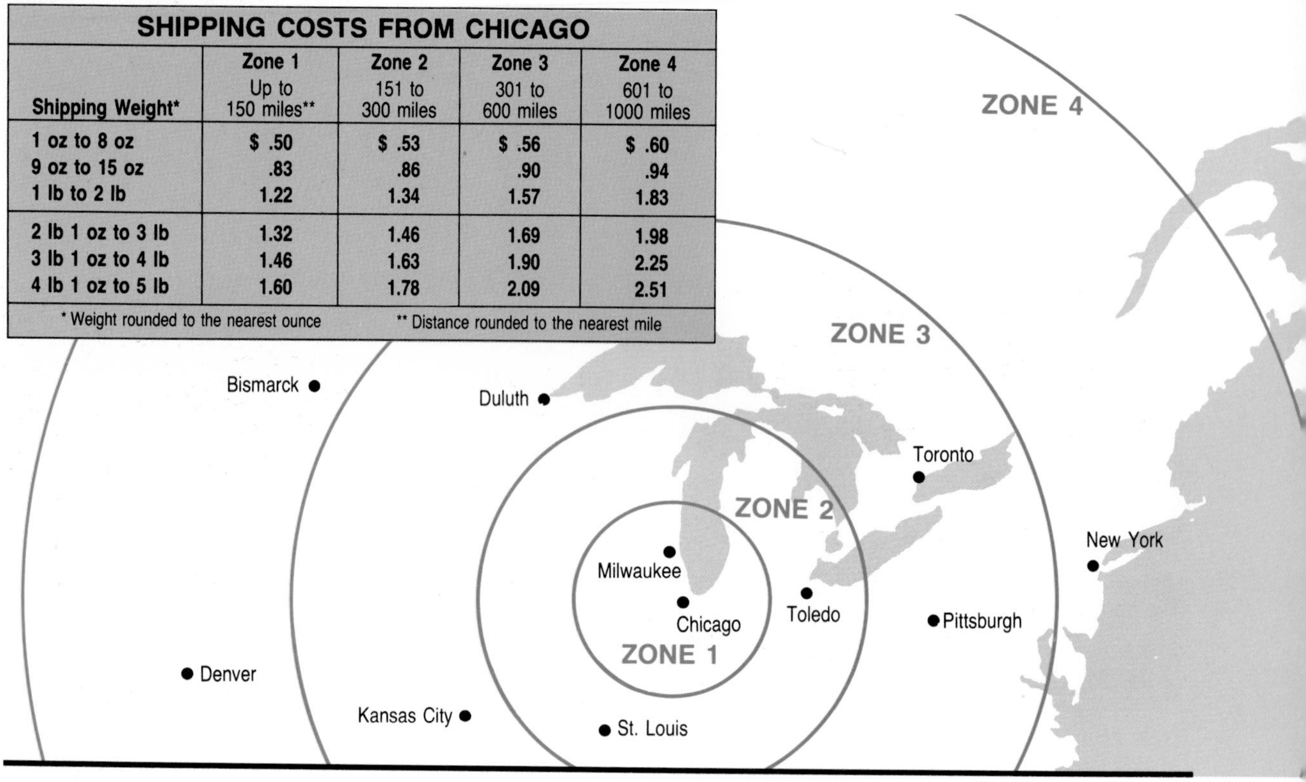

Use the map and the shipping information to solve these problems.

1. How much does it cost to ship a 10-ounce package to zone 4?
2. What is the cost to ship a 4-pound package 800 miles?
3. How much does it cost to ship a 40-ounce package 500 miles? (Remember: 16 ounces = 1 pound.)
4. How much does it cost to ship a 12-ounce package from Chicago to St. Louis?
5. It cost Cindy $1.90 to ship a $3\frac{1}{2}$-pound package from Chicago to her sister. Does Cindy's sister live in Duluth or Toledo?
6. How much would it cost Bob to ship a 4-pound 10-ounce package from Chicago to Bismarck?
7. What is the total cost to ship a 2-pound package and a 1-pound 6-ounce package from Chicago to Milwaukee?
8. How much more does it cost to ship a 5-pound package from Chicago to New York than from Chicago to Kansas City?
9. Can you ship a 20-ounce package from Chicago to Pittsburgh for less than $1.50?
10. What is the total cost to ship a 3-pound package from Chicago to Denver and a 4-pound 2-ounce package from Chicago to Toronto?

SET 10 *(Use after Chapter 10.)*

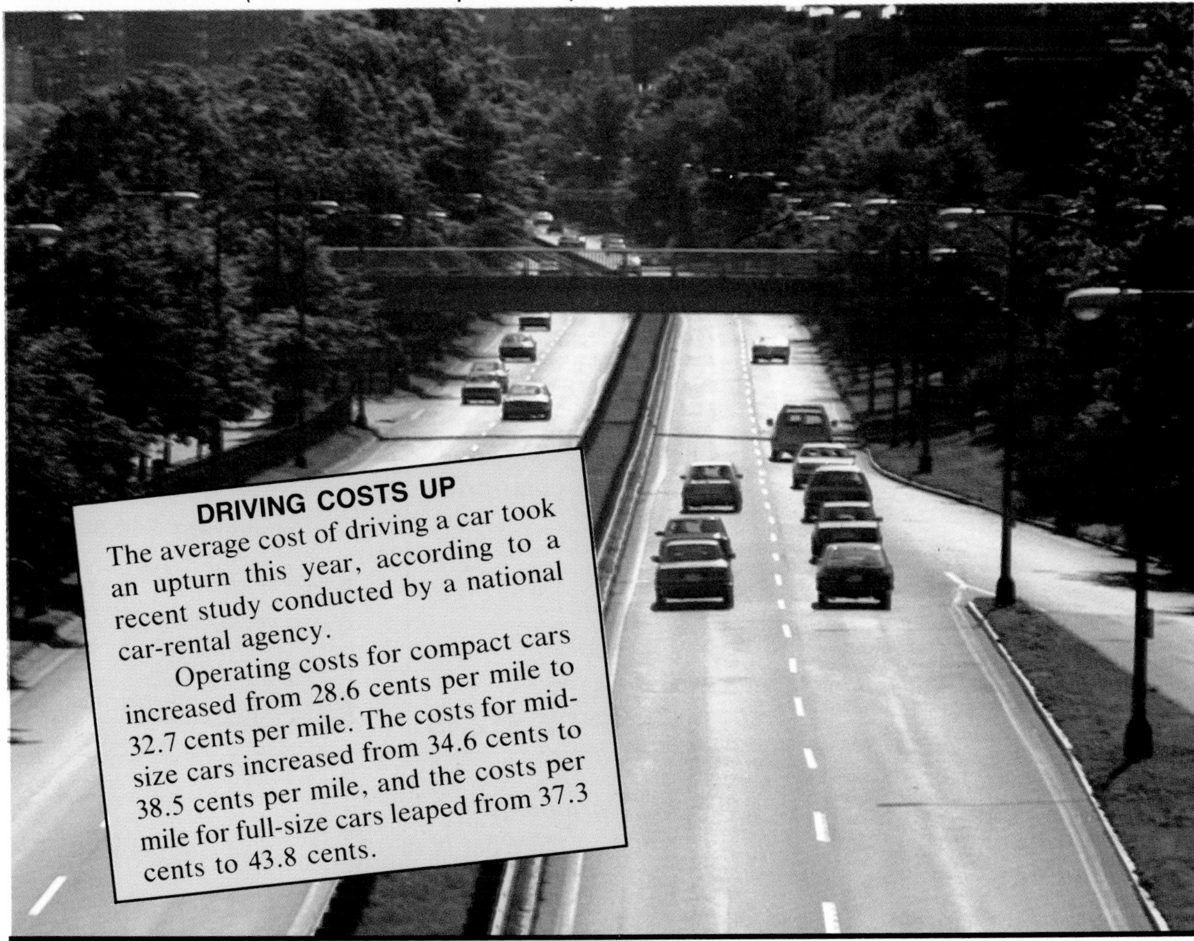

DRIVING COSTS UP

The average cost of driving a car took an upturn this year, according to a recent study conducted by a national car-rental agency.

Operating costs for compact cars increased from 28.6 cents per mile to 32.7 cents per mile. The costs for mid-size cars increased from 34.6 cents to 38.5 cents per mile, and the costs per mile for full-size cars leaped from 37.3 cents to 43.8 cents.

Use the information in the article to solve these problems.

1. Which size car costs 32.7 cents per mile to operate this year?
2. Which size car costs more than 40 cents per mile to operate?
3. Which size car had an operating-cost increase of 6.5 cents per mile?
4. Which size car had an operating-cost increase of 4.1 cents per mile?
5. What was the operating-cost increase for mid-size cars?
6. According to the study, how much does it cost to drive a compact car 200 miles?
7. How much does it cost to drive a mid-size car 200 miles?
8. How much does it cost to drive a full-size car 200 miles?
9. How much more does it cost to drive a mid-size car on a 400-mile trip this year than last year?
10. How much money could you save by driving a compact car on a 500-mile trip rather than a full-size car?

SET 11 *(Use after Chapter 11.)*

SUPER SPECIALS
Telescope
Sale Price
$135.00
Digital Watch
SAVE
$7.77
Now $39.99
Calculator
SALE
$8.80
Reg $10.99
Headphones
25% off
regular price
SALE
PRICE $12.45
Pocket Radio
$33.99
Reg $44.88

Use the information in the ad to solve these problems.

1. What is the regular price of the calculator?

2. What is the sale price of the pocket radio?

3. What is the regular price of the digital watch?

4. Jill bought the telescope at the sale price and saved $19.99. What is the regular price of the telescope?

5. How much money will you save if you buy the calculator at the sale price instead of the regular price?

6. How much money can be saved by buying the pocket radio at the sale price?

7. Greg is paid $3 an hour. How many hours would he need to work to earn enough money to buy a telescope?

8. Pepe earns $1.10 an hour baby-sitting and always saves half of his money. How many hours of sitting will it take him to save enough money to buy a calculator?

9. Shelly and her two friends bought a pocket radio at the sale price. If they share the cost equally, how much will Shelly pay?

10. Joel says that the regular price of the headphones was $18.80. Brad said that the regular price was $16.60. Who is correct, Joel or Brad?

SET 12 *(Use after Chapter 12.)*

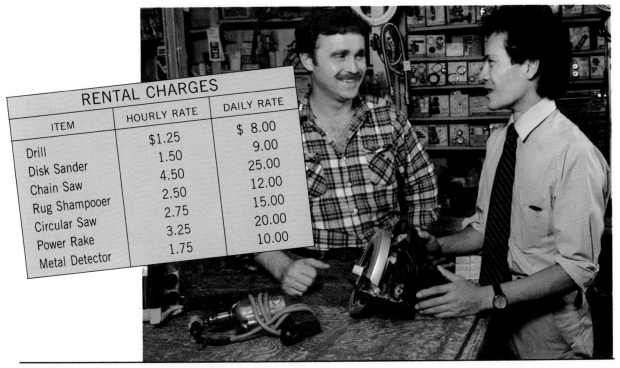

RENTAL CHARGES

ITEM	HOURLY RATE	DAILY RATE
Drill	$1.25	$ 8.00
Disk Sander	1.50	9.00
Chain Saw	4.50	25.00
Rug Shampooer	2.50	12.00
Circular Saw	2.75	15.00
Power Rake	3.25	20.00
Metal Detector	1.75	10.00

Use the rental charges to solve these problems.

1. Which item can you rent for $4.50 per hour?

2. What is the hourly rate to rent a power rake?

3. Which item can you rent for $15.00 per day?

4. What is the daily rate to rent a disk sander?

5. What is the cost of renting a drill for 5 hours?

6. How much does it cost to rent a circular saw for 4 hours?

7. Ray rented a disk sander and rug shampooer for 3.5 hours. What was the total rental cost?

8. If you rent a chain saw for 8 hours, how much cheaper is it to pay the daily rate rather than the hourly rate?

9. Fran rented a metal detector at 10:00 A.M. and returned it at 3:00 P.M. If she paid the hourly rate, what was the rental charge?

10. Tony rented a rug shampooer for 8 hours. How much did he save by paying the daily rate rather than the hourly rate?

11. Sonia paid a deposit of $5.00 on a circular saw. How much more did she owe if she returned the saw 3 hours later and was charged at the hourly rate?

12. Nancy paid a deposit of $10.00 on a power rake. She returned the rake 4 hours later. Based on the hourly rate, how much more did she owe?

SET 13 *(Use after Chapter 13.)*

In the scorebook each X represents a field goal made during the game and is worth 2 points.

Each o represents a successful free throw and is worth 1 point.

Each ● represents a missed free throw.

Team East

Player	Points
Benson, K.	XO●●●X
Evans, E.	XX●XX●
Fuller, M.	●X●
Lufkin, J.	XXO
Patton, R.	XXX●O
Sneller, S.	XXXX●●●O

Team West

Player	Points
Dietz, R.	XXXX●
Gibson, C.	X●OXX
Hauser, T.	XXX●●XO●
McBride, K	X●●XXO
Moody, L.	XOXX●●●●O
Voss, D.	OOX●●

Use the score-book information to solve these problems.

1. Which player on the East team made 4 field goals and 1 free throw?
2. Which West player scored a total of 9 points?
3. Who was the highest scorer for East?
4. Who was the high scorer for West?
5. How many points did Sneller score?
6. How many more points did Dietz score than Gibson?
7. Which player made 100% of his free throws?
8. Which two players for West made 50% of their free throws?
9. How many of the East players made less than 50% of their free throws?
10. Benson attempted a total of 8 field goals. What percent of his field goals did he make?
11. Hauser attempted a total of 10 field goals. What percent of his field goals did he make?
12. Which team's players made an average of 3 field goals?
13. How many points did East score?
14. Which team won the game?

SET 14 *(Use after Chapter 14.)*

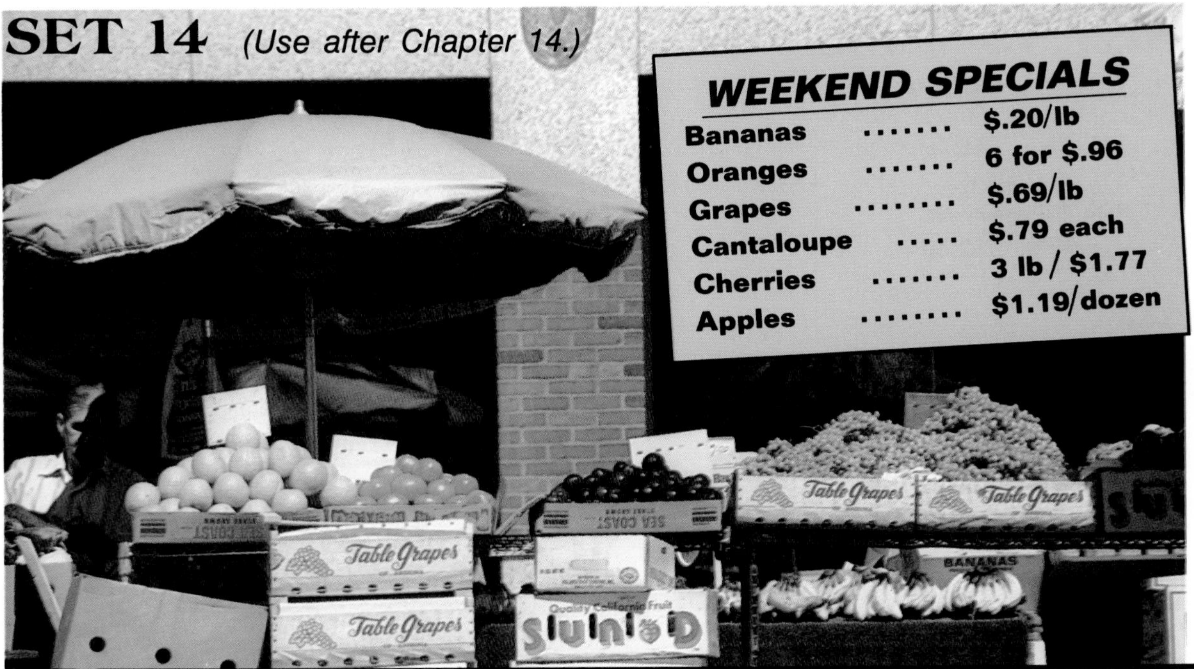

WEEKEND SPECIALS
Bananas .... $.20/lb
Oranges .... 6 for $.96
Grapes .... $.69/lb
Cantaloupe ..... $.79 each
Cherries .... 3 lb / $1.77
Apples $1.19/dozen
Table Grapes
Table Grapes
Table Grapes
Table Grapes
BANANAS
SEA COAST

Use the grocery ad to solve these problems. Round answers to the nearest cent.

1. What is the cost of 2 pounds of grapes?
2. What is the cost of 5 cantaloupes?
3. Can you buy 3 cantaloupes for $2?
4. How many pounds of bananas can you buy for $1?
5. How much would $\frac{1}{2}$ dozen apples cost?
6. What is the cost of a dozen oranges?
7. If you gave the cashier $5 for 2.5 pounds of grapes, how much change would you get?
8. If you wanted to buy only 2 pounds of cherries, how much would they cost? *Hint: What is the cost of 1 pound of cherries?*

Find the total cost of the items on each grocery list.

9.

Grocery List

4 lb grapes

3 cantaloupes

3 lb bananas

10.

Groceries

1 lb cherries

Dozen apples

24 oranges

11.

Market List

24 apples

5 cantaloupes

4 lb bananas

SET 15 *(Use after Chapter 15.)*

NOVELTY ITEMS

TALKING TEETH

They walk, clickety-clack, and yackety-yak.

$2.50

MINI SPY CAMERA

Guaranteed to take pictures. Buy and develop 110 film anywhere! Fits in the palm of your hand. **$1.95**

PHONY ARM CAST

Looks like a real plaster cast with arm sling. A sympathy winner and great excuse.

$2.95

BAG OF LAUGHS

$3.95

Press button for recorded rollicking series of laughs.

SALES TAX TABLE

Amount of Sale	Tax	Amount of Sale	Tax
$0.00 to 0.12	$0.00	3.88 to 4.12	0.16
0.13 to 0.37	0.01	4.13 to 4.37	0.17
0.38 to 0.62	0.02	4.38 to 4.62	0.18
0.63 to 0.87	0.03	4.63 to 4.87	0.19
0.88 to 1.12	0.04	4.88 to 5.12	0.20
1.13 to 1.37	0.05	5.13 to 5.37	0.21
1.38 to 1.62	0.06	5.38 to 5.62	0.22
1.63 to 1.87	0.07	5.63 to 5.87	0.23
1.88 to 2.12	0.08	5.88 to 6.12	0.24
2.13 to 2.37	0.09	6.13 to 6.37	0.25
2.38 to 2.62	0.10	6.38 to 6.62	0.26
2.63 to 2.87	0.11	6.63 to 6.87	0.27
2.88 to 3.12	0.12	6.88 to 7.12	0.28
3.13 to 3.37	0.13	7.13 to 7.37	0.29
3.38 to 3.62	0.14	7.38 to 7.62	0.30
3.63 to 3.87	0.15	7.63 to 7.87	0.31

BALD HEAD WIG

$1.50

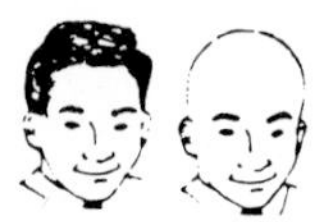

VENUS FLY TRAP

Eats flies, bugs, insects—even meat.

$1.75

Live bulb, instructions, and special soil included.

Use the sales tax table to find the sales tax on each item.

1. Talking Teeth
2. Mini Spy Camera
3. Phony Arm Cast
4. Bag of Laughs
5. Bald Head Wig
6. Venus Fly Trap

Solve.

7. Scott bought a Phony Arm Cast and a Bag of Laughs.
   - **a.** What was the total cost of the items?
   - **b.** What was the sales tax on the total?
   - **c.** What was the total cost including the sales tax?
8. Daphne bought a Mini Spy Camera, a Venus Fly Trap, and Talking Teeth.
   - **a.** What was the total cost of the three items?
   - **b.** What was the sales tax on the total?
   - **c.** What was the total cost including the sales tax?
9. What is the total cost, including the sales tax, for a Phony Arm Cast and a Bald Head Wig?
10. If you have $5.90, do you have enough money to buy a Bag of Laughs and a Venus Fly Trap? *Hint: Don't forget the sales tax.*
11. Cristy bought two novelty items. The sales tax was $.13. What two items did she buy?
12. The sales tax on the two novelty items Brad bought was $.28. What two items did he buy?

SET 16 *(Use after Chapter 16.)*

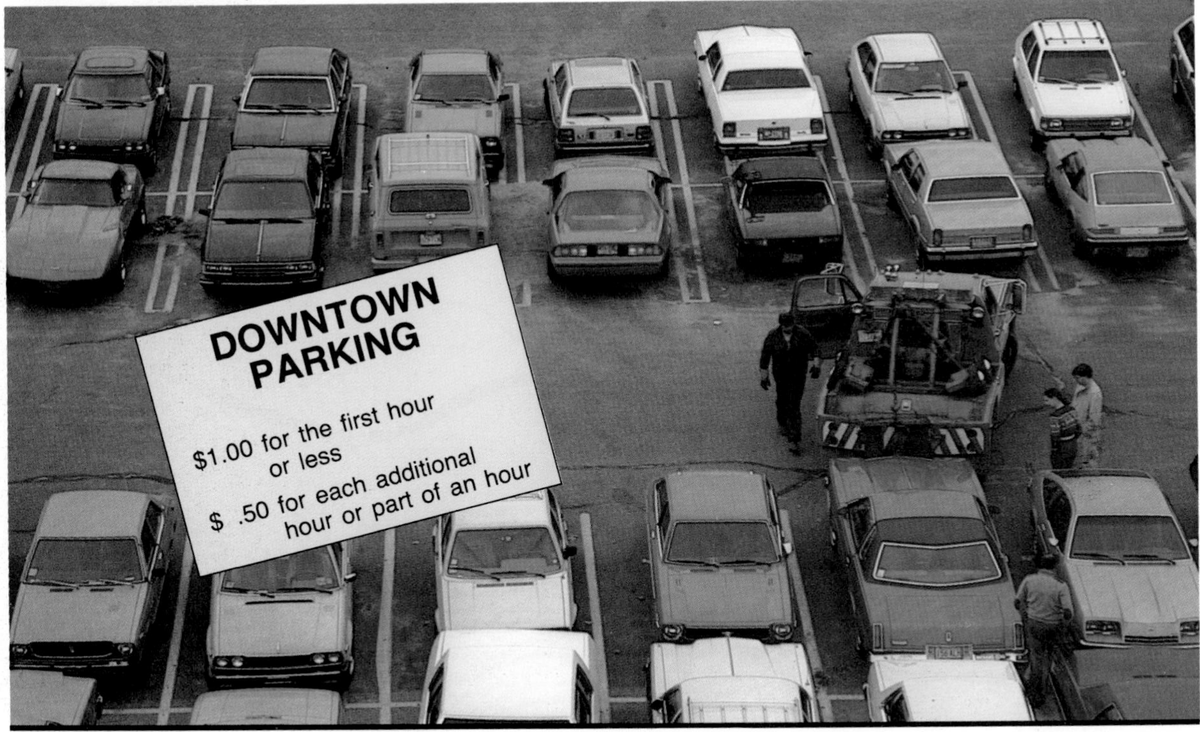
DOWNTOWN
PARKING
$1.00 for the first hour
or less
$ .50 for each additional
hour or part of an hour

Use the parking-rate information to solve these problems.

1. How much does it cost to park a car for the first hour?
2. What is the parking rate for the first two hours?
3. How much does it cost to park a car for 8 hours?
4. How much does it cost to park a car from 11:00 A.M. to 4:00 P.M.?
5. Marty said it would cost $.50 to park a car for one-half hour. Lynn said it would cost $1.00. Who is correct, Marty or Lynn?
6. Maria parked her car from 1:30 P.M. to 4:15 P.M. How much did she pay for parking?
7. Mr. Friendly paid $2.50. Did he park his car for more than 3 hours?
8. What is the maximum number of hours that you can park for $6.00?
9. Ms. Wilson paid $4.50. Did she park her car for less than 10 hours?
10. Brian parked his car for 12 hours. He gave the parking attendant $10.00. How much change did Brian get?
11. Mrs. VerMeer gave the attendant $10.00 and got $2.50 in change. How many hours of parking did she pay for?
12. Andy, Jan, Phil, and Brian parked their jeep for 7 hours. They shared the parking cost equally. How much was Andy's share of the parking cost?

SET 17 *(Use after Chapter 17.)*

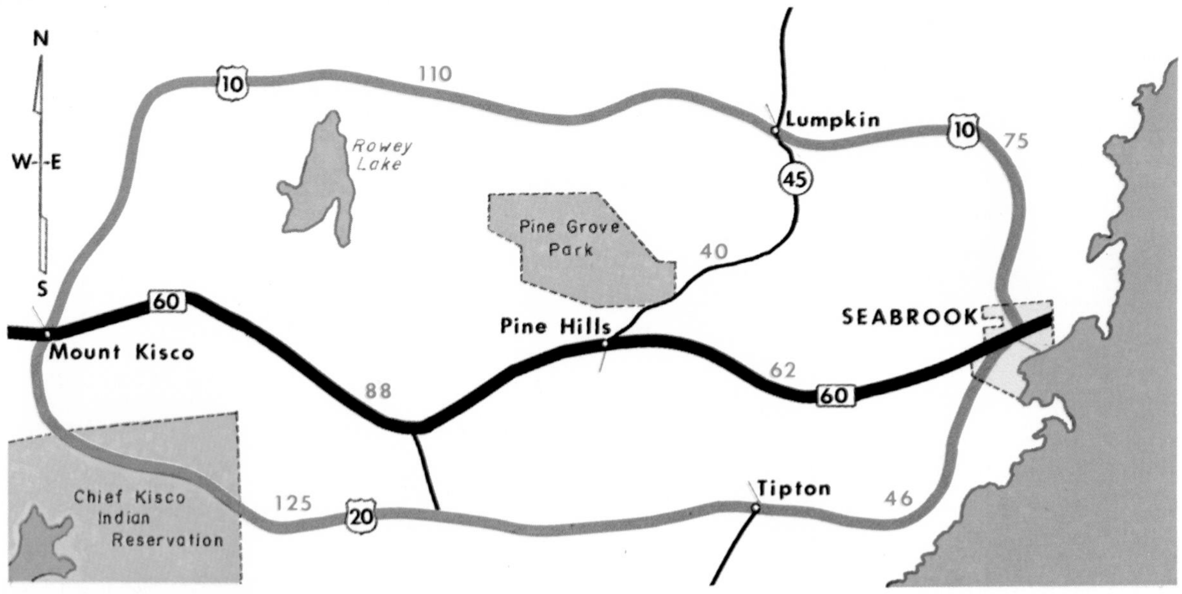

Use the map to solve these problems.

1. Which city is 125 miles from Mount Kisco?
2. Highway 10 goes through which three cities?
3. Which highway from Mount Kisco to Seabrook is 14 miles shorter than Highway 10?
4. Sharon drove from Mount Kisco to Seabrook. Before the trip her car's odometer showed 17,685 miles. After the trip the odometer showed 17,856 miles. Which highway did she take?
5. How many miles per gallon is a car averaging if it takes 5 gallons of gasoline to drive from Lumpkin to Mount Kisco on Highway 10?
6. At a speed of 50 miles per hour, how many hours would it take to get from Tipton to Mount Kisco on Highway 20?
7. How fast (miles per hour) should a driver travel on Highway 10 to get from Lumpkin to Seabrook in 1 hour 30 minutes?
8. You are traveling east on Highway 60. How far are you from Pine Hills if you have traveled 50% of the distance from Mount Kisco to Seabrook?
9. You are traveling east on Highway 60. Your speed is 50 miles per hour. How many hours is the trip from Mount Kisco to Seabrook?
10. If gasoline costs $1.39 per gallon and your car averages 30 miles per gallon, how much will the gasoline cost for your trip on Highway 60 from Mount Kisco to Seabrook?

GLOSSARY

acute angle An angle that measures between 0° and 90°.

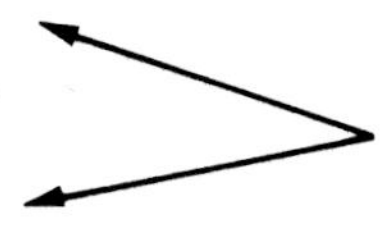

A.M. A symbol used for times after 12:00 midnight and before 12:00 noon.

angle A figure formed by two rays with the same endpoint.

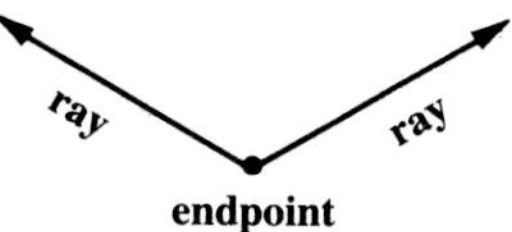

area The number of unit squares that it takes to cover a region.

average The sum of the numbers divided by the number of numbers.

axes Two perpendicular lines used as a reference for graphing ordered pairs.

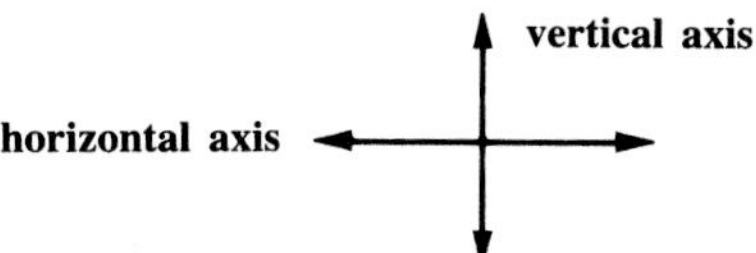

balance The amount of money remaining in an account.

budget A plan for using your money.

Celsius temperature scale (°C) The metric temperature scale, in which 0°C is the freezing point of water and 100°C is the boiling point of water.

centimeter A metric unit of length. 1 centimeter = 0.01 meter.

checking account An account in which money is deposited and held until the bank is told to pay a certain amount by means of a check.

circle A curved plane figure with all points a given distance from the center.

circumference The distance around a circle.

commission The part of the total sales that goes to the salesperson.

common denominator A common denominator for $\frac{1}{2}$ and $\frac{1}{3}$ is 6 because $\frac{1}{2} = \frac{3}{6}$ and $\frac{1}{3} = \frac{2}{6}$. A common denominator is a common multiple of the denominators of two fractions.

common divisor 2 is a common divisor of 4 and 6 because it is a divisor of both 4 and 6.

common multiple 30 is a common multiple of 5 and 6 because it is a multiple of both 5 and 6.

compound interest Interest that is added to the principal at regular intervals. This makes the principal grow and earn more and more interest.

computer language A set of symbols and terms used to tell a computer what to do.

computer program A list of instructions to a computer telling it what to do and when to do it.

cone A space figure with one flat face (known as the base) that is a circle and with one other face that is curved.

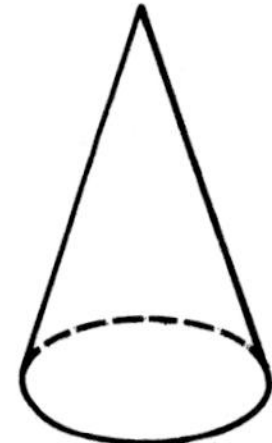

corresponding sides Sides of similar figures that are proportional.

cross products The cross products for the ratios below are 2×10 and 5×4. Two ratios are equal if their cross products are equal.

$$\frac{2}{5} = \frac{4}{10} \text{ because } 2 \times 10 = 5 \times 4$$

cube A rectangular prism whose six faces are squares.

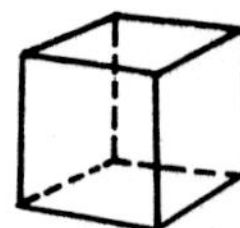

Customary System The system of measurement that uses foot, quart, pound, and Fahrenheit temperature.

cylinder A space figure that has two circular bases that are the same size and are in parallel planes. It has one curved face.

data Pieces of information.

decimal A number such as 3.86 or 0.4 that is written using a decimal point and place value.

decimeter A metric unit of length.
1 decimeter = 0.1 meter.

deductions The amount of money withheld from a person's pay.

degree A unit for measuring angles. This is a 1° (1-degree) angle.

dekameter A metric unit of length.
1 dekameter = 10 meters.

denominator In the fraction $\frac{2}{3}$, the denominator is 3.

deposit A sum of money put into a checking or savings account.

diameter The distance across a circle through its center. The length of the diameter is twice the length of the radius.

difference The answer to a subtraction problem.

digits The basic symbols used to write numerals. In our system, the digits are 0, 1, 2, 3, 4, 5, 6, 7, 8, and 9.

discount An amount subtracted from the regular price of an item.

dividend The number that is divided.

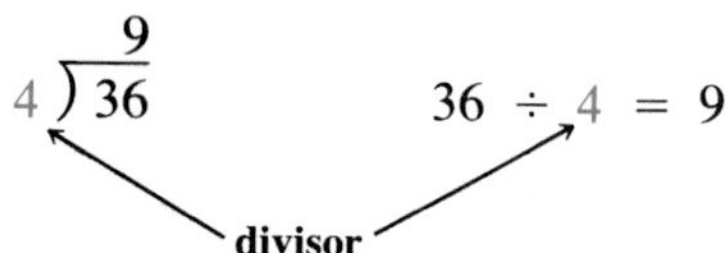

divisor The number that one divides by.

$4\overline{)36}$ with quotient 9 $36 \div 4 = 9$

divisor

down payment The first amount paid when buying on an installment plan.

equal ratios Ratios that indicate the same rate or comparison. The cross product of equal ratios are equal.

equation A sentence with an equal sign such as $3 \times 9 = 27$ or $8 + x = 10$.

equivalent fractions Fractions that name the same number. $\frac{1}{2}$, $\frac{2}{4}$, and $\frac{3}{6}$ are equivalent fractions.

estimate To use rounded numbers to check whether an answer is correct. To estimate $47 + 32$, you would add $50 + 30$. The sum should be about 80.

evaluate an expression To replace a variable in an expression with one of its values and then complete the indicated arithmetic.

even number Zero and multiples of 2.

expectation The probability of winning times the value of the prize.

Fahrenheit temperature scale (°F) The customary temperature scale, in which 32°F is the freezing point of water, and 212°F is the boiling point of water.

finance charge Buying an item on an installment plan costs more than paying cash. The difference is called the finance charge.

formula A general way of expressing a relationship using symbols.

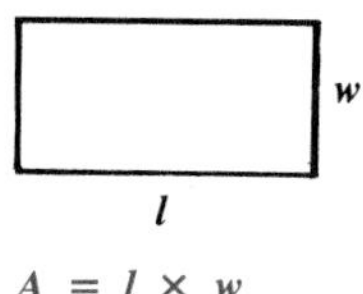

fraction A numeral for part of a group or for part of a region. $\frac{1}{2}$, $\frac{4}{6}$, and $\frac{6}{5}$ are fractions.

frequency table A table showing the number of times different events or responses occur.

gram A metric unit of weight (mass).
1 gram = 0.001 kilogram.

graph A picture used to show numerical information. It can be a bar graph, a picture graph, a circle graph, or a line graph.

greatest common divisor The greatest number that is a divisor of each of two or more numbers.

8 — *1, 2, 4, 8*

12 — *1, 2, 3, 4, 6, 12*

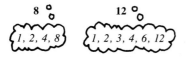

4 is the greatest common divisor of 8 and 12.

gross pay Total pay before deductions.

hectometer A metric unit of length.
1 hectometer = 100 meters.

hexagon A polygon with six sides.

indirect measurement A measurement that is computed from other measurements rather than measured directly.

installment plan A way of buying expensive items. You pay part of the cost (the down payment) when you get the item and then agree to pay a certain amount each month for a certain number of months.

integers The numbers . . . , $^{-}5$, $^{-}4$, $^{-}3$, $^{-}2$, $^{-}1$, 0, $^{+}1$, $^{+}2$, $^{+}3$, $^{+}4$, $^{+}5$, . . .

interest The amount a borrower pays for using the money.

intersecting lines Lines that meet at only one point.

invert To reverse in position. When $\frac{3}{4}$ is inverted, you get $\frac{4}{3}$.

kilogram A metric unit of weight.
1 kilogram = 1000 grams.

kilometer A metric unit of length.
1 kilometer = 1000 meters.

least common denominator The least (smallest) common multiple of two or more numbers. The least common multiple of 6 and 15 is 30.

liter A metric unit of liquid volume.

loan Money that is borrowed for a fixed period of time at a set rate of interest.

long word-name The name for a standard numeral written in words. The long word-name for 6,100,087 is six million, one hundred thousand, eighty-seven.

lower terms To write a fraction in lower terms, divide the numerator and denominator by a common divisor.

lowest terms A fraction is in lowest terms if the greatest common factor of the numerator and denominator is 1.

mainframe computer A large machine costing several hundred thousand dollars. It requires a large staff of operators and programmers. It must be kept in a specially constructed building.

mass The measure of the quantity of matter an object contains.

mean The average of all the numbers.

median If there is an odd number of numbers, the median is the number in the middle. If there is an even number of numbers, the median is the average of the two numbers in the middle.

memory A computer device capable of storing information temporarily or permanently.

meter A metric unit of length.
1 meter = 100 centimeters.

metric system An international system of measurement that uses meter, liter, gram, and Celsius temperature.

milligram A metric unit of weight (mass).
1 milligram = 0.001 gram.

milliliter A metric unit of liquid volume.
1 milliliter = 0.001 liter.

millimeter A metric unit of length.
1 millimeter = 0.001 meter.

mixed number A number that has a whole-number part and a fraction part. $2\frac{3}{4}$ is a mixed number.

mode The number that occurs most often.

multiple A product. 4, 8, 12, 16, 20, and so on, are multiples of 4.

negative number A number that is less than 0.

net pay Pay after deductions; "take-home" pay.

numerator In the fraction $\frac{2}{3}$, the numerator is 2.

obtuse angle An angle that measures between 90° and 180°.

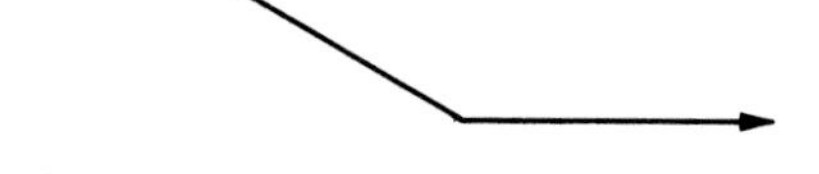

odd number A whole number that is not divisible by 2. The numbers 1, 3, 5, 7, 9, 11, and so on, are odd.

odds The ratio of the number of ways that an outcome can occur to the number of ways that the outcome cannot occur.

operation Addition, subtraction, multiplication, and division are examples of operations.

opposites Two numbers are opposites if their sum is 0.

$$^{-}3 + {}^{+}3 = 0$$
↖ ↗
opposites

ordered pair A pair of numbers that give the location of a point on a grid.

origin The point where axes intersect.

outcome A possible result.

parallel lines Lines in a plane that do not intersect.

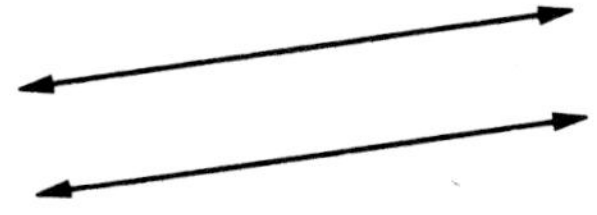

parallelogram A polygon with four sides and two pairs of parallel sides.

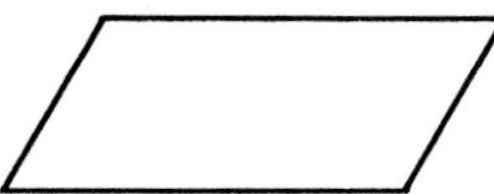

passbook A book issued by a bank when a person opens a savings account. It is used by the bank to record deposits, withdrawals, and interest.

pentagon A polygon with five sides.

percent (%) *Percent* means "per hundred." 5% (5 percent) equals $\frac{5}{100}$.

perimeter The distance around a figure; the sum of the lengths of the sides.

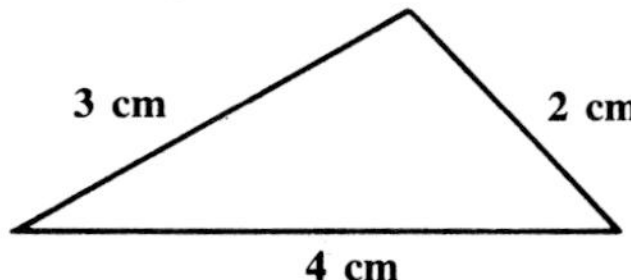

The perimeter is 9 cm.

permutation An arrangement of things in a definite order.

perpendicular lines Two lines that intersect to form right angles.

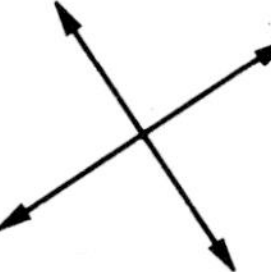

pi The number that is the ratio of the circumference of a circle to its diameter. It is represented by the Greek letter π and is approximately equal to 3.14.

P.M. A symbol used for times after 12:00 noon and before 12:00 midnight.

polygon A closed plane figure made up of segments.

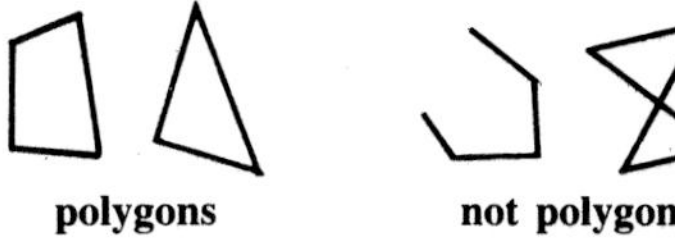

positive number A number greater than 0.

principal An amount of money borrowed.

prism A space figure that has two bases that are the same size and shape and are in parallel planes. The other faces are all rectangles.

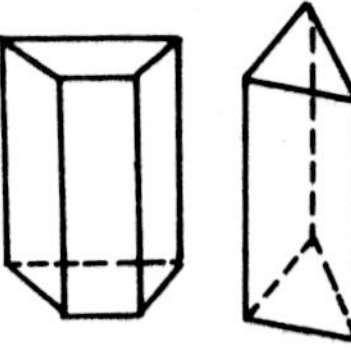

probability The ratio of the number of favorable outcomes to the total number of outcomes.

probability of picking black $= \frac{3}{5}$

product The answer to a multiplication problem.

proportion An equation stating that two ratios are equal.

$$\frac{5}{8} = \frac{30}{48}$$

protractor An instrument used to measure angles.

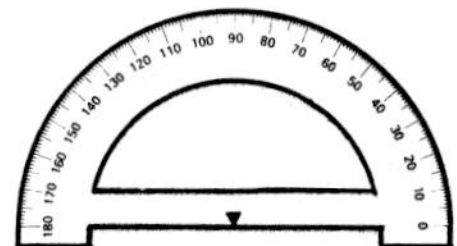

pyramid A solid figure with a face (known as the base) that is any polygon and with all other faces, which are triangles, sharing a common vertex.

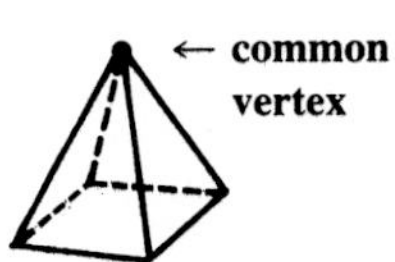

quadrant The regions into which the plane is separated by the horizontal and vertical axes.

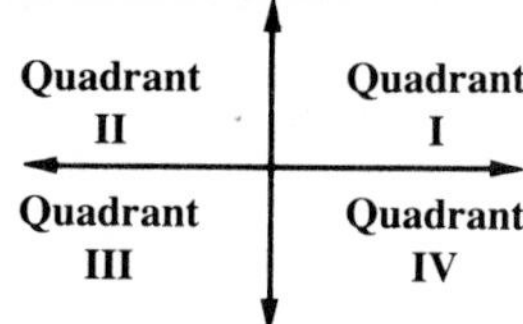

quotient The answer to a division problem.

radius The distance from the center of a circle to the circle. The radius is equal to one half the diameter.

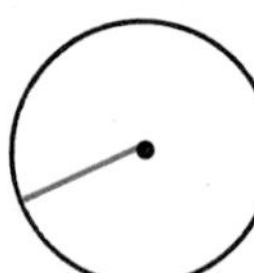

range The difference between the least and greatest numbers.

rate A comparison by division of two quantities.

$$\frac{87 \text{ kilometers}}{2 \text{ hours}}$$

ratio A comparison of two quantities by division. Below, the ratio of squares to circles is 4 to 2, 4:2, or $\frac{4}{2}$.

reciprocal Two numbers are reciprocals when their product is 1.

$$\frac{3}{4} \times \frac{4}{3} = 1$$

↖ ↗
reciprocals

rectangle A polygon with four sides and four right angles.

rectangular prism A prism whose six faces are rectangles.

regular price The price of an item before a discount is subtracted.

remainder In a division problem, the number that is "left over." When it is added to the product of the divisor and quotient, the sum is the dividend.

$$\begin{array}{r} 3 \\ 8 \overline{)29} \\ -24 \\ \hline 5 \end{array} \longleftarrow \textbf{remainder}$$

right angle An angle whose measure is 90°.

round a number To replace a number by another one that is easier to use. You round a number to the nearest ten by choosing the nearest multiple of 10. (5 is rounded up.)

$13 \rightarrow 10$ $27 \rightarrow 30$ $45 \rightarrow 50$

You round a number to the nearest hundred by choosing the nearest multiple of 100.

$487 \rightarrow 500$ $1238 \rightarrow 1200$ $550 \rightarrow 600$

salary Wages paid on a regular basis.

sale price The price of an item after a discount is subtracted.

sample space The set of all possible outcomes of an event.

savings account A bank account in which money is deposited or withdrawn. The money earns interest.

scale drawing A drawing of an object such that the ratio of a unit of length on the drawing to a unit of length on the object is fixed.

segment A part of a line that has two endpoints.

short word-name The name for a standard numeral written using both words and numerals. The short word name for 6,100,087 is 6 million, 100 thousand, 87.

side of an angle One of the rays that make up an angle.

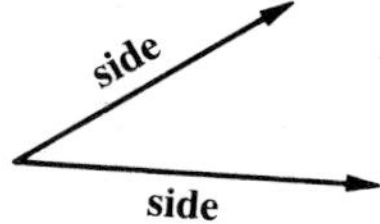

side of a plane figure One of the segments that make up a figure.

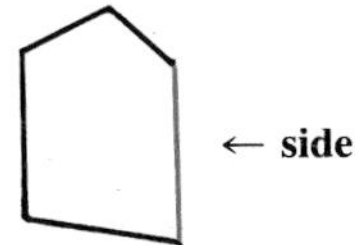

similar figures Two figures that have the same shape.

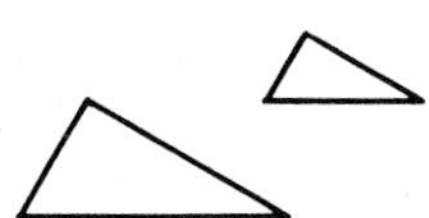

simple interest Interest that is computed by using the formula $I = prt$, where p is principal, r is rate, and t is time.

simplest form A fraction or mixed number is in simplest form if the fraction or fraction-part of the mixed number is less than 1 and in lowest terms.

software Computer programs.

solution A number that makes an equation true.

solve To find all the numbers that make an equation true.

sphere A round space figure shaped like a basketball. All points on a sphere are the same distance from the center.

square A polygon with 4 sides the same length and 4 right angles.

standard numeral The standard numeral for 3 billion, 24 million, 65 is 3,024,000,065.

statistics A branch of mathematics that studies numerical facts as a basis for drawing general conclusions and making predictions.

substitute To replace a variable with a numeral.

$$7a + 3$$
$$7 \cdot 6 + 3$$

sum The answer to an addition problem.

surface area The sum of the areas of all the surfaces of a solid figure.

trapezoid A polygon with 4 sides and exactly 1 pair of parallel sides.

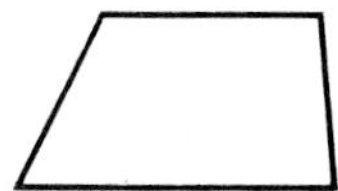

tree diagram A diagram that shows all the possible outcomes of an event.

triangle A polygon with three sides.

triangular prism A prism with two triangular faces in parallel planes.

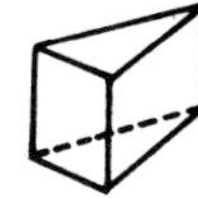

unit price The cost per unit (weight, volume, etc.) of an item.

variable A symbol—usually a letter—that holds the place for a number.

$$8x + 19 = 23$$

volume The amount that a space figure holds.

whole number Any of the numbers 0, 1, 2, 3, 4, and so on.

withdrawal A sum of money taken out of a checking or savings account.

withholdings An amount deducted from a person's pay for the payment of taxes.

SYMBOLS

$<$	is less than	$a{:}b$	the ratio of a to b
$>$	is greater than	$\%$	percent
$=$	is equal to	$^\circ$	degree
$\neq$	is not equal to	π	pi
$\approx$	is approximately equal to	P(2)	the probability of the outcome 2
$'$	foot/feet	$^{+}5$	positive 5
$''$	inch/inches	$^{-}5$	negative 5

FORMULAS

Perimeter of a square	$P = 4 \times s$
Perimeter of a rectangle	$P = 2 \times (l + w)$
Circumference of a circle	$C = \pi \times d$
Area of a rectangle	$A = l \times w$
Area of a square	$A = s \times s$
Area of a parallelogram	$A = b \times h$
Area of a triangle	$A = \frac{1}{2} \times b \times h$
Area of a circle	$A = \pi \times r \times r$
Volume of a prism	$V = B \times h$
Volume of a rectangular prism	$V = l \times w \times h$
Volume of a cylinder	$V = (\pi \times r \times r) \times h$
Volume of a pyramid	$V = \frac{1}{3} \times B \times h$
Volume of a cone	$V = \frac{1}{3} \times (\pi \times r \times r) \times h$
Interest	$I = p \times r \times t$

INDEX

Accounts
  charge, 286–287
  checking, 5, 280–281
  savings, 282–283
Acute angle, 294–295
Addition
  of customary units, 218–219
  of decimals, 22–25
  equations, 386–387
  estimation, 14–15, 24–25
  of fractions, 156–159
  of integers, 364–365
  of mixed numbers, 160–161
  of whole numbers, 6–9
Algebra, 381–402
A.M., 109, 286–287
Angle
  acute, 294–295
  obtuse, 294–295
  right, 294–295
Approximately equal to (≈), 302
Area
  of a circle, 312–313
  of a parallelogram, 308–309
  of a rectangle, 306–307, 331
  of a square, 306–307
  surface, 324–325
  of a triangle, 310–311
Average, 76–77, 114–115
Axis/axes, 374–375
Balance of an account, 27, 281–282
Bar graph, 106–107, 109, 118–119, 121
Base of a figure, 308–311, 328–333
Basic counting principle, 340–341
Billion, 4–5
Bills, 286–287
Budget, 279
Calculators, 36–37, 39, 46–47, 57, 59, 67, 69, 79, 81, 89, 115, 139, 145, 147, 161, 167, 179, 183, 191, 201, 231, 249, 257, 263, 271, 277, 281, 285, 313, 333, 343, 347
Centimeter, 198–203
Change, 61, 71, 157, 257
Charge account, 286–287
Checking account, 5, 280–281
Circle, 302–303, 312–313
Circle graph, 110–111, 118, 121, 132, 248
Circumference, 302–303
Commission, 270
Common denominator, 130–131
Common divisors, 128
Common multiples, 130
Comparing numbers
  decimals, 42–43
  fractions, 132–133
  integers, 362–363
  whole numbers, 32–33
Comparison buying, 274–275
Compound interest, 283
Computers
  at the airport, 49
  in architecture, 357
  in automobiles, 173
  in banking, 27
  calculating a raise, 265
  in cash registers, 71, 151
  computer graphics, 121, 335
  computer language, 399
  gardening, 221
  for home use, 221, 265, 289
  Logo, 399
  in photography, 377
  in schools, 99
  shopping, 289
  software package, 243
  in sports, 315
  in watches, 193
Cone, 320–321, 332–333
Consumer Mathematics
  bills, 286–287
  change, 61, 71, 157, 257
  charge account, 286–287
  checking account, 5, 280–281
  commission, 270

Consumer Mathematics (*continued*)
comparison buying, 274–275
compound interest, 283
coupons, 276–277
deductions, 271
discount, 256–257, 272–273
down payment, 262–263, 349
earning money, 270–271
gross pay, 271
interest, 282–285
loan, 284–285
net pay, 271
paycheck, 271
sale, 272–273, 276–277
savings account, 282–283
take-home pay, 271
taxes, 271, 458
unit price, 274–275
Conversion
customary units, 212–217
metric units, 202–207
Corresponding sides, 238
Cross products, 228–229
Cube, 320–321, 324–325, 328–329
Cup, 214–215, 218–219
Customary system of measurement, 185, 210–219
Cylinder, 320–321, 330–331
Decimals
adding, 22–25
comparing, 42–43
dividing by a decimal, 94–97
dividing a decimal by a whole number, 88–89, 92–93
and fractions or mixed numbers, 146–149
multiplying, 64–65
and percents, 252–253
reading and writing, 16–17
rounding, 20–21, 65
subtracting, 44–47
Decimeter, 200
Deductions, 271
Degree, 294
Dekameter, 200
Denominator, 126
least common, 130–131
Deposit, 27, 281–283
Diameter, 302–303
Difference, 34–37
Discount, 256–257, 272–273
Dividend, 94
Division
by a decimal, 94–97
of a decimal by a whole number, 88–89
equations, 394–395
estimation, 78–79
of fractions, 188–189
of integers, 372–373
of mixed numbers, 190–191
with remainder
as a decimal, 84–85, 96–97
as a fraction, 142–143
as a whole number, 80–81
by 10, 100, 1000, 92–93
of whole numbers, 76–81, 84–85
Divisor, 94
Down payment, 262–263, 349
Edge, 320–321
Equally likely outcomes, 344–347
Equal ratios, 226–227
Equations
addition, 386–387
division, 394–395
multiplication, 392–393
subtraction, 388–389
two-step, 396–397
Equivalent fractions, 126–127
Estimating
differences, 36–39, 46
in measurement, 200–201
products, 56–57, 64
quotients, 78–79
sums, 14–15, 24–25
Evaluate an expression, 384–385
Event, 350
Expectation, 354–355
Expressions
evaluating, 384–385
simplifying, 66–67, 86–87
writing, 371, 382–383
Face, 320–321
Factor, 56

Fahrenheit temperature scale (°F), 362–363
Finance charge, 286–287
Foot, 212–213, 218–219
Formula, 300, 302, 306, 308, 310, 328, 332
Fractions
  adding, 156–159
  comparing, 132–133
  and decimals, 146–149
  dividing, 188–189
  equivalent, 126–127
  multiplying, 178–181
  and percents, 248–251
  and probability, 344–345
  as ratios, 226–227
  reciprocals of, 188–189
  and whole numbers or mixed numbers, 136–139
  of whole numbers, 180–181
  subtracting, 164–167
Frequency table, 104–105, 118
Gallon, 214–215, 218–219
Geometry, 294–299
Gram, 206–207
Graphs
  bar, 106–107, 109, 118–119, 121
  circle, 110–111, 118, 121, 132, 248
  line, 108–109, 113, 121
  picture, 110–111, 119
  of ordered pairs, 374–375
Greater than, 32–33, 42–43, 132–133, 362–363
Gross pay, 271
Hectometer, 200
Height of a figure, 308–311, 328–333
Hexagon, 298
Horizontal axis, 374–375
Hour, 184
Inch, 210–213, 218–219
Indirect measurement, 240–241
Installment plan, 262–263, 349
Integers
  adding, 364–365
  comparing, 362–363
  dividing, 372–373
  multiplying, 370–371
  subtracting, 366–367
Interest, 282–285
  compound, 283
  simple, 284–285
Intersecting lines, 296–297
Inverting a fraction, 188
Kilogram, 206–207
Kilometer, 200–203
Least common denominator, 130–132
Least common multiple, 130
Length
  customary units of, 210–213
  metric units of, 198–203
Less than, 32–33, 42–43, 132–133, 362–363
Line graph, 108–109, 113, 121
Lines
  intersecting, 296–297
  parallel and perpendicular, 296–297
Liquid volume, 204–205, 214–215
Liter, 204–205
Loan, 284–285
Long word name, 4–5
Lower, lowest terms, 128–129
Magic square, 365
Mainframe computer, 265
Maps, 11, 145, 158–159, 170–171, 201, 236–237, 252–253, 362–363
Mass, 206–207
Mean, 114–115
Measurement, 197–224
  of angles, 294–295
  indirect, 240–241
Median, 116–117
Meter, 200–203
Metric system of measurement, 198–207
Mile, 212–213
Milligram, 206–207
Milliliter, 204–205
Millimeter, 198–203
Million, 2–5
Minute, 184–185
Mixed numbers
  adding, 160–161
  and decimals, 146–149
  dividing, 190–191
  and fractions, 136–139
  multiplying, 182–185

Mixed numbers (*continued*)
  and percents, 249, 251
  subtracting, 168–171
Mode, 116–117
Multiple, 54, 130
Multiplication
  of decimals, 64–65
  equations, 392–393
  estimation, 56–57, 64
  of fractions, 178–181
  of integers, 370–371
  of mixed numbers, 182–185
  by 10, 100, 1000, 54, 68
  of whole numbers, 54–61
Multiplication equation, 392–393
Negative integers, 362–367, 370–375
Net pay, 271
Not equal sign (≠), 228–229
Number line, 362
Numerator, 126
Obtuse angle, 294–299
Odds, 352–353
Opposites, 366–367
Ordered pairs, 374–375
Order of operations, 86–87
Origin, 374
Ounce, 216–219
Outcome, 344–345, 350, 352–353
Parallel lines, 296–297
Parallelogram, 298–299, 308–309
Paycheck, 271
Pentagon, 298–299
Percent
  and decimals, 252–253
  and fractions, 248–251
  and mixed numbers, 249
  of a number, 256–259, 262–263
  unknown, 262–263
  of an unknown number, 260–263
Perimeter, 300–301, 307, 331
Permutations, 342–343
Perpendicular lines, 296–297
Pi (π), 302
Picture graph, 110–111, 119
Pint, 214–215, 218–219
Place value, 2–5, 13, 16–17, 32–33, 42–43, 77, 93, 139, 261, 283
P.M., 109, 286–287
Point, 294
Polygons, 298–299
Positive integers, 362–367, 370–375
Possible outcomes, 344–347
Pound, 216–219
Principal, 284–285
Prisms, 320–321, 324–325, 328–329
Probability, 339–360
Problem solving
  checking answers, 69, 161, 167, 191, 231, 303
  choosing appropriate information to solve a problem, 7, 19, 24, 36–37, 46, 49, 60, 66, 76, 84–85, 93–94, 126–127, 133, 142, 146–147, 151, 156–157, 164–165, 168–169, 173, 178, 182–183, 190–191, 198–199, 214–216, 226–227, 230–232, 235, 255, 271, 280–282, 284–287, 322–323, 342–347, 350–351, 354–355, 357, 364, 366, 369, 370, 384–385
  choosing the correct operation, 34, 36, 39, 41, 44, 49, 61, 63, 67, 71, 76–77, 79, 83, 85, 88–89, 91, 93, 95, 97, 113, 115, 143, 145, 147, 151, 163, 173, 181, 183, 191, 199, 209, 215, 217, 219, 221, 235, 237, 249, 255, 261, 265, 277, 287, 289, 307, 329, 349, 357, 369, 385, 391
  conducting an experiment and collecting data, 344–345
  estimating measurements, 294–295
  following directions, 13, 93, 139, 169, 183, 191, 193, 211, 249, 261, 283, 374
  interpreting graphs, 106–113, 118–119, 121, 132–133, 166–167, 248–249, 283, 374–375
  making a drawing, 97, 131, 163, 240–241, 243, 299, 309, 313
  making geometric visualizations, 321–323, 325, 329, 335, 399
  making a list, 157, 259
  reading an ad, 3, 14–15, 41, 58–59, 63, 78–79, 138, 180–181, 205, 256–257, 262, 270, 272–277, 305, 327, 349

Problem solving (*continued*)
reading a map, 11, 145, 158–159, 170–171, 201, 236–237, 252–253, 362–363
reading tables and charts, 2, 4, 6, 8, 21–22, 25, 33–34, 38–39, 42–45, 55, 61, 64, 68, 80–81, 83, 104–105, 114–117, 160–161, 170–171, 187, 189, 219, 228–229, 250–251, 258–259, 279, 299, 352
recognizing when information is missing, 63
selecting data from a drawing, 96, 165, 188, 193, 238–241, 296–297, 300–303, 305–313, 320–321, 324–325, 327–333
solving problems involving more than one step, 19, 65, 67, 77, 91, 135, 145, 179, 187, 209, 217, 237, 255, 327, 349, 357, 369, 391
using computer-displayed information, 27, 99, 221, 243, 265, 289, 315, 399
using equations to solve problems, 386, 389, 393, 395, 397
using a formula, 300–303, 306–313, 328–333
using a guess-and-check strategy, 14–15, 23, 37, 47, 59, 71, 81, 149, 201, 257, 289, 333
using logical reasoning, 3, 9, 33, 39, 45, 57, 65, 115, 127, 129, 131, 137, 141, 143, 169, 181, 203, 213, 215, 217, 229, 297, 299, 321
using a proportion to solve a problem, 232–233, 235–237, 239–241, 243, 262–263
using a tree diagram, 340–341, 346–347, 350–351
Product, 56
Proportion, 228–233, 236–241
Protractor, 294–295
Pyramids, 320–321, 332–333
Quadrant, 374
Quart, 214–215, 218–219
Quotient, 76
Radius, 302–303
Range, 116–117
Rate, 232–233, 284–285
Ratio, 226–227
Reciprocal, 188–189
Rectangle, 298–299, 300–301, 306–307
Rectangular prism, 320–321, 324–325, 328–329
Regular price, 180–181, 256–257, 272–273, 276–277, 388–389
Remainder, 80–81, 84–85, 96–97, 142–143
Right angle, 294–295
Rounding
decimals, 20–21, 65
whole numbers, 12–13, 33, 127
Salary, 270–271
Sale price, 180–181, 256–257, 272–273, 276–277, 388–389
Sales tax, 458
Sample space, 346–347, 350
Savings account, 282–283
Scale drawing, 236–237
Seconds, 184
Segments, 210–211
Short word name, 4–5, 16–17
Side
of an angle, 294
of a plane figure, 298–299
Similar figures, 238–241
Simple interest, 284–285
Simplest form, 140–141
Simplifying expressions, 66–67, 86–87
Social security, 271
Software, 243
Solution, 386
Space figures, 320–323
surface area of, 324–325
volume of, 328–333
Sphere, 320–321
Square, 298–301, 306–307
Standard numerals, 2–5, 16–17
Statistics, 114–117
Substitute, 384–385, 392–397
Subtraction
checking, 38
of customary units, 218–219
of decimals, 44–47
equations, 388–389
estimation, 36–39, 46
of fractions, 164–167

Subtraction (*continued*)
of integers, 366–367
of mixed numbers, 168–171
of whole numbers, 34–39
Sum, 6
Surface area, 324–325
Take-home pay, 271
Taxes, 271, 458
Temperature, 362–363
Time, 3, 35, 184–185, 284–285, 287
Ton, 216–219
Trapezoid, 298–299
Tree diagram, 340–341, 346–347, 350
Triangle, 298–301, 310–311
Triangular prism, 320–321
Unit price, 274–275
Variable, 382
Vertical axis, 374–375
Volume
of cones, 332–333
of cubes, 328–329
of cylinders, 330–331
liquid, 204–205, 214–215
of pyramids, 332–333
of rectangular prisms, 328–329
Whole numbers
addition, 6–9
comparing, 32–33
division, 76–81, 84–85
multiplication, 54–61
reading and writing, 2–5
rounding, 12–13, 33, 127
subtraction, 34–39
Withdrawal, 27, 281–283
Withholdings, 271
Yard, 212–213, 218

8 9 0